LAPLACE AND FOURIER TRANSFORMS FOR ELECTRICAL ENGINEERS

HOLT, RINEHART AND WINSTON

New York
Chicago
San Francisco
Toronto
London

LAPLACE AND

FOR ELECTRICAL

FOURIER TRANSFORMS

ENGINEERS ───────/\\/\\/\\/\\/\\/\\/\\/\\/\\/\\/\\/\\/\\/\\──

EDWARD J. CRAIG
Union College

TO JEANNE AND TERRY,
DAVE, STEVE,
TINA, AND MARY

Preface

The aim of this book is to present the material in as lucid and detailed a manner as possible, particularly in noting the errors that students are most likely to make. Also, many sets of problems have been included throughout the text. It is hoped that this approach will allow the instructor to spend less time on details and free him to concentrate on discussing the more subtle task of reducing a physical problem to a mathematical model.

The book presumes a knowledge of ordinary a-c circuit theory as well as some facility in handling complex numbers. For example, a knowledge of Thévènin's theorem and the superposition theorem is assumed. At least a nodding acquaintance with the loop and nodal methods is really necessary if a course using this text is to be completed in one fifteen-week term.

With regard to the mathematical prerequisites, the student should know how to differentiate and integrate simple functions. A course in differential equations is not really necessary, although it is desirable. An extensive set of problems on the notions of the dummy variable of integration and functional notation is included in the beginning of Chapter 2. Many topics, such as determinants, Cramer's rule, and factoring are included in the text as refreshers. These topics must also be considered prerequisite if the course is to be given in one term.

There is very little about the Laplace transform that I have not learned from Professors M. F. Gardner and K. L. Wildes of the Massachusetts Institute of Technology. These men, along with Professors E. A. Guillemin (also of MIT) and W. K. Linvill (now at Stanford University) have been the inspiration for this book. It has been my desire to integrate the fruits of the work of these men and bring into one volume those techniques that are so necessary to the engineer of today.

So many students have assisted me in this effort that it is not possible to name them all. I do want to thank Union College for granting me sabbatical leave to write this book, and Professor C. F. Goodheart of Union College for his encouragement and help. Thanks also to Mrs. Amelia Di Lella for typing the manuscript, Professor C. F. Rehberg of New York University for his careful reading of the manuscript and many helpful suggestions, and to Mrs. Joanne Smith for assistance in the preparation of the first draft.

EDWARD J. CRAIG

Schenectady, New York

February 1964

Contents

chapter

1

A Preview of the Book

1.1 Introduction

The author has always believed that his greatest experiences in formal education came when two or more seemingly unrelated ideas were brought together under one larger idea. The most remarkable of all these experiences for the author was the joining of what engineers call the *transient* and the *steady-state*. This synthesis was originally achieved by Jean Baptiste Joseph Fourier (1768–1830), and it produced three offspring: Fourier series, Fourier transforms, and Laplace transforms.

This volume is written primarily for electrical engineers, because it is they who are most concerned with the transmission of information in frequency or radio bands and to whom the notion and concept of frequency response is most important. Other applications of Fourier's offspring are mentioned in the text and problems; in many instances, their applications to other fields are as important as they are in electrical engineering.

The Laplace* transform will be the first of this group to be considered. In a period where a microsecond is considered a long time, the *speed* or response time of a network to rapidly varying signals is extremely important. Even in a device as ordinary as a television set, the video circuits must respond to changes in voltage levels in less than a microsecond if a well-defined picture is to appear on the screen. Thus the initial behavior of a network when a signal is suddenly applied to it is very important to the designer. The Laplace transform is a straightforward *algebraic* method for determining the transient behavior of a linear network.

The Fourier series will be discussed next, and its relationship to the Laplace transform will be emphasized. The notion of harmonics

*Named for Pierre Simon, Marquis de Laplace (1749–1827).

or overtones in periodic functions will be related directly to transient behavior. Moreover, in spite of the integrals that appear in the definitions of the Laplace transform and Fourier series, the text will show that transforms and series can be obtained in most cases of practical interest *without evaluating any integrals*. Thus, one of the large stumbling blocks to learning in this area can be sidestepped.

A mathematical *periodic* function has no beginning and no end. The function sin t, for example, is defined for all values of t from $-\infty$ to $+\infty$. There are no such signals in reality. Although some musical notes are sinusoidal in form, these notes certainly do not last forever. Practical time signals are of finite duration, and the electrical engineer, especially, knows that these signals can be thought of as containing frequencies. For example, suppose a certain audio amplifier can be shown to amplify all sinusoidal signals equally from 50 cps to 10 kc (10,000 cps). The amplifier can also be shown to amplify voice signals with good fidelity. It is reasonable to assume that even though no voice signal is periodic, it must contain frequencies in the range of the amplifier. Furthermore, as the amplifier's pass-band is continually made smaller, voice signals become more and more distorted. It is intuitively assumed that nonperiodic (or aperiodic) functions can be viewed in what is now referred to as the *frequency domain*. It is the Fourier transform that permits a mathematical representation of the frequency character of aperiodic functions of time. As with the Fourier series, the Fourier transforms can, for the most part, be derived directly from the Laplace transform.

Thus, one algebraic technique will enable the electrical engineer to solve most transient circuit problems, evaluate the Fourier series for periodic functions, and find the frequency spectrum for nonperiodic signals.

In the three sections below, each of the techniques will be summarized and examples of their use will be given. It is not anticipated that the reader will understand completely all the steps in the examples, but they will give a general picture of the objectives of this book.

1.2 The Laplace Transform*

The Laplace transform is used strictly as an *operational* calculus. An operational calculus is a technique by which the solution of differential

---

* There are two forms of the Laplace transform, the unilateral and the bilateral. Only the unilateral form is discussed and implied in this book.

equations is obtained by transforming the equations to algebraic equations. The usefulness of the method is based on the premise that algebra is easier than calculus. It was Oliver Heaviside (1850–1925) who popularized the technique with the presentation of his operational calculus. His work is substantially equivalent to the Laplace transform, the latter being better suited, perhaps, to future applications.

In the chapters to follow, each step in the solutions of transient circuit problems will be taken up in turn and mastered. The example below is designed to indicate the goal of this study.

Experience shows us that if an electric network is excited by a battery or other constant voltage source, ultimately there will in almost every case be steady currents and constant potentials everywhere in the network. (There are a few startling exceptions to this statement when the networks considered contain no resistances. For the present it will be assumed that the networks in question do contain some resistances.) These voltages and currents are described as the *steady-state*. If the source is a sinusoid of constant frequency, then all currents and voltages will eventually become sinusoids of the same frequency. Again, these final conditions are the steady-state, in this case the *sinusoidal steady-state*.

The behavior of a network and its currents and voltages in the interval between the application of the source and the establishment of steady-state conditions is referred to as the *transient*. Consider, for example, the speed of a car entering a modern high-speed highway. The speed of the car while it is on the approach to the highway is usually about 30 mph. Assuming that the prevailing speed on the highway is 65 mph, the car enters an accelerating lane at 30 mph, accelerates to 65 mph, and then enters the highway. This period of acceleration is the transient, and it is certainly important to the man designing the accelerating lane to know the approximate distance covered during this transient for the average car that is to use the highway. Note also that the transient is sandwiched in between two steady-states, 30 and 65 mph.

A similar example involving an electric circuit would be the charging of a capacitance through a resistance by a battery. Figure 1.1 depicts a capacitance, C, of 1 μf (microfarad), which is charged to a potential of 10 volts. Since the charge on the capacitance is proportional to the potential

$$q = Cv$$

then there must be $q = 10 \times 10^{-6} = 10^{-5}$ coulomb of charge on the capacitance. (Specifically this means that the top or positive plate has an excess positive charge of 10^{-5} coulomb, and the bottom plate has an excess 10^{-5} coulomb of negative charge. Actually the total algebraic charge on the capacitance is always zero.)

Note in Fig. 1.1 that the switch k is open; hence, the charge on the capacitance has no choice but to remain where it is. Suppose that at the instant the switch k is closed, a stopwatch is started. Then, at time zero $(t = 0)$, the 20-volt battery is connected to the capacitance through the 500,000-ohm resistance.

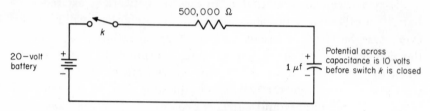

Fig. 1.1   *Battery charging a capacitance.*

The overall result of this operation will be to raise the potential across the capacitance to 20 volts. Since the charge is proportional to the potential, the charge will double its initial value after a certain period of time—that is, it will become 2×10^{-5} coulomb.

In general the engineer has to know how long the transient will last, and in many applications he must know exactly what the transient will look like. In order to answer these questions he must call upon Kirchhoff's and Ohm's laws.

Ohm demonstrated that the potential across a resistance is proportional to the rate at which charge flows through the resistance. If this rate is denoted by i, the current in amperes, then the potential across the resistance in Fig. 1.1 is v_r, with

$$v_r = Ri = 5 \times 10^5 i$$

But

$$i = \frac{dq}{dt}$$

the rate at which positive charge collects on the top plate of the capacitance. Thus

$$v_r = 5 \times 10^5 \frac{dq}{dt}$$

Kirchhoff's voltage law states that the sum of the potentials across

the resistance and capacitance must be equal to the battery voltage
after the switch is closed. Since the capacitance potential is simply
$q/C = q/10^{-6} = 10^6 q$, then

$$5 \times 10^5 \frac{dq}{dt} + 10^6 q = 20$$

Dividing through by 5×10^5 yields

$$\frac{dq}{dt} + 2q = 4 \times 10^{-5}$$

This equation is known as a linear differential equation with
constant coefficients: *linear* since the unknown, q, and its derivatives
appear in the first degree only (that is, there are no terms of the type
q^2 or $q\,dq/dt$, etc.); *differential* because of the presence of the derivative
(or, in general, derivatives); *constant coefficients* as distinct from time-
varying coefficients such as those in the equation

$$30 = (\sin t)\,\frac{dq}{dt} + e^{-t} q$$

In the networks to be considered in this text, circuit-element values
will always be constants; hence all problems relating to these networks
can be reduced to the problem of solving one or more simultaneous
linear differential equations with constant coefficients.

The Laplace transform is a straightforward algebraic technique
for solving this type of equation. It is based on the principle that all
realistic functions of time can be transformed to functions of a new
variable, s, in such a manner that differentiation is transformed into
multiplication by s, and integration into division by s. For example,
consider the function defined as zero for $t < 0$ and equal to Ae^{-at}
for $t > 0$, with A and a constants and $e = 2.71828\ldots$, the base of the
natural logarithms. It will be shown that this function has a Laplace
transform

$$\frac{A}{s + a}$$

Interestingly enough, almost all transforms of any engineering
importance can be shown to be related to this transform. For example,
if $a = 0$, then the function is zero for negative t and is a constant, A,
for positive t. This is called the *Heaviside step function*, or simply, a step
function. Figure 1.2 shows the function Ae^{-at}, $t > 0$, for values of a of
-1, 0, and $+1$.

Note the discontinuity of these functions at $t = 0$. This discontinuity may be unsettling at first, but it is digestible, as will be seen.

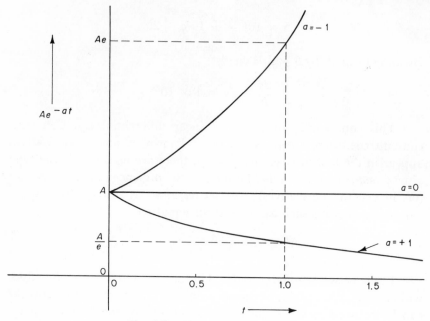

Fig. 1.2   *The exponential function.*

The whole objective of the operational method, as indicated previously, is to change the problem from calculus to algebra. Going back to the capacitance-charging problem, we have the equation

$$\frac{dq}{dt} + 2q = 4 \times 10^{-5}$$

We may begin by supposing that the transform of q or $q(t)$, since it is a function of time, is $Q(s)$, a function of s. Then the transform of dq/dt must be $sQ(s)$. The transform of the constant must be $4 \times 10^{-5}/s$, for 4×10^{-5} is the function Ae^{-at} with $A = 4 \times 10^{-5}$ and $a = 0$. Then the transformed equation should be

$$sQ(s) + 2\,Q(s) = \frac{4 \times 10^{-5}}{s}$$

This is not quite correct. For reasons that will become apparent later, the transform of the derivative is not exactly $sQ(s)$, but it is $sQ(s) - q(0-)$, where $q(0-)$ is the value of the charge on the capacitance *just before* the switch is thrown. Since this is known to be 10^{-5} coulomb, then the correct equation is actually

$$sQ(s) - 10^{-5} + 2\,Q(s) = \frac{4 \times 10^{-5}}{s}$$

We now solve for $Q(s)$ by ordinary algebraic methods:

$$(s + 2)\,Q(s) = 10^{-5} + \frac{4 \times 10^{-5}}{s} = 10^{-5}\frac{(s + 4)}{s}$$

or

$$Q(s) = 10^{-5}\,\frac{s + 4}{s(s + 2)}$$

At this point the denominator of the rational fraction in s usually has to be factored. In this simple example it is already in factored form. The next step is to arrange the transform $Q(s)$ so that the function $q(t)$ can be deduced from it. This is done by what is called a partial-fraction expansion. Thus constants C_1 and C_2 are to be found such that

$$\frac{10^{-5}\,(s + 4)}{s\,(s + 2)} = \frac{C_1}{s} + \frac{C_2}{s + 2}$$

The reasons for this will be apparent, since the inverse transform of C_1/s is just C_1, and that of $C_2/(s + 2)$ is $C_2 e^{-2t}$ (both, of course, for $t > 0$ only).

There are many ways of determining C_1 and C_2. The method used below is not the simplest, but it is nevertheless easy to follow. The two fractions are combined into one with a least common denominator $s(s + 2)$:

$$\frac{C_1}{s} + \frac{C_2}{s + 2} = \frac{C_1(s + 2) + C_2 s}{s(s + 2)} = \frac{(C_1 + C_2)s + 2C_1}{s(s + 2)}$$

Comparing the numerator of the last fraction with the transform $Q(s)$, we have

$$10^{-5}\,s + 4 \times 10^{-5} = (C_1 + C_2)\,s + 2C_1$$

If these are to be identical for all values of s, then

$$C_1 + C_2 = 10^{-5}$$

$$2C_1 = 4 \times 10^{-5}$$

and hence $C_1 = 2 \times 10^{-5}$ and $C_2 = -10^{-5}$. Then

$$Q(s) = \frac{10^{-5}\,(s + 4)}{s(s + 2)} = \frac{2 \times 10^{-5}}{s} - \frac{10^{-5}}{s + 2}$$

so $q(t) = 2 \times 10^{-5} - 10^{-5}\, e^{-2t}$ for $t > 0$. Since q was 10^{-5} before the switch was closed, a plot of q versus t would be as shown in Fig. 1.3.

The function e^{-2t} approaches zero as t becomes large, but it never actually attains the value of zero. Thus, we must say that the transient lasts forever, if we wish to be mathematically rigorous. However, a table of e^{-x} indicates that when $x = 5$, $e^{-5} = 0.006738$. In the example above this occurs when $t = 2.5$. The reciprocal of the coefficient of t in the exponent is commonly referred to as the *time constant*. Thus the time constant for the transient in the example is $\frac{1}{2}$ sec. The transient is usually said to last about five time constants.

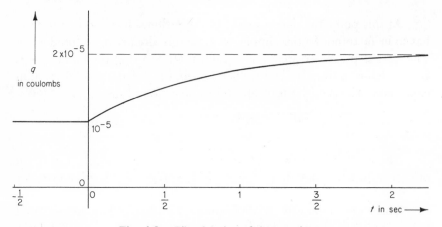

Fig. 1.3　*The charging of the capacitance.*

Chapters 2 through 6 are devoted to the general analysis of electric networks and transient response by the use of the Laplace transform as outlined above. Chapter 6, in particular, includes an introduction to matrix algebra, and shows how any linear lumped-constant network, however complicated, can be solved in a perfectly straightforward manner.

1.3 The Fourier Series

A function of time is said to be *periodic* and to have a period T sec if after every time interval T the signal repeats exactly the behavior of the previous T sec. Note in Fig. 1.4 that if the first T sec of the somewhat strange but repetitious wave were cut out with scissors, the result would be the function appearing in Fig. 1.5. (Observe that the cut

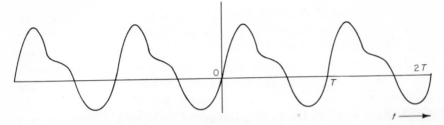

Fig. 1.4 *A periodic wave.*

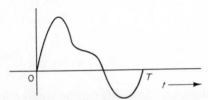

Fig. 1.5 *One period only of the wave of Fig. 1.4.*

does not have to come from 0 to T. Any section whose base is T sec long is a period.)

Probably the most familiar periodic function is the sinewave or sinusoid. The sinewave with period T can be expressed mathematically as $A \sin (2\pi t/T)$. In this text the most general of all sinusoids will always be written as $A \cos (2\pi t/T + \theta)$; A will be a positive real number, called the *amplitude* of the sinusoid, and θ will be the *phase* of the sinusoid in radians. θ may be any positive or negative real number. When $\theta = -\pi/2$ the cosine expression reduces to the sinewave: $\sin (2\pi t/T)$. For this and other values of θ, the cosine function is plotted versus t, as in Fig. 1.6.

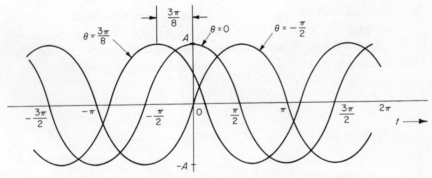

Fig. 1.6 *A cos $(2\pi t/T + \theta)$ for different values of θ.*

It was Fourier who first demonstrated that *any* periodic function (bounded, piecewise-continuous) can be represented as a sum of sinusoids and a constant. If the reciprocal of the period T is denoted by the frequency f, then these sinusoids are all harmonically related; that is, the frequencies of the sinusoids are all integral multiples of the fundamental frequency, $f = 1/T$. Specifically, if $p(t)$ represents the periodic wave of Fig. 1.4, Fourier insists that there exists a set of numbers $c_0, c_1, c_2, \ldots,$ and $\theta_1, \theta_2, \ldots,$ such that

$$p(t) = \frac{1}{T}\left\{c_0 + 2c_1 \cos\left(\frac{2\pi t}{T} + \theta_1\right) + 2c_2 \cos\left(\frac{4\pi t}{T} + \theta_2\right)\right.$$

$$\left. + 2c_3 \cos\left(\frac{6\pi t}{T} + \theta_3\right) + \ldots\right\}$$

Using summation notation, this can be written in compact form as

$$p(t) = \frac{c_0}{T} + \frac{2}{T}\sum_{n=1}^{\infty} c_n \cos\left(\frac{2\pi nt}{T} + \theta_n\right)$$

(The reader may wonder why the $1/T$ is brought out as a factor and not assumed to be part of the constants c_n. The reason will become apparent shortly.)

Fourier went on to show that the constants c_n and θ_n could be easily determined from the Laplace transform of *one* period of the periodic wave. Specifically, if $P(s)$ is the Laplace transform of one period of the periodic wave, $p(t)$, then the magnitude of $P(j2\pi n/T)$ is c_n and its argument or angle is θ_n. Thus

$$P\left(\frac{j2\pi n}{T}\right) = c_n\underline{/\theta_n} = c_n e^{j\theta_n}$$

Again an example is in order, but it must be followed with some faith, since all the techniques involved have not been covered.

Consider the "square" wave of Fig. 1.7. Figure 1.8 shows one period of this square wave. It must be taken on faith at this point that the Laplace transform of this single rectangular pulse is given by

$$P(s) = \frac{A(e^{Ts/4} - e^{-Ts/4})}{s}$$

If s is now replaced by $j2\pi n/T$, then

$$P\left(\frac{j2\pi n}{T}\right) = \frac{A(e^{jn\pi/2} - e^{-jn\pi/2})}{2jn\pi/T}$$

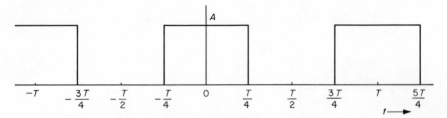

Fig. 1.7 *A square wave.*

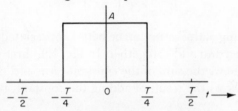

Fig. 1.8 *One period of the square wave of Fig. 1.7.*

But $(e^{jx} - e^{-jx})/2j = \sin x$, so the last expression can be written

$$P\left(\frac{j2\pi n}{T}\right) = \frac{AT}{n\pi} \sin\left(\frac{n\pi}{2}\right)$$

According to Fourier, the magnitude of this complex number (it is real in this example, but not in general) is c_n, and its angle is θ_n, for all $n = 0,1,2,\ldots$. Note that $n = 0$ yields an indeterminate form. This happens quite frequently, but it can be avoided by using L'Hôpital's rule, or, what is equivalent, by replacing $\sin(n\pi/2)$ by $n\pi/2$, since the sine approaches the angle for small angles. Thus

$$c_0 = \frac{AT}{2}$$

$$c_1 = \frac{AT}{\pi}, \qquad \theta_1 = 0$$

$$c_2 = 0$$

$$c_3 = \frac{AT}{3\pi}, \qquad \theta_3 = \pi \text{ (or } -\pi)$$

(Note that c_3 could be $-AT/3\pi$ with $\theta_3 = 0$.) Apparently $c_n = AT/n\pi$ when n is odd, and the signs alternate. $c_n = 0$ when n is even.

If these results are now substituted into the general expression for the Fourier series, we have

$$p(t) = \frac{c_0}{T} + \frac{2}{T} \sum_{n=1}^{\infty} c_n \cos\left(\frac{2\pi nt}{T} + \theta_n\right)$$

$$p(t) = \frac{A}{2} + \frac{2A}{\pi} \sum_{n=1,3,5,\ldots}^{\infty} \frac{(-1)^{(n-1)/2}}{n} \cos\left(\frac{2\pi nt}{T}\right)$$

$$= \frac{A}{2} + \frac{2A}{\pi} \cos\left(\frac{2\pi t}{T}\right) - \frac{2A}{3\pi} \cos\left(\frac{6\pi t}{T}\right)$$

$$+ \frac{2A}{5\pi} \cos\left(\frac{10\pi t}{T}\right) - \cdots$$

The meaning of this series can be better appreciated if the individual terms are plotted and added together. In Fig. 1.9, three sketches appear. Figure 1.9(a) shows the sum of the constant term and the fundamental. Figure 1.9(b) shows the result of adding the constant, the fundamental,

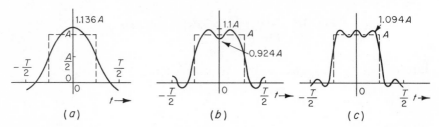

Fig. 1.9 (a) *Constant and fundamental.* (b) *Constant, first, and third harmonics.* (c) *Constant, first, third, and fifth harmonics.*

and the third harmonic. Figure 1.9(c) is the sum of the constant, the fundamental, and the third and fifth harmonics. The figures clearly indicate that as more and more terms are added to the series, the resulting waveform does approach more and more closely the square wave to which it is equivalent.

The discovery of the Fourier series has permitted engineers to associate specific meanings with the word frequency: frequency refers to a sinusoid only. Although the rectangular wave of the example may be spoken of by the layman as having a frequency $1/T$, the engineer recognizes from its nonsinusoidal nature that harmonics—that is, frequencies of integral multiples of $1/T$—must be present. Furthermore it is possible to design a filter that will remove the higher harmonics and produce at its output a pure sinusoid: the fundamental or any one of the higher harmonics. Devices have been designed that can present on the face of a cathode-ray tube a plot of the amplitudes of the harmonics versus frequency. Such devices are called *spectrum analyzers*.

A striking example of the audio effects of nonsinusoidal waveforms is that a well-trained ear can distinguish easily between different musical instruments even if they are all playing the same note. The frequency of any note is its *fundamental* frequency (pitch). The fact that different instruments have different qualities (timbre) is due solely to the fact that their waveforms (hence harmonic contents) differ.

Chapter 7 treats the Fourier series and the notion of frequency spectra for periodic waveforms.

1.4 The Fourier Transform

The differences between the Fourier transform and the Laplace transform are subtle. At first glance it will appear that to obtain the Fourier transform from the Laplace transform we merely write $j\omega$ for s, and there the difference ends. This is true for the most part, but untrue for some situations.

The electrical engineer uses the Fourier transform to assist him in what might be called spectrum analysis. Thus, whereas the Laplace transform is used to solve transient circuit problems, the Fourier transform is used to give the student some insight into what is now known as the *frequency domain*.

This is the day of the high-fidelity sound system. Hi-Fi's (a term used to identify a system that reproduces audio signals with high fidelity) consist of amplifiers that reproduce sinusoidal signals in the range of 20 cps to 20,000 cps. The usual criterion is a "flat" response; that is, all sinusoids of a given amplitude and with a frequency in the range stated should be amplified by the same amount. Thus a sinusoid of magnitude 1 volt may be amplified to 100 volts at any signal frequency in the interval 20 cps to 20 kc. (This is not, however, all that is really necessary for the faithful reproduction of audio signals.)

The band of frequencies mentioned above is chosen because the lowest note on the piano is about 27.5 cps and the highest tone a good human ear can hear has a frequency below 20 kc. This reasoning seems plausible enough as an argument for establishing the 20-cps to 20-kc range as appropriate for a high-fidelity system, especially if music signals are to be transmitted. However, it does not necessarily follow that voice signals or speech will be amplified without distortion simply because music is. Nevertheless, an experiment with a voice signal over a high-fidelity system (or even a low-fidelity system such as the telephone) does reveal that the signal is, in fact, amplified without noticeable distortion. It must be possible, then, to characterize nonperiodic signals in the frequency domain, even though the signals appear to be completely unrelated to sinusoidal signals.

Consider, for example, a single pulse that is never repeated. The triangular pulse of Fig. 1.10 is chosen since it is easy to draw, but any shape would do as well. If a system *can* transmit this signal without distortion once, it should be able to do it again. Thus, if the signal were repeated T sec later, where T is larger than the pulse length δ, then the system should be capable of transmitting this signal again without distortion. In fact, the system should be able to transmit the signal over and over again, if it could be produced periodically with period T. This is shown in Fig. 1.11.

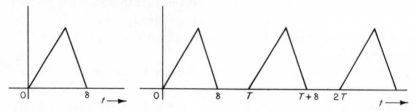

Fig. 1.10 *A pulse.*   **Fig. 1.11** *The pulse of Fig. 1.10 repeated periodically.*

Thus, any signal, if it is of finite duration (δ), can be made into a periodic function with $T > \delta$. We may say that the criterion for faithful reproduction is the same for the lone signal as it is for the periodic signal, and that this should be true for *any* period $T > \delta$. In other words the system should reproduce the signal accurately, no matter how large a period elapses before its repetition.

If a periodic signal is constructed from the aperiodic signal in the manner suggested above, it is possible to obtain for it a Fourier series and a *line* spectrum—that is, a series of harmonics with the fundamental frequency $1/T$. If this is done for all values of T as T goes from δ to $+\infty$, it can be shown that all of the resulting line spectra have something in common: they all have the same *envelope*. Thus for any aperiodic signal there is a function of frequency f; this function is the envelope of all spectra that can be constructed by the periodic repetition of this signal. The envelope is called the *Fourier transform* of the signal.

Since all practical signals have both definite beginnings and definite ends, they fall into this classification, and each is said to possess a continuous spectrum. This spectrum is the Fourier transform of the signal. Hence a strict mathematical interpretation can be made of time-signals in the frequency domain.

The engineer now has two ways of viewing a communication system or problem: in the time domain (transient) and in the frequency domain (transform). Some problems are better suited to one domain than the other, but the ability to view a situation from two entirely different angles is essential to the engineer.

As indicated in the beginning of this section, for all practical signals—signals that have beginnings and ends—the Fourier transform is obtained by simply replacing the letter s in the Laplace transform by $j\omega = j2\pi f$. There are, however, signals that do not have beginnings or ends and whose transforms are mathematically very simple. For some of these functions the Fourier transform is quite different from the Laplace transform. In fact, some signals have Fourier transforms but no Laplace transforms, and others have Laplace transforms but no Fourier transforms.

It would be wrong to suggest that signal transmission is the only area of engineering in which Fourier transforms are important. In the theory of probability the *characteristic function* of a probability density function is its Fourier transform (or the conjugate thereof). The entire field of *information theory* rests on the theory of probability, and a thorough knowledge of Fourier transforms is essential to this field.

Many probability density functions are not practical signals in the sense used previously. The Gaussian function, for example, is defined from $-\infty$ to $+\infty$. For this and other functions the Fourier transform is definitely *not* obtained by substitution of $j\omega$ for s.

1.5 Objectives

The chapters that follow have two goals: (1) *power*, to provide powerful tools with which transient circuit problems can be solved; (2) *sophistication*, to enhance comprehension of the frequency domain and to emphasize its relation to the time domain.

It will be noted that each technique is studied separately, and most sections are followed by a group of practice problems. In many cases a chapter is also followed by a set of problems, designed to tie together all the ideas of that chapter and unite it with those chapters preceding it.

chapter

2

Sources, Signals, and Circuits

2.1 Introduction

This chapter defines the sources and elements that are to be used, discusses the mathematical notations to be used, introduces the step function and its derivative, and presents the loop and nodal methods of writing circuit equations in the time domain. The last section deals with the exponential function, which will be used continuously in the chapters that follow.

2.2 Sources

The Voltage Source

As are all elements in circuit theory, the voltage source is a fictitious device. Actual energy sources, however, can be approximated arbitrarily closely by an ideal voltage (or current) source in combination with one or more of the circuit elements: resistance, capacitance, or inductance. A battery, for example, can be approximated very closely by an ideal voltage source in series with a small resistance.

An ideal voltage source, hereinafter referred to simply as a voltage source, is a two-terminal device; the potential difference across it is a specified and fixed time signal. This time signal may be any function of time desired: a constant, a sinusoid, any periodic function, or any aperiodic function—even the electrical equivalent of the human voice in any of its many moods.

The important idea to remember is that the specific time signal exists across the terminals *no matter what* is connected to the terminals. The symbol used in this text for a voltage source is that which appears in Fig. 2.1. The wiggle in the circle is not intended to imply that the

source is necessarily a sinusoid; it is there only for identification purposes. In all cases, either the letters $e(t)$, indicating an emf that varies
with time (this includes constants also, which do not really vary with
time), or an actual function, such as 10 sin (377t), will be written to the
side of the source. One terminal will be marked with a plus ($+$) sign,
and the other will be marked with a minus ($-$) sign. These marks do
not, however, mean that the terminal so marked is electrically charged

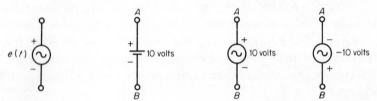

Fig. 2.1 *A voltage source.*   **Fig. 2.2** *A battery and two equivalent voltage sources.*

positively or negatively, nor do they mean that the terminal marked
($+$) is always positive with respect to the other terminal. What the
signs *do* mean is that whenever the signal written next to the source is
positive, the potential has the polarity shown, but when that signal is
negative, the actual polarity is *opposite* that shown.

A symbol other than that shown in Fig. 2.1 is sometimes used for a
constant voltage source or battery. This symbol appears in Fig. 2.2(a),
and though it is not used in this text, the figure does emphasize the
convention used in the text with regard to signs or polarity marks.
Figure 2.2(a) depicts a battery, the large plate (the longer line) of which
is usually considered to be the positive plate. Figure 2.2(b) shows this
source as it is represented in this text. Figure 2.2(c) shows an alternative
representation of the same source. Note that a change in the algebraic
sign of the source requires that the polarity marks be *reversed*. It may be
difficult at first to accustom ourselves to the idea of negative potential,
but it is to our advantage to generalize in this manner at the outset of
this study.

To avoid a contradiction, one rule must be established immediately:
No two (or more) voltage sources may be placed in parallel *with each other unless*
for every instant of time *they have exactly the same voltage values across them.*
Since a short-circuit can be thought of as a voltage source (of zero volts
for all time), this rule naturally excludes the short-circuiting of a voltage
source.

It is assumed in all cases in this text that there is no resistance,
capacitance, or inductance associated with a voltage source unless the

symbol for the element appears connected to the source. Thus, it will never be assumed that a source has an internal resistance or impedance. If the actual source being represented does have an internal impedance, it will appear as a circuit element connected to the source.

The Current Source

Like the voltage source, the current source is an ideal source without impedance.* It is a device that causes a positive charge to move through it at a specified *rate* no matter what may be connected to it. (If nothing is connected to it then it showers the charge into the air.) Clearly, the current source should always be provided with a return path for the charge.

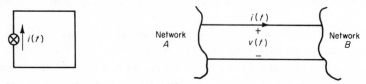

Fig. 2.3 *A current source.*   **Fig. 2.4** *A two-wire line connecting two networks.*

Figure 2.3 is an example of the symbol used in this text for a current source. Note that a return path for the charge is provided in the form of a short-circuit. As with the voltage source, the arrow and the time signal $i(t)$ indicate the direction and amount of the current that the source is delivering. The current will have the direction of the arrow only when the signal is positive. When the signal is negative, the current will have the opposite direction.

The cross in the circle is not representative of a characteristic; it is used only to distinguish the current source from the voltage source. As in the case of the voltage source, the algebraic sign of the source may be changed, provided the direction of the arrow is reversed.

Again, to avoid an almost obvious contradiction, the following rule must be established: *No two (or more) current sources may be connected*

---

*Sometimes the internal impedance of a voltage source is said to be zero ohms, since a voltage source of zero volts is indistinguishable from a short-circuit, or zero resistance. In like manner, a current source delivering zero amperes is indistinguishable from an open circuit. Thus the internal impedance of a current source is usually said to be *infinite*. It would be more proper, perhaps, to refer to a current source as a source without admittance.

in series *unless the current values and their directions are exactly the same* for all instants of time. An open circuit is a current source of zero amperes; hence a current source can never be open-circuited.

2.3 Power and Energy

The time rate at which work is done in an electric circuit is an instantaneous function of time just as are the voltage and current. By definition, the direction of power flow *at any instant* over a two-wire line is the same as the direction of the current at that instant in the wire that is more positive. Specifically, in Fig. 2.4, if at time t_0:

    1. $v(t_0)$ and $i(t_0)$ are both positive, power is going to the right.

    2. $v(t_0)$ and $i(t_0)$ are both negative, power is going to the right.

    (Note here that despite the polarity marks, the bottom line is the more positive and the current in that line is going to the right.)

    3. $v(t_0)$ is positive and $i(t_0)$ is negative, power goes to the left.

    4. $v(t_0)$ is negative and $i(t_0)$ is positive, power goes to the left.

If $p(t)$ is defined as the instantaneous power going to the right in Fig. 2.4, then

$$p(t) = v(t)\, i(t) \text{ watts} \qquad (2.1)$$

from which we note that power is a nonlinear quantity and will not be invariant under linear transformations such as Thévenin's theorem, the superposition theorem, and so on. (See Probs. 2.15 and 2.16 at the end of Sec. 2.7.)

If $W(t)$ represents the total energy in joules that has moved to the right in Fig. 2.4, then

$$p(t) = \frac{dW(t)}{dt} \qquad (2.2)$$

and

$$W(t) = \int_{-\infty}^{t} p(t)\, dt \qquad (2.3)$$

It will be noted in Eq. (2.3) that the lower limit of the integral is chosen as $-\infty$; this is all-inclusive. Clearly no energy could have moved to the right (or to the left for that matter) before the circuits were connected. The lower limit should be the time the circuit was first energized. Since $p(t)$ is zero before then, the value of the integral from $-\infty$ to that point in time will be zero; so, with this convention, Eq. (2.3) is both mathematically and actually correct. In this text the inverse of differentiation with respect to t will always be a *definite* integral with lower limit $-\infty$ and upper limit t. The problems following this section cover in detail functional notation and the operations of differentiation and its inverse.

The circuit that we are usually interested in studying is one that is energized or altered at some specific time. For convenience, this time is almost always chosen as $t = 0$, and t can be envisioned as the reading of a stopwatch that is clicked on just as the switch is thrown. Then, from Eq. (2.3), the energy delivered *before* this time is obtained by replacing t with 0 in the upper limit only:

$$W(0) = \int_{-\infty}^{0} p(t)\ dt \tag{2.4}$$

But it is known that Eq. (2.3) can be divided into two integrals

$$W(t) = \int_{-\infty}^{0} p(t)\ dt + \int_{0}^{t} p(t)\ dt$$

Combining this last equation with Eq. (2.4) gives

$$W(t) = \int_{0}^{t} p(t)\ dt + W(0) \text{ for } t > 0 \tag{2.5}$$

Using Eq. (2.1) in Eq. (2.5), we have

$$W(t) = \int_{0}^{t} v(t)i(t)\ dt + W(0), \ t > 0 \tag{2.6}$$

Eqs. (2.5) and (2.6) indicate that $W(t)$ cannot be calculated unless $v(t)$ and $i(t)$ are known for all values of time, or that $v(t)$ and $i(t)$ must be known at least for positive t, and that $W(0)$ must be given. In all problems in this text either $W(0)$ or information by which $W(0)$ can be obtained will be given. If this is not the case, then $W(0)$ will be assumed to be zero.

PROBLEMS

2.1   The symbol $v(t)$ is read v of t, and means that the voltage v has a value that depends on the time t. The value of the voltage at $t = 2$ sec is represented as $v(2)$, the value at $t = -3$ sec is $v(-3)$, and so on. Let $v(t) = e^{-t}$ for positive t, and zero for negative t.

(a)   Use a set of tables or a slide rule and evaluate $v(0+)$. [$v(0+)$ means the limit of $v(\epsilon)$ as ϵ approaches zero through positive values. The function $v(t)$ is undefined at $t = 0$.] Also evaluate $v(1)$, $v(-1)$, $v(2)$, $v(3)$, $v(4)$, and $v(5)$.

(b) Using the results of part (a), plot carefully $v(t)$ versus t in the interval $-3 < t < 5$.

2.2 For $v(t) = e^{-t}$, $t > 0$, and $v(t) = 0$, $t < 0$, plot

(a) $5v(t)$ (b) $2v(t-1)$ (c) $v(-t)$ (d) $-2v(3-t)$

2.3 If $v(t) = 2 - 3t + t^3$, then functional notation means that $v(x) = 2 - 3x + x^3$, $v(\sin y) = 2 - 3 \sin y + (\sin y)^3$, and $v(z^2) = 2 - 3z^2 + z^6$. In other words, whatever appears in the parentheses after the letter v, this quantity or function is to be substituted for t in the explicit expression to which $v(t)$ is equivalent. For the $v(t)$ of this problem evaluate

(a) $\int_{-2}^{4} v(t)\, dt$ (b) $\int_{0}^{t} v(t)\, dt$

(c) $\int_{-2}^{4} v(y)\, dy$ (d) $\int_{0}^{t} v(x)\, dx$

$$\text{Answer to (d): } 2t - \frac{3t^2}{2} + \frac{t^4}{4}$$

2.4 Let $F(t) = df(t)/dt$. Then $F(\zeta) = df(\zeta)/d\zeta$. Then, by the usual rules of integration

$$\int_{0}^{t} F(t)\, dt = f(t) - f(0)$$

Use this result to prove that

$$\int_{0}^{t} F(t)\, dt = \int_{0}^{t} F(x)\, dx = \int_{0}^{t} F(y)\, dy = \int_{0}^{t} F(\zeta)\, d\zeta$$

The variables t, x, y, and ζ *under* the integral sign (not the t in the upper limit) are called *dummy* variables of integration. Why are they called this?

2.5 The previous problems indicate that the definite integrals in them are functions of the *limits* of the integration rather than the dummy variables of integration. Hence

$$f(x) = \int_{-x}^{2} e^{-t}\, dt$$

is indeed a function of x and not t, as can be seen by carrying out the integration and substituting the limits. But

$$g(t) = \int_{-t}^{t^2} e^{-x}\, dx$$

is a function of t alone. Evaluate $f(x)$ and $g(t)$.

2.6 Let $g(t)$ and $h(t)$ be two arbitrary functions of t. Prove that if

$$i(t) = \int_{g(t)}^{h(t)} F(x)\ dx$$

then

$$\frac{di(t)}{dt} = F[h(t)]\frac{dh(t)}{dt} - F[g(t)]\frac{dg(t)}{dt}$$

Hint: Let $F(x) = df(x)/dx$.

2.7　Demonstrate the truth of the theorem of Prob. 2.6 by letting $F(x) = \cos x$
[$f(x)$ must then be $\sin x$], $g(t) = -t$, and $h(t) = t^2$.

(*a*)　Evaluate

$$i(t) = \int_{-t}^{t^2} \cos x\ dx$$

(*b*)　From the results of (*a*) find $di(t)/dt$.

(*c*)　Write out

$$F[h(t)]\frac{dh(t)}{dt} - F[g(t)]\frac{dg(t)}{dt}$$

and show that it is the same as the answer to part (*b*).

2.8　Using the results of Prob. 2.6, show that

$$\frac{d}{dt}\left(\int_{a}^{t} F(y)\ dy\right) = F(t)$$

where a is a constant. This proves that an inverse of differentiation
with respect to time is a definite integral with a constant lower limit
and an upper limit of t.

2.9　In the integral

$$\int_{0}^{5} x^3\ dx$$

change the dummy variable of integration x to $-3y$; that is, let $x = -3y$.
Show that the integral then becomes

$$81 \int_{0}^{-5/3} y^3\ dy$$

Evaluate the two integrals and show that they yield the same result.

Answer: 156.25

2.10　In the integral

$$I(t) = \int_{0}^{10} e^{-tx}\ dx$$

the dummy variable of integration is x, since this is the variable that
appears in the differential dx. t is to be treated as a constant so far as the
integration is concerned. Evaluate the integral.

Answer: $\dfrac{1 - e^{-10t}}{t}$

2.11 The symbols

$$\frac{\partial f(t,x)}{\partial x} \quad \text{and} \quad \frac{\partial f(t,x)}{\partial t}$$

are called *partial* derivatives. $f(t,x)$ is functional notation for a mathematical expression that contains *two* variables, x and t, as, for example, e^{-tx} in Prob. 2.10. The differentiation

$$\frac{\partial f(t,x)}{\partial x}$$

simply means that differentiation is to be performed with respect to x as though t were a constant, and

$$\frac{\partial f(t,x)}{\partial t}$$

means that differentiation is to be performed with respect to t, treating x as though it were a constant. Using this convention, evaluate

(a) $\dfrac{\partial e^{-tx}}{\partial x}$ (b) $\dfrac{\partial e^{-tx}}{\partial t}$ (c) $\dfrac{\partial \sin(3t^2x)}{\partial x}$ (d) $\dfrac{\partial \sin(3t^2x)}{\partial t}$

Answers: (b) $-xe^{-tx}$

(d) $6tx\cos(3t^2x)$

2.12 A theorem that will be of value to us in transform work can now be proved. Define

$$\frac{\partial f(t,x)}{\partial t} = \lim_{\Delta t \to 0} \frac{f(t + \Delta t,x) - f(t,x)}{\Delta t}$$

and

$$\frac{dI(t)}{dt} = \lim_{\Delta t \to 0} \frac{I(t + \Delta t) - I(t)}{\Delta t}$$

Further, let

$$I(t) = \int_a^b f(t,x)\, dx$$

where a and b are constants. From the integral relation between f and I, it must be true that

$$I(t + \Delta t) = \int_a^b f(t + \Delta t,x)\, dx$$

Formulate

$$\frac{I(t + \Delta t) - I(t)}{\Delta t}$$

and show that

$$\frac{dI(t)}{dt} = \int_a^b \left[\frac{\partial f(t,x)}{\partial t}\right] dx$$

(It is necessary here to assume that the limit of an integral is equal to the integral of the limit. This assumption is true when a and b are finite and $f(t,x)$ is continuous in both variables x and t).

2.13. Since

$$\frac{\partial e^{-tx}}{\partial t} = -xe^{-tx}$$

(Prob. 2.11), evaluate

$$\int_0^{10} -xe^{-tx}\,dx$$

(*a*) by direct integration (integration by parts), and (*b*) by differentiation of the answer to Prob. 2.10.

2.14. Prove that if

$$Q(s) = \int_{-\infty}^{\infty} q(t)e^{-st}\,dt$$

then

$$\frac{dQ(s)}{ds} = -\int_{-\infty}^{\infty} tq(t)e^{-st}\,dt$$

[The integral $Q(s)$ is *improper* because of the infinite limits. Using here the results of Prob. 2.12 can be justified only if the integral converges uniformly and absolutely in what will be known as a *region* in the *s*-plane. We should be aware of this distinction, but for the time being we need not be concerned about it.]

2.4 Resistance

The resistance element is defined as a device in which the existing current is at all times proportional to the potential across it. Figure 2.5 shows the symbol to be used for a resistance.

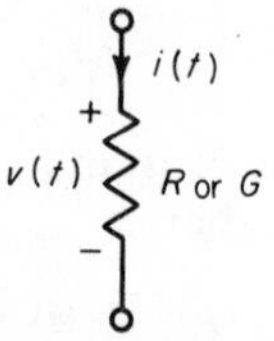

Fig. 2.5   *A resistance.* $v(t)$ R or G $i(t)$ +   −

In this figure note that the current direction is defined as positive in the direction plus to minus. This convention will always be used for passive elements in this text. With this convention as given, Ohm's law states that

$$v(t) = Ri(t) \qquad (2.7)$$

where R is the resistance in ohms, or

$$i(t) = Gv(t) \qquad (2.8)$$

where G is the conductance in mhos (ohm spelled backwards). Evidently

$$R = 1/G \qquad (2.9)$$

If these equations are substituted into Eq. (2.1), then

$$p(t) = v(t)i(t) = i^2(t)\,R = v^2(t)G = \frac{v^2(t)}{R} \qquad (2.10)$$

As with the sources, there are no pure resistances. Devices that approximate resistances under certain conditions are called *resistors*.

The power expressed by Eq. (2.10) is transformed from electric energy to energy in some other form. Usually this new energy is heat. In any event the energy disappears from the circuit.

2.5 Capacitance

The capacitance is a theoretical device that stores electric energy. The practical equivalent device is called a capacitor. Figure 2.6* depicts the symbol to be used for a capacitance. Note that as with the resistance, the current direction is from plus to minus.

Fig. 2.6 *A capacitance.*

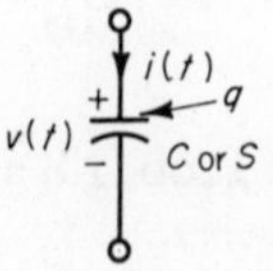

The relationship between the current and voltage for a capacitance comes from two basic laws of electricity. The first is that charge is conserved; that is, electric charge can neither be created nor destroyed. Thus, for example, any positive charge that flows in the top wire toward the top plate must terminate on the plate. It cannot move across the space between the plates. The charge being placed on the top plate may be thought of as coming from the bottom plate. In effect, it is removed from the bottom plate by the circuit to which it is connected—hence the charge on the top plate is always numerically equal to but of opposite sign from that on the bottom plate.

---

*For reasons concerned primarily with the radiation of the stored energy, and to avoid voltage or current breakdown of capacitors, the plate that is physically nearer the outside of the capacitor should be connected to a point where there is no time-varying potential or to a point of lower direct potential. For this reason, a curved line is drawn to indicate the outside plate (or outside foil; many capacitors are made with metal foil used for the plates).

Conservation of charge indicates that since the charge on the capacitance must come through the wires leading to it, then the charge q on the top plate must be related to the current by

$$i(t) = \frac{dq}{dt} \tag{2.11}$$

or

$$q = \int_{-\infty}^{t} i(t) \, dt \tag{2.12}$$

The second law that forms the relationship between the potential and the current is Coulomb's law. The pertinent result of this law is that the potential between the plates is directly proportional to the charge on the plates, the proportionality factor being defined as the capacitance in farads. Thus

$$v(t) = \frac{q}{C} \tag{2.13}$$

If Eq. (2.13) is combined with Eq. (2.12), the volt-ampere relation becomes

$$v(t) = \frac{1}{C} \int_{-\infty}^{t} i(t) \, dt \tag{2.14}$$

and, if the results of Prob. 2.8 are used,

$$i(t) = C \frac{dv(t)}{dt} \tag{2.15}$$

Equation (2.14) can be written as

$$v(t) = \frac{1}{C} \int_{0}^{t} i(t) \, dt + \gamma \tag{2.16}$$

where $\gamma = v(0)$ will be used to denote the initial voltage across the capacitance, that is, its value at $t = 0$. In this text the forms of the volt-ampere relations to be used are those of Eqs. (2.15) and (2.16). The reciprocal of C is defined as the elastance and denoted by the letter S. No use is actually made of G or S in this text, simply because it is not necessary; these quantities are rarely used in practice. Thus if a number is written near a resistance or capacitance, we are to assume that the former means ohms and the latter means farads, unless the contrary is specifically stated.

As a matter of interest, a unit has been defined for the elastance S.

It is the *daraf*. (It will be left as an exercise for the student to determine the origin of this word.)

If Eq. (2.15) is substituted into Eq. (2.3), then

$$W(t) = \int\limits_{-\infty}^{t} Cv(t) \left[\frac{dv(t)}{dt}\right] dt = \int\limits_{v(-\infty)}^{v(t)} Cv(t) \, dv(t) = \frac{1}{2} \, Cv^2(t) \bigg|_{v(-\infty)}^{v(t)}$$

Since the capacitance was not in existence at $t = -\infty$, it could not have had any potential across it, so $v(-\infty) = 0$. Clearly any value of time, such as t_0, would be appropriate for the lower limit, provided that before t_0 either no charge existed on the capacitance or that $v(t_0) = 0$. Thus

$$W(t) = \frac{1}{2} \, Cv^2(t) \text{ joules} \tag{2.17}$$

Thus the capacitance stores energy, the energy at any instant being dependent only on the potential across the device at that instant.

2.6 Inductance

An inductance is a device that stores magnetic energy. The basic laws that govern the behavior of this device are not as easy to visualize as those governing the behavior of the capacitance. Although present knowledge of the actual nature of charges is sparse, for convenience we can visualize them as small marbles rolling around in the wires and collecting on the plates.

The inductance, on the other hand, has no such simple (albeit not very accurate) artifice by which its behavior can be explained. Michael Faraday did devise one, however. For the inductance, Faraday's counterpart of charge for a capacitance is a *flux-linkage*. Flux-linkages resemble rubber bands linked around wires carrying current. Just as the behavior of a capacitance is related to the electric field effects of stationary charges, the behavior of the inductance is related to the magnetic field effects of moving charges. Flux lines are fictitious lines of magnetic force. One such flux line is shown in Fig. 2.7, where the symbol for an inductance is shown. Since inductors—that is, the devices that most nearly approximate the theoretical inductance—are manufactured by winding coils of wire, the symbol is pictorial in origin. Note that, as with the resistance and capacitance, the current is directed plus to minus.

The number of flux-linkages is the product of the number of flux lines and the number of turns that the flux lines link. As with charge on a capacitance, a flux-linkage is conserved. Specifically, it is impossible to change the flux-linkages of a short-circuited coil just as it is impossible to change the charge on an open-circuited capacitance. No attempt

Fig. 2.7   *An inductance.*

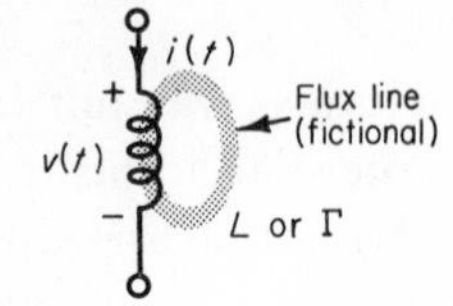

will be made at this point to explain the last two remarks by physical reasoning. A true understanding of the magnetic behavior of electricity can only be achieved by a study of electromagnetic field theory. The only attempt here to justify the notion of flux-linkages will be a mathematical analogy to charge.

If the flux-linkages of a coil are denoted by λ, then, by definition, the flux-linkages are

$$\lambda = \int_{-\infty}^{t} v(t)\ dt \qquad (2.18)$$

Note the similarity between this equation and Eq. (2.12); however, no attempt to devise a physical connection between flux-linkages and the integral of the voltage will be made here. Memorize the relations, and be certain to study electro-magnetics in order to attain some appreciation of the meaning of the terms used.

The current in the coil is proportional to the flux-linkages, the proportionality factor being defined as the inductance L of the coil in henrys. Thus

$$\lambda = Li* \qquad (2.19)$$

Combining Eqs. (2.18) and (2.19) yields the desired volt-ampere relations

$$i(t) = \frac{1}{L} \int_{-\infty}^{t} v(t)\ dt \qquad (2.20)$$

---

*Flux-linkages derive their name from the linking of ϕ flux lines about N turns of wire. Thus $\lambda = N\phi$ is an alternate definition if all ϕ lines link all N turns. Such a definition makes Eq. (2.21) read $v = N d\phi/dt$, which is, perhaps, the more familiar form of Faraday's law.

and

$$v(t) = L\frac{di(t)}{dt} \tag{2.21}$$

Equation (2.20) can be written with a zero in the lower limit, as before

$$i(t) = \frac{1}{L}\int_0^t v(t)\,dt + \rho \tag{2.22}$$

where $\rho = i(0)$ will be used to denote the initial current in the inductance, that is, the current at $t = 0$. Equations (2.21) and (2.22) are the relations to remember.

As with the other two elements, the reciprocal of L is defined as Γ, but it has no standard unit designation, due undoubtedly to the peculiar appearance of henry spelled backwards. However, unlike the reciprocals of resistance and capacitance, we will use the reciprocal of the inductance quite frequently, although never for a single inductance. When it appears, we will go ahead and use the unit *yrneh* (rhymes with Ernie).

It will be explained in the next section that when Γ is used with mutually coupled coils, the inductance of a coil in henrys will *not* be the reciprocal of its reciprocal inductance in yrnehs. Remember for now that $\Gamma \neq 1/L$ when there are two or more mutually coupled coils.

As indicated in the beginning of this section, the inductance is an energy-storage device. Substituting Eq. (2.21) into Eq. (2.3) [assuming $i(-\infty)$ is zero for the same reason that the voltage across the capacitance is zero at $t = -\infty$] yields

$$W(t) = \tfrac{1}{2} Li^2(t) \text{ joules} \tag{2.23}$$

Then the energy stored at any instant in the inductance depends only on the current that exists at that moment in the coil.

2.7 Mutual Inductance

When two inductors are brought near each other, the current in one of them affects the behavior of the other. Specifically, a time-varying current in one induces a voltage in the other. Using the flux-linkage concept, flux caused by current in one coil links the other coil. The voltage induced in the opposite coil is proportional to the rate of change of the current in the other coil and vice versa, the proportionality factor being defined as the mutual inductance in henrys M. Figure 2.8(*a*) depicts the symbols used for the individual coils and the mutual inductance. The dots at the ends of the coils have a very specific meaning: they indicate the polarity of the induced voltage. If a current i is directed into the dotted end of one coil, then the potential induced in the other coil will be

$$e = M\frac{di}{dt}$$

and the plus sign will be the dotted end of the other coil. Conversely, if the current is directed into the undotted end of the first coil, then the dotted end of the other coil will be negative.

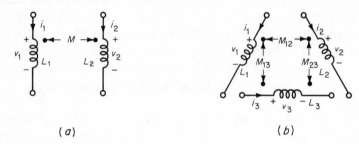

(*a*)   (*b*)

Fig. 2.8   (*a*) *Two mutually coupled coils.* (*b*) *Three mutually coupled coils.*

In Fig. 2.8(*b*) three coils are shown, each coupled to the others. Note that three mutuals and three sets of dots (some dots do double duty) are required to specify completely all the coupling coefficients and polarities. The placement of the dots are determined by the manner in which the coils are wound and the direction in which the flux of one coil links the other. Rules for determining this are stated in Probs. 2.27 and 2.29. Thus the dots are an essential part of the information of the circuit. Several of the problems that follow this section illustrate this point.

For two coupled coils in which both currents are directed *into* (or out of) the dots and in which the voltages are defined as plus to minus in the direction of current [as in Fig. 2.8(*a*)], the volt-ampere relations are

$$v_1(t) = L_1\frac{di_1(t)}{dt} + M\frac{di_2(t)}{dt}$$

$$v_2(t) = M\frac{di_1(t)}{dt} + L_2\frac{di_2(t)}{dt}$$

(2.24)

These equations may be solved for the currents by integrating both sides from 0 to t:

$$\int_0^t v_1 \, dt = L_1 \left[i_1(t) - i_1(0) \right] + M \left[i_2(t) - i_2(0) \right]$$

(2.25)

$$\int_0^t v_2 \, dt = M \left[i_1(t) - i_1(0) \right] + L_2 \left[i_2(t) - i_2(0) \right]$$

If the first equation of (2.25) is multiplied through by L_2/M, and the second is subtracted from the result, we obtain

$$\frac{L_2}{M} \int_0^t v_1 \, dt - \int_0^t v_2 \, dt = \left(\frac{L_1 L_2}{M} - M \right) \left[i_1(t) - i_1(0) \right]$$

If we multiply both sides of the last result by $M/(L_1 L_2 - M^2)$ and re-arrange terms, we have

$$i_1(t) = \frac{L_2}{L_1 L_2 - M^2} \int_0^t v_1 \, dt - \frac{M}{L_1 L_2 - M^2} \int_0^t v_2 \, dt + i_1(0)$$

In an entirely similar way we can solve for i_2, giving

$$i_2(t) = -\frac{M}{L_1 L_2 - M^2} \int_0^t v_1 \, dt + \frac{L_1}{L_1 L_2 - M^2} \int_0^t v_2 \, dt + i_2(0)$$

If we now define

$$\Gamma_1 = \frac{L_2}{\Delta L} \qquad \Gamma_m = \frac{M}{\Delta L} \qquad \Gamma_2 = \frac{L_1}{\Delta L} \qquad \Delta L = L_1 L_2 - M^2$$

(Δ stands for determinant here, not an increment), then the last two equations can be written

$$i_1(t) = \Gamma_1 \int_0^t v_1 \, dt - \Gamma_m \int_0^t v_2 \, dt + \rho_1$$

(2.26)

$$i_2(t) = -\Gamma_m \int_0^t v_1 \, dt + \Gamma_2 \int_0^t v_2 \, dt + \rho_2$$

The expressions relating the Γ terms to the L terms are correct if only two coils are mutually coupled; they are incorrect if more than two coils are coupled magnetically. Note that Γ_1, for example, is the reciprocal of L_1 *only if M is zero*. This is the reason for the statement near the conclusion of the previous section.

If there are more than two coils, say for example the three in Fig. 2.8(b), then the volt-ampere relations can be written as

$$v_1 = L_1 \frac{di_1}{dt} + M_{12} \frac{di_2}{dt} + M_{13} \frac{di_3}{dt}$$

$$v_2 = M_{12} \frac{di_1}{dt} + L_2 \frac{di_2}{dt} - M_{23} \frac{di_3}{dt} \qquad (2.27)$$

$$v_3 = M_{13} \frac{di_1}{dt} - M_{23} \frac{di_2}{dt} + L_3 \frac{di_3}{dt}$$

Note that the sign before M_{23} is negative, since for these two coils the currents do not both enter the dotted ends.

The inverse relations for Eq. (2.27) can also be written, but it is not possible to determine the signs of the mutual terms (see Prob. 2.29). Also, the individual coefficients are not given by any relation between L and Γ thus far mentioned. The technique for obtaining Γ from L and M is discussed in Chapter 6. It amounts to solving a set of simultaneous equations, as has been done here for the two-coil case.

In any event it is worthwhile to present the inverted equations to demonstrate their form, and to emphasize the fact that only one initial current appears in each equation. As before noted, $\rho_1 = i_1(0)$, $\rho_2 = i_2(0)$, and $\rho_3 = i_3(0)$.

$$i_1(t) = \Gamma_{11} \int_0^t v_1 \, dt \pm \Gamma_{12} \int_0^t v_2 \, dt \pm \Gamma_{13} \int_0^t v_3 \, dt + \rho_1$$

$$i_2(t) = \pm \Gamma_{12} \int_0^t v_1 \, dt + \Gamma_{22} \int_0^t v_2 \, dt \pm \Gamma_{23} \int_0^t v_3 \, dt + \rho_2 \qquad (2.28)$$

$$i_3(t) = \pm \Gamma_{13} \int_0^t v_1 \, dt \pm \Gamma_{23} \int_0^t v_2 \, dt + \Gamma_{33} \int_0^t v_3 \, dt + \rho_3$$

It is well to point out at this time a physical limitation on the parameters. Though it will not be proved here,* the mutual inductance between any two coils cannot exceed the geometric mean of the self-inductances of the coils. In this connection a quantity k, defined by

$$k = \frac{M}{\sqrt{L_1 L_2}} < 1 \qquad (2.29)$$

is called the *coefficient of coupling* of the coils.

---

*See Probs. 2.19 and 2.20 following this section.

PROBLEMS

2.15. In Sec. 2.3, on power and energy, a statement was made that since power is nonlinear, it will not remain invariant under a linear transformation. To illustrate the meaning of this statement, consider the two circuits in Fig. 2.9.

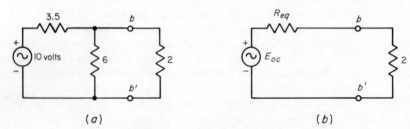

Fig. 2.9 *Problem 2.15.*

(a) For the circuit of Fig. 2.9(a), calculate the power delivered to the 2-ohm resistance and the power supplied by the 10-volt source.

(b) For the circuit in Fig. 2.9(b) calculate the Thévènin equivalent— that is, find E_{oc} and R_{eq}—so that the circuits are equivalent at the terminals b and b'.

(c) For the Thévènin equivalent obtained in (b), calculate the power dissipated in the 2-ohm resistance and the power supplied by the source E_{oc}. Compare the power requirements of the source and the power dissipated by the 2-ohm resistance in both cases.

2.16. Use the principle of superposition to solve for the current in the 2-ohm resistance in the circuit of Fig. 2.10; that is, calculate the current and power dissipated in the resistance when the current source is replaced by an open circuit, and then calculate the power and current again when the voltage source is replaced by a short-circuit. Compare their algebraic sums with the actual power and current in the resistance when both sources are present.

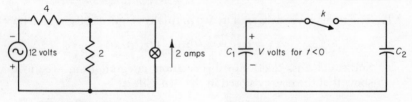

Fig. 2.10 *Problem 2.16.*   **Fig. 2.11** *Problem 2.17.*

2.17. The capacitances C_1 and C_2 appear in the circuit of Fig. 2.11. Before $t = 0$, the switch k is open, C_1 is charged to a potential of V volts, where V is a constant, and C_2 is uncharged. At $t = 0$ the switch k is closed.

(a) What is the charge on C_1 (in terms of V and C_1) before $t = 0$?

(b) What is the energy stored on C_1 and C_2 before $t = 0$?

(c) Assuming that charge is conserved, and noting that the potential across both capacitances must be the same for $t > 0$, what will be the voltage across the capacitances and the total energy stored after the switch is closed? Observe that the energy stored is *less* than it was before.

(d) Since conservation of charge in (c) obviously violates the law of conservation of energy, then assume that the total energy stored after the switch is closed is the same as that stored on C_1 before $t = 0$. Calculate the voltage and total charge on C_1 and C_2 after $t = 0$. This indicates that the law of conservation of energy negates the law of conservation of charge, since more charge exists after the switch is closed than existed before $t = 0$.

(e) Which solution is correct: (c), (d), or neither? If (c) is correct, where did the energy go? If (d) is correct, where did the extra charge come from? (We could always go into the laboratory and find out. The only difficulty in a laboratory experiment of this kind is that the measurement of voltage is difficult because the capacitors start to discharge through the voltmeter as soon as it is connected. If the voltmeter resistance is very high, and large capacitances are used, good results can be obtained.) (See also Probs. 2.79 and 2.80 at the end of this chapter.)

Answer to (c): $\dfrac{C_1}{C_1 + C_2}\, V$ volts $\dfrac{C_1^2}{2(C_1 + C_2)} V^2$ joules

Answer to (e):   Part (c) is correct. The energy went into either heat, light, sound, or radiation.

2.18. In the relations between the inductance and the reciprocal inductance parameters for two coupled coils, derived immediately preceding Eq. (2.26), show that if $\Delta\Gamma = \Gamma_1\,\Gamma_2 - \Gamma_m^2$, then $\Delta\Gamma = 1/\Delta L$. Also show that

$$L_1 = \frac{\Gamma_2}{\Delta\Gamma}, \; M = \frac{\Gamma_m}{\Delta\Gamma}, \text{ and } L_2 = \frac{\Gamma_1}{\Delta\Gamma}$$

2.19. The total power delivered to two mutually coupled coils is given by

$$p(t) = v_1(t)i_1(t) + v_2(t)i_2(t)$$

Substitute Eqs. (2.24) into this relation, integrate from $-\infty$ to t, and show that the energy stored in the two coils is

$$W(t) = \tfrac{1}{2}\left[L_1 i_1^2(t) + 2\,M i_1(t)i_2(t) + L_2 i_2^2(t)\right]$$

2.20. In the expression appearing for $W(t)$ in Prob. 2.19, substitute $M = k\sqrt{L_1 L_2}$ and complete the square by adding and subtracting $\tfrac{1}{2}k^2 L_2 i_2^2(t)$ to the right-hand side of the equation. Deduce that, since

$W(t)$ must always be positive (there is no such thing as negative stored energy) and the currents can have any positive or negative values, $k^2 \leq 1$.

2.21. Show that the coefficient of coupling can be expressed in terms of reciprocal inductance by

$$k = \frac{\Gamma_m}{\sqrt{\Gamma_1 \Gamma_2}}$$

2.22. An ideal transformer is defined as a pair of coupled coils for which the coefficient of coupling is unity, and the inductances L_1 and L_2 are very large; that is, they tend towards infinity such that their ratio always remains constant. Naturally there are in reality no ideal transformers, but there are transformers with coefficients of coupling of 0.98 and very large inductances.

(a) Assuming that $k = 1$, show that Eqs. (2.24) imply that $v_1(t)$ and $v_2(t)$ are proportional to each other. Find this proportionality factor.

(b) The ideal transformer has the symbol appearing in Fig. 2.12. It is characterized by the following relations:

$$v_1(t) = a v_2(t)$$

$$i_1(t) = -\frac{i_2(t)}{a}$$

where a is a constant.
Show that the device neither dissipates nor stores energy.

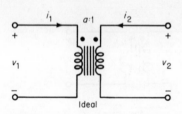

Fig. 2.12 *An ideal transformer.*   **Fig. 2.13** *Problem 2.22(c).*

(c) Show that the circuit of Fig. 2.13 has the same volt-ampere relations as those of Eqs. (2.24) when $M = \sqrt{L_1 L_2}$ [note that, from part (b), $i_1' = -\sqrt{L_2/L_1}\, i_2$]. Conclude from this that, as L_1 and L_2 become infinite, the closely coupled coils $(k = 1)$ approach an ideal transformer with a turns-ratio of $\sqrt{L_1/L_2}$ to 1.

2.23. (a) Show that the volt-ampere relations of the circuit appearing in Fig. 2.14 are exactly the same as Eqs. (2.24). Thus, *any* pair of mutually coupled coils can be represented by three inductances and an ideal transformer. Note that the turns-ratio a of the transformer could be any number at all. Is there any reason for this?

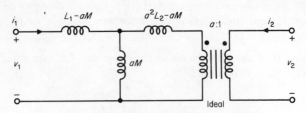

Fig. 2.14 *Problem 2.23(a).*

(b) Set $a = \sqrt{L_1/L_2}$ in Fig. 2.14, and show that it is equivalent to Fig. 2.15.

(c) Set $a = L_1/M$ in the circuit of Fig. 2.14, and draw the transformer equivalent circuit. Label the element values.

(d) Repeat (c), but for $a = M/L_2$.

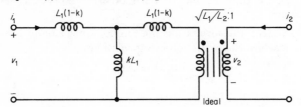

Fig. 2.15 *One common transformer equivalent circuit.*

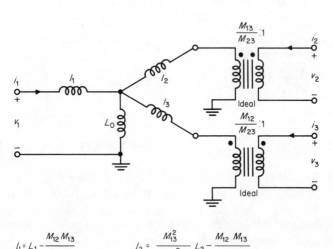

$$l_1 = L_1 - \frac{M_{12}M_{13}}{M_{23}} \qquad l_2 = \frac{M_{13}^2}{M_{23}^2}L_2 - \frac{M_{12}M_{13}}{M_{23}}$$

$$l_3 = \frac{M_{12}^2}{M_{23}^2}L_3 - \frac{M_{12}M_{13}}{M_{23}} \qquad \text{and} \qquad L_0 = \frac{M_{12}M_{13}}{M_{23}}$$

Fig. 2.16 *Equivalent circuit of the three-winding transformer.*

2.24. Show that the circuit of Fig. 2.16 has the volt-ampere relations

$$v_1 = L_1 \frac{di_1}{dt} + M_{12} \frac{di_2}{dt} + M_{13} \frac{di}{dt}$$

$$v_2 = M_{12} \frac{di_1}{dt} + L_2 \frac{di_2}{dt} + M_{23} \frac{di_3}{dt}$$

$$v_3 = M_{13} \frac{di_1}{dt} + M_{23} \frac{di_2}{dt} + L_3 \frac{di_3}{dt}$$

2.25. Show that Figs. 2.17(a) and 2.17(b) have the same volt-ampere relations, and hence, in this sense at least, it is possible to produce a *negative* inductance.

2.26. Show that Figs. 2.18(a) and 2.18(b) have the same volt-ampere relations.

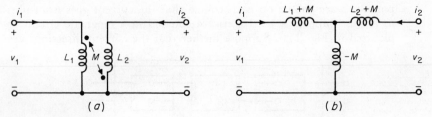

Fig. 2.17 *A pair of negatively coupled coils and its* **T** *equivalent.*

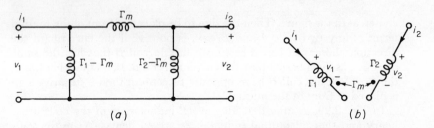

Fig. 2.18 *A pair of mutually coupled coils and its π equivalent.*

2.27. A general rule can be developed for obtaining the relative positions of dots to mark polarity: Take the first coil (at random), place a dot at one end of it, and imagine that a current is forced into the end thus chosen. Using the right-hand rule, determine the direction of the flux produced by this current as the flux passes through all the other coils. Then choose any one of the other coils, and determine by the right-hand rule which end should receive the current to produce a flux going in the *same* direction as the flux produced by the first coil. Place the dot at that end of the second coil. A repetition of this with all coil pairs will establish all the dot pairs necessary.

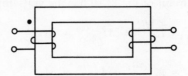

Fig. 2.19   *Two coils coupled by an iron core.*

In the iron-core magnetic circuit shown in Fig. 2.19, find the dotted end of the coil on the right that corresponds to the dot shown for the coil on the left.

2.28. It is possible to write the volt-ampere equations directly from the magnetic circuit without recourse to the dots. The task here is really one of finding the correct signs to place in front of the mutual terms. The self-inductances are always positive if the current directions and potentials are chosen on each coil so that the current goes from plus to minus. Suppose several coils are coupled in a magnetic circuit as pictured in Fig. 2.20. Suppose further that the current directions are

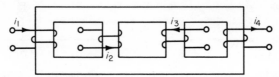

Fig. 2.20   *Four mutually coupled coils.*

chosen as in the figure. Then the sign to be placed in front of the mutual terms of any two coils *A* and *B*, say, is positive if the current (in the direction chosen) in coil *A* sets up a flux in coil *B* that has the same direction as the flux set up by the current in coil *B*. If, on the other hand, the two fluxes in coil *B* have opposite directions, then a negative sign is placed in front of the mutual.

In Fig. 2.20, assume that all the self-inductances of the coils are 1 henry and that all mutual inductances are $\frac{1}{4}$ henry. Write the volt-ampere relations for the four coils.

2.29. In the case of *two* coupled coils, the dot notation has significance. It is very convenient to remember these two rules: (1) If a positive potential is applied to the *dotted* terminal of one coil, the *induced* voltage in the other coil will be *positive* at the dotted end. Alternatively, on increasing current into the dotted end of a coil induces in the other coil a voltage that is positive at the dotted end. (2) If an increasing current is applied to the *dotted* end of one coil, the *induced* current in the other coil will increase in a direction *out* of the dotted end. Alternatively, a positive potential applied to the dotted end of one coil causes an increasing current to come out of the dotted end of the other coil.

These rules come in handy when writing mesh and nodal equations, but whereas rule (1) applies no matter how many coils there may be, rule (2) applies for the two-coil case only, and may or may not apply when there are three or more coils coupled.

To demonstrate when rule (2) does not apply, consider the circuit of Fig. 2.21. In this circuit, $L_1 = 2$, $L_2 = 6$, $L_3 = \frac{1}{4}$, and the magnitudes of the mutuals are $M_{12} = M_{23} = 1$ and $M_{13} = \frac{1}{2}$.

(a) Write the volt-ampere relations for the three coils in the form

$$v_1 = L_1 \frac{di_1}{dt} \cdots$$

(b) Show that the coefficient of coupling between any two coils is less than one.

$$\text{Answer: } k_{12} = \frac{1}{\sqrt{12}} \qquad k_{13} = \frac{1}{\sqrt{2}} \qquad k_{23} = \sqrt{\frac{2}{3}}$$

(c) Place the dots in the appropriate positions in Fig. 2.22.

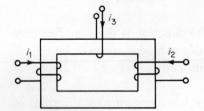
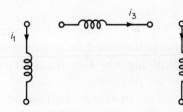

Fig. 2.21 *Three mutually coupled coils.*   **Fig. 2.22** *Problem 2.29(c).*

(d) Invert the equations obtained in (a) to obtain

$$i_1(t) = \rho_1 + 2\int_0^t v_1\,dt + \int_0^t v_2\,dt - 8\int_0^t v_3\,dt$$

$$i_2(t) = \rho_2 + \int_0^t v_1\,dt + \int_0^t v_2\,dt - 6\int_0^t v_3\,dt$$

$$i_3(t) = \rho_3 - 8\int_0^t v_1\,dt - 6\int_0^t v_2\,dt + 44\int_0^t v_3\,dt$$

Note that the sign of the $\int_0^t v_2\,dt$ term in the first equation and that of the $\int_0^t v_1\,dt$ term in the second equation (the sign of Γ_{12}) could not have been obtained by using rule (2) above.

2.8 The Heaviside Step Function

Since the engineer is concerned with "practical" signals—signals that are zero before some time and that are of finite duration—there is a definite need for some compact notation to indicate this. The rectangular function pictured in Fig. 2.23 is known as a *step function*, defined by

$$\mathbf{1}(t) = \begin{cases} 1 & \text{for } t > 0 \\ 0 & \text{for } t < 0 \end{cases} \tag{2.30}$$

Besides conserving space, there is a good reason for representing such an unusual function by a simple notation. Thus $\mathbf{1}(t)$ will always be used to represent this function *only*.*

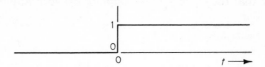

Fig. 2.23 *The unit or Heaviside step function,* $\mathbf{1}(t)$.

One of the many advantages of this function is that any function $f(t)$ that is defined for negative values of t can be made zero by simply multiplying it by $\mathbf{1}(t)$. Thus $e^{-t}\mathbf{1}(t)$ is identically zero for $t < 0$ and equal to e^{-t} for positive t.

We can realize another advantage when we employ the rules of functional notation discussed in Probs. 2.1 and 2.2. Since the step function jumps from zero to one at $t = 0$, then $\mathbf{1}(x)$ jumps from zero to one as x goes from negative to positive values. Similarly, $\mathbf{1}(-t)$ jumps from zero to one when $-t$ goes from negative to positive values. But $-t$ goes from negative to positive values when t goes from positive to negative values. Then $\mathbf{1}(-t)$ is equal to one for negative t and zero for positive t.

In a similar fashion, $\mathbf{1}(t-a)$ is equal to one for $t > a$, and zero for $t < a$. In this text it will never be assumed that a function such as e^{-t} is zero for any values of t unless a step function multiplies the function. The letters $f(t)$ or $g(t)$ may well include step functions in their definitions, but never such expressions as $\sin \beta t$ or e^{at^2}. The last two functions will be assumed to be continuous and to exist for all values of t. If, for example, we wish to define a function that is equal to $\cos 5t$ for positive t only, and to zero for negative t, then we must express the result as $\cos 5t\mathbf{1}(t)$. Failure to do this leads to confusion.

The step function is not defined for $t = 0$. At $t = 0+$, that is, just a little more positive than zero, it is equal to 1. Similarly, at $t = 0-$

---

*The $\mathbf{1}(t)$ is Heaviside's notation; $u(t)$—u for unit—is also commonly used.

it is equal to zero.* Generally the value at $t = 0$ is left undefined. When a value must be assigned there are numerous good reasons for setting the value at $\frac{1}{2}$. One such reason might be the equation

$$\mathbf{1}(t) + \mathbf{1}(-t) = 1$$

for all values of t, including zero.

When two functions are identical except at a point (or points) of discontinuity, mathematicians denote this by placing the equals sign in parentheses. Thus

$$\mathbf{1}(t) \ (=) \ [\mathbf{1}(t)]^2$$

since both sides of the equation are zero for negative t, and unity for positive t. The equation above is read: "$\mathbf{1}$ of t equals, almost everywhere, $\mathbf{1}$ of t squared."

Evidently the two are not equal to each other at $t = 0$ if any value for the function is assigned there (except, of course, zero or one). If, for example, the value of $\frac{1}{2}$ were used for the step function at $t = 0$, then the left side would be $\frac{1}{2}$ and the right side $\frac{1}{4}$. Since this point tends to be confusing, we shall not dwell on it for the time being, and assume that the value is $\frac{1}{2}$ at $t = 0$.

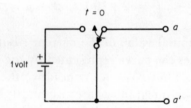

Fig. 2.24 *Battery - switch equivalent of the step function.*

Figure 2.24 shows a 1-volt battery and switch. For negative values of t the switch is in the position shown, with the battery disconnected and the terminals a and a' short-circuited.

At $t = 0$, the switch is thrown up so the short-circuit is suddenly removed and the battery placed across terminals a and a'. The potential at a and a' is therefore zero for negative t and 1 volt for positive t. Hence the potential across the terminals a and a' is simply $\mathbf{1}(t)$.

Evidently, practical sources made from batteries (or constant-

---

*$0+$ and $0-$ are not values of time such as $t = -1$ or $t = +1$. A limiting process is understood, such as $f(0-) = \lim_{\epsilon \to 0} f(\epsilon)$ where ϵ moves through negative values toward zero.

voltage sources) and switches can be made to synthesize step functions. What happens when a step function of voltage is applied to a resistance?

In Fig. 2.25(a), a step function of 10 volts is applied to a resistance of 5 ohms. From Ohm's law, Eq. (2.7), the current must be ⅕ the voltage at all times, hence

$$i(t) = 2\mathbf{1}(t)$$

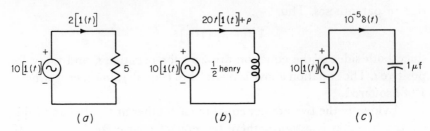

Fig. 2.25   *A step voltage applied to R, L, and C.*

In Fig. 2.25(b), the same 10-volt step is applied to an inductance of ½ henry. From Eq. (2.22)

$$i(t) = 2 \int_0^t 10\,\mathbf{1}(t)\ dt + \rho$$

(as before, ρ is the initial value of the current). But the integration is simply the area under the curve represented by the integrand between the lower and upper limits. When t is negative the integrand is zero. When t is positive the integrand is a constant 10; hence, the integral is the area of a rectangle 10 units high and t units long. Then

$$i(t) = 20\,t + \rho \qquad \text{for}\ \ t > 0$$

and

$$i(t) = \rho \qquad \text{for}\ \ t < 0$$

But this could have been written as

$$i(t) = 20t\,\mathbf{1}(t) + \rho$$

Note here that the result of the integration contains a step function. ρ cannot be determined from the problem as stated. It indicates the possibility that some energy was stored in the coil before it was hit by the 10-volt source.

This leads to a general rule that can be formulated for those cases when $\mathbf{1}(t)$ appears under an integral sign.

THEOREM 2.1.

$$\int_{-a}^{t} f(x)\,\mathbf{1}(x)\ dx = \mathbf{1}(t) \int_{0}^{t} f(x)\ dx \qquad (2.31)$$

when a is positive. That is, when the step function appears under the integral then it can be taken outside of the integral as a multiplier, *providing* the lower limit is changed from its negative value to zero and t replaces the dummy variable of integration in the step function.
Proof: Since the integrand is zero for negative x, then no area under the integrand can be obtained until the upper limit t is positive. Hence the integral is zero for negative t, and for $t = 0$ in particular. Thus

$$\int_{-a}^{t} f(x)\mathbf{1}(x)\ dx = \int_{-a}^{0} f(x)\mathbf{1}(x)\ dx + \int_{0}^{t} f(x)\mathbf{1}(x)\ dx = \int_{0}^{t} f(x)\mathbf{1}(x)\ dx$$

But $\mathbf{1}(x)$ is unity for all intervals from 0 to any positive quantity, so

$$\int_{-a}^{t} f(x)\mathbf{1}(x)\ dx = \begin{cases} \int_{0}^{t} f(x)\ dx \text{ for } t > 0 \\ \\ 0 \qquad\qquad \text{ for } t < 0 \end{cases}$$

Therefore

$$\int_{-a}^{t} f(x)\mathbf{1}(x)\ dx = \mathbf{1}(t) \int_{0}^{t} f(x)\ dx, \text{ q.e.d.}*$$

For the case when the lower limit is positive the reader is referred to Prob. 2.34 at the end of this section.

In Fig. 2.25(c), the step voltage is applied to a capacitance of one microfarad (10^{-6} farad). From Eq. (2.15)

$$i(t) = 10^{-6} \frac{d}{dt} [10\,\mathbf{1}(t)] = 10^{-5} \frac{d}{dt} [\mathbf{1}(t)]$$

(The voltage across the capacitance jumps to 10 volts after $t = 0$. If it had a potential of γ volts initially, then the actual voltage applied to the capacitance would be $(10 - \gamma)\,\mathbf{1}(t) + \gamma$. This can be seen by drawing a picture of the capacitance voltage versus time. In this example it is tacitly assumed that $\gamma = 0$). Evidently the derivative of the step function is required; since the derivative is the slope, then the derivative must be zero for all values of time, except, of course, at $t = 0$, where the derivative does not exist at all. But this is not so. The capacitance will

Quod Erat Demonstrandum: which was to be proved.

be charged to 10 volts, and hence it must have 10^{-5} coulombs of charge on it. This charge must have come through the wires, so a current must have existed.

The derivative of the step function is usually called *the unit impulse* or the *Dirac delta function*.

Thus, *by definition*

$$\delta(t) = \frac{d}{dt}[\mathbf{1}(t)] \tag{2.32}$$

This is not a very satisfactory definition. Let us see if we can discover more about this unusual function. Since an inverse of differentiation is integration from $-\infty$ to t

$$\int_{-\infty}^{t} \delta(x)\ dx = \mathbf{1}(x)\ \Big|_{-\infty}^{t} = \mathbf{1}(t) - \mathbf{1}(-\infty)$$

But $\mathbf{1}(-\infty) = 0$, so

$$\int_{-\infty}^{t} \delta(x)\ dx = \mathbf{1}(t) \tag{2.33}$$

(Note that *any* negative number for a lower limit would yield the same result.)

We can conclude from this that for $t < 0$, the delta function has no area under it. Therefore

$$\delta(t) = 0 \qquad \text{for} \qquad t < 0 \tag{2.34}$$

For any value of $t > 0$, the left-hand side is unity, so as t goes from $0-$ to $0+$ the integral picks up a unit of area. For all positive values of t, the function still has a value of unity; hence

$$\delta(t) = 0 \qquad \text{for} \qquad t > 0 \tag{2.35}$$

Both Eqs. (2.34) and (2.35) agree with the usual concept of a derivative. But somehow the delta function has no value except at $t = 0$, and it has unit area under it.

There is actually no rigorous way that this situation can be handled, that is, no way of representing the delta function so that it looks anything like the functions we have met in the past.* There are many heuristic or physical ways of viewing this function, however, and the function

---

*There are modern theories which handle the delta function rigorously. See, for example, A. ERDÉLYI, *Operational Calculus and Generalized Functions*. New York: Holt, Rinehart and Winston, 1962.

does prove to be useful. One of the advantages of the function so far as this text is concerned will be that its Laplace transform is unity— that is, $+1$. This fact alone will be invaluable to us, so some effort must be expended to establish rules for the mathematical use of the impulse function and to help the reader get some physical idea of what an impulse looks like, however inaccurate the picture might be.

Suppose we start by rationalizing a little. Since nothing in nature changes from one thing to another in *zero* time, let us redefine the step function as

$$\mathbf{1}(t) = \begin{cases} 0 \text{ for } t < \dfrac{-\epsilon}{2} \\[2ex] \dfrac{t}{\epsilon} + \dfrac{1}{2} \text{ for } \dfrac{-\epsilon}{2} < t < \dfrac{\epsilon}{2} \\[2ex] 1 \quad \text{for} \quad t > \dfrac{\epsilon}{2} \end{cases}$$

This function is shown in Fig. 2.26. If we imagine that ϵ is very small, we could not distinguish it from the step function of Fig. 2.23. The time scale in Fig. 2.26 is blown up tremendously so the behavior near the origin can be seen easily.

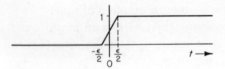

Fig. 2.26 *Approximate step function.*

The function in Fig. 2.26 does have a derivative in the usual sense, the slope being zero for $t < -\epsilon/2$, $1/\epsilon$ for $|t| < \epsilon/2$, and zero for $t > \epsilon/2$. This function is plotted in Fig. 2.27, and it is seen that it is a large rectangular pulse of height $1/\epsilon$ and base ϵ. It has unit area under it, and hence it seems to satisfy all our requirements. In the limit, as ϵ is made smaller and smaller, the pulse grows larger and larger. It seems to become a rectangular pulse of infinite height and zero base, with unit area under it. Since this definition is nonsensical, we shall settle on a pulse several light-years high with unit area under it.

The real difficulty with the impulse comes not in its physical meaning, but in its mathematical use. Most of the situations in which the impulse appears are covered in the list of definitions below. In each

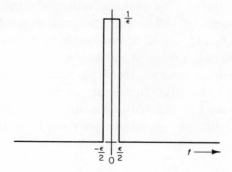

Fig. 2.27   *The impulse or delta function.*

case we shall not try to prove the relations as a theorem. What is done by way of "proof" is to show that the statement leads to a result to which some physical sense can be applied.

Definitions

   1. Since $\delta(t)$ occurs at $t = 0$, then $\delta(t-a)$ is a unit impulse at $t = a$.

   2. Then

$$\delta(t) = \delta(-t) \tag{2.36}$$

that is, the impulse is an even function of time.

   3. If A is a constant, then $A\delta(t)$ is an impulse at $t = 0$ with an area of A under it. If A is negative, then the area is below the $t = 0$ axis; that is, the pulse is negative.

   4. Since $\delta(t)$ has value only near $t = 0$, then for $f(t)$ a continuous function at $t = 0$,

$$f(t)\,\delta(t) = f(0)\,\delta(t) \tag{2.37}$$

Similarly, if $f(t)$ is continuous at $t = a$, then

$$f(t)\,\delta(t-a) = f(a)\,\delta(t-a) \tag{2.38}$$

Both of these results come from the physical fact that since the impulse is so narrow $f(t)$ is nearly constant over the duration of the pulse length. This changes the height of the pulse, but not its length, so the area changes from unity to whatever the height of the function is at the time the impulse occurs.

   5. In consequence of Eqs. (2.33) and (2.37), we have

$$\int_a^t f(x)\delta(x)\,dx = \int_a^t f(0)\delta(x)\,dx = f(0)\,\mathbf{1}(t) \tag{2.39}$$

if the lower limit of the integral is *negative*. (If the lower limit is positive, the integral has the value $-f(0)\mathbf{1}(-t)$, but this will not be used in this text. However, this result should be verified. If the lower limit is zero it is undefined, although an acceptable value might be $f(0)[\mathbf{1}(t) - 1/2]$).

6. Using the ordinary rules of differentiating a product and using Eq. (2.37), we have

$$\frac{d\,[f(t)\,\mathbf{1}(t)]}{dt} = \mathbf{1}(t)\,\frac{df(t)}{dt} + f(0)\delta(t) \qquad (2.40)$$

7. It is sometimes desirable to change the variable or argument of the delta function. To this end it is necessary to define

$$\delta(at) = \frac{\delta(t)}{a} \qquad a > 0 \qquad (2.41)$$

The reason may be made apparent by noting that from Eq. (2.33)

$$\mathbf{1}(t) = \int_{-b}^{t} \delta(at)\;d(at)$$

if b is positive.
But $d(at) = a\,dt$, so

$$\mathbf{1}(t) = \int_{-b/a}^{t/a} a\delta(at)\;dt$$

But also

$$\mathbf{1}(t) = \int_{-b/a}^{t/a} \delta(t)\;dt$$

since the lower limit is negative, and $\mathbf{1}(t/a) = \mathbf{1}(t)$. Then the integrands of the equations must be rectangular pulses with equal areas, hence Eq. (2.41). This is discussed in Prob. 2.45.

8. It will be agreed at the outset that the product of an impulse and a discontinuous function *at the point of the discontinuity* will be meaningless. Thus, for example, $\mathbf{1}(t)\delta(t)$ will be undefined.

The use of the impulse requires a new kind of sophistication. Consider, for example, the contact of a bat with a pitched ball in the game of baseball. Let us suppose that the ball is pitched, and just before it comes in contact with the bat it has a velocity of v_1 meters per sec. The bat then hits the ball squarely, and after a momentary contact between bat and ball, the ball leaves the bat with a velocity v_2 in the *opposite* direction.

A force, $f(t)$, is exerted on the ball for a very short interval, Δt, and Newton's law requires that

$$f(t) = m \frac{dv}{dt}$$

where m is the mass of the ball in kilograms. Let $t = 0$ just as the bat comes in contact with the ball, and let $t = \Delta t$ be the instant the ball leaves the bat.

The batter is only interested in the *velocity* (both magnitude and direction) with which the ball leaves the bat. If the batter's objective is to hit a home run, then he is indeed interested in its velocity, because that will determine how far it will go. (Similar analogies could be drawn in which the ball is at rest until contact is made; for example, a golf club and a golf ball.) If both sides of the force equation above are integrated from 0 to t, then

$$v(t) + v_1 = \frac{1}{m} \int_0^t f(t) \, dt$$

or

$$v(t) = \frac{1}{m} \int_0^t f(t) \, dt - v_1$$

Here the negative sign in front of v_1 means negative velocity toward the field, that is, positive velocity toward the catcher.

Note that since the ballplayer is interested in the ball's terminal velocity only, and the force $f(t)$ is zero after Δt sec (since the ball is no longer in contact with the bat)

$$v_2 = \frac{1}{m} \int_0^{\Delta t} f(t) \, dt - v_1$$

Figure 2.28 shows what the force $f(t)$ might look like plotted versus t. But the batter really cares only about the *area* under the curve, for this area will determine the final velocity of the ball. The shape of the curve is of no interest to a batter. Since the bat is in contact with the ball for such a short time, then $f(t)$ could be considered an impulse whose area is simply $m(v_1 + v_2)$.

Thus, in many situations the area under a tall short pulse is the only thing that interests a designer. In these cases the use of the delta function is indicated, and it will prove to be an approximation that

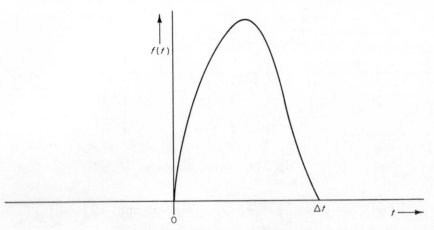

Fig. 2.28   *The force of a bat on a ball.*

is valuable to the engineer, since it will simplify the mathematics. However, when the pulse is long enough that its actual shape is important, then the impulse should *not* be used. For example, the man who designs the bat in the example above really cares about the maximum force the bat is likely to have to withstand. Usually the bat is designed so that when struck parallel to the grain it can withstand without fracture the maximum force that an average player is likely to impart to the ball.

It is seen that in the example above, the use of the impulse and its physical interpretation may be either convenient or very misleading, depending on the application. Only through experience with this idea will we be able to distinguish between those cases where it is a convenience and those where it is not proper to use the delta function at all.

Going back to the example of Fig. 2.25(c), the current in the capacitance must be

$$i(t) = 10^{-5} \, \delta(t)$$

that is, an impulse whose area is 10^{-5}. (See also Probs. 2.79 and 2.80 at the end of this chapter.)

The symbol to be used to denote an impulse is shown in Fig. 2.29. It consists of an arrow pointing to $+\infty$ if the area under the curve is positive, with the area written next to the arrow in parentheses. If the area is negative, the arrow will point down to $-\infty$, again with the area written in parentheses. Thus, in Fig. 2.29, the impulses shown can be represented symbolically from left to right as

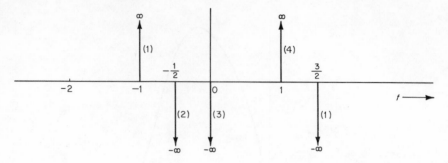

Fig. 2.29 *A group of impulses.*

$$\delta(t+1) \quad -2\delta\left(t+\frac{1}{2}\right) \quad -3\delta(t) \quad 4\delta(t-1) \quad \text{and} \quad -\delta\left(t-\frac{3}{2}\right)$$

EXAMPLE 2.1. It is often necessary to find the derivatives and the integrals of time signals having discontinuities within them. Figure 2.30 indicates one such function, $f(t)$. Find the derivative $df(t)/dt$ and the integral $\int_{-\infty}^{t} f(t) \ dt$ of this function.

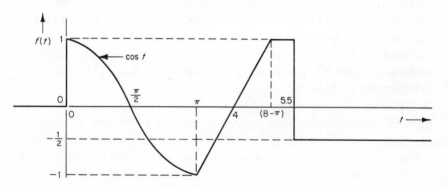

Fig. 2.30 *A function whose derivative and integral are sought.*

Solution: As we move from negative t through zero, we encounter a discontinuity. By definition, the derivative of this is an impulse whose area is equal to the amount of the discontinuity. Thus the derivative has a unit positive impulse at $t = 0$ (because the function *rises* at $t = 0$). After $t = 0$ the function is identical with the function cos t, whose derivative is known to be $-\sin t$. At $t = \pi$, however, the slope becomes a constant of $1/(4-\pi)$, so the derivative is constant until $t = 8 - \pi \doteq 4.8584$. At this point the slope becomes zero and remains at zero until $t = 5.5$. At this point a negative discontinuity occurs of magnitude

$3/2$ at $t = 5.5$. From this point on the slope is always zero. Figure 2.31 is a graph of $df(t)/dt$.

The integral of the function shown in Fig. 2.30 is conceptually somewhat more difficult. When we integrate from $-\infty$ to t, we are really performing many integrations, since the result is different for each value of t. For any fixed t the result is equal to the area under the curve from $-\infty$ up to this fixed t, remembering that the area below the t axis is negative and the area above the axis is positive.

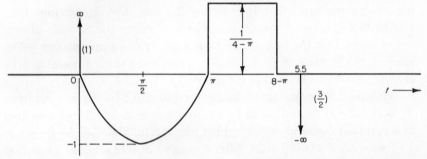

Fig. 2.31 *The derivative of the function of Fig. 2.30.*

In Fig. 2.30 there is no area under the curve from $-\infty$ to $t = 0$. As t moves to the right from zero we see that the area is positive, and we continue to accumulate positive area until we reach the point $\pi/2$. After this time the additional area accumulated is negative, so the value of the integral falls. It will continue to fall until $t = 4$, at which point it will be at its most negative value. Between $t = 4$ and $t = 5.5$ it will pick up positive area, but at $t = 5.5$ and thereafter the only area picked up will be negative, and the integral must head for $-\infty$.

Specifically: in the first interval, with $0 < t < \pi$, we have

$$\int_0^t \cos t \, dt = \sin t \, \Big|_{t=0}^{t=t} = \sin t$$

Thus the integral will be identical to $\sin t$ in this interval. In the interval $\pi < t < 8-\pi$

$$f(t) = \frac{1}{(4-\pi)} (t-4)$$

and the integral of this from π on is

$$\int_\pi^t \frac{t-4}{4-\pi} \, dt = \frac{1}{(4-\pi)} \left(\frac{t^2}{2} - 4t \right) \Big|_{t-\pi}^t = \frac{(t-\pi)(t-8+\pi)}{2(4-\pi)}$$

Notice that this is merely the integral of $f(t)$ from $t = \pi$ and that the integral from $-\infty$ must be this *plus* the value of area accumulated up to $t = \pi$. In this case this is sin π, which happens to be zero. The total accumulated area up to $t = 4$ in this case is that value of the integral last written when $t = 4$. Furthermore, the last result is the equation of a parabola whose vertex is at $t = 4$ and that opens upwards. At $t = 4$ we obtain $(\pi - 4)/2$. This should be clear to us, since it is the area of a triangle whose base is $(4 - \pi)$ and whose height is unity. The minus sign indicates that it is below the line, also an obvious fact. Furthermore, without substituting $t = 8 - \pi$ into the formula above, it is evident that the integral must rise to zero as t approaches $8 - \pi$, since in the interval from 4 to $8 - \pi$ exactly the same amount of area is added as was subtracted in the interval $\pi < t < 4$.

Figure 2.32 indicates the function represented by the integral from $-\infty$ to t of $f(t)$. Note that as t goes from $8 - \pi$ to 5.5, it picks up area at a constant *rate*, and at 5.5 it must have accumulated $(5.5 - 8 + \pi) \times 1 = \pi - 2.5 \doteq 0.6416$ units. After t passes 5.5, area is lost at a constant rate of $\frac{1}{2}$ unit per sec.

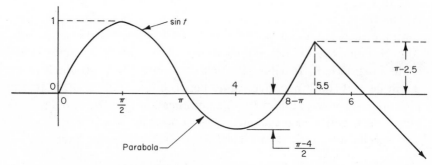

Fig. 2.32   *The integral from* $-\infty$ *to* t *of the function pictured in Fig. 2.30.*

EXAMPLE 2.2. Integrate the function pictured in Fig. 2.33.
Solution: The accumulated area is zero until $t = 1$, at which time it becomes $+2$ immediately. In the interval from 1 to 2, one unit is lost at a constant rate, making the integral $2 - 1 = 1$ at $t = 2-$. One unit is then suddenly lost at $t = 2$, bringing the total back to zero at $t = 2+$. Then $\frac{1}{2}$ unit is picked up at a parabolic rate from 2 to 3, and beyond $t = 3$ area is picked up at the rate of 1 unit per sec. The solution appears in Fig. 2.34.

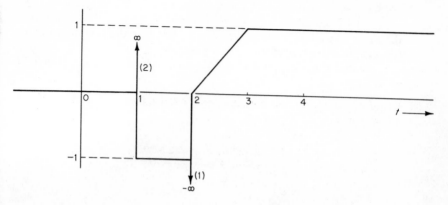

Fig. 2.33 *Example 2.2.*

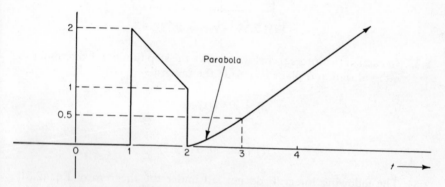

Fig. 2.34 *The integral of the function pictured in Fig. 2.33.*

PROBLEMS

2.30. Sketch the functions below.

    (a) $\sin t\, \mathbf{1}\,(t)$

    (b) $e^{-2t}\,[\mathbf{1}(t) - \mathbf{1}(t-2)]$

    (c) $\mathbf{1}\!\left(t+\dfrac{\gamma}{2}\right) - \mathbf{1}\!\left(t-\dfrac{\gamma}{2}\right)$

    (d) $\mathbf{1}(4-t) - \mathbf{1}(t)$

    (e) $\mathbf{1}(t) - \dfrac{1}{2}$

2.31. An *even* function is defined as a function that does not change if t is replaced by $-t$. Stated in another way, an even function is identical to the function obtained when the graph of that function is rotated 180 deg about the vertical axis at $t = 0$ (or held in front of a mirror). An *odd* function is defined as a function whose sign is changed when t is replaced by minus t. The graph has to be rotated 180 deg about the t-axis as well as the vertical axis to reproduce the original function (the graph appears upside down in a mirror).

Show that the function $1(t) - \frac{1}{2}$ is an odd function if $1(t)$ is defined as $\frac{1}{2}$ at $t = 0$.

2.32. Using step-function notation, express the current issuing from terminals a and a' in Fig. 2.35.

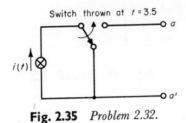

Fig. 2.35   *Problem 2.32.*

2.33. In each of the integrals below, remove the step function from under the integral sign and place it outside the integral.

$$(a) \int_{-3}^{t} e^{-x} \, 1(x) \, dx$$

$$(b) \int_{-4}^{t} \sin 30y \, 1(y+2) \, dy$$

2.34. The following integrals do not fall under the theorem of Eq. (2.31). Evaluate these integrals and express the results in closed form, using the step function. It is suggested that the student sketch the graph and integrate it. The result must hold for all values of t, both positive and negative.

$$(a) \int_{0}^{t} 1(4-t) \, dt$$

$$(b) \int_{2}^{t} e^{-t/2} \, 1(t) \, dt$$

Answer to (b): $2(1 - e^{-t/2}) \, 1(t) - \left(2 - \frac{2}{e}\right)$

2.35. Evaluate the following integrals, expressing the result with the step function wherever convenient.

$$(a) \int_{-\infty}^{t} t^2 \, 1(t) \, dt$$

$$(b) \int_{-\infty}^{t} \frac{t^4}{5} \, 1(t) \, dt$$

2.36. Show that if

$$f_n(t) = \frac{t^n}{n!} \mathbf{1}(t)$$

for n a positive integer or zero, then

$$f_{n-1}(t) = \frac{df_n(t)}{dt}$$

for $n \geq 1$. $n! = n(n-1)(n-2)\ldots(3)(2)(1)$, and *by definition* $0! = 1$.

2.37. Evaluate the following integrals:

(a) $\int_{-2}^{t} e^{-2t} \delta(t+1)\, dt$

(b) $\int_{2}^{t} e^{-2t} \delta(t-1)\, dt$

(c) $\int_{-\infty}^{t} e^{-st} \delta(t)\, dt$

(d) $\int_{-\infty}^{t} [\sin \beta t\, \delta(t) + \mathbf{1}(t)]\, dt$

(e) $\int_{-\infty}^{t} e^{-t^2} e^{-st} \delta(t+5)\, dt$

2.38. Differentiate

(a) $\cos \beta t\, \mathbf{1}(t)$ (b) $5 \sin \omega t\, \mathbf{1}(t)$ (c) $e^{-t^2} \mathbf{1}(t)$

2.39. Assume that in Fig. 2.36, the triangular pulse is an impulse, that is, that ϵ is very small. Sketch carefully the derivative of this function, and obtain the *unit doublet*. Label the amplitudes in terms of ϵ, and calculate the area of the pulses. As ϵ approaches zero do the pulses approach two impulses?

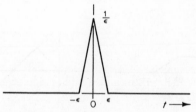

Fig. 2.36 *Triangular approximation of the unit impulse.*

2.40. Given that

$$f = \frac{\omega}{2\pi}$$

express $\delta(\omega)$ in terms of $\delta(f)$ and $\delta(f)$ in terms of $\delta(\omega)$.

2.41. A baseball with a mass of 0.156 kg (5.5 oz) is thrown toward a batter with a velocity of 38.00 meters per sec (85 mph). If the force exerted by the bat on the ball is given by

$$f(t) = F_m \sin 1000\pi t \, [\mathbf{1}(t) - \mathbf{1}(t - 10^{-3})] \text{ newtons}$$

what must the constant F_m be in order that the ball leave the bat with a velocity of 53.67 meters per sec (120 mph)? F_m is the maximum force exerted by the bat on the ball. The force in pounds may be obtained by dividing the force in newtons by 4.45.

2.42. Sketch carefully the following integrals:

$$(a) \int_0^t \sin t \, \mathbf{1}(t) \, dt \qquad (b) \int_0^t \cos t \, \mathbf{1}(t) \, dt$$

2.43. For each of the functions sketched in Fig. 2.37, sketch the derivative and the integral from $-\infty$ to t.

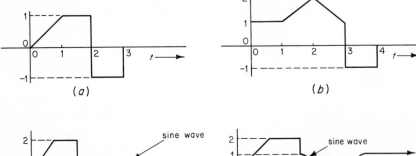

(a)

(b)

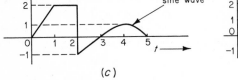

(c)

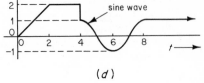

(d)

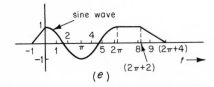

(e)

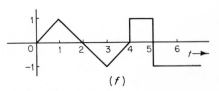

(f)

Fig. 2.37 *Problem 2.43.*

2.44. For each of the functions in Fig. 2.38, find the integral from $-\infty$ to t.

2.45. Let

$$\delta(t) = \frac{1}{\epsilon} \qquad \text{for} \qquad |t| < \frac{\epsilon}{2}$$

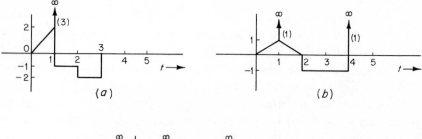

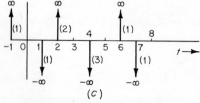

Fig. 2.38 *Problem 2.44.*

$$\delta(t) = 0 \qquad \text{for} \qquad |t| > \frac{\epsilon}{2}$$

(a) Plot $\delta(4t)$.

(b) What is the area under $\delta(4t)$?

(c) What is the area under $[\delta(t)]^2$? As $\epsilon \to 0$, does $\delta^2(t)$ have any meaning at all?

2.9 Nodal Equations

There are many ways in which circuit equations may be written. In this text only two methods are used, the *nodal* method and the *loop* method. It is generally, but not always, true that one of these approaches is the best for a specific problem.

In the nodal (or node-voltage) approach, the variables are defined as the potentials from all nodes to ground, the *reference* node. Thus we must search out all points that can have different voltages. A *node* is defined as that collection of points in the circuit that must have the same potential. Since a straight line is to be used to denote wire without resistance (or inductance and capacitance), then all straight lines in a schematic diagram are nodes or parts of nodes.

Consider the circuit of Fig. 2.39(a). The nodes of this circuit are outlined by heavy lines in Fig. 2.39(b), and in Fig. 2.39(c) the nodes are clearly outlined by dotted enclosures, or "balloons."

The reference or *datum* node can be any node. Usually it is chosen as the node that has the greatest number of wires leading to it. It is commonly referred to as *ground*.

At each node for which the voltage to ground is not known, we define an unknown nodal voltage, such as $v_1(t)$, $v_2(t)$, and $v_3(t)$ in Fig. 2.39(c). Note that one node, whose potential is not known, is not given a separate symbol but is instead labeled $v_2(t) + e_{s2}(t)$. This is a useful sleight-of-hand procedure, for much trouble can be experienced if too many node-voltages are defined. In Fig. 2.39 note that the presence of the source $e_{s2}(t)$ implies that the potential to the left of this source must

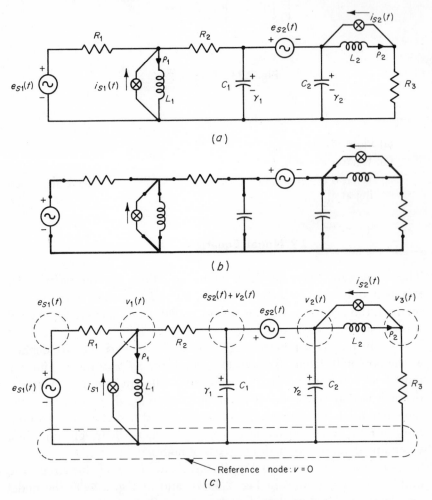

Fig. 2.39 *A circuit with its nodes outlined.*

always be larger than the one to the right by $e_{s2}(t)$ volts. $e_{s2}(t)$ represents a known function of time; hence, if $v_2(t)$ were known, the potential to the left of the source would have to be larger than this by exactly $e_{s2}(t)$ volts. We could just as well have labeled the node to the left $v_s(t)$ and the node to the right $v_s(t) - e_{s2}(t)$. Note that the node in the upper left is not defined as a separate unknown either, since this node too must always be $e_{s1}(t)$ volts more positive than ground.

Having seen how the variables are chosen, it is now necessary to write as many equations relating these variables as there are unknown node voltages. In Fig. 2.39 this means writing three equations for the three unknowns v_1, v_2, v_3. To do this it is only necessary to write Kirchhoff's first (current) law for each node v_1, v_2, and v_3. Not only is it *not* necessary to write an equation for the upper left-hand node (where the potential is known to be e_{s1}); it is likely to be written incorrectly. Remember that, in general, the current in a voltage source is *not* zero, and this current is unknown. It is, then, not possible to write an equation for this node without introducing a new unknown, that is, one representing the current in the source.

Since only as many equations as unknowns are necessary, it is clear that only three equations will be required for Fig. 2.39.

The rule used to write the equation is *current in equals current out.* To keep things in order, the current will always be assumed in this text to *leave* a node through passive elements, and to arrive at the node from current sources only.

To this end we must be familiar with the three volt-ampere relations for the elements of circuits. The ones needed are those that express current in terms of voltage:

$$i(t) = \frac{1}{L} \int_0^t v(t) \, dt + \rho$$

$$i(t) = \frac{C \, dv(t)}{dt}$$

and

$$i(t) = \frac{v(t)}{R}$$

for the inductance, capacitance, and resistance, respectively.

EXAMPLE 2.3. Write the nodal equations for the circuit of Fig. 2.39. *Solution:* Consider the node marked $v_1(t)$ in Fig. 2.39(c). There are three passive elements connected to the node, and one current source. The current to the *left* in R_1 is the voltage across it, plus-to-minus to the left, divided by R_1; that is $[v_1(t) - e_{s1}(t)]/R_1$. Note that the current is expressed in terms of the unknown variable v_1 and the known quantities e_{s1} and R_1, and that the potential at the node for which the equation is being written appears first. Though v_1 is not known, it can be assumed that, it is larger than e_{s1}; hence, the current would go to the left. Even if v_1 proves to be smaller than e_{s1}, the algebraic sign will take care of the erroneous assumption and the expression for current will still be correct.

The current away from the node in L_1 is

$$\frac{1}{L_1} \int_0^t [v_1(t) - 0] \, dt + \rho_1$$

or simply

$$\frac{1}{L_1} \int_0^t v_1(t) \, dt + \rho_1$$

where the letter ρ will be used, as before, to denote the initial currents in the inductances; that is, $\rho_1 = i_{L_1}(0)$, $\rho_2 = i_{L_2}(0)$.

In like manner the current to the right in R_2 is simply

$$\frac{v_1(t) - [e_{s2}(t) + v_2(t)]}{R_2}$$

since the potential at its right end is $e_{s2} + v_2$.

The source current entering the node is $i_{s1}(t)$, so *current in equals current out* leads to the equation

$$\frac{[v_1(t) - e_{s1}(t)]}{R_1} + \frac{1}{L_1} \int_0^t v_1(t) \, dt + \rho_1 + \frac{[v_1(t) - e_{s2}(t) - v_2(t)]}{R_2} = i_{s1}(t)$$

The next step is to collect terms so that only expressions with the unknowns appear on the left, and everything else goes on the right. Thus the last equation can be written

$$\left[\frac{1}{R_1} + \frac{1}{R_2} + \frac{1}{L_1} \int_0^t (-) \, dt \right] v_1(t) - \frac{1}{R_2} v_2(t) = i_{s1}(t) + \frac{e_{s1}(t)}{R_1} + \frac{e_{s2}(t)}{R_2} - \rho_1$$

where the symbol

$$\left[\int_0^t (-) \, dt \right] v_1(t) \quad \text{means} \quad \int_0^t v_1(t) \, dt$$

The next step is to jump to the node labeled $v_2(t)$. The current leaving this node through C_2 is $C_2\, dv_2(t)/dt$; that leaving through L_2 is $1/L_2 \int_0^t [v_2(t) - v_3(t)]\, dt + \rho_2$; but that leaving through the source $e_{s2}(t)$ cannot be determined by a volt-ampere relation.

However, the current leaving node 2 through the source e_{s2} has to be the same as the currents leaving the node $e_{s2}(t) + v_2(t)$ through the resistance R_2 and the capacitance C_1. In other words, when two nodes are joined by an ideal voltage source, we must look beyond the source to find a way of expressing its current in terms of the unknown voltages v_1, v_2, or v_3 and the element values of the network. Thus the current through e_{s2} to the left is the sum of the current in R_2 to the left, $[e_{s2}(t) + v_2(t) - v_1(t)]/R_2$, and the current down through C_1, $C_1\, d[e_{s2}(t) + v_2(t)]/dt$. Finally, the current entering the node through a current source is $i_{s2}(t)$, so the second node equation is

$$C_2\, \frac{dv_2(t)}{dt} + \frac{1}{L_2} \int\limits_0^t [v_2(t) - v_3(t)]\, dt + \rho_2$$

$$+ \frac{e_{s2}(t) + v_2(t) - v_1(t)}{R_2} + C_1\, \frac{d[e_{s2}(t) + v_2(t)]}{dt} = i_{s2}(t)$$

Collecting terms as before gives

$$- \frac{1}{R_2}\, v_1(t) + \left[(C_1 + C_2)\, \frac{d(-)}{dt} + \frac{1}{R_2} + \frac{1}{L_2} \int\limits_0^t (-)\, dt \right] v_2(t)$$

$$- \left[\frac{1}{L_2} \int\limits_0^t (-)\, dt \right] v_3(t) = i_{s2}(t) - \frac{e_{s2}(t)}{R_2} - C_1\, \frac{de_{s1}(t)}{dt} - \rho_2$$

At this point we note that much time and energy can be saved by shortening the notation. For one thing the (t) after the variables can be dropped; it is easily borne in mind that the functions depend on time. But, more important, the operators d/dt and $\int_0^t (-)\, dt$ can be shortened considerably. There is no standard notation in mathematics for these, but the one used most frequently is

$$p(-) = \frac{d(-)}{dt} \tag{2.42}$$

that is

$$pf(t) = \frac{d[f(t)]}{dt}$$

In like manner, the inverse of differentiation can be defined as

$$\frac{(-)}{p} = \int_0^t (-)\, dt \qquad (2.43)$$

that is

$$\frac{f(t)}{p} = \int_0^t f(t)\, dt$$

It must be clearly understood that p and $1/p$ are *not* algebraic factors, nor are they reciprocals of each other in the algebraic sense. They are introduced only to shorten the time it takes to write a set of equations. They do have other advantages, however. One is that they make the volt-ampere relations used in the nodal method easier to remember.

$$i(t) = \frac{v(t)}{Lp} + \rho$$

$$i(t) = Cpv(t) \qquad (2.44)$$

$$i(t) = v(t)/R$$

If we now proceed to write the third and final equation for the circuit of Fig. 2.39, it is seen that, at the node labeled $v_3(t)$, the current going to the left in L_2 is with the new notation $(v_3 - v_2)/(L_2 p) - \rho_2$. Notice the minus in front of ρ_2. This is necessary, since ρ_2 is defined in Fig. 2.39(a) as positive to the right, but we want the initial value of the current going to the left. The current going down in R_3 is v_3/R_3, and the source current entering the node is $-i_{s2}$. Note also the minus sign here.

If all three currents are put in equation form, then

$$\frac{1}{L_2 p}(v_3 - v_2) - \rho_2 + \frac{v_3}{R_3} = -i_{s2}$$

Collecting terms as before, we have

$$-\frac{1}{L_2 p}v_2 + \left(\frac{1}{R_3} + \frac{1}{L_2 p}\right)v_3 = -i_{s2} + \rho_2$$

If the equations for the first two nodes are rewritten with the operator p, and the (t)'s are dropped, the three nodal equations become:

$$\frac{1}{R_1}+\frac{1}{R_2}+\frac{1}{L_1 p}\Big]v_1 \qquad\qquad -\frac{1}{R_2}v_2 \qquad\qquad = i_{s1} +\frac{e_{s1}}{R_1}+ \frac{e_{s2}}{R_2} - p_1$$

$$-\frac{1}{R_2}v_1 +\Big[(C_1+C_2)p+\frac{1}{R_2}+\frac{1}{L_2 p}\Big]v_2 \quad -\frac{1}{L_2 p}v_3 = i_{s2} - \frac{e_{s2}}{R_2} - C_1 p e_{s1} - p_2$$

$$-\frac{1}{L_2 p}v_2 +\Big[\frac{1}{R_3}+\frac{1}{L_2 p}\Big]v_3 = -i_{s2} + p_2 \qquad (2.45)$$

Note the care employed to write the equation for node 1 first, node 2 second, and node 3 third. Also note the effort to align in columns the coefficients of the same unknowns in the three equations and to place everything but the coefficients of the unknowns on the right-hand sides of the equations. This procedure is very important for the following reasons.

Although it is important that we know how to go about writing these equations, an error of *one sign* or the omission of but one term can mean that all the hard labor that follows will produce an erroneous result. Careless "misteaks" are a bane of the engineering profession, and it is sensible to take precautions against them.

Writing the equations, of course, is merely the first step. After a little practice it will become routine; however, it is important at this point for the equation-writer to stop and check his work. Experience has taught that going back over work in the same manner as the first time is likely to be misspent energy, for the same mistake is often made twice. Fortunately, a different kind of check is available.

Look at Eqs. (2.45) and Fig. 2.39(a). Note that there are three elements soldered to node v_1. They are R_1, R_2, and L_1. Look at the coefficient of v_1 in the equation for node 1. The fact that they are the same elements and that they all have plus signs is not mere chance. Look at the coefficient of v_2 in the equation for node 2. C_1, C_2, R_2, and L_2 appear. Now look at nodes v_2 and $e_{s2} + v_2$. The elements soldered to these nodes, both having v_2 in their label, are the same as in that coefficient. Again, this is not mere chance. A general rule may be formulated: *The coefficient of v_k in the kth equation will be the sum of the admittances (reciprocal impedances) of all the elements soldered to node v_k and, in the event a voltage source is soldered to v_k, those elements connected to the other terminal of the voltage source.*

For purposes of checking coefficients it is easier to replace each *voltage* source by a short circuit, then the rule becomes easier to use. If all voltage sources are replaced by short circuits, opposite terminals of these sources are reduced to one node. Figure 2.40 shows the circuit of Fig. 2.39 with the two voltage sources missing. The circuit has only three nodes plus the reference node, and the coefficients of the appropriate voltages are easy to determine.

Now look at the coefficient of v_2 in the first equation, and that of v_1 in the second. Not only are they the same, but they both have *minus* signs. The *principal diagonal* of the set of coefficients is made up of the coefficients of v_1 in the first equation, v_2 in the second equation, and v_3 in the third equation. Evidently the principal diagonal goes from the upper left to the lower right. All other coefficients are off the principal diagonal. Note that the coefficients on the principal diagonal are all positive, and those off the diagonal are all negative. This will always be the case, with the one exception that with mutually coupled coils, the off-diagonal terms may have a positive sign.

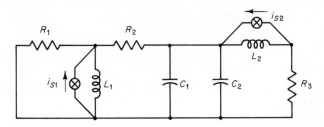

Fig. 2.40   *The circuit of Fig. 2.39 with the voltage sources replaced by short circuits.*

But the coefficient of v_2 in the first equation, and that of v_1 in the second equation, is $1/R_2$, and this is the only element that is soldered to *both* node 1 and node 2 in Fig. 2.40. Look at all the other off-diagonal elements. In every case the variable number and the equation number give the numbers of the two nodes to which the element given in the coefficient is soldered.

The left-hand side of the equations can be written by inspection, with the possible exception of those cases that involve mutual inductance. However, the right-hand side of the equations is not easy to write by inspection, although there are tricks we can employ. For example, the right-hand side must contain all current sources connected to the appropriate node. Its sign will be positive if the current enters the node and negative if it leaves the node. Thus, for example, i_{s2} leaves node 3, so the right-hand side of equation 3 has $-i_{s2}$ in it. All initial inductance currents on the right-hand side will appear as positive if the current enters the node and negative if the current leaves the node. All terms containing voltage sources will have positive coefficients on the right-hand side if the positive terminal of the source is nearer the node for which the equation was written than the negative terminal.

Procedure: No attempt should be made to write the equations by inspection until the basic notions and techniques of the method have been mastered. Begin by writing the equations as has been done in the text; that is, actually applying Kirchhoff's current law to each node in the problem and then checking the results using the rules given above. Because of the work that remains to be done in order to obtain a solution to the problem, always arrange the equations exactly as they appear in Eqs. (2.45), even to the extent that within the coefficients themselves the C's are written first, the $1/R$'s second, and the $1/L$'s last. Neatness and order cannot be overemphasized in this work.

EXAMPLE 2.4. Write the circuit equations (called the integro-differential equations) for the network of Fig. 2.41, using the nodal method.

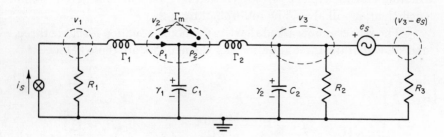

Fig. 2.41 *Example 2.4.*

Solution: The currents leaving node v_1 through passive elements are v_1/R_1 and the current in the inductance. But the current in the inductance (reciprocal inductance) consists of three terms; the initial current ρ_1, the self term $\Gamma_1(v_1-v_2)/p$, and a mutual term representing the voltage across the reciprocal inductance Γ_2. The magnitude of the current in the first coil, induced by the voltage across the second coil, is $\Gamma_m(v_2-v_3)/p$. But v_2-v_3 is the voltage across the coil Γ_2 "dot-to-undot," and, by rule (2) of Prob. 2.29, this causes a current to come out of the dotted end of coil Γ_1. Then the sign of the mutual term is positive, since this is the direction desired for this current. Since there is a current source supplying node 1, the right-hand side of this equation is $i_s(t)$.

$$\frac{v_1}{R_1} + \frac{\Gamma_1(v_1-v_2)}{p} + \frac{\Gamma_m(v_2-v_3)}{p} = i_s - \rho_1$$

(Note that ρ_1 is the only ρ term appearing in the equation.) Collecting terms, we have

$$\left[\frac{1}{R_1} + \frac{\Gamma_1}{p}\right] v_1 - \left[\frac{\Gamma_1 - \Gamma_m}{p}\right] v_2 - \frac{\Gamma_m}{p} v_3 = i_s - \rho_1$$

Note here that the coefficient of v_2 might be positive if $\Gamma_m > \Gamma_1$. This is the exception referred to in Example 2.3.

Proceeding to node 2, the current to the *left* in Γ_1 is $+ \Gamma_1(v_2 - v_1)/p - \Gamma_m(v_2 - v_3)/p - \rho_1$, the current down in C_1 is $C_1 p v_2$, and the current to the right in Γ_2 is $\Gamma_2(v_2 - v_3)/p - \Gamma_m(v_2 - v_1)/p - \rho_2$.

No current source is connected to this node, so after rearranging terms, the equation becomes

$$-\frac{\Gamma_1 - \Gamma_m}{p} v_1 + \left[C_1 p + \frac{\Gamma_1 + \Gamma_2 - 2\Gamma_m}{p}\right] v_2 - \frac{\Gamma_2 - \Gamma_m}{p} v_3 = \rho_1 + \rho_2$$

Another clue to help check results is that if Γ_m does appear in a diagonal coefficient, it will always be multiplied by ± 2.

The reader is now asked to write the nodal equation for node three, and show that the three equations for the network are those below.

$$\left[\frac{1}{R_1} + \frac{\Gamma_1}{p}\right] v_1 \qquad -\frac{(\Gamma_1 - \Gamma_m)}{p} v_2 \qquad -\frac{\Gamma_m}{p} v_3 = i_s - \rho_1$$

$$-\frac{(\Gamma_1 - \Gamma_m)}{p} v_1 + \left[C_1 p + \frac{\Gamma_1 + \Gamma_2 - 2\Gamma_m}{p}\right] v_2 \qquad -\frac{(\Gamma_2 - \Gamma_m)}{p} v_3 = \rho_1 + \rho_2$$

$$-\frac{\Gamma_m}{p} v_1 \qquad -\frac{(\Gamma_2 - \Gamma_m)}{p} v_2 + \left[C_2 p + \frac{1}{R_2} + \frac{1}{R_3} + \frac{\Gamma_2}{p}\right] v_3 = \frac{e_s}{R_3} - \rho_2$$

Notice that in every case the coefficients are symmetric; that is, the coefficient of v_1 in equation 3 is the same as the coefficient of v_3 in equation 1, the coefficient of v_2 in equation 3 is the same as the coefficient of v_3 in equation 2, and so on. Note also that the initial currents in the coils appear with opposite signs in the different equations. This will always be the case if the initial current appears in two equations. Note that in Example 2.3, ρ_1 appeared in only one equation, since the other end of the coil L_1 was terminated at ground.

Notice that the rules for checking the equations all apply in this example, but that the appearance of Γ_m cannot be easily checked. It is possible to work out a check for this, but it is entirely too complicated for the general case (more than two coils) and too infrequently used.

PROBLEMS

In all of the examples that follow, use p and $1/p$ to represent d/dt and $\int_0^t (-)\, dt$. Be certain to include the initial currents ρ in the equations, and arrange the equations so that the equation for node 1 is first, the equation for node 2 is second, and so on. Also align the variables in columns: v_1 first, v_2 second, and so on. In the coefficients of the variables, place the terms Cp first, $1/R$ second, and $1/Lp$ third. Maintain the same order even if one is missing. Everything involving current sources, voltage sources, and initial currents must go to the right-hand side of the equation. Check each result using the checks outlined at the end of Example 2.3.

2.46. Write the nodal equation for the network pictured in Fig. 2.42.

2.47. Write the nodal equation for the network pictured in Fig. 2.43.

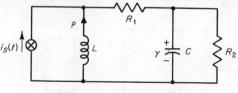

Fig. 2.42 *Problem 2.46.*   **Fig. 2.43** *Problem 2.47.*

2.48. Write the nodal equations for the network in Fig. 2.44.

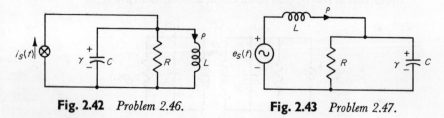

Fig. 2.44 *Problem 2.48.*

2.49. Write the nodal equations for the network in Fig. 2.45.

2.50. Write the nodal equations for the network in Fig. 2.46.

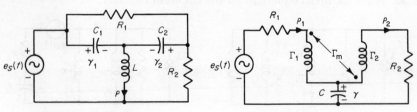

Fig. 2.45 *Problem 2.49.*   **Fig. 2.46** *Problem 2.50.*

2.51. Write the nodal equations for the network in Fig. 2.47. Assume $\rho_1 = \rho_2 = 0$.

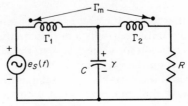

Fig. 2.47   *Problem 2.51.*

2.52. The equivalent circuit for a pentode i-f amplifier stage appears in Fig. 2.48. Write the two nodal equations for the network. *Note:* calculate Γ_1, Γ_2, and Γ_m first. $i_s(t) = 2 \sin 10^4 t \, \mathbf{1}(t)$, $L_1 = 10^{-3}$ henry, $L_2 = 0.1$ henry, and $M = 6 \times 10^{-3}$ henry. Assume that no energy is stored in the circuit at $t = 0$; that is, all essential conditions are zero.

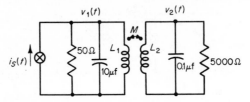

Fig. 2.48   *Problem 2.52.*

2.53. Write the nodal equations in v_1 and v_2 for the network in Fig. 2.49.

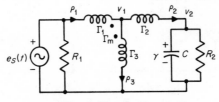

Fig. 2.49   *Problem 2.53.*

2.54. Write the nodal equations for the circuit in Fig. 2.50.

2.55. Write the nodal equations for the circuit in Fig. 2.51.

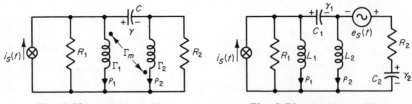

Fig. 2.50   *Problem 2.54.*   **Fig. 2.51**   *Problem 2.55.*

2.10 Mesh (Loop) Equations

The second, and perhaps more common approach to writing the equations of a network is based on the definition of a mesh or loop current. In the mesh method the variables chosen are mesh currents, and Kirchhoff's second, or *voltage*, law is used to write the equations.

A network is said to be *mappable* when it can be laid out on the surface of a sphere or plane in such a way that no wires cross over one another. In Fig. 2.52(*a*), the network looks unmappable, but it is actually mappable with a little alteration, as is shown in Fig. 2.52(*b*). The network of Fig. 2.52(*c*) is not mappable, however.

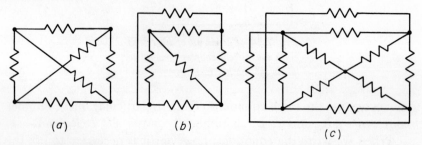

Fig. 2.52   *Two mappable networks and one unmappable network.*

When a network is mappable the simplest set of loop currents that can be used are the mesh currents. A mesh is nothing but a hole in the network, and the group of elements that form the boundary of that hole.

When attempting to determine the number of mesh currents to define, we must be certain to remove all current sources from the circuit, that is, to replace all current sources by open circuits. The reasons for this will be apparent shortly.

After the current sources have been removed, it is then a simple matter to count the openings in the circuit and to note the meshes for which equations must be written. In the event that the network is not mappable, some of the holes (loops) will be in the third dimension. A general discussion of this appears in Chapter 6. In this section, only mappable networks will be considered.

Consider the circuit of Fig. 2.53. If both current sources are removed, we obtain Fig. 2.54, which has two meshes as indicated by the clockwise circular arrows. Note that this not only indicates the number of current variables required, but also tells us which elements and voltage sources

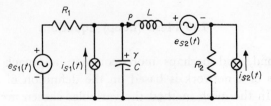

Fig. 2.53   *A two-mesh network.*

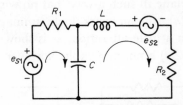

Fig. 2.54   *The circuit of Fig. 2.53 with the current sources removed to place the meshes in evidence.*

to use in writing the mesh equations. Thus, in particular, mesh number 1 consists of e_{s1}, R_1, and C. Mesh number 2 consists of C, L, R_2, and e_{s2}.

When we write the equations, however, it is necessary to use the original circuit. In Fig. 2.55 this circuit is redrawn; note that there are really *four* meshes in it, and that the figure shows four mesh currents. Note, however, that two of the meshes have mesh currents that are either known functions of time, such as $-i_{s2}$ in the mesh at the far right, or defined in terms of a known function of time and another mesh current, such as the second mesh from the left, which has a mesh current of $i_1 + i_{s1}$. The reason for this is based on the definition of a mesh current.

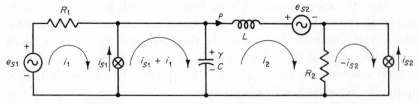

Fig. 2.55   *The circuit of Fig. 2.53 with the mesh currents defined.*

The *mesh current* is a fictitious current circulating within a mesh. The actual current in any branch in a mesh is made up of one or more mesh currents; it is, in fact, the algebraic sum of the mesh currents that course through the branch. Thus, only i_2 exists in L, so the current to the right in that element is equal to i_2. But $i_1 + i_{s1}$ and i_2 exist in C, so the current down in C is $i_{s1} + i_1 - i_2$, or the current up in C is $i_2 - i_{s1} - i_1$. With this definition, the current up in the current source i_{s1} must be the mesh current on its right less the mesh current on its left. But, by definition, the current in the source must be i_{s1} at all times, so the mesh currents on its left and right cannot be independent. Thus, knowing the right-hand current automatically yields the left-hand current, and vice versa.

It is seen in Fig. 2.55 that the two mesh currents in the two meshes on the left are defined so that their difference is indeed equal to the source current. Note that i_1 need not have been placed in the far left. It could have been placed in the second mesh, but then the first mesh current would have had to be $i_1 - i_{s1}$. This is shown in Fig. 2.56. The i_1's of Figs. 2.55 and 2.56 are not equal to each other, of course.

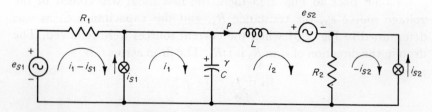

Fig. 2.56 *The circuit of Fig. 2.53 with a different definition for the mesh currents.*

If a network is to be solved by the mesh method, it is advantageous to choose the mesh currents all in a clockwise (or all in a counter-clockwise) direction. As will be seen, this leads to negative off-diagonal coefficients, as in the nodal method, and provides one more check on the work without the necessity of learning additional techniques. It is possible in some networks to choose mesh-current directions so that they alternate; this leads to positive off-diagonal terms. This latter approach cannot always be used, as will be seen by referring to Fig. 2.60 and Prob. 2.58 at the end of this section. Because the basic method is complicated enough, we are advised to begin by choosing all mesh currents in a clockwise direction and to continue this until we are thoroughly familiar with the method. The following examples are designed to demonstrate the writing of mesh-current equations.

EXAMPLE 2.5. Write the two mesh-current equations for the network of Fig. 2.55.
Solution: As indicated previously, the potential drop across each element

in a mesh is to be expressed in terms of one or more mesh currents. Proceeding around the loop, sum all the potential drops in the passive elements, and set them equal to the sum of all the voltage sources that tend to produce current in the loop in the direction of the loop or mesh current.

One word of caution is necessary: *never include a current source in any mesh or loop equation.* The reason for this is simple. A mesh equation is a summation of voltages, and the voltage across a current source is never known at the outset of a problem. If it is to be used as part of a mesh, then its potential must be defined as a new variable, and an additional equation must be written; this is to be avoided. This warning is often ignored, the source *is* used in the loop, and its voltage is assumed to be zero. But if the potential across a current source is zero, then what is it doing in the network? It is certainly delivering no power (see Eq. 2.1). To repeat: *a current source is never a branch in a loop or mesh.*

Going back to Fig. 2.55 then, the first mesh will consist of the voltage source e_{s1}, the resistance R_1, and the capacitance C, as was determined in Fig. 2.54 when the current sources were removed. The drop in the direction of i_1 in R_1 is $i_1 R_1$. The drop across C is

$$\frac{i_{s1} + i_1 - i_2}{Cp} + \gamma$$

The sum of these two drops must equal the rise due to the source:

$$i_1 R_1 + \frac{i_{s1} + i_1 - i_2}{Cp} + \gamma = e_{s1}$$

Collecting coefficients of like variables and putting everything else on the right-hand side of the equation gives

$$\left[R_1 + \frac{1}{Cp}\right] i_1 - \frac{1}{Cp} i_2 = e_{s1} - \frac{i_{s1}}{Cp} - \gamma$$

For mesh 2, the drop across the inductance is $Lp i_2$, the drop (going down) through R_2 is $R_2[i_2 - (-i_{s2})] = R_2(i_2 + i_{s2})$ and the drop across C (from bottom to top) is $(i_2 - i_{s1} - i_1)/(Cp) - \gamma$. The source e_{s2} tends to drive current in a direction opposite the direction of i_2, so it will appear with a minus sign on the right-hand side of the equation. The equation is then

$$-\frac{1}{Cp} i_1 + \left[Lp + R_2 + \frac{1}{Cp}\right] i_2 = -e_{s2} - R_2 i_{s2} + \frac{i_{s1}}{Cp} + \gamma$$

If, as before, the two equations are written together, keeping like variables in the same columns and writing mesh 1 first, then

$$\left[R_1 + \frac{1}{Cp}\right] i_1 \qquad\qquad - \frac{1}{Cp} i_2 \; = \; e_{s1} - \frac{i_{s1}}{Cp} - \gamma$$

$$- \frac{1}{Cp} i_1 + \left[Lp + R_2 + \frac{1}{Cp}\right] i_2 \; = \; - e_{s2} - R_2 i_{s2} + \frac{i_{s1}}{Cp} + \gamma$$

Just as in the nodal method, the coefficients on the principal diagonal are all positive, and those off the diagonal are all negative. Moreover, the coefficients off the diagonal are symmetric; that is, the coefficient of i_2 in equation 1 is the same as the coefficient of i_1 in equation 2. In addition, this coefficient is the only element in the network that is in both mesh 1 and mesh 2. Furthermore, the diagonal coefficients are seen to be the elements of the mesh for which the appropriate equation was written. Thus (with the possible exception of the case with mutual inductance), the left-hand side of the equations could have been written by inspection.

As for the right-hand side of the equations, the voltage sources are those in the appropriate mesh and have a minus sign if the polarity opposes the direction of the mesh current. The same is true of the initial voltage on the capacitance. The current sources appear with the elements with which they are in parallel, and the sign is positive if the direction of the source is the same as that of the mesh current through the parallel element.

Thus it is seen that mesh equations also can be written by inspection; however, this method should not be used except as a check.

Note that the initial voltages across the capacitances did not appear in the nodal equations, and the initial currents in the coils did not appear in the mesh equations. When the equations are transformed in Chapter 4 it will be seen that these missing initial conditions are required. Thus the initial currents in the inductances and the initial voltages on the capacitances are called *essential* initial conditions, for the complete solution of the circuit cannot be determined without them.

Note also that when the mesh method is used, the volt-ampere relations that should be used are the inverse of Eqs. (2.44); that is,

$$v = Ri$$

$$v = Lp\,i \tag{2.46}$$

$$v = \frac{i}{Cp} + \gamma$$

EXAMPLE 2.6. Write the mesh-current equations for the circuit shown in Fig. 2.57.

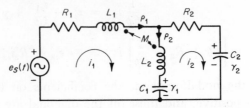

Fig. 2.57   *Example 2.6.*

Solution: Starting in the upper left-hand corner of mesh 1, the drop left-to-right in R_1 is $i_1 R_1$, and in L_1 it is $L_1 p i_1$. There is an additional drop in L_1, however, because of the current in L_2. Again, using rule (1) of Prob. 2.29, the current into the dotted end of coil 2 produces a drop dot-to-undot in coil 1. Therefore $M p (i_1 - i_2)$ actually produces a *rise* in coil L_1, since we are moving clockwise around the loop and collecting drops. Therefore the drop in L_1 because of the mutual term is $- M p (i_1 - i_2)$.

There will be a self-inductance drop in L_2 of $L_2 p (i_1 - i_2)$, also a mutual drop because of i_1 in L_1. Since i_1 comes out of the dotted end of L_1, the induced voltage in L_2 as a result of i_1 will be positive on the bottom of L_2; that is, it will be a negative drop or a positive rise. Hence the total drop across L_2 is $L_2 p (i_1 - i_2) - M p i_1$. Finally, there is a drop of $(i_1 - i_2)/(C p) + \gamma_1$ across the capacitance C_1. Since all these drops must equal the rise in the source, then the equation for mesh 1 is

$$R_1 i_1 + L_1 p i_1 - M p (i_1 - i_2) + L_2 p (i_1 - i_2) - M p i_1 + \frac{i_1 - i_2}{C_1 p} + \gamma_1 = e$$

and, after collecting terms, this becomes

$$\left[(L_1 + L_2 - 2M) p + R_1 + \frac{1}{C_1 p} \right] i_1 - \left[(L_2 - M) p + \frac{1}{C_1 p} \right] i_2 = e_s - \gamma_1$$

Write the equation for mesh 2 and show that it is

$$- \left[(L_2 - M) p + \frac{1}{C_1 p} \right] i_1 + \left[L_2 p + R_2 + \frac{1}{C_1 p} + \frac{1}{C_2 p} \right] i_2 = \gamma_1 - \gamma_2$$

Notice the care with which the equations are written. Also note that the derivative term comes first, the constant second, and the integral last in the coefficients. This is the same procedure that should be used in the nodal method, except, of course, the positions of L and C

are now interchanged. Note also that if M appears in a principal diagonal term, it is always preceded by a ± 2, as in the reciprocal inductance case. Furthermore, the off-diagonal terms *could* be positive if $M > L_2$. This is the only time that the off-diagonal terms can become positive if all mesh currents are chosen with the same direction.

PROBLEMS

In all the problems that follow, use the p and $1/p$ notation for d/dt and $\int_0^t (-) \, dt$. Be certain to include the initial voltages γ across the capacitances in the equations, and arrange the equations so that the equation for mesh 1 is first, for mesh 2 is second, and so on. Also align the variables in columns with i_1 first, i_2 second, and so on. In the coefficients of the variables write the terms Lp first, R second, and $1/Cp$ last. Even if a coefficient does not have all three, maintain relative order. Every term involving voltage sources, current sources, or initial capacitance voltages should go to the right-hand side of the equations. Check each result by comparing the final equations with the original network.

2.56. Write the mesh equation for the network of Fig. 2.58.

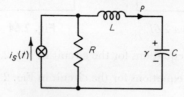

Fig. 2.58 *Problem 2.56.*

2.57. Write the mesh equation for the circuit of Fig. 2.59.

2.58. Write the mesh equations for the circuit of Fig. 2.60,

(a) with all mesh currents clockwise.

(b) with not all mesh currents in clockwise directions.

Note that it is not possible to choose current directions so that all off-diagonal terms are positive.

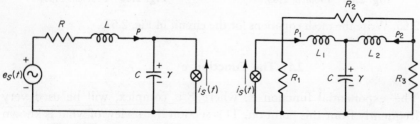

Fig. 2.59 *Problem 2.57.*   **Fig. 2.60** *Problem 2.58.*

2.59. Write the mesh equations for the circuit in Fig. 2.61.

2.60. Write the mesh equations for the circuit in Fig. 2.62.

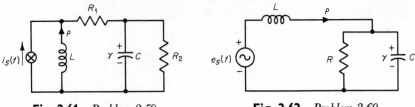

Fig. 2.61   *Problem 2.59.*   **Fig. 2.62**   *Problem 2.60.*

2.61. Write the mesh equations for the circuit in Fig. 2.63.

2.62. Write the mesh equations for the circuit in Fig. 2.64.

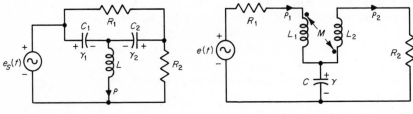

Fig. 2.63   *Problem 2.61.*   **Fig. 2.64**   *Problem 2.62.*

2.63. Write the mesh equations for the circuit in Fig. 2.65.

2.64. Write the mesh equations for the circuit in Fig. 2.66.

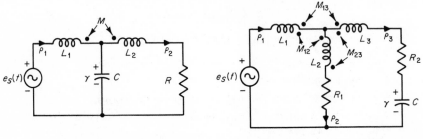

Fig. 2.65   *Problem 2.63.*   **Fig. 2.66**   *Problem 2.64.*

2.65. Write the mesh equations for the circuit in Fig. 2.67.

2.11 The Function e^z

The exponential function e^z, where z is complex, will be used very frequently from this point on. This section is a review of what is known about this important function.

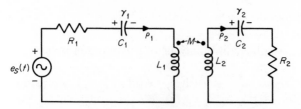

Fig. 2.67   *Problem 2.65.*

The Case Where z is Real

When z is real, the function will be denoted here by e^x. A plot of e^x and e^{-x} appears in Fig. 2.68. Observe that as $t \to \infty$ e^x becomes

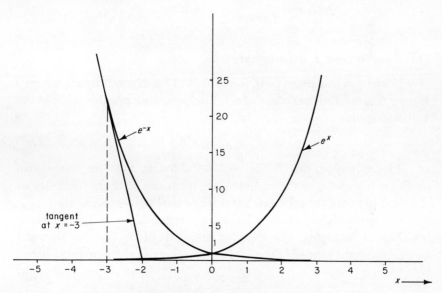

Fig. 2.68   *Graphs of e^x and e^{-x}.*

infinite and e^{-x} approaches (but never reaches) zero. The slopes of the curves (derivatives) are

$$\frac{de^x}{dx} = e^x \quad \text{and} \quad \frac{de^{-x}}{dx} = - e^{-x}$$

Any section of the exponential function looks like any other section with but a change in amplitude. For example, the ratio of $e^{(x+1)}$ to e^x is the same no matter what x is: $e = 2.71828. \ldots$ If at any point on the curve a tangent is drawn to the curve, it will intersect the zero axis one unit away from the point of tangency along the x-axis. If the exponential function is $e^{-x/a}$, then the tangent at any point x_0 will intersect the x-axis at $x_0 + a$.

The particular combinations of the exponentials

$$\frac{e^x + e^{-x}}{2} = \cosh x \quad \text{and} \quad \frac{e^x - e^{-x}}{2} = \sinh x$$

are called the hyperbolic cosine and hyperbolic sine. In like manner the hyperbolic functions tanh x, coth x, sech x, and csch x are defined in terms of the sine and cosine by

$$\tanh x = \frac{(\sinh x)}{(\cosh x)} \quad \coth x = \frac{(\cosh x)}{(\sinh x)}$$

$$\text{sech } x = \frac{1}{(\cosh x)} \quad \text{csch } x = \frac{1}{(\sinh x)}$$

The Case Where z is Imaginary

When z is imaginary, the function will be denoted by e^{jy}, where y is real. A clear understanding of this function is not possible without the Euler formula:

$$e^{jy} = \cos y + j \sin y \tag{2.47}$$

This equation can be derived by showing that the Maclaurin series for both sides of the equation are identical. It is not necessary at this time to prove the relation, but it is essential that we know it.

Evidently the function e^{jy} has both a real and an imaginary part; it is therefore complex. The complex conjugate of Eq. (2.47) is obtained by changing the sign of $j \, (= \sqrt{-1})$ everywhere in the equation; hence

$$e^{-jy} = \cos y - j \sin y \tag{2.48}$$

If Eqs. (2.47) and (2.48) are added, and the result solved for $\cos y$, then the result is

$$\cos y = \frac{e^{jy} + e^{-jy}}{2} \tag{2.49a}$$

Similarly, if the equations are subtracted, and the result solved for $\sin y$, then

$$\sin y = \frac{e^{jy} - e^{-jy}}{2j} \tag{2.49b}$$

We should be thoroughly familiar with Eqs. (2.47) through (2.49).

In fact, we should know them so well that when we see an equation such as

$$e^{-j2\pi x^2} - e^{j2\pi x^2} = \phi$$

we should see the sinusoid immediately. The result can be obtained by multiplying numerator and denominator by $-2j$.

$$\phi = -2j \times \frac{e^{-j2\pi x^2} - e^{j2\pi x^2}}{-2j}$$

$$= -2j \times \left(\frac{e^{j2\pi x^2} - e^{j2\pi x^2}}{2j}\right)$$

$$= -2j \sin(2\pi x^2)$$

This is only one of the interesting properties of e^{jy}. From Eq. (2.47), the magnitude of the function must be the square root of the sum of the squares of its real and imaginary parts; hence

$$|e^{jy}| = \sqrt{\cos^2 y + \sin^2 y} = 1 \tag{2.50}$$

Thus, no matter what y is, the magnitude of e^{jy} is always unity. If Eq. (2.47) is plotted as a complex number with the abscissa the real part and the ordinate the imaginary part, then it is a vector (phasor) of unit length and angle of y radians. This is shown in Fig. 2.69, where it is apparent that the real part is $\cos y$ and the imaginary part is $\sin y$.

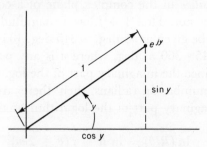

Fig. 2.69 *The complex number* e^{jy}.

It is common practice in electrical engineering to write complex numbers in *polar* form, that is, as a magnitude and a phase angle. For examples, $3 + j4 = 5\underline{/53.1°}$, $5 - j12 = 13\underline{/-67.4°}$, and so on. If the complex number e^{jy} is written in this form, then

$$e^{jy} = 1 \underline{/y} \text{ radians} = 1 \underline{/57.2958\,y°} \tag{2.51}$$

The Case Where z is Complex

If z is complex, then it will be represented by $z = x + jy$, so $e^z = e^{(x+jy)}$. Then, by the ordinary rule of exponents, and using Eq. (2.51),

$$e^{x+jy} = e^x e^{jy} = e^x \underline{/y} \text{ radians} \qquad (2.52)$$

Thus when z is complex, with real part x and imaginary part y, e^x is the magnitude of the complex number and y is its (phase) angle.

The Inverse of the Exponential

The inverse of the exponential is the natural logarithm. Thus if

$$f = e^z \qquad (2.53)$$

then

$$\ln f = z \qquad (2.54)$$

In the general case when z is complex, Eqs. (2.53) and (2.54) become

$$f = e^x \underline{/y} \text{ radians} \qquad (2.55)$$

and

$$x + jy = \ln f \qquad (2.56)$$

from which we conclude that the logarithm of a complex number to the base e is the logarithm of its magnitude plus j times its angle in radians.

While the *position* in the complex plane of a complex number is unique, its angle is not. Thus $1 + j$ has a magnitude of $\sqrt{2} \doteq 1.414$, but its angle may be given as 45 deg, -315 deg, 405 deg and so on. In fact its angle is $(45 + 360\ n)$ deg, where n is any positive or negative integer or zero. Since the imaginary part of the logarithm is the angle of the complex number in radians, then there are infinitely many values for the imaginary part of the logarithm of any number. Thus

$$\ln (R\underline{/\theta}) = \ln R + j\,(\theta + 2\pi n) \qquad (2.57)$$

where θ is in radians and n is any integer. Thus the logarithm is multivalued, and in working the problems following this section this should be taken into consideration.

EXAMPLE 2.7. Write e^{-2-j5} in rectangular and polar form.
Solution: From Eq. (2.52), the magnitude of the complex number is $e^{-2} = 1/e^2 = 0.135335$, and its angle is -5 radians or $-5 \times 180/\pi$deg $= -286.479$ deg $= +73.521$ deg. Hence

$$e^{-2-j5} = 0.135335\underline{/73.521°}$$
$$= 0.0383 + j0.1295$$

EXAMPLE 2.8. Express $e^{5\underline{/30°}}$ in polar and rectangular form.

Solution: Since $5\underline{/30°} = 4.33 + j2.5$, then

$$e^{5\underline{/30°}} = e^{4.33}\underline{/2.5 \text{ radians}} = 75.94\underline{/143.24°}$$
$$= -60.9 + j45.4$$

EXAMPLE 2.9. Express ln $(5\underline{/30°})$ in rectangular form.

Solution: $30° = 0.523$ radians, so

$$\ln (5\underline{/30°}) = \ln 5 + j(0.523 + 2n\pi)$$
$$= 1.61 + j(0.523 + 2n\pi)$$

EXAMPLE 2.10. Express ln $(10-j30)$ in rectangular form.

Solution: Since $10 - j30 = 31.6\underline{/-71.55°} = 31.6\underline{/-1.25 \text{ radians}}$, then

$$\ln (31.6\underline{/-1.25}) = \ln 31.6 - j(1.25+2n\pi)$$
$$= 3.45 - j(1.25+2n\pi)$$

PROBLEMS

2.66. Express the following in polar and rectangular form.

(a) e^{3-j10} (b) e^{-1+j2} (c) $e^{-3\underline{/200°}}$ (d) $e^{0.5\underline{/-300°}}$

Answers: (b) $0.368\underline{/114.6°}$ (d) $1.284\underline{/24.8°}$

2.67. Express the following in rectangular form.

(a) ln $(3-j10)$ (b) ln $(-4-j2)$ (c) ln $(3/5 \text{ radians})$
(d) ln $(13\underline{/-206.5°})$

Answers: (b) $1.498 - j(2.68+2n\pi)$ (d) $2.565 - j(3.61+2n\pi)$

2.68. Show that the function $f(t) = t^n e^{-at}$, where n is an integer and a is a positive constant, has a maximum value of $e^{-n}(n/a)^n$. Show also that its derivative is always negative for $t > n/a$.

2.69. Show that

$$\lim_{t \to \infty} t^n e^{-at} = \lim_{t \to \infty} \frac{t^n}{e^{at}} = \begin{cases} 0 & \text{if } a > 0 \\ \infty & \text{if } a \leq 0 \end{cases}$$

2.70. Express tan θ in terms of exponentials.

2.71. Prove the following identities:

(a) $\sin^2 \dfrac{\theta}{2} = \dfrac{1}{2} - \dfrac{e^{j\theta}}{4} - \dfrac{e^{-j\theta}}{4}$

(b) $2Ae^{\alpha t} \cos (\beta t + \theta) = Ae^{j\theta}e^{(\alpha + j\beta)t} + Ae^{-j\theta}e^{(\alpha - j\beta)t}$

2.72. (a) Let S_n be the sum of the first n terms of a geometric series
$$S_n = a + ar + ar^2 + \ldots + ar^{n-1}$$
Show that since
$$rS_n = ar + ar^2 + ar^3 + \ldots + ar^n$$
then
$$S_n = a \frac{1 - r^n}{1 - r}$$

(b) Use the result of part (a) to prove the identity
$$e^{j(n-1)\theta/2} \frac{\sin (n\theta/2)}{\sin (\theta/2)} = 1 + e^{j\theta} + e^{j2\theta} + \ldots + e^{j(n-1)\theta}$$

2.73. Show by direct substitution that

(a) $e^{-as} + 1 = 0$ if $s = \dfrac{j(2n-1)\pi}{a}$, $n = 0, \pm 1, \pm 2$, etc.

(b) $e^{-as} - 1 = 0$ if $s = \dfrac{j2n\pi}{a}$, $n = 0, \pm 1, \pm 2$, etc.

2.74. Conclude from the previous problem that if $f = e^z = e^{x+jy}$, then $\ln f = x + j(y + 2n\pi)$, with n any positive or negative integer or zero, as asserted in Eq. (2.57).

CHAPTER PROBLEMS

2.75. The value of the current in the source of Fig. 2.70 is
$$i_s(t) = 5(1 - e^{-2t})\mathbf{1}(t)$$
Find: (a) $v_r(t)$, (b) $v_L(t)$, (c) the voltage across the source, (d) the instantaneous power delivered by the source, and (e) the energy delivered by the source from $t = 0$ to $t = t$ [that is, $W(t)$].

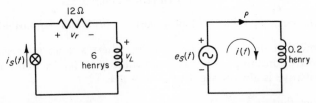

Fig. 2.70 *Problem 2.75.*   **Fig. 2.71** *Problem 2.76.*

2.76. In the circuit of Fig. 2.71 it is given that $\rho = 1$ amp and $e_s(t) = e^{-2.5t}\mathbf{1}(t)$. Find the time expression for $i(t)$ and calculate the energy stored in the inductance at $t = 0$ and at $t = \infty$.

2.77. The *L-C* "tank" circuit in Fig. 2.72 is lossless and is oscillating at its resonant frequency $\omega_0 = 1/(\sqrt{LC})$.

(a) If $v(t) = v_0 \cos t/(\sqrt{LC})$ for all $-\infty < t < +\infty$, and if it is known that $\rho = 0$ [that is, $i_L(0) = 0$], find $i_L(t)$.

(b) If $W_L(t)$ is the instantaneous stored energy in *L*, and $W_c(t)$ is the instantaneous stored energy in *C*, find $W_L(t)$ and $W_c(t)$.

Show that the total energy stored at all times is $CV_0^2/2$ joules.

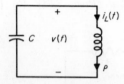

Fig. 2.72 *Problem 2.77.*

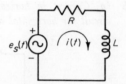

Fig. 2.73 *Problem 2.78.*

2.78. If it is known that $i(t) = Ae^{-Rt/L}\mathbf{1}(t)$, what must $e_s(t)$ be in the circuit of Fig. 2.73?

Hint: draw $i(t)$ and then differentiate it.

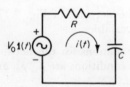

Fig. 2.74 *Problem 2.79.*

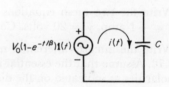

Fig. 2.75 *Problem 2.80.*

2.79. If there is no energy stored on the capacitance of Fig. 2.74 at $t = 0$, find $i(t)$ and the total energy supplied by the source $0 < t < \infty$. Find the energy supplied to the capacitance, and deduce the energy lost in *R*. Find the limit of the energy lost in *R* as $R \to 0$.

2.80. If there is no energy stored on the capacitance in Fig. 2.75 at $t = 0$, find $i(t)$ and the energy supplied by the source $0 < t < \infty$. This is evidently the same as the energy stored on *C*. Note that as $\beta \to 0$ in this problem, the final circuit is the same as that in Fig. 2.74 when $R \to 0$, but the answers are different.

2.81. The magnetic horizontal and vertical deflection systems of a kinescope (TV picture tube) require currents in their coils that look like the signal pictured in Fig. 2.76(*a*). If the frequency is 15,750 cps (for the 525 horizontal lines per picture, 30 pictures per sec), and the coil is represented by the circuit of Fig. 2.76(*b*) with $R = 30\ \Omega$, $L = 0.01$ henry, find $v(t)$. Sketch $v(t)$ versus time.

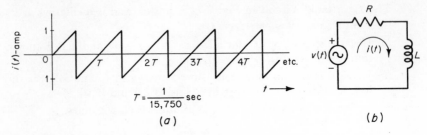

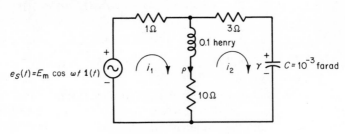

Fig. 2.76 (a) *Current in horizontal deflection coil* (*Prob. 2.81*). (b) *Equivalent circuit for horizontal deflection coil.*

Fig. 2.77 *Problem 2.82.*

2.82. Write the two mesh equations for the network of Fig. 2.77. Assume $\rho = -1$ amp, $\gamma = 20$ volts. Collect variables.

2.83. Write the integro-differential mesh equations for the network of Fig. 2.78. Assume that the essential initial conditions are ρ_1, ρ_2, and γ, with polarities as indicated on the diagram.

2.84. Write the nodal equations for the network of Fig. 2.78.

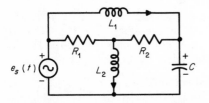

Fig. 2.78 *Problems 2.83 and 2.84.*

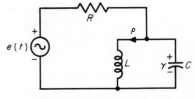

Fig. 2.79 *Problem 2.85.*

2.85. For the circuit pictured in Fig. 2.79,
   (a) write the mesh equations.
   (b) write the nodal equation.

2.86. For the circuit pictured in Fig. 2.80,
   (a) write the integro-differential mesh-current equations.
   (b) write the integro-differential nodal equations.
   (c) Using only the equations obtained in (b), set

$$e_s(t) = \mathbf{1}(t) \qquad \rho_1 = \rho_2 = 0 \qquad \Gamma_1 = 1 \qquad \Gamma_m = 2 \qquad \Gamma_2 = 8$$
$$R = 10 \qquad C = 10^{-6}$$

Draw a circuit with current sources *only* that has the same equations as (*b*). Describe, sketch, or write mathematical expressions for the current source(s) used.

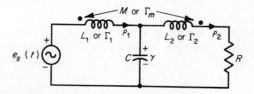

Fig. 2.80 *Problem 2.86.*

2.87. A unit step voltage is applied to the coupled coils in the circuit of Fig. 2.81. Write the single nodal equation in $v(t)$ and solve this equation for $v(t)$. Sketch $v(t)$ versus t.

Hint: If the equation is differentiated, the result will be a linear, first-order, first-degree equation of the simplest type.

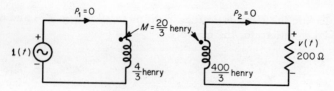

Fig. 2.81 *Problem 2.87.*

2.88. In the circuit of Fig. 2.82,

$$\rho_1 = \alpha \qquad \rho_2 = \beta \qquad v_c(0) = \gamma$$

Write the mesh-current equations for the network.

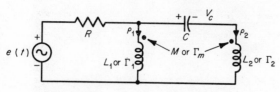

Fig. 2.82 *Problems 2.88 and 2.89.*

2.89. Write the nodal equations for the circuit in Fig. 2.82.

2.90. Write the nodal equations for the network of Fig. 2.83.

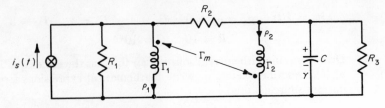

Fig. 2.83 *Problem 2.90.*

2.91. A bridged-T network is pictured in Fig. 2.84. Assume that all essential initial conditions are zero. Write the mesh equations for the network.

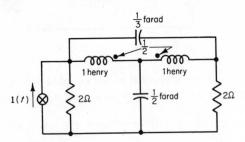

Fig. 2.84 *Problems 2.91 and 2.92.*

2.92. Calculate the Γ terms for the circuit pictured in Fig. 2.84 and write the nodal equations for the network.

chapter

3

The Laplace Transform

3.1 The Unilateral Transform

The objective of the Laplace transform is to change a function of the real variable t to a function of a new variable s. We wish to force all functions of time into a new frame of reference in which the dimension time is replaced by something entirely different. This new dimension is called the complex frequency s. We have at present only one objective in doing this: we want the operation of differentiation with respect to time to be transformed into multiplication by s, and the operation of integration with respect to time to become division by s.

The new variable s is complex; that is, it is really a combination of two real variables, σ and ω. Thus

$$s = \sigma + j\omega \tag{3.1}$$

σ is the real part of s, and ω is its imaginary part. σ has units of nepers per sec, and ω has units of radians per sec. Their combination, the variable s, has units of (time)$^{-1}$.

Definition

Let $f(t)$ be a function of time with the following two properties: (1) There exists a time t_0 such that

$$f(t) = 0 \quad \text{for} \quad t < t_0 \tag{3.2}$$

Thus $f(t)$ has a step function in its definition. If $g(t)$ is a continuous function from $-\infty$ to $+\infty$, such as e^{-t}, then it does *not* have a Laplace transform. But for *any* t_0, $f(t) = e^{-t}\,\mathbf{1}(t - t_0)$ does have the property mentioned, and does have a Laplace transform. (2) There exists a real number σ_e, such that, for $Re\,[s] = \sigma > \sigma_e$

$$\lim_{t \to \infty} f(t)e^{-\sigma t} = 0 \tag{3.3}$$

87

The condition mentioned in Eq. (3.3) is sometimes referred to as requiring $f(t)$ to be of *exponential order*.* In essence we are merely stating that $f(t)$ cannot go to infinity faster than the exponential $e^{\sigma t}$.

Fortunately there are very few common functions that do not satisfy the requirements of Eq. (3.3). One such function is $e^{t^2}\mathbf{1}(t)$, and this is mentioned in Prob. 3.1 (f), following this section.

Unlike for Eq. (3.3), *no* common function with which the student is familiar satisfies Eq. (3.2). Thus, the importance of the step function in this work now becomes clear.

Assuming from this point on that $f(t)$ is a function that satisfies both Eqs. (3.2) and (3.3), then it has a Laplace transform $F(s)$, given by

$$F(s) = \int_{-\infty}^{\infty} f(x)e^{-sx}\,dx \qquad (3.4)\dagger$$

where x is the dummy variable of integration. s may have any complex value so long as $\sigma > \sigma_a$.

σ_a is called the *abscissa of absolute convergence*. The reason for this name is clear when we plot the so-called s-plane. In plotting functions of one variable, such as t, we need only a two-dimensional picture, one dimension of which is t. Since s consists of two variables, we need at least three dimensions to plot a function of s—one for σ, one for ω, and one (or two) for $F(s)$. The s-plane is that plane formed by choosing $j\omega$ as the ordinate and σ as the abscissa. This is shown in Fig. 3.1. Note in Fig. 3.1 that the equation $\sigma = 3$ is the equation of a straight line parallel to the $j\omega$ axis. Thus if σ_a were $+3$ for some function, then the Laplace transform of that function would be defined only for those values of s to the right of the line $\sigma = 3$. In general the transform is not defined on the line itself. It will be assumed that, for all functions considered in this text, $\sigma_a = \sigma_e$; that is, the abscissa of absolute convergence

---

*σ_e is called the *abscissa of exponential order*. The condition in Eq. (3.3) is a *sufficient* but not a *necessary* condition for the existence of the Laplace transform. As will be seen in Eq. (3.4), it is only necessary that the integral definition of the transform converge uniformly and absolutely for s such that $Re[s] > \sigma_a$, where σ_a is some finite real number called the *abscissa of absolute convergence*. For all functions of practical interest, $\sigma_e = \sigma_a$, except for the one noted in Prob. 3.64.

†This is not to be confused with the bilateral Laplace transform, which has an identical definition but does not require of the function $f(t)$ the property mentioned in Eq. (3.2). The bilateral transform has not found any wide usage in electrical engineering. Because of Eq. (3.2), the lower limit in Eq. (3.4) could have been written as t_0, since the integrand is identically zero for all t less than t_0. Making the lower limit $-\infty$ merely generalizes the notation.

is identical to the abscissa of exponential order, the latter being more easily evaluated.*

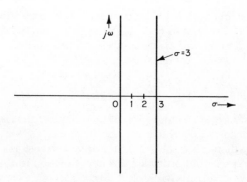

Fig. 3.1 *The s plane.*

EXAMPLE 3.1. Which of the following functions possess Laplace transforms?

(a) $\sin 3t$ (c) $\mathbf{1}(-t)$

(b) $\mathbf{1}(t)$ (d) $e^{t^2} [\mathbf{1}(t) - \mathbf{1}(t-1)]$

Solutions: (a) $\sin 3t$ does not possess a Laplace transform; since this function is defined for t all the way to $-\infty$, it does not satisfy Eq. (3.2).

(b) $\mathbf{1}(t)$ satisfies Eq. (3.2). Does it satisfy Eq. (3.3)?

$$\lim_{t \to \infty} \mathbf{1}(t)e^{-\sigma t} = \lim_{t \to \infty} e^{-\sigma t} = 0$$

if and only if $\sigma > 0$. Thus $\sigma_e = 0$ for this function. $\mathbf{1}(t)$ does have a Laplace transform, and it is defined for all values of s in the right-half s plane.

(c) $\mathbf{1}(-t) = 1$ for all values of negative t. It does not satisfy Eq. (3.2) and hence it does not have a Laplace transform.

(d) $e^{t^2} [\mathbf{1}(t) - \mathbf{1}(t-1)]$ is zero for all $t < 0$. Hence it satisfies Eq. (3.2). The function is zero for $t > 1$, so

$$\lim_{t \to \infty} e^{t^2} [\mathbf{1}(t) - \mathbf{1}(t-1)] e^{-\sigma t} = 0$$

no matter what σ is, since the entire expression vanishes when t is greater than 1. Then $\sigma_e = -\infty$; that is, the Laplace transform of the function not only exists, but is defined for all values s in the entire s plane.

---

*One exception to this rule will be encountered in this text. (See Prob. 3.64.)

PROBLEMS

3.1. Which of the functions listed below have Laplace transforms? For those functions that satisfy both Eqs. (3.2) and (3.3), and hence have Laplace transforms, find σ_e, the abscissa of exponential order. Assume that if $\sigma_e = +\infty$ the transform does not exist.

(a) e^t (b) $e^t \mathbf{1}(t)$ (c) $e^t \mathbf{1}(t+1)$ (d) $e^t \mathbf{1}(1-t)$ (e) $\sin \beta t \mathbf{1}(t)$

(f) $e^{t^2} \mathbf{1}(t)$ (g) $t^2 \mathbf{1}(t)$ (h) $e^{j\omega_0 t} \mathbf{1}(t)$ (i) $e^{st} \mathbf{1}(t)$ (j) $e^{-at} \mathbf{1}(t)$

3.2. Let $f(t)$ satisfy Eqs. (3.2) and (3.3) of this chapter; that is, let $f(t)$ have a Laplace transform. Then it must also have a $\sigma_e < +\infty$. Prove that if $z = a + jb$, then $e^{zt}f(t)$ also has a Laplace transform and that the abscissa of exponential order for this new function is $a + \sigma_e$; that is

$$\sigma_e \,[\text{for } e^{zt}f(t)] = a + \sigma_e \,[\text{for } f(t)]$$

3.3. Use the results of Prob. 2.69 to show that the σ_e of $t^n \mathbf{1}(t)$ is 0.

3.4. Let $p(t)$ be a function that is zero for $t < t_0$ *and* for $t > t_1$, where $t_1 > t_0$. Thus $p(t)$ has values different from zero only in the interval $t_0 < t < t_1$. Show that $p(t)$ has a Laplace transform by showing that it satisfies Eqs. (3.2) and (3.3). Show also that if the transform is denoted by $P(s)$, $P(s)$ is defined for *all* values of s; that is, $\sigma_e = -\infty$.

3.2 The Inverse Laplace Transform

It is apparent at the outset that different functions of time should not have the same transform. In the course of using the Laplace transform it is necessary to obtain the solution desired—a function of time—from its transform. This process is known as finding the *inverse* Laplace transform. Clearly there must be no ambiguity as to what this inverse is; otherwise the entire procedure would be useless. Though a proof of the formula for the inverse transform is not given until Chapter 8, it is stated here:

If $F(s)$ is the Laplace transform of $f(t)$

$$f(t) = \frac{1}{2\pi j} \int_{c-j\infty}^{c+j\infty} F(s)e^{ts}\, ds \qquad (3.5)$$

where c is any constant greater than σ_a.

Equation (3.5) will not be used to obtain the inverse transform in this text, since the integral contained therein cannot be evaluated in most cases without a knowledge of functions of a complex variable. This knowledge is not necessary for the understanding and use of the Laplace transform.

Equation (3.5) is here intended to indicate the uniqueness of the transform. Thus Eq. (3.5) indicates that for *every* transform $F(s)$ there exists one, and only one, function of time $f(t)$.

As with the step function, the inverse transform does not uniquely establish the value of a function at a point of discontinuity. Thus two functions that are equal to each other *almost everywhere* in the sense used in Sec. 2.8 will have the same Laplace transforms. The *Cauchy principal value* of the integral of Eq. (3.5) always yields a value at a point of discontinuity that is halfway between the values of the function to the left and right of this point. This is one reason for assuming $\mathbf{1}(0) = \frac{1}{2}$.

3.3 Transforms of Functions

In spite of the integral definition of the Laplace transform in Eq. (3.4), it is possible to obtain the transforms of almost all important functions of time without integrating at all. To this end this section is divided into subsections; in each a theorem is stated, proved, and used to obtain the transform of a new class of functions. Most subsections are followed by problems intended to demonstrate how the theorems immediately preceding them are used.

The Transform of 1(t)

The Laplace transform of $\mathbf{1}(t)$ can be obtained by substituting it into Eq. (3.4) and performing the integration

$$F(s) = \int_{-\infty}^{\infty} \mathbf{1}(x)e^{-sx}\,dx = \int_{0}^{\infty} e^{-sx}\,dx = \frac{e^{-sx}}{-s}\bigg|_{0}^{\infty}$$

Now if the real part of $s = Re\,[s] = \sigma > 0$ [$\sigma_e = 0$ for the function $\mathbf{1}(t)$ from example (b) in Sec. 3.1], then e^{-sx} is zero at the upper limit ∞. At the lower limit $e^{-sx} = e^0 = 1$, so

$$F(s) = \frac{1}{s} \qquad (3.6)$$

This result must be memorized, for it will be used frequently.

The Transform of $af(t)$

Let $f(t)$ be transformable, with transform $F(s)$. Then, for any constant a, the function $af(t)$ possesses a Laplace transform $aF(s)$.

Proof: Since $F(s) = \int\limits_{-\infty}^{\infty} f(x)\, e^{-sx}\, dx$

then

$$\mathscr{L}[af(t)] = \int\limits_{-\infty}^{\infty} af(x)e^{-sx}\, dx = a \int\limits_{-\infty}^{\infty} f(x)e^{-sx}\, dx$$

$$\mathscr{L}[af(t)] = aF(s) \qquad \text{Q.E.D.} \tag{3.7}$$

EXAMPLE 3.2. Since the Laplace transform of $\mathbf{1}(t)$ has been shown to be $1/s$, then the Laplace transform of $5\mathbf{1}(t)$ is $5/s$, the transform of $-2\mathbf{1}(t)$ is $-2/s$, and so on.

The Transform of $[f(t) + g(t)]$

Let $f(t)$ and $g(t)$ be transformable and have transforms $F(s)$ and $G(s)$ respectively. (Note that lower-case letters are used for functions of time t, and capital letters for transforms, that is, functions of s.) Then the Laplace transform of $[f(t)+g(t)]$ is $[F(s)+G(s)]$ for s in the common region of convergence of $\mathscr{L}[f(t)]$ and $\mathscr{L}[g(t)]$.
Proof: By the definition of the Laplace transform

$$\mathscr{L}[f(t) + g(t)] = \int\limits_{-\infty}^{\infty} [f(x) + g(x)]e^{-sx}\, dx$$

But the integral of a sum is equal to the sum of the integrals, so

$$\mathscr{L}[f(t) + g(t)] = \int\limits_{-\infty}^{\infty} f(x)e^{-sx}\, dx + \int\limits_{-\infty}^{\infty} g(x)e^{-sx}\, dx$$

But the right-hand side is simply the sum of the transforms of $f(t)$ and $g(t)$; hence

$$\mathscr{L}[f(t) + g(t)] = F(s) + G(s) \qquad \text{Q.E.D.} \tag{3.8}$$

Anti-Theorem Number One

A pitfall into which many fall can be avoided at this time by doing the unusual: stating something that is *not* true. If $f(t)$ and $g(t)$ are transformable, and have transforms $F(s)$ and $G(s)$ respectively, then the transform of $f(t) \times g(t)$ is *not* $F(s) \times G(s)$.*

Proof: The statement above is true if we could find but one example for which it is true. This type of proof is not the most satisfying, but the author knows of *no* two functions for which $\mathscr{L}[f(t)g(t)] = F(s)G(s)$. Almost any pair of functions will do. Since we have the transform of only one function at present, that is, $\mathbf{1}(t)$, let us use $f(t) = \mathbf{1}(t)$ and $g(t) = \mathbf{1}(t)$. Then $F(s) = G(s) = 1/s$.

But

$$f(t)g(t) = \mathbf{1}(t)\mathbf{1}(t) = [\mathbf{1}(t)]^2$$
$$(=) \mathbf{1}(t)$$

(see Sec. 2.8).

Then the Laplace transform of $f(t)g(t)$ is simply $1/s$, and

$$\frac{1}{s} \neq F(s)G(s) = \frac{1}{s^2} \qquad \text{Q.E.D.}$$

Complex Translation

Let $f(t)$ be a transformable function with transform $F(s)$, and let $z = a + jb$ be any complex constant. Then the transform of $e^{zt}f(t)$ exists and is $F(s-z)$.

Proof: By definition

$$\mathscr{L}[e^{zt}f(t)] = \int_{-\infty}^{\infty} e^{zx}f(x)e^{-sx}\, dx$$

$$= \int_{-\infty}^{\infty} f(x)e^{zx-sx}\, dx = \int_{-\infty}^{\infty} f(x)\, e^{-(s-z)x}\, dx$$

But the last integral is simply the Laplace transform of $f(t)$ with $(s-z)$ written in place of s. Since

$$F(s) = \int_{-\infty}^{\infty} f(x)e^{-sx}\, dx$$

---

*It is entirely possible that some pairs of functions do what this anti-theorem says they do not, though the author is ignorant of such a pair. $F(s)G(s)$ is the transform of

$$q(t) = \int_{-\infty}^{\infty} f(x)g(t-x)\, dx$$

as will be shown in Chapter 8 in the section on "Convolution."

then

$$F(s-z) = \int_{-\infty}^{\infty} f(x) \, e^{-(s-z)x} \, dx$$

so

$$\mathscr{L}[e^{zt}f(t)] = F(s-z) \qquad \text{Q.E.D.} \tag{3.9}$$

Comment: From Prob. 3.2, the abscissa of exponential order of the new transform differs from that of the old by the real part of z.

EXAMPLE: 3.3. In the theorem above, let $f(t) = \mathbf{1}(t)$, and $F(s) = 1/s$. Then

$$\mathscr{L}[e^{-at}\mathbf{1}(t)] = \frac{1}{s+a} \qquad \text{with} \quad \sigma_e = -a \tag{3.10}$$

$$\mathscr{L}[e^{at}\mathbf{1}(t)] = \frac{1}{s-a} \qquad \text{with} \quad \sigma_e = +a \tag{3.11}$$

$$\mathscr{L}[e^{j\beta t}\mathbf{1}(t)] = \frac{1}{s-j\beta} \qquad \text{with} \quad \sigma_e = 0 \tag{3.12}$$

$$\mathscr{L}[e^{-j\beta t}\mathbf{1}(t)] = \frac{1}{s+j\beta} \qquad \text{with} \quad \sigma_e = 0 \tag{3.13}$$

These transforms [Eqs. (3.10) through (3.13)] will be used so frequently in this text that they should be memorized.

PROBLEMS

3.5. Use the exponential forms for $\cos \beta t$ and $\sin \beta t$ given in Eqs. (2.49a) and (2.49b) to find the Laplace transforms of (a) $\cos \beta t \, \mathbf{1}(t)$ (b) $\sin \beta t \, \mathbf{1}(t)$ (c) $e^{-\alpha t} \cos (\beta t + \theta)\mathbf{1}(t)$. [See Prob. 2.71(b).]

$$\text{Answers: } (a) \, \frac{s}{s^2 + \beta^2} \qquad (c) \, \frac{(s+\alpha) \cos \theta - \beta \sin \theta}{(s+\alpha)^2 + \beta^2}$$

The answers to (a) and (b) should be memorized.

3.6. Find the Laplace transforms of
(a) $\sinh \beta t \, \mathbf{1}(t)$ (b) $\cosh \beta t \, \mathbf{1}(t)$
(See Sec. 2.11).

3.7. Given that the Laplace transform of $[\mathbf{1}(t) - \mathbf{1}(t-a)]$ is $(1 - e^{-as})/s$, what is the transform of $e^{-bt}[\mathbf{1}(t) - \mathbf{1}(t-a)]$?
Sketch the two functions of time carefully.

The Transform of $df(t)/dt$, $t > 0$

When the integro-differential equations were written for the circuits in the examples and problems of Chapter 2, the notation $1/p$ was used for $\int_0^t (-)\, dt$. The lower limit was chosen as zero because it was agreed that, if any switching action took place, it would take place at $t = 0$. Furthermore, the equations as written were those that held for $t > 0$. The closing or opening of a switch alters a circuit; hence, the transient behavior of interest occurs only after the switch is operated.

Since the Laplace transform is to be used for the solution of these equations, it will be necessary to transform both sides of the equations for $t > 0$ only. This can be accomplished by multiplying both sides of the equations by $\mathbf{1}(t)$ and transforming the result.

A minor problem arises in this connection, however. A decision has to be made about the unit impulse at $t = 0$. Do we or do we not want to use this function as a source and/or in a response? If we do, we may not multiply the function by $\mathbf{1}(t)$, since it was agreed in Sec. 2.8 [part 8 following Eq. (2.41)] that the impulse and the step function were not to be multiplied. Consider, for example, the circuit of Fig. 3.2. In Fig. 3.2 an impulsive current source of $10^{-5}\, \delta(t)$ amp is applied to a $1 - \mu f$ capacitance. The result is that the capacitance voltage jumps 10 volts higher.

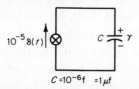

$$C = 10^{-6} f \quad = 1\,\mu f$$

Fig. 3.2 *Charging a capacitance.*

The solution of this problem is simple enough, since the capacitance current must be the derivative of the voltage across it multiplied by C. The only way the current could be an impulse is for the voltage to have a discontinuity in it. Since the amount of the discontinuity and the area of the impulse are equal

$$v(t) = \gamma + 10\,\mathbf{1}(t)$$

satisfies all the conditions of the problem. To see this, differentiate $v(t)$ with respect to t, and multiply by 10^{-6}. The derivative of a constant is zero, and the derivative of $\mathbf{1}(t)$ is $\delta(t)$, so

$$\frac{dv(t)}{dt} = 10\,\delta(t)$$

and $10^{-6}\,dv/dt = 10^{-5}\,\delta(t)$.

Now if our attention is focused on the behavior after $t = 0+$, we would have to consider the effect of the impulsive source, as was done here, and then note that the initial capacitance voltage is not γ, but $\gamma + 10$ at $t = 0+$. This seems unnecessary, and is not to our best advantage.

The current practice in electrical engineering is toward the increased use of the impulse response of systems, so $t = 0+$ is no longer used. To ensure that an impulse at $t = 0$ is not missed, the lower limit of all integrals will be chosen as $0-$, and all initial conditions will be stated for $t = 0-$ *. Thus ρ will represent the current in an inductance *just before* $t = 0$, and the corresponding volt-ampere relation will be

$$i(t) = \frac{1}{L}\int\limits_{0-}^{t} v(t)\,dt + \rho$$

Similarly, γ will represent the value of the initial capacitance voltage at $t = 0-$, and $1/p$ will be refined to mean $\int_{0-}^{t} (-)\,dt$. It is important to reiterate that in most cases it will not matter, since without either impulsive currents or voltages the values of these voltages and currents will be the same at $0+$ as they are at $0-$. A helpful reminder is this simplified rule: *When in doubt, use zero minus.*

Going back to the integro-differential equations of a network, it is seen that all the behavior after $t = 0$, and the behavior from $0-$ to $0+$, can be retained if we multiply both sides of the equations by a step function that occurs just before $t = 0$. In our notation this could be symbolized by $\mathbf{1}(t - 0-)$, but this will be shortened to $\mathbf{1}(t-)$. Then, by definition

$$\mathbf{1}(t-) \equiv \lim_{\epsilon \to 0} \mathbf{1}(t + \epsilon) \tag{3.14}$$

where $\epsilon > 0$. Thus

$$\mathbf{1}(t-)\,\delta(t) = \delta(t)$$

---

*$0+$ and $0-$ are used as though they were numbers such as $-\frac{1}{2}$ or $+5$. They are not. The value of a function $f(t)$ at $t = 0+$, $f(0+)$, means the limit of $f(\epsilon)$ as ϵ goes to zero through positive values. Similarly, $f(0-)$ means the limit of $f(\epsilon)$ as ϵ goes to zero through negative values.

and this is the *only* reason for the introduction of $\mathbf{1}(t-)$. In every other sense it may be used interchangeably with $\mathbf{1}(t)$.

THEOREM 3.1. If $f(t)\mathbf{1}(t-)$ is transformable, and has a transform $F(s)$, then the transform of $\dfrac{df(t)}{dt}\,\mathbf{1}(t-)$ is $[sF(s) - f(0-)]$.

Proof: By the definition of the Laplace transform

$$\mathscr{L}\left[\frac{df(t)}{dt}\,\mathbf{1}(t-)\right] = \int_{-\infty}^{\infty} \frac{df(x)}{dx}\,\mathbf{1}(x-)e^{-sx}\,dx$$

but the integrand is zero from $-\infty$ to $0-$ because of the presence of $\mathbf{1}(x-)$, so the lower limit of the integral may be changed to $0-$ and the $\mathbf{1}(x-)$ dropped.

$$\mathscr{L}\left[\frac{df(t)}{dt}\,\mathbf{1}(t-)\right] = \int_{0-}^{\infty} \frac{df(x)}{dx}\,e^{-sx}\,dx$$

The integral may now be evaluated by parts.* Let $u = e^{-sx}$, $du = -se^{-sx}\,dx$, $v = f(x)$, $dv = [df(x)/dx]\,dx$. Then, since $\int u\,dv = uv - \int v\,du$

$$\int_{0-}^{\infty} \frac{df(x)}{dx}\,e^{-sx}\,dx = e^{-sx} f(x) \Big|_{0-}^{\infty} - \int_{0-}^{\infty} - sf(x)\,e^{-sx}\,dx$$

But $e^{-s0-} = e^0 = 1$, so at the lower limit, $e^{-sx}f(x) = f(0-)$. At the upper limit the expression must vanish, since the transformability of $f(t)\mathbf{1}(t-)$ insures that an abscissa of exponential order σ_e exists, making

$$\lim_{x \to \infty} f(x)e^{-\sigma x} = 0$$

for σ greater than σ_e.

In the integral on the right-hand side, s is not a function of the dummy variable x, so it may be brought outside of the integral sign; hence

$$\mathscr{L}\left[\frac{df(t)}{dt}\,\mathbf{1}(t-)\right] = s\int_{0-}^{\infty} f(x)\,e^{-sx}\,dx - f(0-)$$

---

*The function $df(x)/dx$ may contain impulses, so the right to integrate by parts is thus in doubt. So long as the rules presented in Sec. 2.8, Eqs. (2.36) through (2.40), are adhered to, this can be shown to be legitimate.

But the integral on the right-hand side is simply the Laplace transform of $f(t)\mathbf{1}(t-)$, so

$$\mathscr{L}\left[\frac{df(t)}{dt}\,\mathbf{1}(t-)\right] = sF(s) - f(0-) \qquad \text{Q.E.D.} \qquad (3.15)$$

EXAMPLE 3.4. Find the Laplace transform of $\delta(t)$.

Solution: This transform can be found very easily by noting that $\delta(t)$ is the derivative of $\mathbf{1}(t)$ and that $\mathbf{1}(0-) = 0$; hence

$$\mathscr{L}[\delta(t)] = s\frac{1}{s} - 0 = 1 \qquad (3.16)$$

As indicated previously, this is one of the main reasons for using impulses in our work. This transform can be obtained easily by integration also, since

$$\mathscr{L}[\delta(t)] = \int_{-\infty}^{\infty} \delta(x)\, e^{-sx}\, dx$$

But from Eq. (2.37), $e^{-sx}\,\delta(x) = e^0\,\delta(x) = \delta(x)$. Hence

$$\mathscr{L}[\delta(t)] = \int_{-\infty}^{\infty} \delta(x)\, dx = 1$$

EXAMPLE 3.5. Use the theorem of this section to find the Laplace transforms of $[df(t)/dt]\mathbf{1}(t-)$ when

$$(a) \quad f(t) = \cos \beta t$$
$$(b) \quad f(t) = \cos \beta t\,\mathbf{1}(t)$$

Solutions: (*a*) If $f(t) = \cos \beta t$, then $f(t)\mathbf{1}(t-) = \cos \beta t\,\mathbf{1}(t-)$; the transform of this function was obtained in Prob. 3.5(*a*) and found to be $s/(s^2+\beta^2)$. $f(0-) = 1$, so the required transform is

$$\frac{s^2}{s^2 + \beta^2} - 1 = \frac{-\beta^2}{s^2 + \beta^2}$$

(*b*) When $f(t) = \cos \beta t\,\mathbf{1}(t)$, the function will be unaltered when multiplied by $\mathbf{1}(t-)$, so $F(s)$ is again $s/(s^2+\beta^2)$. But this time $f(0-)$ is zero, so the required transform is

$$\frac{s^2}{s^2 + \beta^2}$$

Why the difference in the two answers? The answer to this question can be made quite clear by referring to Fig. 3.3. In Fig. 3.3(*a*), $\cos \beta t$ is sketched. The function goes from $-\infty$ to $+\infty$. In Fig. 3.3(b), the derivative $-\beta \sin \beta t$ is sketched, and in Fig. 3.3(c), the derivative multiplied by $\mathbf{1}(t-)$ is shown, $-\beta \sin \beta t \mathbf{1}(t-)$. Figure 3.3($d$) depicts $\cos \beta t \mathbf{1}(t)$. The derivative of this must have an impulse of value 1 at the origin because of the discontinuity of the function there. This can be obtained

(a)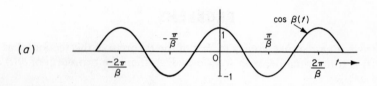

(b)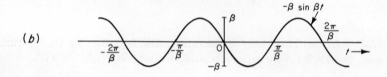

(c)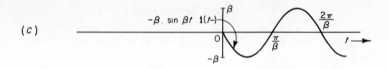

(d)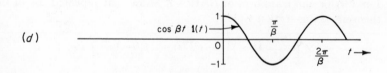

(e)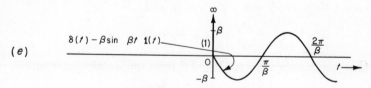

Fig. 3.3 *Example 3.5.*

mathematically also, using Eq. (2.40). Fig. 3.3(e) shows the derivative of $\cos \beta t \mathbf{1}(t)$. Comparison of Figs. 3.3(c) and 3.3(e) shows that the functions differ only by the impulse at the origin. But the transform of this impulse is unity, so the transforms of the two functions should differ by just this amount.

PROBLEMS

3.8. Prove, in a manner similar to that of the theorem of this section, that if $f(t)$ is transformable, with transform $F(s)$, then the transform of $df(t)/dt$ is $sF(s)$.

3.9. Find $Y(s)$, the Laplace transform of $y(t)\mathbf{1}(t-)$, when it is known that

$$\frac{dy(t)}{dt} + 2\,y(t) = 1 \qquad \text{for} \qquad t > 0$$

given that $y(0-) = -1$.
Hint: multiply both sides of the differential equation by $\mathbf{1}(t-)$, transform both sides of the equation, and solve algebraically for $Y(s)$.

$$\textit{Answer:} \ \ Y(s) = \frac{1-s}{s(s+2)}$$

3.10. Find $G(s)$, the Laplace transform of $g(t)\mathbf{1}(t-)$, when it is known that

$$5\frac{dg(t)}{dt} + g(t) = 3e^{-t/5} \quad \text{for} \quad t > 0$$

given that $g(0-) = 0$. [See Eq. (3.10). It is important to memorize this equation.]

$$\textit{Answer:} \ \ G(s) = \frac{3/5}{(s+1/5)^2}$$

3.11. Let $F(s)$ be the transform of $f(t)\mathbf{1}(t-)$. Show that repeated use of the theorem of this section yields

$$\mathscr{L}\left[\frac{d^2f(t)}{dt^2}\,\mathbf{1}(t-)\right] = s^2F(s) - sf(0-) - f'(0-)$$

where $f'(0-)$ is the value of $df(t)/dt$ at $t = 0-$.

3.12. Use the results of Prob. 3.11 to find the transform of $y(x)\mathbf{1}(x-)$ if it is known that $y(0-) = 5, y'(0-) = 0$, and

$$\frac{d^2y}{dx^2} + 4y = 0 \quad \text{for} \quad x > 0$$

Can you deduce what $y(x)\mathbf{1}(x-)$ is from the transform obtained?

$$\textit{Ans:} \ \ Y(s) = \frac{5s}{s^2+4}$$

3.13. In each of the examples below, find the transform of the derivative with respect to time of the function given when the derivative is multiplied by $\mathbf{1}(t-)$.

(a) e^{-at} (b) $e^{-at}\mathbf{1}(t)$ (c) e^{at} (d) $e^{j\beta t}\mathbf{1}(t)$ (e) $\sin \beta t$ (f) $\cosh \beta t$
(g) $\sinh \beta t\mathbf{1}(t)$

Answers: (b) $\dfrac{s}{s+a}$ (c) $\dfrac{a}{s-a}$ (f) $\dfrac{\beta^2}{s^2-\beta^2}$

For (f) and (g), see Sec. 2.11.

The Transform of $\int\limits_{0-}^{t} f(t)\, dt, \quad t > 0$

In solving integro-differential equations the expression

$$\frac{f(t)}{p} = \int\limits_{0-}^{t} f(t)\, dt$$

appears frequently. We need to know how to express the transform of this expression in terms of $F(s)$, the transform of $f(t)\mathbf{1}(t-)$.

THEOREM 3.2. Let $f(t)\mathbf{1}(t-)$ be transformable, with transform $F(s)$; then the transform of $\left\{\int\limits_{0-}^{t} f(t)\, dt\right\}\mathbf{1}(t-)$ is simply $F(s)/s$.

Proof: The transform of $\left\{\int\limits_{0-}^{t} f(t)\, dt\right\}\mathbf{1}(t-)$ is, by definition

$$\mathcal{L}\left[\left\{\int\limits_{0-}^{t} f(t)\, dt\right\}\mathbf{1}(t-)\right] = \int\limits_{-\infty}^{\infty}\left\{\int\limits_{0-}^{x} f(t)\, dt\right\}\mathbf{1}(x-)\, e^{-sx}\, dx$$

Note that only the t in the upper limit is replaced by the dummy variable of integration, x. (See Prob. 2.4).

The integration is to be done by parts. It will be noted that the $\mathbf{1}(x-)$ may be removed from under the integral sign if the lower limit is changed to $0-$. Set $u = \int_{0-}^{x} f(t)\, dt$, $du = f(x)\, dx$ (Prob. 2.8), $v = e^{-sx}/(-s)$, and $dv = e^{-sx}\, dx$. Then $\int u\, dv = uv - \int v\, du$ yields

$$\mathcal{L}\left[\left\{\int\limits_{0-}^{t} f(t)\, dt\right\}\mathbf{1}(t-)\right] = \left[\frac{e^{-sx}}{-s} \times \int\limits_{0-}^{x} f(t)\, dt\right]\Bigg/\limits_{0-}^{\infty} - \int\limits_{0-}^{\infty}\frac{e^{-x}}{-s}f(x)\, dx$$

But the first term on the right is zero at both limits, at the upper limit because the transformability of the integral is assumed and hence a σ_e

must exist, and at the lower limit because the integral from $0-$ to $0-$ is zero. $1/s$ can be factored out of the integral on the right-hand side of the equation, so

$$\mathscr{L}\left[\left\{\int_{0-}^{t} f(t)\,dt\right\}\mathbf{1}(t-)\right] = \frac{1}{s}\int_{0-}^{\infty} f(x)e^{-sx}\,dx = \frac{F(s)}{s} \qquad \text{Q.E.D.} \qquad (3.17)$$

PROBLEMS

3.14. In Prob. 2.36 a class of functions were defined

$$f_n(t) = \frac{t^n}{n!}\,\mathbf{1}(t)$$

It was also stated that for n any positive integer

$$f_{n-1}(t) = \frac{df_n(t)}{dt}$$

providing that $0! = 1$. If both sides of the latter equation are integrated from $0-$ to t

$$f_n(t) = \int_{0-}^{t} f_{n-1}(t)\,dt$$

for n any positive integer. Since all $f_n(t)$ are zero for negative t, Theorem 3.2 applies. Since $f_0(t) = \mathbf{1}(t)$, prove that

$$\mathscr{L}[f_n(t)] = \frac{1}{s^{n+1}}$$

3.15. Find $Y(s)$, the transform of $y(t)\mathbf{1}(t-)$, if it is known that

$$\int_{0-}^{t} y(x)\,dx + 3y(t) = 2, \quad \text{for} \quad t > 0$$

$$\textit{Answer:} \quad \frac{2/3}{s + 1/3}$$

3.16. Find $Z(s)$, the transform of $z(x)\mathbf{1}(x-)$, if it is known that $z(0-) = -1$ and

$$\frac{dz(x)}{dx} + 2z(x) + \int_{0-}^{x} z(y)\,dy = 10 \quad \text{for} \quad x > 0$$

$$\textit{Answer:} \quad Z(s) = \frac{10-s}{(s+1)^2}$$

3.17. For the circuit pictured in Fig. 3.4, write the mesh equation in $i(t)$ after the switch k is thrown upward. Let $\rho = 1$ amp and $\gamma = -1$ volt. Solve for the transform $I(s)$—that is, the transform of $i(t)\mathbf{1}(t-)$.

$$\text{Answer: } I(s) = \frac{s + 22}{s^2 + 4s + 20}$$

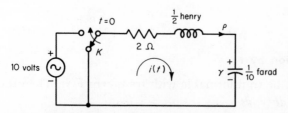

Fig. 3.4   *Problems 3.17 and 3.18.*

3.18. In Prob. 3.17 and the associated circuit of Fig. 3.4, what would the transform of $i(t)\mathbf{1}(t-)$ be if the switch k had *not* been thrown at $t = 0$, all other conditions remaining the same?

3.19. Find the transform of $v(t)\mathbf{1}(t-)$ in the circuit of Fig. 3.5, given that $\rho = \frac{1}{2}, \gamma = 3$.

$$\text{Answer: } V(s) = \frac{3(s + 5000)}{s^2 + 100s + 10^7}$$

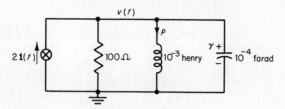

Fig. 3.5   *Problem 3.19.*

3.20. For each of the functions below find the transform of the function when it is multiplied by $\mathbf{1}(t-)$, and then use the theorem of this section to find the transforms of the integrals of the functions for $t > 0$, that is, $\mathbf{1}(t-) \int_{0-}^{t} f(t) \, dt$. Evaluate the integrals and find the transforms of the resulting functions to check your answers.

(a) e^{-at} (b) e^{at} (c) $\sin \beta t$ (d) $\cos \beta t$ (e) t (f) t^2 (g) 1

Solution to (c):

$$\mathscr{L}\left[\sin \beta t \, \mathbf{1}(t-)\right] = \frac{\beta}{s^2 + \beta^2}$$

$$\mathscr{L}\left[\mathbf{1}(t-) \int_{0-}^{t} \sin \beta t \, dt\right] = \frac{\beta}{s(s^2 + \beta^2)}$$

$$\mathbf{1}(t-) \int_{0-}^{t} \sin \beta t \, dt = \mathbf{1}(t-)\left[\frac{-\cos \beta t}{\beta}\Big/_{0-}^{t}\right] = \mathbf{1}(t-)\left[\frac{1 - \cos \beta t}{\beta}\right]$$

$$\mathscr{L}\left\{\mathbf{1}(t-)\left[\frac{1-\cos\beta t}{\beta}\right]\right\} = \frac{1}{\beta}\,\mathscr{L}\left[\mathbf{1}(t) - \cos\beta t\,\mathbf{1}(t)\right] = \frac{1}{\beta}\left[\frac{1}{s} - \frac{s}{s^2+\beta^2}\right]$$

$$= \frac{\beta}{s(s^2+\beta^2)} \qquad \text{(Check.)}$$

Multiplication by t

Let $f(t)$ be transformable with transform $F(s)$. Then the transform of $tf(t)$ is $-dF(s)/ds$.

Proof: By definition, the transform of $f(t)$ is

$$F(s) = \int_{-\infty}^{\infty} f(x)\,e^{-sx}\,dx$$

If both sides of the equation are differentiated with respect to s, then, by Prob. 2.12:*

$$\frac{dF(s)}{ds} = \int_{-\infty}^{\infty} \frac{\partial}{\partial s}\left[f(x)e^{-sx}\right]dx$$

But $\dfrac{\partial}{\partial s}[f(x)e^{-sx}] = -xf(x)e^{-sx}$, so, multiplying both sides by -1

$$-\frac{dF(s)}{ds} = \int_{-\infty}^{\infty} xf(x)e^{-sx}\,dx$$

But the right-hand side is simply the transform of $tf(t)$, so

$$\mathscr{L}[tf(t)] = -\frac{dF(s)}{ds} \qquad \text{Q.E.D.} \tag{3.18}$$

EXAMPLE 3.6. (*a*) Since the transform of $\mathbf{1}(t)$ is $1/s$, the transform of $t\mathbf{1}(t)$ is

$$-\frac{d}{ds}\left(\frac{1}{s}\right) = \frac{1}{s^2}$$

(*b*) The transform of $\delta(t)$ is 1. Then the transform of $t\delta(t)$ is $(-d/ds)(1) = 0$. This agrees with the definition

$$f(t)\,\delta(t) = f(0)\,\delta(t)$$

---

*Strictly speaking, $f(x)e^{-sx}$ should be continuous in x and s and the uniform and absolute convergence of the integral assumed. The continuity of $f(x)$ is not necessary, however, if we adhere to the rules already established.

(c) The transform of $\cosh \beta t \, \mathbf{1}\,(t)$ is $\dfrac{s}{s^2-\beta^2}$. Then the transform of $t \cosh \beta t \, \mathbf{1}(t)$ is

$$- \frac{d}{ds}\left[\frac{s}{s^2-\beta^2}\right] = \frac{s^2+\beta^2}{(s^2-\beta^2)^2}$$

PROBLEMS

3.21. Use the theorem of multiplication by t to find the transforms of

   (a) $te^{-at}\mathbf{1}(t)$ (b) $te^{at}\mathbf{1}(t)$ (c) $t \sin \beta t \, \mathbf{1}(t)$ (d) $t \cos \beta t \, \mathbf{1}(t)$

$$\text{\textit{Answer to} (c): } \frac{2\beta s}{(s^2+\beta^2)^2}$$

3.22. Show that if as in Probs. 2.36 and 3.14

$$f_n = \frac{t^n}{n!}\,\mathbf{1}(t)$$

and

$$F_n(s) = \frac{1}{s^{n+1}}$$

the transform of $tf_n(t)$ is $(n+1)F_{n+1}(s)$.

3.23. Use the *complex translation theorem* to prove that if

$$g_n(t) = \frac{t^n}{n!}\,e^{-at}\,\mathbf{1}(t)$$

then

$$G_n(s) = \frac{1}{(s+a)^{n+1}}$$

3.24. If $F(s)$ is the Laplace transform of $f(t)\mathbf{1}(t-)$, show that the transform of

$$t\,\frac{df(t)}{dt}\,\mathbf{1}(t-)$$

is

$$-\left[s\,\frac{dF(s)}{ds} + F(s)\right]$$

and that the transform of $t\,\dfrac{d^2f(t)}{dt^2}\mathbf{1}(t-)$ is

$$-\left[s^2\,\frac{dF(s)}{ds} + 2sF(s) - f(0-)\right]$$

3.25. Use the results of Prob. 3.24 to transform the following differential equation for $t > 0$.

$$t\frac{d^2f(t)}{dt^2} + \frac{df(t)}{dt} + tf(t) = 0$$

$$\text{Answer: } (s^2+1)\frac{dF(s)}{ds} + sF(s) = 0$$

3.26. Show by direct substitution in the answer to Prob. 3.25 that

$$F(s) = \frac{C}{\sqrt{s^2+1}}$$

satisfies the differential equation. For the differential equation in t in Prob. 3.25, the solution that has the value 1 at $t = 0$ is called $J_0(t)$, the Bessel function of the first kind, order zero. It will be shown by the *initial value theorem* what C must be to make the $F(s)$ of this problem the transform of $J_0(t)\mathbf{1}(t)$.

The Real Translation Theorem

Let $f(t)$ be transformable with transform $F(s)$. The transform of $f(t-a)$ is $e^{-as}F(s)$. (Although a is usually thought of as a positive number, it can be negative or complex as well. In general the theorem is used for any complex number a).
Proof: By definition

$$\mathscr{L}[f(t)] = F(s) = \int_{-\infty}^{\infty} f(x)e^{-sx}\,dx$$

and

$$\mathscr{L}[f(t-a)] = \int_{-\infty}^{\infty} f(x-a)e^{-sx}\,dx$$

Substituting $y = x - a$ for the dummy variable of integration makes $f(x-a) = f(y)$, $e^{-sx} = e^{-s(y+a)}$, $dx = d(y+a) = dy$; the lower limit will be $-\infty - a = -\infty$, and the upper limit will be $+\infty - a = \infty$.

$$\mathscr{L}[f(t-a)] = \int_{-\infty}^{\infty} f(y)e^{-s(y+a)}\,dy = \int_{-\infty}^{\infty} f(y)e^{-sy}\,e^{-as}\,dy$$

In the last integral on the right, e^{-as} does not depend on y, so it can be taken out from under the integral sign.

$$\mathscr{L}[f(t-a)] = e^{-as}\int_{-\infty}^{\infty} f(y)e^{-sy}\,dy = e^{-as}F(s) \tag{3.19}$$

since this last integral is the same as the one for $F(s)$ in the foregoing definition but with y as the dummy variable of integration. (Review Prob. 2.4 if this is not clear.)

This theorem has great practical utility. Its use is best seen from graphs. In essence it says that if the transform of $f(t)$ is known, the transform of $f(t)$ slid to the right a units is the same as the transform of $f(t)$ but multiplied by e^{-as}. Conversely, if $f(t)$ is slid to the left b units, the transform of the new function is e^{bs} times the original transform.

EXAMPLE 3.7. Find the transform of the rectangular pulse pictured in Fig. 3.6.

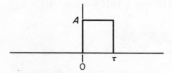

Fig. 3.6 *A rectangular pulse.*

Solution: The rectangular pulse can be thought of as a step function at $t = 0$; then, at $t = \tau$, the step is removed; that is, a negative step is added. But the transform of the step A units high is A/s, so the transform of a step moved to the right τ units is simply $e^{-\tau s}A/s$, and the transform of a negative step is just the negative of this. Then the transform of the pulse is

$$F(s) = \frac{A}{s}\left(1 - e^{-\tau s}\right)$$

EXAMPLE 3.8. Find the transform of the "handy housewives' kitchen stepladder" shown in Fig. 3.7.

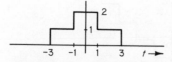

Fig. 3.7 *The "handy house- wives' kitchen step- ladder".*

Solution: Here we see that the function is made up of a step at $t = -3$, another step at $t = -1$, a negative step at $t = 1$, and finally a negative step at $t = 3$. Thus the transform can be written

$$\mathcal{L}[\text{"hhks" } (t)] = \frac{e^{3s} + e^{s} - e^{-s} - e^{-3s}}{s}$$

EXAMPLE 3.9. Find the inverse transform of cosh (as).
Solution: From Sec. 2.11

$$\cosh (as) = \frac{e^{as} + e^{-as}}{2}$$

But $\frac{1}{2}$ is the transform of an impulse at $t = 0$ with area $\frac{1}{2}$, so $e^{as}/2$ must be the transform of the impulse at $t = -a$, and $e^{-as}/2$ must be the transform of an impulse at $t = a$, each with area $\frac{1}{2}$. The inverse transform, then, is

$$f(t) = \frac{1}{2} [\delta(t+a) + \delta(t-a)]$$

and it is shown in Fig. 3.8.

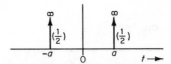

Fig. 3.8   *The inverse transform*
of cosh(as).

EXAMPLE 3.10. Find the transform of the "stairway-to-the-stars" pictured in Fig. 3.9.

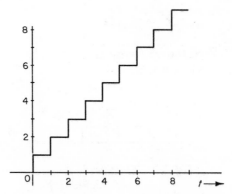

Fig. 3.9   *The "stairway to the stars".*

Solution: The function pictured can be thought of as a succession of steps, each occurring at $t = 0$ and the positive integers, so the transform is simply

$$F(s) = \frac{1}{s}[1 + e^{-s} + e^{-2s} + e^{-3s} + e^{-4s} + \cdots]$$

But, for the real part of s positive, the series can be summed (see Prob. 3.28) to $1/(1-e^{-s})$, and hence

$$\mathscr{L}\left[\text{``stts''}(t)\right] = F(s) = \frac{1}{s(1-e^{-s})}$$

PROBLEMS

3.27. Use the *real translation theorem* to find the transforms of each of the pulses pictured in Fig. 3.10.

$$\text{Answers: } (b)\ \frac{A}{a}\left[\frac{1-e^{-as}}{s}\right]^2 \qquad (f)\ \sinh(as).$$

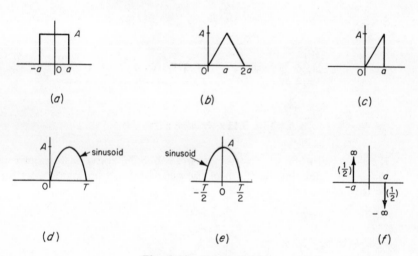

(a)   (b)   (c)

(d)   (e)   (f)

Fig. 3.10 *Problem 3.27.*

3.28. In Prob. 2.72 it was shown that if

$$S_n = a(1+r+r^2+ \ldots + r^{n-1})$$

then S_n could be written as

$$S_n = a\frac{(1-r^n)}{(1-r)}$$

(a) Show that as $n \to \infty$ the sum $\lim_{n \to \infty} S_n$ exists provided that $|r| < 1$, and that the sum is

$$S = \lim_{n \to \infty} S_n = \frac{a}{1-r}$$

(*b*) The series

$$S_1 = A(1 + e^{-as} + e^{-2as} + \cdots) = \frac{A}{1 - e^{-as}}$$

and

$$S_2 = A(1 - e^{-as} + e^{-2as} - \cdots) = \frac{A}{1 + e^{-as}}$$

will be expressible in the closed forms shown if $|e^{-as}| < 1$. Show that this is true for all s such that $\mathrm{Re}[s] > 0$.

3.29. Use the *real translation theorem* and the results of Prob. 3.28 to prove that if $p(t)$ is a pulse of finite duration, such as that shown in Fig. 3.11(*a*), and has a transform $P(s)$, then the transform of a periodic function (for positive t only) made by repeating $p(t)$ every T seconds is

$$\frac{P(s)}{1 - e^{-Ts}}$$

Such a periodic function is shown in Fig. 3.11(*b*).

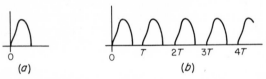

(*a*)   (*b*)

Fig. 3.11   *Problem 3.29.*

3.30. If $p(t)$ is a pulse of finite duration, as in Prob. 3.29, and it has a transform $P(s)$, show that the transform of the periodic function (again only for positive t) shown in Fig. 3.12 is

$$\frac{P(s)}{1 + e^{-Ts}}$$

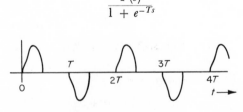

Fig. 3.12   *Problem 3.30.*

3.31. Starting with the transform of the pulse obtained for the signal of Prob. 3.27(*d*), Fig. 3.10(*d*), find the transform of the rectified sine wave pictured in Fig. 3.13. Express the result in closed form.

3.32. Using the transform of the rectangular pulse shown in Fig. 3.14(*a*) as a starting point, express in closed form the transform of the square wave pictured in Fig. 3.14(*b*).

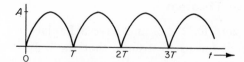

Fig. 3.13 *Problem 3.31.*

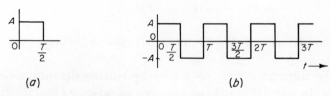

(a)   (b)

Fig. 3.14 *Problem 3.32.*

3.33. Find the Laplace transform of the periodic wave $(t>0)$ pictured in Fig. 3.15.

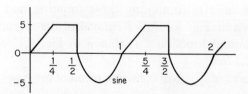

Fig. 3.15 *Problem 3.33.*

3.34. Find the transform of the periodic function pictured in Fig. 3.16.

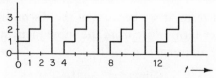

Fig. 3.16 *Problem 3.34.*

3.35. Find the transform of $e^{-at}[1(t) - 1(t - \beta)]$.

3.36. Use the results of Probs. 3.29 and 3.30 to find the inverse transforms of each of the following functions. (It is simplest to sketch the answers.)

(a) $\dfrac{1 + e^{-s}}{s(1 + e^{-2s})}$

(b) $\dfrac{1 + e^{-\pi s}}{(s^2 + 1)(1 - e^{-2\pi s})}$

(c) $\dfrac{2}{s^2}(1 - e^{-s}) - \dfrac{2}{s}e^{-2s}$

(d) $\dfrac{\cosh(as)}{s}$

(e) $\dfrac{1 - e^{-s/2} + e^{-s}}{s + 2}$

(f) $\dfrac{\beta}{s^2 + \beta^2}[1 + e^{-2\pi s/\beta}]$

The Initial Value Theorem

Let $f(t)$ be zero for $t < 0$ and have a Laplace transform $F(s)$. It will be convenient for us to assume that the only discontinuities in $f(t)$ will be step discontinuities and impulses. Then with $f(0+) = \lim\limits_{\epsilon \to 0} f(\epsilon)$, $\epsilon > 0$

$$\lim_{s \to \infty} sF(s) = f(0+) \tag{3.20}$$

(It is to be understood that s approaches infinity through real positive values.)

Proof: The theorem is true no matter how many discontinuities* $f(t)$ may have. In fact $f(t)$ may have impulses for positive t and the theorem is still valid. $f(t)$ may not, however, have an impulse at $t = 0$.

Let $f(t)$ be divided into two functions, $f_c(t)$, which will be continuous for all t (and hence zero at $t = 0$), and $f_d(t)$, which will consist of nothing but step functions and impulses. An example of this division is shown in Fig. 3.17 where an $f(t)$ containing three impulses and three discontinuities is shown in Fig. 3.17(a). Removal of the discontinuities produces the continuous function $f_c(t)$ shown in Fig. 3.17(b), and $f_d(t)$ is shown in Fig. 3.17(c).

The transform of $f_d(t)$ will consist of terms of the type

$$F_d(s) = \frac{f(0+)}{s} + \frac{1}{s}(A_1 e^{-t_1 s} + A_2 e^{-t_2 s} + \ldots)$$
$$+ (a_1 e^{-b_1 s} + a_2 e^{-b_2 s} + \ldots)$$

where the $f(0+)/s$ term arises because of the discontinuity occuring at $t = 0$ and the other terms arise from the subsequent step functions and impulses. Since for all integers n

$$\lim_{s \to \infty} s^n e^{-as} = 0$$

when a is positive, then

$$\lim_{s \to \infty} sF_d(s) = f(0+) \tag{3.21}$$

Since

$$f(t) = f_d(t) + f_c(t)$$

then

$$F(s) = F_d(s) + F_c(s)$$

and

---

*Strictly speaking, the discontinuities must be *countable;* that is, we must be able to associate them with the positive integers in some way so that we can identify a *first,* a *second,* and so on.

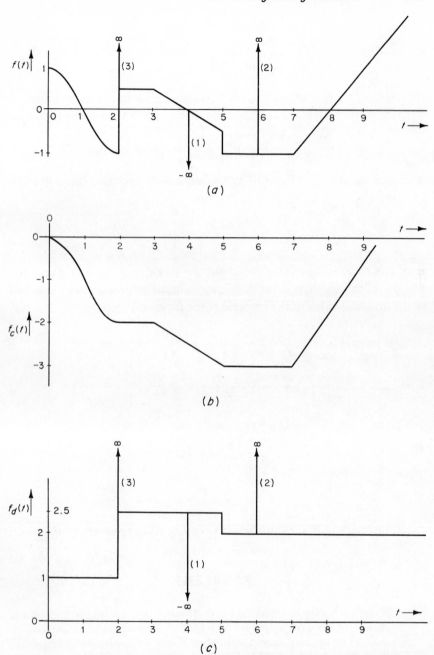

Fig. 3.17 *The splitting of a function, containing impulses and step functions, into a continuous function $f_c(t)$ and a discontinuous function $f_d(t)$. The latter contains nothing but impulses and step functions.*

$$\lim_{s \to \infty} sF(s) = f(0+)$$

if and only if

$$\lim_{s \to \infty} sF_c(s) = 0$$

Since $f_c(t)$ is continuous, its derivative will have no impulses in it, so there must exist a pair of positive, finite constants A and a such that

$$\left| \frac{df_c(t)}{dt} \right| \leqslant Ae^{at} \quad \text{for all } t > 0$$

This can be seen in that $f_c(t)$ is transformable and that therefore an abscissa of exponential order exists. But

$$sF_c(s) = \int_0^\infty \frac{df_c(x)}{dx} e^{-sx} \, dx$$

from the differentiation theorem and the fact that $f_c(0) = 0$. Since the integral of the absolute value of a function must be greater than or equal to the absolute value of the integral of the function, then

$$\left| sF_c(s) \right| = \left| \int_0^\infty \frac{df_c(x)}{dx} e^{-sx} \, dx \right| \leqslant \int_0^\infty \left| \frac{df_c(x)}{dx} \right| e^{-\sigma x} \, dx$$

$$\leqslant \int_0^\infty Ae^{ax} e^{-\sigma x} \, dx = \int_0^\infty Ae^{(a-\sigma)x} \, dx = \frac{A}{(\sigma - a)}$$

Then

$$\left| sF_c(s) \right| \leqslant \frac{A}{(s - a)}$$

when s is positive real ($s = \sigma$), so

$$\lim_{s \to \infty} sF_c(s) = 0$$

The combination of this result with Eq. (3.21) proves the theorem.

PROBLEMS

3.37. Show that if $F(s)$ is a ratio of polynomials in s, then (*a*) the theorem of this section does not apply if the degree of the numerator polynomial is equal to or greater than the degree of the denominator polynomial, (*b*) $f(0+) = 0$ if the degree of the numerator polynomial is two or more less than the degree of the denominator polynomial, (*c*) $f(0+)$ equals the ratio of the coefficients of the highest degree terms in s if the degree of the numerator is exactly one less than the degree of the denominator.

3.38. Show that if $f(t)$ has an impulse at $t = 0$, then, in a sense

$$\lim_{s \to \infty} sF(s) = f(0)$$

Note: It is wrong to conclude that if $sF(s)$ approaches infinity as s becomes infinite, there is an impulse at $t = 0$. (See Prob. 3.63, for example.)

3.39. Given are the following functions, which are continuous at $t = 0$. Find $F(s)$, the transform of the function multiplied by $\mathbf{1}(t)$, and show that $\lim_{s \to \infty} sF(s) = f(0)$.

   (a) e^{-at} *(b)* $e^{j\omega t}$ *(c)* $\cos \beta t$ *(d)* $\sin \beta t$

3.40. In Prob. 3.26 find C in the transform $F(s) = C/(\sqrt{s^2 + 1})$ so that $f(0) = 1$. This establishes the transform of $\mathcal{J}_0(t)\mathbf{1}(t)$.

Change of Scale

If $f(t)$ is transformable with transform $F(s)$, then $f(at)$ has a transform $(1/a)F(s/a)$.

Remarks: Sometimes the numbers appearing in a transform are made a little easier to handle if the time scale is changed. For example, microseconds and milliseconds are often easier than seconds to work with. If the microsecond is chosen as the unit of time after the transform has already been found using the second, then the transform has to be divided by $a = 10^{-6}$ and s has to be replaced by $s/10^{-6} = 10^6 s$. If a millisecond is to be used, then $a = 10^{-3}$.

This theorem has, of course, other uses. For example it was shown that the transform of $\mathcal{J}_0(t)\mathbf{1}(t)$ was $1/(\sqrt{s^2 + 1})$ (see Prob. 3.40). If we wanted the transform of $\mathcal{J}_0(\alpha t)\mathbf{1}(\alpha t) = \mathcal{J}_0(\alpha t)\mathbf{1}(t)$, it would simply be

$$\frac{1}{\alpha} \frac{1}{\sqrt{(s/\alpha)^2 + 1}} = \frac{1}{\sqrt{s^2 + \alpha^2}}$$

Proof: By definition

$$F(s) = \int_{-\infty}^{\infty} f(x)\, e^{-sx}\, dx$$

so

$$F\left(\frac{s}{a}\right) = \int_{-\infty}^{\infty} f(x)\, e^{-sx/a}\, dx$$

Also, by definition

$$\mathcal{L}\,[f(at)] = \int_{-\infty}^{\infty} f(ay)\, e^{-sy}\, dy$$

If the substitution $y = x/a$, $dy = dx/a$ is made in the last integral, then

$$\mathscr{L}[f(at)] = \int_{-\infty}^{\infty} f(x)\, e^{-sx/a}\, \frac{dx}{a} = \frac{1}{a} \int_{-\infty}^{\infty} f(x)\, e^{-sx/a}\, dx$$

$$= \frac{F(s/a)}{a} \qquad \text{Q.E.D.} \tag{3.22}$$

PROBLEMS

3.41. Find the transforms of each of the functions below, and use the change of scale theorem to find the transforms of the same functions when t is replaced by at.

(a) $\delta(t)$ [see also Eq. (2.41)]   (b) $\mathbf{1}(t)$ (c) $\sin t\mathbf{1}(t)$

(d) $\cos t\mathbf{1}(t)$ (e) $e^{-t}\mathbf{1}(t)$

3.42. Find the transform of the rectangular pulse in Fig. 3.18(a) using the time unit of 1 sec. Repeat this for Fig. 3.18(b), but now use the time unit as $1\,\mu$sec. Show that with $a = 10^{-6}$ the second transform could have been obtained from the first by the change of scale theorem.

(a)   (b)

Fig. 3.18   *Problem 3.42.*

3.4 Summary

All the important results of this chapter appear in Tables 3.1 and 3.2. The first group of theorems in Table 3.1 apply to any transformable function of time $f(t)$. The only requirements for this, it will be recalled, are that $f(t)$ be identically zero for t less than some finite time t_0 and that $f(t)$ be of exponential order; that is, a σ_e must exist such that $\lim_{t \to \infty} f(t)e^{-\sigma t} = 0$ for all $\sigma > \sigma_e$.

The second group of theorems in Table 3.1 apply only to functions defined for $t > 0-$, and are used in the solution of integro-differential equations obtained from the analysis of electric circuits or mechanical systems.

Table 3.2 is a list of seven transform pairs that should be memorized as quickly as possible. Problems 3.43 through 3.48 are designed to assist us in remembering the most important of these seven, that is, the first two. As will be seen shortly, these two are the key pairs that will allow us to find the inverse transforms of transient voltages and currents.

Table 3.1 Laplace Transform Theorems

Function of Time		Transform
$f(t)$	(1)	$F(s)$
$g(t)$	(2)	$G(s)$
$af(t)$	(3)	$aF(s)$
$f(t) + g(t)$	(4)	$F(s) + G(s)$
$f(t)g(t)$	(5)	[NOT $F(s)G(s)$]
$e^{zt}f(t)$	(6)	$F(s-z)$
$\dfrac{df(t)}{dt}$	(7)	$sF(s)$
$\displaystyle\int_{-\infty}^{t} f(t)\, dt$	(8)	$\dfrac{F(s)}{s}$
$tf(t)$	(9)	$-\dfrac{dF(s)}{ds}$
$f(t-a)$	(10)	$e^{-as}F(s)$
$f(at)$	(11)	$\left(\dfrac{1}{a}\right)F\left(\dfrac{s}{a}\right)$
Useful in the Solution of Integro-Differential Equations		
$f(t)\mathbf{1}(t-)$	(12)	$F(s)$
$\dfrac{df(t)}{dt}\mathbf{1}(t-)$	(13)	$sF(s) - f(0-)$
$\mathbf{1}(t-)\displaystyle\int_{0-}^{t} f(t)\, dt$	(14)	$\dfrac{F(s)}{s}$
$\displaystyle\lim_{s \to \infty} sF(s)$	(15)	$f(0+)$

Table 3.2 Key Laplace Transforms

Function of Time		Function of s
$\dfrac{A}{(n-1)!} \; t^{n-1} \, e^{-\alpha t} \, \mathbf{1}(t)$	(1)	$\dfrac{A}{(s+\alpha)^n}$
$\dfrac{2A}{(n-1)!} \; t^{n-1} \, e^{-\alpha t} \cos\,(\beta t+\theta)\mathbf{1}(t)$	(2)	$\dfrac{A\underline{/\theta}}{(s+\alpha-j\beta)^n} + \dfrac{A\underline{/-\theta}}{(s+\alpha+j\beta)^n}$
$\mathbf{1}(t)$	(3)	$\dfrac{1}{s}$
$t\mathbf{1}(t)$	(4)	$\dfrac{1}{s^2}$
$e^{-at}\mathbf{1}(t)$	(5)	$\dfrac{1}{s+a}$
$\cos \beta t \; \mathbf{1}(t)$	(6)	$\dfrac{s}{s^2+\beta^2}$
$\sin \beta t \; \mathbf{1}(t)$	(7)	$\dfrac{\beta}{s^2+\beta^2}$

PROBLEMS

3.43. A careful study of Table 3.1 indicates an apparent contradiction. Pairs (8) and (14) have the same transform, but different functions. Does this mean that the Laplace transform is not unique for each function, or is there an error in the table? If the table is correct, then why the confusion?

3.44. The first pair given in Table 3.2 were obtained in Prob. 3.23. Use the appropriate values of A, α, and n to find the transforms of

(a) $2t^2e^{3t}\mathbf{1}(t)$ (b) $\dfrac{t^3}{3} \; e^{-t/2}\mathbf{1}(t)$ (c) $t^5\mathbf{1}(t)$

In your solution make it clear which values you chose for A, α, and n.

3.45. Use the first pair in Table 3.2 to find the inverse transform of each of the following functions.

(a) $\dfrac{3}{(s+5)^3}$ (b) $\dfrac{2}{(s-2)^2}$ (c) $\dfrac{-10}{(s+2)^5}$ (d) $\dfrac{6}{s^{10}}$

3.46. Observe that in pair (2) of Table 3.2 the transform is a combination of two terms just like the term of pair (1), except that in the first fraction of pair (2), A is replaced by a complex number whose magnitude is A and whose angle is θ, and α is replaced by the complex number $\alpha - j\beta$. The second fraction in the transform of pair (2) is seen to be the conjugate of the first (if s is considered real, of course), since $A/-\theta$ is the conjugate of A/θ, and $\alpha + j\beta$ is the conjugate of $\alpha - j\beta$.

Take pair (1) and replace A by A/θ and $A/-\theta$, and replace α by $\alpha - j\beta$ and $\alpha + j\beta$, and inverse transform each fraction separately. Combine the two functions of time thus obtained and show that pair (2) is indeed correct.

3.47. Use pair (2) of Table 3.2 to find the inverse transforms of the following functions.

(a) $\dfrac{5/30°}{s + 1 - j3} + \dfrac{5/-30°}{s + 1 + j3}$

(b) $\dfrac{3/45°}{(s + 2 - j14)^2} + \dfrac{3/-45°}{(s + 2 + j14)^2}$

(c) $\dfrac{4/205°}{(s + 3 + j10)^3} + \dfrac{4/155°}{(s + 3 - j10)^3}$

(d) $\dfrac{1 - j}{s - j30} + \dfrac{1 + j}{s + j30}$

(e) $\dfrac{\sqrt{2}j}{(s - 2 - j5)^5} - \dfrac{\sqrt{2}j}{(s - 2 + j5)^5}$

3.48. "If the denominator of a transform goes to zero for a value of s in the right-half plane, the function of time will explode." Comment on this statement by considering the positions of the roots of the denominators of the transforms

$$\frac{1}{s + 1}, \quad \frac{1}{s - 1} \quad \text{and} \quad \frac{1}{s - j} + \frac{1}{s + j}.$$

Relate these roots to the behavior of their inverse transforms as t becomes large.

CHAPTER PROBLEMS

3.49. Using the theorems for real differentiation and integration, find the transforms of $[df(t)/dt\mathbf{1}(t-)]$ and $\mathbf{1}(t-) \int_{0-}^{t} f(t)\,dt$ if $f(t)$ is

(a) $5e^{-3t}$ (b) $5e^{-3t}\mathbf{1}(t)$ (c) $5e^{-3t}\mathbf{1}(t+1)$ (d) $5e^{-3t}\mathbf{1}(t-1)$

3.50 Given that the transform of $\mathcal{J}_0(t)\mathbf{1}(t)$ is $1/(\sqrt{s^2+1})$, find the transforms of

(a) $\dfrac{d\mathcal{J}_0(t)}{dt}\mathbf{1}(t)$ (b) $e^{-t}\mathcal{J}_0(t)\mathbf{1}(t)$ (c) $t\mathcal{J}_0(t)\mathbf{1}(t)$ (d) $\mathcal{J}_0(t+4)\mathbf{1}(t+4)$

(e) $\mathcal{J}_0(t-2)\mathbf{1}(t-2)$

3.51. Find the transform of the rectangular pulse in Fig. 3.19(*a*). Use this transform and the theorems of this chapter to find the transforms of each of the functions pictured in Fig. 3.19(*b*), (*c*), (*d*), (*e*), and (*f*).

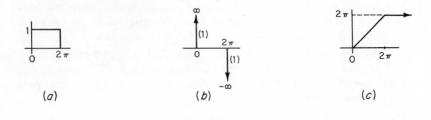

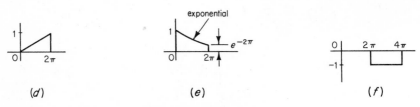

Fig. 3.19   *Problem 3.51.*

3.52. The gamma function, denoted by $\Gamma(y)$, is sometimes called the factorial function, for it is a continuous function which, at the positive integers, is equal to $(y-1)!$ Thus $\Gamma(3) = 2! = 2$, $\Gamma(5) = 4! = 24$, and so on. The integral below is known to converge to the gamma function for all positive y.

$$\Gamma(y) = \int_0^\infty z^{y-1} e^{-z} \, dz$$

Make the substitution $z = sx$, and show that

$$\mathscr{L}\left[\frac{t^{y-1}}{\Gamma(y)}\mathbf{1}(t)\right] = \frac{1}{s^y}$$

In particular, show that this result is the same as the result of Prob. 3.14 when y is an integer.

3.53. Given that the Bessel function of the first kind and order one, $\mathcal{J}_1(t)$, is related to $\mathcal{J}_0(t)$ by

$$\mathcal{J}_1(t) = -\frac{d\mathcal{J}_0(t)}{dt}$$

find the transform of $\mathcal{J}_1(t)\mathbf{1}(t)$.

Answer: $\dfrac{1}{\sqrt{s^2+1}\,(\sqrt{s^2+1}+s)}$

3.54. For $n > 1$, the Bessel function of the first kind and order n is related to the Bessel functions of the first kind and orders $n - 1$ and $n - 2$ by

$$J_n(t) = -2 \frac{dJ_{n-1}(t)}{dt} + J_{n-2}(t)$$

Use this to find the transform of $J_2(t)\mathbf{1}(t)$.

3.55. It is asserted that the Laplace transform of $J_n(t)\mathbf{1}(t)$ is given by

$$\mathcal{L}[J_n(t)\mathbf{1}(t)] = \frac{1}{\sqrt{s^2 + 1} \ (\sqrt{s^2 + 1} + s)^n}$$

Prove this by substituting this relation into the transform of the equation given in Prob. 3.54. Note that the result also holds for $n = 1$ and 0. It is necessary to observe from the initial value theorem that $J_n(0) = 0$ for $n \neq 0$.

3.56. Use the change of scale theorem and the relation given in Prob. 3.55 to find the transform of $J_n(\alpha t)\mathbf{1}(t)$.

3.57. It is asserted that

$$\mathcal{L}\left[\frac{J_n(t)}{t}\mathbf{1}(t)\right] = \frac{1}{n \ (\sqrt{s^2 + 1} + s)^n}$$

Prove that this is true by using the theorem for multiplication by t and the results of Prob. 3.55.

3.58. Sketch carefully the inverse transforms of the following functions.

(a) sinh s (b) cosh s (c) tanh s (d) coth s (e) csch s
(f) sech s

3.59. Prove that

$$\mathcal{L}\left[\frac{\sin \beta t}{t}\mathbf{1}(t)\right] = \tan^{-1}\frac{\beta}{s}$$

3.60. Use the initial value theorem and the results of the previous problem to find the value of $(\sin \beta t)/t$ at $t = 0$. Check your result with L'Hôpital's rule.

3.61. Show that

$$\mathcal{L}\left[\frac{e^{-\alpha t} - e^{-\beta t}}{t}\mathbf{1}(t)\right] = \ln\frac{s + \beta}{s + \alpha}$$

3.62. Use the initial value theorem and L'Hôpital's rule to find and check the value of $(e^{-\alpha t} - e^{-\beta t})/t$ in the previous problem at $t = 0$.

3.63. (a) Given that $\Gamma(1/2) = \sqrt{\pi}$, use the results of Prob. 3.52 to show that

$$\mathcal{L}\left[\frac{\mathbf{1}(t)}{\sqrt{t}}\right] = \sqrt{\frac{\pi}{s}}$$

(b) See if the initial-value theorem works for this function. (See Prob. 3.38).

3.64. Consider the function

$$f(t) = \sum_{n=0,1,2}^{\infty} \delta(t - n)$$

$$= \delta(t) + \delta(t - 1) + \ldots$$

(a) Show that

$$F(s) = \frac{1}{1 - e^{-s}}$$

(b) Show that $F(s)$ exists (is less than infinity) for all s for which $\sigma > 0$.

(c) Show that σ_e, the abscissa of exponential order, is $+\infty$ for $f(t)$. This is the only practical example used in this book in which σ_e does not exist and yet the transform does. $\sigma = 0$ is known as the abscissa of absolute convergence σ_a, and this will be the only function considered for which $\sigma_a \neq \sigma_e$. Others might exist, but they will certainly be unusual functions.

chapter

4

The Transformed Equations, Transfer Functions

4.1 Transforming the Integro-Differential Equations

The discussion of Chapter 2 covered the writing of the mesh and nodal equations of a network. If these equations are written for the situation after $t = 0$, that is, after the switch is actuated, then they are valid for $t > 0$ only. This can be represented symbolically by multiplying each term on both sides of the equation by the step function $\mathbf{1}(t)$. In the event one term contains an impulse (either explicitly or implicitly), then to be certain of not missing the impulse both sides are to be multiplied by $\mathbf{1}(t-)$.

The next step is to transform each term on both sides of the equations, defining unknown transforms such as the mesh and nodal variables by $I_2(s)$ or $V_3(s)$, the transforms of $i_2(t)$ and $v_3(t)$ respectively.

The Left-Hand Side

We have been careful to write on the left-hand side of the mesh and nodal equations only those terms arising from voltages or currents in the passive elements; the initial capacitance voltages, inductive currents, and sources have all been placed on the right-hand side of the equations. The terms on the left-hand side consist of one or more of the five possible types listed below.

1. $Cpv(t)\,\mathbf{1}(t-)$. When this term is transformed according to the discussion of the transform of $df(t)/dt$, $t > 0$, the result is

$$CsV(s) - Cv(0-)$$

But it was agreed that $v(0-) = \gamma$, so the transform of the expression is

$$CsV(s) - C\gamma \tag{4.1}$$

$C\gamma$ is a constant, and hence must be the transform of an impulse. Then Eq. (4.1) is the same as the transform of a current in a capacitance uncharged at $t = 0$, but in parallel with a current source that is an impulse at $t = 0$ with area $C\gamma$. Alternatively, the current could be considered to be the current in a capacitance C whose voltage at $t = 0-$ is zero, but the capacitance is in series with a constant voltage source of γ volts. This is shown in Fig. 4.1, where the three possible situations

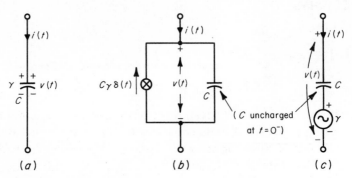

Fig. 4.1   *Three situations in which the transformed volt-ampere relation for the current is* $CsV(s) - C\gamma$.

are pictured. For each of the three circuits, the Laplace transform of the current is given by Eq. (4.1).

Figure 4.1 suggests that if a capacitance in a circuit with initial charge is to be handled on the nodal basis, its handling will be facilitated if its initial voltage is drawn in the circuit as an impulsive current source in parallel with the capacitance and with a value $C\gamma$. Alternatively, if it is to be handled on the mesh-current basis, with the voltage across the capacitance expressed in terms of the current, then the equation

$$I(s) = CsV(s) - C\gamma$$

may be solved for $V(s)$, yielding

$$V(s) = \frac{I(s)}{Cs} + \frac{\gamma}{s} \tag{4.2}$$

But this is just the transform of

$$v(t)\,\mathbf{1}(t-) = \mathbf{1}(t-)\int_{0-}^{t} i(t)\,dt + \gamma\,\mathbf{1}(t-)$$

or $v(t) = i(t)/Cp + \gamma$ multiplied by $\mathbf{1}(t-)$.

The simplicity of these results leads directly to an idea: *Why draw the circuit in the time domain at all; why write the integro-differential equations?* Why not start by drawing a *transformed* network such as that pictured in Fig. 4.2(*b*) or (*c*)? As will be seen, this is not only possible, but time-saving as well.

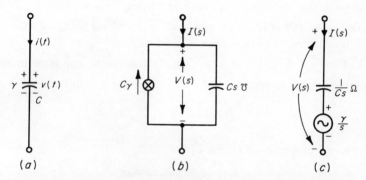

(*a*)　　　　　(*b*)　　　　　(*c*)

Fig. 4.2 (a) *The capacitance in the time-domain with initial voltage γ.*
(b) *The transformed capacitance, with Cs as its admittance and 1/(Cs) as its impedance. The initial voltage now appears as a current source of $C\gamma$. (c) The transformed capacitance, with 1/Cs as its impedance and Cs as its admittance, but with the initial voltage appearing as a voltage source of γ/s volts.*

Rule. If a circuit is to be analyzed by the nodal method, then all capacitances in the circuit should be replaced by admittances of Cs mhos, and placed in parallel with a transformed current source of $C\gamma$. The units of $C\gamma$ are coulombs, but this is because the dimension of a transformed variable is always multiplied by time. Thus, amperes transform into amp-sec, or coulombs, volts transform into volt-sec, or flux linkages. However, since transforms will be thought of as density functions in the frequency domain, it will be more convenient if we use the units amp/cps and volts/cps for the transforms of currents and voltages rather than coulombs and flux linkages.

Rule. If a circuit is to be analyzed by the mesh method, then each capacitance should be replaced by an impedance of $1/(Cs)$ ohms in series with a voltage source of γ/s volts/cps.

2. $v(t)/R\mathbf{1}(t-)$. The transform of the current in a resistance can be written in terms of the transform of the voltage by

$$I(s) = \frac{V(s)}{R} \tag{4.3}$$

and this can be solved for $V(s)$:

$$V(s) = RI(s) \qquad (4.4)$$

It is clear that these relations are exactly the same as those in the time domain, so transforming the resistance requires no new knowledge.

Rule. If a network is to be solved by the nodal method, all resistances should be entered as admittances of $1/R$ mhos.

Rule. If a network is to be solved by the mesh method, all resistances should be entered as impedances of R ohms.

3. $\mathbf{1}(t-) \left\{ 1/L \int_{0-}^{t} v(t) \, dt + \rho \right\}$. The transform of the current in an inductance *that is not mutually coupled to another coil* is simply

$$I(s) = \frac{V(s)}{Ls} + \frac{\rho}{s} \qquad (4.5)$$

or, if the expression is solved for $V(s)$

$$V(s) = LsI(s) - L\rho \qquad (4.6)$$

But Eq. (4.6) is the transform of $L \, di(t)/dt \, \mathbf{1}(t-)$, so the inductance is analogous to the capacitance. Figure 4.3 shows the transformed equivalent of an inductance. In Fig. 4.3(b), the initial current appears as a current source in parallel with an admittance of $1/(Ls)$ mhos, the current having a value of ρ/s amp/cps. Figure 4.3(c) shows the inductance as an impedance of Ls ohms in series with a voltage source of $L\rho$ volts/cps [the transform of an impulsive voltage source of $L\rho \, \delta(t)$].

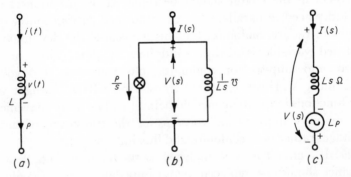

Fig. 4.3 *The two forms of the transformed inductance when a coil is not coupled to another coil.*

Rule. If a network is to be solved by the nodal method, all inductances not coupled to other inductances are to be replaced by an admittance of $1/(Ls)$ mhos in parallel with a current source of ρ/s amp/cps.

Rule. If the network is to be solved using the mesh method, all inductances not coupled to other inductances are to be replaced by an impedance of Ls ohms in series with a voltage source of $L\rho$ volts/cps.

Note carefully the directions of the sources in Figs. 4.2 and 4.3. In every case, if the direction of the current source is compared with that of the voltage source, the arrow has the same direction as the $(-)$ to $(+)$ direction, these arrows and polarity marks bearing the same relation to the initial conditions that they represent.

4. *Mutual reciprocal inductance.* When coils are coupled to each other, the simplest representation is that of the nodal method. As will be seen, each coil is replaced by an admittance of Γ/s, and a current source of ρ/s is placed in parallel with the reciprocal inductance, the current ρ being the initial current in the coil as with the uncoupled inductance in 3. This is shown in Fig. 4.4. Again, no new techniques are needed.

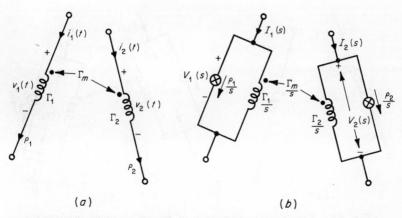

(a)   (b)

Fig. 4.4 *Transform representation of mutually coupled reciprocal inductances.*

That these statements are true can be deduced by referring to Eqs. (2.26), which are reproduced here:

$$i_1(t) = \Gamma_1 \int_{0-}^{t} v_1 \, dt - \Gamma_m \int_{0-}^{t} v_2 \, dt + \rho_1$$

$$i_2(t) = -\Gamma_m \int_{0-}^{t} v_1 \, dt + \Gamma_2 \int_{0-}^{t} v_2 \, dt + \rho_2$$

(2.26)

If Eqs. (2.26) are multiplied by $\mathbf{1}(t-)$ and transformed, the result is

$$I_1(s) = \frac{\Gamma_1}{s} V_1(s) - \frac{\Gamma_m}{s} V_2(s) + \frac{\rho_1}{s}$$

$$I_2(s) = -\frac{\Gamma_m}{s} V_1(s) + \frac{\Gamma_2}{s} V_2(s) + \frac{\rho_2}{s}$$

(4.7)

If we use the ordinary rules (current into one dot induces a current out of the other—valid for two coils only) for the mutual reciprocal inductance, it is seen that the equations for the network of Fig. 4.4(*b*) are the same as Eqs. (4.7).

5. *Mutual inductance*. The case for mutual inductance is more complicated—sufficiently complicated, in fact, that it is advisable to use current sources for the initial currents as in Fig. 4.5(*b*), impedances of *Ls*, and mutual impedance *Ms*. Admittedly, current sources are confusing when the mesh method is used, but they are not as confusing as the task of representing the initial currents as voltage sources.

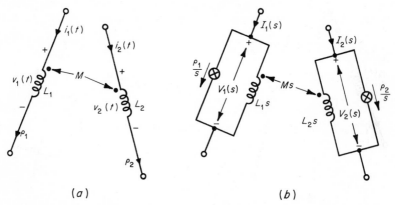

(*a*) (*b*)

Fig. 4.5 *Transform representation of mutually coupled inductances.*

Because of the difficulty that has been implied here, Matrix Algebra is introduced in Chapter 6, and with this tool all these problems can be resolved in a straightforward manner. The difficulties are demonstrated by the following example, which will hold for two coupled coils only.

EXAMPLE 4.1. Show that the circuit of Fig. 4.6(*b*) is the transformed equivalent of the two coupled coils in Fig. 4.6(*a*) and hence a voltage source representation of the initial conditions.

Solution: The volt-ampere relations for the circuit can be transformed as follows:

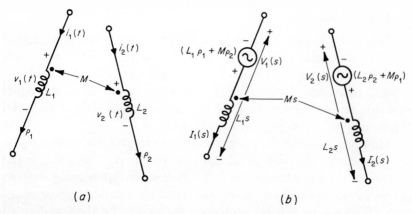

(a)　　　　　　　　　　　　　　　(b)

Fig. 4.6 *Two coupled coils and their transformed equivalent.*

$$v_1(t) = L_1 \frac{di_1(t)}{dt} + M \frac{di_2(t)}{dt}$$

$$v_2(t) = M \frac{di_1(t)}{dt} + L_2 \frac{di_2(t)}{dt}$$

If both sides are multiplied by $1(t-)$ and transformed

$$V_1(s) = L_1 s I_1(s) + M s I_2(s) - L_1 \rho_1 - M \rho_2$$

$$V_2(s) = M s I_1(s) + L_2 s I_2(s) - L_2 \rho_2 - M \rho_1$$

The last two equations indicate that the transformed source magnitudes must be $(L_1\rho_1 + M\rho_2)$ and $(L_2\rho_2 + M\rho_1)$. Notice that even if ρ_2 is *zero*, there is *still* a source in series with each inductance even though the current source representation would show only one current source. This result is sometimes confusing when first encountered.

A general rule for these impulsive voltage sources can be formulated. They are the sum of the flux linkages of the coils at $t = 0-$. The signs of the mutual terms come into play here, however, and it is easier to write the integro-differential equations of the network and then transform them than to attempt to establish a rule that will be used so infrequently that it will be difficult to remember.

We are faced with a decision at this point: when coils are coupled mutually and a transformed network is to be used, is it best to use current sources in parallel with the coils no matter which method is to be employed in solving the network, or is it best to write the integro-differential equations of the network and then transform them? This text tends to emphasize the former approach.

The Right-Hand Side

When the integro-differential equations were written, the initial values of the inductive currents were placed in evidence for nodal equations and the initial capacitance voltages were placed in evidence for mesh equations. These initial conditions were placed on the right-hand side of the equations; when they are multiplied by $1(t-)$ and transformed, they become constants divided by s.

However, whether the nodal method or mesh method is used in the foregoing discussion, the initial currents in the coils and the initial voltages on the capacitances are taken care of by representing them as sources in the transformed network. Thus these terms appear automatically when the network equations are written for the transformed network.

The only other terms in these equations are those that represent the sources. These can be handled in the network itself by finding the transforms of the sources [after they are multiplied by $1(t-)$] and representing the sources in the transformed network by the Laplace transforms of their time expressions. Again this is best demonstrated with an example.

EXAMPLE 4.2. For the circuit pictured in Fig. 4.7, draw the transformed network and write the transformed equations for the network. First use the nodal method and then use the mesh method. When the equations are transformed, put all terms not containing the unknowns on the right-hand side of the equations, and combine them all into one rational fraction, with the coefficient of the highest powered term in s in the denominator as unity. Then multiply both sides of the equations by a constant or a constant times s so there are no $1/s$ terms on the principal diagonal and all the coefficients of the variables on the main diagonal are polynomials in s, with the highest power of s having a coefficient of unity.

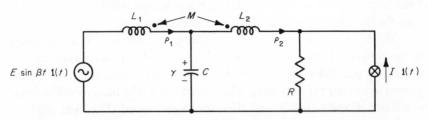

Fig. 4.7 *A circuit whose mesh and nodal equations are to be transformed.*

Note. Although algebra is easier than calculus, this is where most errors in this study are made: the writing and solving of the simultaneous equations. The work here is sometimes considered uninteresting and sometimes even exasperating. However, the chances of arriving at a correct solution are enhanced considerably by adopting an orderly approach to writing the equations. The method outlined here might seem to require a lot of effort, but following it can help avoid errors. Generally, errors in algebra cannot be detected by "checking" the work, so the fastest method of solving a problem is to do it correctly the first time.

(The process by which the transformed equations are converted to a set of transforms for the unknown variables is sometimes referred to as *turning the crank.*)

Solution (The Nodal Method): There are two nodes in the network; label them v_1 and v_2. Draw the transformed network. This appears in Fig. 4.8. Note that since the nodal method is to be used, the elements are written as *admittances* and the initial conditions appear as *current* sources.

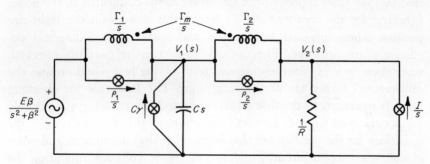

Fig. 4.8 *The network of Fig. 4.7 transformed for the nodal method.*

Using the concept that current out of the nodes in the passive elements equals current into the nodes from current sources, and treating the positive terminal of the voltage source as a known node (for which an equation will *not* be written), then the two equations are

$$\frac{\Gamma_1}{s}\left[V_1(s) - \frac{E\beta}{s^2 + \beta^2}\right] + \frac{\Gamma_m}{s}[V_2(s) - V_1(s)] + CsV_1(s)$$

$$+ \frac{\Gamma_2}{s}[V_1(s) - V_2(s)] + \frac{\Gamma_m}{s}\left[\frac{E\beta}{s^2+\beta^2} - V_1(s)\right] = \frac{\rho_1}{s} - \frac{\rho_2}{s} + C\gamma$$

$$\frac{\Gamma_2}{s}[V_2(s) - V_1(s)] + \frac{\Gamma_m}{s}\left[V_1(s) - \frac{E\beta}{s^2 + \beta^2}\right] + \frac{1}{R}V_2(s) = \frac{I}{s} + \frac{\rho_2}{s}$$

where the Γ terms are given by

$$\Gamma_1 = L_2/\varDelta L \qquad \Gamma_2 = L_1/\varDelta L \qquad \Gamma_m = M/\varDelta L \qquad \varDelta L = L_1 L_2 - M^2$$

If we collect the coefficients of the variables, then

$$\left[Cs + \frac{\Gamma_1 + \Gamma_2 - 2\Gamma_m}{s}\right] V_1(s) - \left[\frac{\Gamma_2 - \Gamma_m}{s}\right] V_2(s) = \frac{(\Gamma_1 - \Gamma_m)E\beta}{s(s^2 + \beta^2)}$$

$$+ \frac{\rho_1 - \rho_2 + C\gamma s}{s}$$

$$- \left[\frac{\Gamma_2 - \Gamma_m}{s}\right] V_1(s) + \left[\frac{1}{R} + \frac{\Gamma_2}{s}\right] V_2(s) = \frac{\Gamma_m E\beta}{s(s^2 + \beta^2)}$$

$$+ \frac{I + \rho_2}{s}$$

At this point the equations should be checked. The coefficients of the diagonal elements should be the self-admittances at each node; that is, they shall represent the circuit elements connected to the node. Ignoring for the moment the Γ_m terms, the sources on the right are positive when directed toward the node, and the off-diagonal coefficients are negative. The mutual terms can be partially checked, since there is a $2\Gamma_m$ in the diagonal term of the first equation and the off-diagonal terms are of the same sign. The best rule for checking these is to return to the first equation and check each term separately for accuracy of sign. It is worth the effort at this time to rewrite the equations for the coils alone; that is, imagine that the sources and other elements are open circuits, and use the node voltages (including the source node) to write the currents at the nodes resulting from the coils alone.

If we are satisfied that the equations are correct, we now multiply the first equation by s/C and the second equation by Rs, and express the right-hand sides as single fractions.

$$\left[s^2 + \frac{\Gamma_1 + \Gamma_2 - 2\Gamma_m}{C}\right] V_1 - \left[\frac{\Gamma_2 - \Gamma_m}{C}\right] V_2 =$$

$$\frac{\gamma s^3 + (\rho_1 - \rho_2)s^2/C + \gamma\beta^2 s + (\Gamma_1 - \Gamma_m)E\beta/C + (\rho_1 - \rho_2)\beta^2/C}{s^2 + \beta^2}$$

$$-R(\Gamma_2 - \Gamma_m)V_1 + (s + R\Gamma_2) V_2 = \frac{(I + \rho_2)Rs^2 + (I + \rho_2)R\beta^2 + R\Gamma_m E\beta}{s^2 + \beta^2}$$

The equations are now written in a form that will make their solution as simple as possible. In the next section (Sec. 4.2) we will discuss ways of proceeding from this point.

Solution (The Mesh Method): Figure 4.9 is the transformed circuit for the mesh method. Note that the initial inductive currents are still represented by current sources. The equations are

$$L_1 s \left[I_1(s) - \frac{\rho_1}{s} \right] - Ms \left[I_2(s) - \frac{\rho_2}{s} \right] + \frac{I_1(s) - I_2(s)}{Cs} = -\frac{\gamma}{s} + \frac{E\beta}{s^2 + \beta^2}$$

$$\frac{I_2(s) - I_1(s)}{Cs} + L_2 s \left[I_2(s) - \frac{\rho_2}{s} \right] - Ms \left[I_1(s) - \frac{\rho_1}{s} \right] + R \left[I_2(s) + \frac{I}{s} \right] = \frac{\gamma}{s}$$

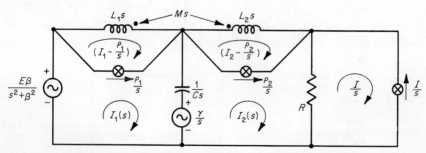

Fig. 4.9 *The transformed network for the mesh method.*

Collecting terms

$$\left[L_1 s + \frac{1}{Cs} \right] I_1 - \left[Ms + \frac{1}{Cs} \right] I_2 = -\frac{\gamma}{s} + \frac{E\beta}{s^2 + \beta^2} + L_1 \rho_1 - M\rho_2$$

$$- \left[Ms + \frac{1}{Cs} \right] I_1 + \left[L_2 s + R + \frac{1}{Cs} \right] I_2 = L_2 \rho_2 - M\rho_1 + \frac{\gamma}{s} - \frac{RI}{s}$$

The equations should now be checked carefully; then the first equation should be multiplied by s/L_1 and the second by s/L_2, and the right-hand sides combined into single fractions:

$$\left(s^2 + \frac{1}{L_1 C} \right) I_1 - \left[\frac{M}{L_1} s^2 + \frac{1}{L_1 C} \right] I_2 =$$

$$\frac{(\rho_1 - M\rho_2/L_1)s^3 - \gamma s^2/L_1 + [(\rho_1 - M\rho_2/L_1)\beta^2 + E\beta/L_1]s - \beta^2 \gamma/L_1}{s^2 + \beta^2}$$

$$- \left[\frac{M}{L_2} s^2 + \frac{1}{L_2 C} \right] I_1 + \left[s^2 + \frac{R}{L_2} s + \frac{1}{L_2 C} \right] I_2 = \left(\rho_2 - \frac{M\rho_1}{L_2} \right) s + \frac{\gamma - RI}{L_2}$$

The example chosen here is rather complicated. The circuit does not look too complicated at first, but the equations do. Fortunately, we are not often called upon to solve a problem of such complexity and to retain all the literal element values. Usually the element values are given numerically; hence, the algebra is somewhat simplified. A simpler example is given below; however, make a real effort to understand the previous example, especially the handling of the mutual inductance. Time spent at this point verifying the equations will prove to be well worthwhile.

EXAMPLE 4.3. Write the equations for the circuit pictured in Fig. 4.10 using both the nodal and mesh methods. As before, draw the transformed network, write the equations, and reduce them to the form where the diagonal coefficients and the denominator of the right-hand side are polynomials, the coefficient of the highest power in s being unity.

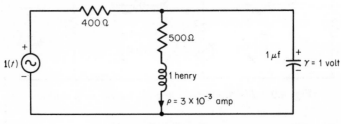

Fig. 4.10 *Example 4.3.*

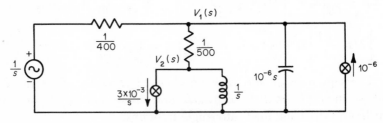

Fig. 4.11 *The transformed network.*

Solution (Nodal Method): The transformed network appears in Fig. 4.11.

$$\text{Node 1:} \quad \frac{V_1(s) - 1/s}{400} + \frac{V_1(s) - V_2(s)}{500} + 10^{-6}sV_1(s) = 10^{-6}$$

$$\text{Node 2:} \quad \frac{V_2(s) - V_1(s)}{500} + \frac{V_2(s)}{s} = -\frac{3 \times 10^{-3}}{s}$$

Collecting terms, we have

$$\left[\frac{1}{500} + \frac{1}{400} + 10^{-6}\,s\right] V_1 - \frac{1}{500}\,V_2 = \frac{400 \times 10^{-6}\,s + 1}{400s}$$

$$-\frac{1}{500}\,V_1 + \left[\frac{1}{500} + \frac{1}{s}\right] V_2 = -\frac{3 \times 10^{-3}}{s}$$

Multiplying the first equation by 10^6, and the second by $500s$, we have

$$(s + 4500)\,V_1 - 2000V_2 = \frac{s + 2500}{s}$$

$$-sV_1 + (s + 500)\,V_2 = -1.5$$

Note how much simpler the work is when numerical coefficients are used. The fact that mutual inductance was absent also helped.

Solution (The Mesh Method): The transformed circuit appears in Fig. 4.12.

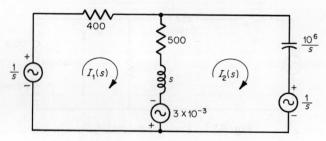

Fig. 4.12   *The transformed circuit.*

Mesh 1: $400I_1 + 500(I_1 - I_2) + s(I_1 - I_2) = 3 \times 10^{-3} + \dfrac{1}{s}$

Mesh 2: $s(I_2 - I_1) + 500(I_2 - I_1) + \dfrac{10^6}{s}\,I_2 = -\dfrac{1}{s} - 3 \times 10^{-3}$

Collecting terms

$$(s+900)\,I_1 - (s+500)\,I_2 = \frac{3 \times 10^{-3}\,s + 1}{s}$$

$$-(s+500)I_1 + \left(s+500+\frac{10^6}{s}\right)I_2 = -\frac{3 \times 10^{-3}s+1}{s}$$

Multiplying the second equation by s gives

$$(s+900)I_1 - (s+500)I_2 = \frac{3 \times 10^{-3}s+1}{s}$$

$$-(s^2+500s)I_1 + (s^2+500s+10^6)I_2 = -(3 \times 10^{-3}s+1)$$

PROBLEMS

In each of the circuits of the problems that follow, write the equations of the circuit and collect coefficients of like variables. If any of the coefficients on the diagonal contain a $1/s$ term, multiply that equation by s. Multiply each equation through by a constant so the highest power of s in the diagonal coefficients is unity. Then write the right-hand side of each equation as a single fraction, the denominator of which is a polynomial in s (*no* $1/s$ terms) and the coefficient of the highest power of which is unity.

4.1.   Write the nodal equations for the circuit of Fig. 4.13.

$$Answer: \left(s+\frac{5}{3}\right) V_1 - \frac{s}{6} V_2 = \frac{500/3}{s}; \; - sV_1 + (s+5)V_2 = 100$$

4.2.   Write the mesh equations for the circuit of Fig. 4.13.

$$Answer: (s+2)I_1 - 2I_2 = \frac{10}{s}; \; - I_1 + (s+6)I_2 = - 1$$

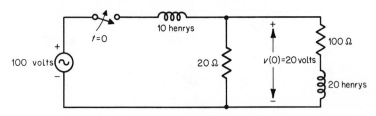

Fig. 4.13   *Problems 4.1 and 4.2.*

4.3.   Write the nodal equations for the circuit of Fig. 4.14.

4.4.   Write the mesh equations for the circuit of Fig. 4.14.

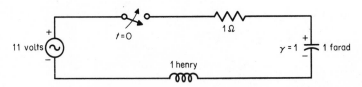

Fig. 4.14   *Problems 4.3 and 4.4.*

4.5.   Count the number of meshes and the number of nodes in the circuit of Fig. 4.15 and write the equations for the method that requires the fewer equations.

4.6.   Write the nodal equations for the network of Fig. 4.16, given that $\rho = 0.1$ amp and $\gamma = \sqrt{3}$ volt.

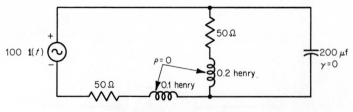

Fig. 4.15 *Problem 4.5.*

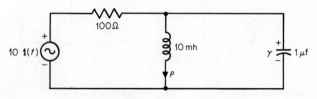

Fig. 4.16 *Problem 4.6.*

4.7. Count the number of meshes and nodes in the network of Fig. 4.17 and write the equations using the method that requires the fewer equations.

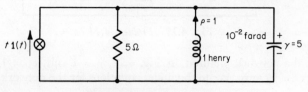

Fig. 4.17 *Problem 4.7.*

4.8. Write the mesh equations for the circuit of Fig. 4.18.

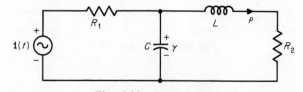

Fig. 4.18 *Problem 4.8.*

4.9. Write the nodal equations for the network of Fig. 4.19.

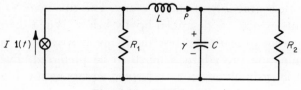

Fig. 4.19 *Problem 4.9.*

4.10. The circuit pictured in Fig. 4.20 is at rest at $t = 0$; that is, there is no energy stored in the circuit. Write the nodal equations for the circuit for $t > 0$.

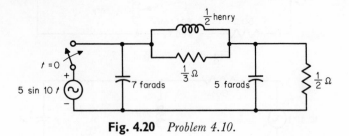

Fig. 4.20   *Problem 4.10.*

4.11. Write the mesh equations for the circuit of Fig. 4.21.

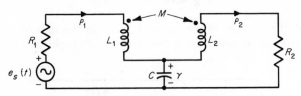

Fig. 4.21   *Problem 4.11.*

4.12. For the network pictured in Fig. 4.22, $\gamma = 1$ volt, $\rho_1 = 1$ amp, and $\rho_2 = -\frac{1}{2}$ amp. Write the nodal equations for the network.

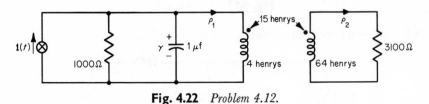

Fig. 4.22   *Problem 4.12.*

4.2 Solving the Equations

When there are fewer than four equations to be solved simultaneously, Cramer's rule is probably as simple as any. This rule involves the use of determinants, which are described briefly below. When there are four or more equations, the use of determinants involves excessive labor and a Gauss elimination procedure is much to be preferred. Even so, the solution of four simultaneous transformed equations involves a major effort on the part of an individual and is rarely undertaken unless an entire day can be spent on it. Problems this complex are usually solved on computers.

If N is the number of equations, then the labor involved in the solution of a problem increases at least by N^2, and more probably N^3. Thus three equations in three unknowns can be expected to take from two to three times as long to solve as a problem with two equations in two unknowns. Knowing this, it is advisable to note the number of nodes and loops in a problem and to use the method that requires the fewer equations.

The presence of nonzero initial conditions markedly increases the labor involved, so an application that does not require the initial conditions to be other than zero is a simpler problem than the general case.

Determinants

A determinant is represented by a square array of elements. If the determinant has N rows and N columns—hence N^2 elements—it is said to be of *order N*.

The determinant has a value which is the sum of $N!$ products. These products are obtained by multiplying elements together, taking N at a time. For each of these products, no two of the N elements going into the product are in the same row or column. Different signs $(+)$ or $(-)$ are placed in front of these products, depending on which elements are combined to form them.

The simplest method to use in evaluating determinants is the *Laplace development*. This development involves the successive reduction of the order of a determinant by the use of cofactors.

Definitions

1. The minor determinant of any element in an Nth-order determinant is a determinant of order $N - 1$ and is obtained by striking out all the elements of the original determinant that lie in the same row and column as the element whose minor is sought.

2. The cofactor of an element of an Nth-order determinant is its minor determinant multiplied by ± 1. The cofactor of any element is equal to its minor if the sum of the row and column numbers of the element is even. The cofactor is the negative of the minor if the sum of the row and column numbers is odd.

EXAMPLE 4.4. Find the indicated cofactors of the elements of the following determinant.

$$\begin{vmatrix} (s+2) & -s/2 & 1 \\ 2s & (3s-4) & 0 \\ -3 & -2s & (s^2+1) \end{vmatrix}$$

(*a*) *Cofactor of the* 1 − 1 *element.* The 1 − 1 element is the element of the first row, first column. Strike out row 1 and column 1.

$$\begin{vmatrix} \cancel{(s+2)} & \cancel{-s/2} & \cancel{1} \\ 2s & (3s-4) & 0 \\ -3 & -2s & (s^2+1) \end{vmatrix}$$

The minor determinant, which remains, is

$$M_{11} = \begin{vmatrix} (3s-4) & 0 \\ -2s & (s^2+1) \end{vmatrix}$$

Since $1 + 1 = 2$ is even, C_{11}, the cofactor of element 1–1, is given by

$$C_{11} = (-1)^{1+1}M_{11} = M_{11}$$

or

$$C_{11} = \begin{vmatrix} (3s-4) & 0 \\ -2s & (s^2+1) \end{vmatrix}$$

(*b*) *Cofactor of the* 1–2 *element.* The 1–2 element is the element in the first row, second column. (The row number is always given first.) This time $1 + 2 = 3$ is odd, so $C_{12} = -M_{12}$.

$$\begin{vmatrix} \cancel{(s+2)} & \cancel{s/2} & \cancel{1} \\ 2s & (3s+4) & 0 \\ -3 & -2s & (s^2+1) \end{vmatrix}$$

so

$$M_{12} = \begin{vmatrix} 2s & 0 \\ -3 & (s^2+1) \end{vmatrix} \quad \text{and} \quad C_{12} = -\begin{vmatrix} 2s & 0 \\ -3 & (s^2+1) \end{vmatrix}$$

(*c*) In a similar manner we may verify the following results.

$$C_{13} = \begin{vmatrix} 2s & (3s-4) \\ -3 & -2s \end{vmatrix} \qquad C_{21} = -\begin{vmatrix} -s/2 & 1 \\ -2s & (s^2+1) \end{vmatrix}$$

$$C_{22} = \begin{vmatrix} (s+2) & 1 \\ -3 & (s^2+1) \end{vmatrix} \qquad C_{23} = -\begin{vmatrix} (s+2) & -s/2 \\ -3 & -2s \end{vmatrix}$$

$$C_{31} = \begin{vmatrix} -s/2 & 1 \\ (3s-4) & 0 \end{vmatrix} \qquad C_{32} = - \begin{vmatrix} (s+2) & 1 \\ 2s & 0 \end{vmatrix}$$

$$C_{33} = \begin{vmatrix} (s+2) & -s/2 \\ 2s & (3s-4) \end{vmatrix}$$

The value of a determinant is the sum of the products of the elements of any row or any column and the cofactors of the elements. If, for example, we wanted to evaluate the determinant of the example above, we could choose any row or column at random, say the second row, and find the value, D, of the determinant to be

$$D = 2sC_{21} + (3s-4)C_{22} + 0C_{23} \tag{4.8}$$

It is seen that this rule reduces the third-order determinant to three second-order determinants (actually only two in the example, since the 2–3 element is zero). For each of these determinants the order of each of the cofactors can then be reduced again to two first-order determinants. Finally, by definition, the value of a first-order determinant is the element itself.

A determinant is evaluated then by reducing an Nth order determinant to N $(N-1)$th-order determinants, and each of these in turn to $N-1$ $(N-2)$th-order determinants, and so on, until we finally have nothing but first-order determinants.

The use of determinants in solving simultaneous equations is feasible for two or three equations, but rarely for more than this. As indicated previously, this has to do with the total number of multiplications and additions involved, and elimination procedures are more efficient for situations in which there are four or more equations. To this end it is convenient to describe shorthand techniques for the evaluation of second- and third-order determinants. No such shorthand rule is given for orders higher than the third, because no simple rule exists that is worth remembering. Those who plan to use determinants frequently should look elsewhere for a more thorough treatment.*

The second-order determinant can be evaluated by subtracting the product of the two elements on the diagonal that goes from the lower left to the upper right from the product of the two terms on the principal diagonal. In the example above

---

*See, for example, GUILLEMIN (3). (The number in parentheses refers to the Bibliography at the end of this book.)

$$C_{21} = - \begin{vmatrix} -s/2 & 1 \\ -2s & s^2+1 \end{vmatrix} = - \left[\left(\frac{-s}{2} \right)(s^2+1) - (-2s)1 \right] = \frac{s^3}{2} - \frac{3s}{2}$$

Thus, products going down to the right are positive, and products going up to the right are negative. As an exercise, verify the value of C_{22} as $s^3 + 2s^2 + s + 5$.

The value of the third-order determinant can now be found by substituting these values into Eq. (4.8):

$$D = 2s \left(\frac{s^3}{2} - \frac{3s}{2} \right) + (3s-4)(s^3+2s^2+s+5)$$

$$= 4s^4 + 2s^3 - 8s^2 + 11s - 20$$

The third-order determinant can be solved directly using a scheme similar to the one for the second order. Six products can be formed by using an *almost* diagonal scheme; those going down to the right are positive, and those going up to the right are negative. This can be seen using the determinant of the example given and noting the arrows in the determinant below. The solid arrows indicate positive products, and the dashed arrows negative products.

$$D = (s+2)(3s-4)(s^2+1) + (2s)(-2s)(1) + (-s/2)(0)(-3)$$
$$- (-3)(3s-4)(1) - (2s)(-s/2)(s^2+1) - (-2s)(0)(s+2)$$
$$= 4s^4 + 2s^3 - 8s^2 + 11s - 20.$$

This last technique requires a little less writing, but it is apparent that the complexity and labor increases rapidly with the order of the determinant.

As stated previously, no such "diagonal" rule exists for fourth-order determinants or higher. One could be fabricated, no doubt, but there would have to be $4! = 24$ products of four elements each for a fourth-order determinant and it seems hardly worthwhile. With fourth-order determinants, either the Laplace development or other schemes are used to reduce the order of the determinant to three, and the third-order determinants are evaluated using the diagonal scheme above.

Cramer's Rule

If a set of simultaneous linear equations is written so that all variables appear aligned in columns, and if the variables are erased, the left-hand sides of the equations form the determinant of the coefficients, D.

Now, let the determinant formed by replacing the third column of this determinant by the right-hand sides of the equations be called D_3. Cramer's rule states that the value of the third variable is D_3/D. Similarly, the value of any variable, say the one in the kth column, is simply D_k/D, where D_k is the same as D except that the right-hand sides of the equations replace the kth column.

EXAMPLE 4.5. Solve the following equations for $I_2(s)$.

$$(s+2)I_1(s) \quad - (s/2)I_2(s) \quad + I_3(s) = -3/s^2$$
$$2sI_1(s) \quad + (3s-4)I_2(s) \qquad = 0$$
$$-3I_1(s) \quad - 2sI_2(s) \quad + (s^2+1)I_3(s) = 5/s$$

Solution: According to Cramer's rule,

$$I_2(s) = \frac{\begin{vmatrix} (s+2) & -3/s^2 & 1 \\ 2s & 0 & 0 \\ -3 & 5/s & (s^2+1) \end{vmatrix}}{\begin{vmatrix} (s+2) & -s/2 & 1 \\ 2s & (3s-4) & 0 \\ -3 & -2s & (s^2+1) \end{vmatrix}}$$

The denominator determinant is simply the one of Example 4.4 and has already been evaluated. The two zeros in row 2 of the numerator determinant indicate that the Laplace development of that determinant according to the elements of the second row will consist of one term only; that is

$$D_2 = -(2s) \begin{vmatrix} -3/s^2 & 1 \\ 5/s & (s^2+1) \end{vmatrix} = \frac{6}{s}\left(s^2 + \frac{5}{3}s + 1\right)$$

making

$$I_2(s) = \frac{6\left(s^2 + \frac{5}{3}s + 1\right)}{s(4s^4 + 2s^3 - 8s^2 + 11s - 20)}$$

$$= \frac{1.5\left(s^2 + \frac{5}{3}s + 1\right)}{s\left(s^4 + \frac{1}{2}s^3 - 2s^2 + \frac{11}{4}s - 5\right)}$$

(Note the care taken here to make the coefficients of the highest power in s equal to unity. This is aimed at avoiding mistakes.)

The beauty of Cramer's rule is that all sets of simultaneous equations have solutions so long as there are as many equations as unknowns, and, of course, so long as the denominator determinant, D, does not vanish.

Gauss Elimination Procedure

The method of solving simultaneous equations that requires the fewest operations is known as the Gauss (or Gauss-Jordan) procedure; it consists of reducing the set of equations from a square array to a triangular one.

EXAMPLE 4.6. Solve the equations of Example 4.5 by the Gauss-Jordan elimination procedure.

Solution: If all the variables are wanted, then the equations may be left as they are. If, however, only $I_2(s)$ is desired, then the terms containing $I_2(s)$ should be written last. As will be seen, this will lead to the fewest operations. The equations of the example are rewritten as

(1) $(s+2)I_1(s) + I_3(s) \qquad -\frac{s}{2}I_2(s) \qquad\qquad = \frac{-3}{s^2}$

(2) $2sI_1(s) \qquad\qquad\qquad +(3s-4)I_2(s) \quad = 0$

(3) $-3I_1(s) \quad + (s^2+1)I_3(s) \quad -2sI_2(s) \qquad\qquad = \frac{5}{s}$

Equation (1) is now multiplied through by $-2s/(s+2)$ and added to equation (2). This makes equation (2) become equation (2'):

$$-\frac{2s}{s+2}I_3(s) + \left[\frac{s^2}{s+2} + 3s - 4\right]I_2(s) = \frac{6}{s(s+2)}$$

(2') $\quad -2sI_3(s) + (4s^2+2s-8)I_2(s) = \frac{6}{s}$

Equation (1) is now multiplied by $3/(s+2)$ and added to equation (3), yielding equation (3'):

(3') $(s^3+2s^2+s+5)I_3(s) - \left(2s^2+\dfrac{11}{2}s\right)I_2(s) = \left(\dfrac{5s^2+10s-9}{s^2}\right)$

If equations (1) (2') and (3') are now written together, we have

(1) $(s+2)I_1 \quad + I_3 \qquad\qquad -\dfrac{s}{2}I_2 \qquad = \dfrac{-3}{s^2}$

(2') $\qquad\qquad -2sI_3 \quad + (4s^2+2s-8)I_2 \quad = \dfrac{6}{s}$

(3') $\qquad (s^3+2s^2+s+5)I_3 - \left(2s^2+\dfrac{11}{2}s\right)I_2 = \dfrac{(5s^2+10s-9)}{s^2}$

It should be clear now why the first equation was multiplied by the appropriate factors and added to equations (2) and (3): I_1 is now missing from the new second and third equations. I_3 will now be eliminated from the last equation, using equation (2'), by multiplying that equation by $(s^3+2s^2+s+5)/2s$ and adding it to equation (3'), yielding equation (3''):

(3'') $\dfrac{4s^5 + 10s^4 - 4s^3 - 5s^2 + 2s - 40}{2s}I_2 = \dfrac{3s^3 + 11s + 13s + 6}{s^2}$

or

$$I_2(s) = \dfrac{1.5\left(s^3+\dfrac{11}{3}s^2+\dfrac{13}{3}s+2\right)}{s\left(s^5+\dfrac{5}{2}s^4-s^3-\dfrac{5}{4}s^2+\dfrac{1}{2}s-10\right)}$$

This is not the same answer as that obtained by Cramer's rule; it is, however, equivalent to the previous answer, since both numerator and denominator have a factor of $(s+2)$; thus

$$I_2(s) = \dfrac{1.5\cancel{(s+2)}\left(s^2+\dfrac{5}{3}s+1\right)}{s\cancel{(s+2)}\left(s^4+\dfrac{1}{2}s^3-2s^2+\dfrac{11}{4}s-5\right)}$$

Note that with the elimination procedure we run the risk of introducing extraneous factors, which we do not with the determinant approach. The saving in operations by this procedure is at least partially counterbalanced by new difficulties.

If $I_3(s)$ is also desired, the solution for $I_2(s)$ may now be substituted into equation (2′) and the result solved for $I_3(s)$. Finally, $I_1(s)$ may be obtained by using the solutions for $I_2(s)$ and $I_3(s)$ in equation (1). The reason the $I_2(s)$ terms were written last is now apparent; the last variable is obtained first.

You may decide for yourself which procedure you prefer. The problems below specify the methods to be used. A little experience will permit you to choose the method most to your liking.

PROBLEMS

4.13. Evaluate the following determinants:

(a) $\begin{vmatrix} 3 & 0 & -1 \\ 2 & 2 & 3 \\ 1 & -2 & 1 \end{vmatrix}$ (b) $\begin{vmatrix} (s+1) & -s \\ -s & (s+1) \end{vmatrix}$ (c) $\begin{vmatrix} 4 & 0 & 1 & 2 \\ 2 & 3 & -1 & -2 \\ 0 & 4 & 6 & 2 \\ 1 & 3 & 4 & 7 \end{vmatrix}$

Note: (c) has to be done by a Laplace development or some other scheme to reduce its order.

Answer: (a) 30   (b) $2s + 1$ (c) 534

4.14. Solve the following simultaneous equations for $I_1(s)$, using (a) Cramer's rule, and (b) the Gauss elimination procedure.

$$(s^2 + 2s + 1)I_1(s) - sI_2(s) = \frac{1}{s}$$

$$- sI_1(s) + (s+3)I_2(s) = 3$$

4.15. Solve the following set of equations for $V_2(s)$, using (a) Cramer's rule, and (b) the Gauss elimination procedure.

$$(s+3)V_1(s) - V_2(s) - V_3(s) = 0$$
$$- V_1(s) + 4V_2(s) = 0$$
$$- V_1(s) + (s+2)V_3(s) = \frac{1}{s}$$

Answer: $V_2(s) = \dfrac{\dfrac{1}{4}}{s\left(s^2 + \dfrac{19}{4}s + \dfrac{9}{2}\right)}$

4.16. Draw the transformed network for the circuit of Fig. 4.23, write the equations, and solve for $V_0(s)$.

Answer: $V_0(s) = \dfrac{\gamma s^3 + (I_m - \rho_1)s^2/C + \gamma\beta^2 s - \rho_1\beta^2/C}{(s^2 + \beta^2)\,[s^2 + s/(R_2 C) + 1/(LC)]}$

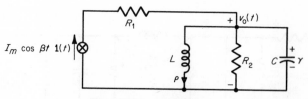

Fig. 4.23 *Problem 4.16.*

4.3 Transfer Functions

Now that we have demonstrated how the transform equations are written and solved, let us direct our attention to an analysis of such a solution and toward the introduction of the concept of the transfer function.

When a network is transformed, all the initial conditions appear as sources. The principle of superposition tells us that all the currents and voltages in a network except those of the sources depend on all of the sources in the network. In many applications only one voltage or current needs to be known; this voltage or current is called the *output signal*. The output signal will depend on all the sources in a network and will be the sum of the responses of all sources, taken when each source acts alone.

EXAMPLE 4.7. The output signal in the circuit pictured in Fig. 4.24 will be the voltage v_2. (It could be any current or voltage; v_2 is chosen arbitrarily.) Write and solve the nodal equations for the network for the transform $V_2(s)$ and express it in such a way that the effects of each source and initial condition are placed in evidence.

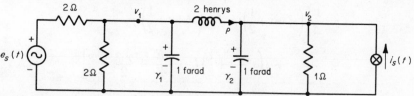

Fig. 4.24 *A circuit whose transfer functions are to be obtained.*

Solution: (*a*) Draw the transformed network. (This appears in Fig. 4.25.)
(*b*) Write the equations of the transformed network.

$$\left(s+1+\frac{1}{2s}\right) V_1 \qquad -\frac{1}{2s} V_2 = \gamma_1 - \frac{\rho}{s} + \frac{E_s(s)}{2}$$

$$-\frac{1}{2s} V_1 + \left(s+1+\frac{1}{2s}\right) V_2 = \frac{\rho}{s} + \gamma_2 + I_s(s)$$

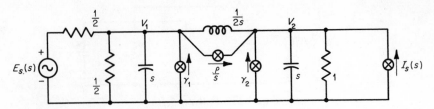

Fig. 4.25 *The transformed network.*

Multiplying both equations by s and solving by Cramer's rule for $V_2 = V_2(s)$ gives

$$\left(s^2+s+\frac{1}{2}\right) V_1 \qquad -\frac{1}{2} V_2 = \frac{sE_s(s)}{2} + \gamma_1 s - \rho$$

$$-\frac{1}{2} V_1 + \left(s^2+s+\frac{1}{2}\right) V_2 = \rho + \gamma_2 s + sI_s(s)$$

$$V_2(s) = \frac{\begin{vmatrix} \left(s^2+s+\dfrac{1}{2}\right) & \left(\dfrac{sE_s}{2}+\gamma_1 s-\rho\right) \\[2mm] \dfrac{-1}{2} & (\rho+\gamma_2 s+sI_s) \end{vmatrix}}{\begin{vmatrix} \left(s^2+s+\dfrac{1}{2}\right) & \dfrac{-1}{2} \\[2mm] \dfrac{-1}{2} & \left(s^2+s+\dfrac{1}{2}\right) \end{vmatrix}}$$

$$= \frac{1}{\Delta}\left[\left(s^2+s+\frac{1}{2}\right)\rho + s\left(s^2+s+\frac{1}{2}\right)\gamma_2 \right.$$

$$\left. + s\left(s^2+s+\frac{1}{2}\right)I_s + \frac{sE_s}{4} + \frac{\gamma_1 s}{2} - \frac{\rho}{2}\right]$$

where Δ is the denominator determinant, which can be shown to be

$$\Delta = s(s^3+2s^2+2s+1)$$

Thus

$$V_2(s) = \frac{0.25}{s^3 + 2s^2 + 2s + 1} E_s(s) + \frac{s^2 + s + 1/2}{s^3 + 2s^2 + 2s + 1} I_s(s)$$

$$+ \frac{s+1}{s^3 + 2s^2 + 2s + 1}\rho + \frac{0.5}{s^3 + 2s^2 + 2s + 1}\gamma_1 + \frac{s^2 + s + 1/2}{s^3 + 2s^2 + 2s + 1}\gamma_2$$

Now study the last equation for $V_2(s)$, and note the following.

(1) If all sources but $E_s(s)$ were zero, and this includes the initial condition sources, then the first term on the right would be the transform of $v_2(t)$. $E_s(s)$ would have to be known, of course, before an inverse transformation could result. Observe that reducing a current source to zero means replacing it by an *open* circuit.

(2) If all the sources except $I_s(s)$ were zero, the second term on the right would be the transform of $v_2(t)$ as a result of this current source. In fact, for any source or initial condition, with all the rest zero, the term corresponding to the source would be the transform of $v_2(t)$ when the source acted alone. *Conclusion:* When several sources are present, $v_2(t)$ can be thought of as the sum of the individual $v_2(t)$'s obtained by considering each source acting independently. This is just the principle of superposition.

(3) Note that the denominator polynomials of all terms are alike. Actually, until $E_s(s)$ and $I_s(s)$ are known, the total denominator of the first two terms cannot be determined. It will be shown in Sec. 4.4 that the *character* of the transient is completely determined by the factor $s^3 + 2s^2 + 2s + 1$ in the denominator. It will be shown that to determine this character it is first necessary to factor the denominator polynomial in order to write the transforms as the sum of expressions, each being a special case of the key pairs of Table 3.2.

Definition

The transfer function $H(s)$ is that function of s which when multiplied by the transform of the input signal yields the transform of the output signal, *provided that* all other independent sources or initial conditions are zero.*

The input signal in the definition is any source chosen to be the input. For example, if in Example 4.7 all initial conditions are zero and $I_s(s)$ is zero, the transfer function with $e_s(t)$ the input and $v_2(t)$ the output is

$$\frac{V_2(s)}{E_s(s)} = \frac{0.25}{s^3 + 2s^2 + 2s + 1}$$

---

*The sources that have been described are independent sources, since the values of these sources have nothing to do with the network to which they are connected. In the study of *active* circuits, however, *dependent* sources appear in the equivalent circuits. The values of these sources depend on other variables (current or voltage) in the network. When the superposition principle, Thévènin's theorem, or the notion of the transfer function is used, these dependent sources are *never* set equal to zero. (See Probs. 4.28, 4.30 and 4.35(c) and (d).)

But if $i_s(t)$ is considered the input, the transfer function would be

$$\frac{V_2(s)}{I_s(s)} = \frac{s^2 + s + 1/2}{s^3 + 2s^2 + 2s + 1}$$

Similarly, if γ_1 were the input, the transfer function would be the coefficient of γ_1 in the expression for $V_2(s)$ in Example 4.7.

With regard to transfer functions, only these rules need be re-membered: (1) The input and output signals must be identified. Both may be currents, both voltages, or one a current and the other a voltage. (2) The transfer function assumes that all initial conditions are zero, as well as all other sources, except, of course, dependent sources. The principal reasons for this are based upon convenience and the fact that the character of the transient can be obtained with zero initial conditions.

It may happen that a circuit can be solved more easily by the mesh method, even though the output signal is a voltage, that is, not a mesh current. Similarly, the output signal may be a current with the nodal method leading to fewer equations. In cases such as these, choose the method that leads to fewer equations, and express the transform of output signal in terms of the variables used, using the appropriate volt-ampere relation. Then solve for the required variables and obtain the desired transform.

EXAMPLE 4.8. Find the transfer function relating the voltage across the 50-$k\Omega$ (50,000-ohm) resistance to $e_s(t)$ in Fig. 4.26.

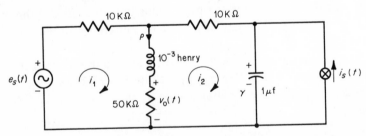

Fig. 4.26   *A circuit for which a transfer function is sought.*

Solution: There are three nodes but only two meshes. The mesh method is chosen. Notice that $v_0(t)$ can be obtained only if both i_1 and i_2 are known, since

$$v_0(t) = 5 \times 10^4 \, (i_1 - i_2)$$
$$V_0(s) = 5 \times 10^4 \, (I_1 - I_2)$$

Hence both I_1 and I_2 have to be found.

Setting $\rho = \gamma = i_s(t) = 0$ (since only the transfer function with $e_s(t)$ as the source is required) and drawing the transformed network in Fig. 4.27, we can write the transform equations

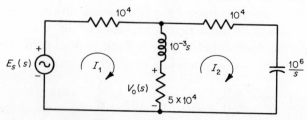

Fig. 4.27   *The transformed network.*

$$(10^{-3}s + 6 \times 10^4)I_1 - (10^{-3}s + 5 \times 10^4)I_2 = E_s(s)$$

$$- (10^{-3}s + 5 \times 10^4)I_1 + \left(10^{-3}s + 6 \times 10^4 + \frac{10^6}{s}\right)I_2 = 0$$

Multiplying the first equation by 10^3 and the second by $10^3 s$, we have

$$(s + 6 \times 10^7)I_1 - (s + 5 \times 10^7)I_2 = 10^3 E_s$$

$$- (s^2 + 5 \times 10^7 s)I_1 + (s^2 + 6 \times 10^7 s + 10^9)I_2 = 0$$

The denominator determinant is

$$\begin{vmatrix} (s + 6 \times 10^7) & -(s + 5 \times 10^7) \\ -s(s + 5 \times 10^7) & (s^2 + 6 \times 10^7 s + 10^9) \end{vmatrix} = 2 \times 10^7 (s^2 + 5.5 \times 10^7 s + 3 \times 10^9)$$

so

$$I_1(s) = \frac{5 \times 10^{-5}(s^2 + 6 \times 10^7 s + 10^9)}{s^2 + 5.5 \times 10^7 s + 3 \times 10^9} E_s(s)$$

and

$$I_2(s) = \frac{5 \times 10^{-5} s(s + 5 \times 10^7)}{s^2 + 5.5 \times 10^7 s + 3 \times 10^9} E_s(s)$$

Since $5 \times 10^4 (I_1 - I_2)$ is actually what is desired

$$V_0(s) = 5 \times 10^4 \frac{5 \times 10^{-5} E_s(s)(s^2 + 6 \times 10^7 s + 10^9 - s^2 - 5 \times 10^7 s)}{s^2 + 5.5 \times 10^7 s + 3 \times 10^9}$$

$$= \frac{2.5 \times 10^7 (s + 100)}{s^2 + 5.5 \times 10^7 s + 3 \times 10^9} E_s(s)$$

so the transfer function $H(s)$ is

$$H(s) = \frac{V_0(s)}{E_s(s)} = \frac{2.5 \times 10^7 \,(s+100)}{s^2+5.5 \times 10^7 s+3 \times 10^9} \qquad (answer)$$

It is interesting to note that if $s = 0$ then the inductance has zero impedance, and the capacitance infinite impedance. For $s = 0$ then, the transfer function is simply the function that would be obtained if the source were a direct voltage source. Drawing the network for d–c requires only that all inductances be replaced by short-circuits, all capacitances by open-circuits. This is done in Fig. 4.28. The simple resistance network that results is just a voltage divider, so

$$\frac{V_0(s)}{E_s(s)} \bigg|_{s=0} = \frac{5 \times 10^4}{6 \times 10^4} = \frac{5}{6}$$

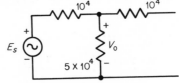

Fig. 4.28   *The circuit at* $s = 0$ (*d-c*).

Setting $s = 0$ in the transfer function, we obtain

$$H(s) \bigg|_{s=0} = \frac{2.5 \times 10^7 \times 100}{3 \times 10^9} = \frac{5}{6} \qquad (Check)$$

This check does not assure the individual that the answer is correct, but it is comforting.

4.4 Transfer Functions and the Sinusoidal Steady-State

The transfer function has another very important interpretation. If all initial conditions are zero, then the impedances of the inductances become simply Ls and those of the capacitances $1/(Cs)$. But these are almost the same as the impedances of these elements in the sinusoidal steady-state. In the latter case the impedances are $j\omega L$ and $1/(j\omega C)$. It appears that if we let $s = j\omega$, the transfer function could be interpreted as the ratio of the *complex amplitude* of the output signal to the *complex amplitude* of the input signal. This is, in fact, the case.

This is probably the most remarkable result of our study, and it will be embellished considerably. It says, in effect, that if we know the *frequency response* of a network, that is, the ratio of the complex amplitudes of output to input for all frequencies, we will also know the transient behavior of the network. Conversely, if we know the transient behavior, then we also know the entire behavior in the sinusoidal steady-state.

EXAMPLE 4.9. Analyze the circuit of Fig. 4.29 for both transient response and frequency response.

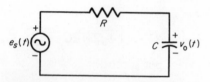

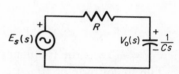

Fig. 4.29 *A circuit whose transient behaviour and frequency response are to be determined.*

Fig. 4.30 *The transformed network*

Solution: The transformed network appears in Fig. 4.30. Since the circuit is simply a voltage divider, we can determine by inspection that

$$H(s) = \frac{V_0(s)}{E_s(s)} = \frac{1/Cs}{R+1/Cs} = \frac{1/RC}{s+1/RC}$$

Transient: The *character* of the transient is determined by the inverse transforming of $H(s)$. The inverse transform of $H(s)$ is called the *impulse response*, since if $e_s(t)$ is $\delta(t)$, then $E_s(s) = 1$ and $V_0(s) = H(s)$. The inverse transform of

$$\frac{1/RC}{s+1/RC}$$

is simply

$$\frac{1}{RC} e^{-t/RC} \mathbf{1}(t)$$

This tells us that no matter what $e_s(t)$ is, part of the total solution will be a term $Ae^{-t/RC}\mathbf{1}(t)$, where A is some constant. The circuit, then, causes changes in the input to be smoothed out exponentially, a steady condition being achieved only when $e^{-t/RC}$ is small. Since $e^{-5} \doteq 0.00674$, then the transient will have died away in $5RC$ seconds. RC is called the time-constant of the circuit in seconds, and as a rule-of-thumb transients are said to die out in four or five time-constants.

Sinusoidal Steady-State: If this were a problem in the sinusoidal steady-state, the input signal would be set equal to

$$e_s(t) = E_m \cos(\omega t + \theta)$$

and this would be abbreviated to the complex voltage $E_m\underline{/\theta}$. Similarly, the output signal would be represented as

$$v_0(t) = V_m \cos (\omega t + \phi)$$

and abbreviated to the complex voltage $V_m\underline{/\phi}$. The complex ratio of these two in terms of frequency is what is commonly referred to as the *frequency response*, which is, of course, just $H(j\omega)$.

$$\frac{V_m\underline{/\phi}}{E_m\underline{/\theta}} = \frac{1/(j\omega C)}{R+1/(j\omega C)} = \frac{1}{1+j\omega RC} = \frac{1}{1+j2\pi fRC}$$

where $f = \omega/2\pi$ is the frequency in cycles per second.

The magnitude of $H(j\omega)$ is

$$\left| H(j\omega) \right| = \frac{V_m}{E_m} = \frac{1}{\sqrt{1+(2\pi fRC)^2}}$$

This is plotted versus frequency in Fig. 4.31. The frequency f_0 is commonly called the half-power or 3-db frequency, and is given by

$$f_0 = \frac{1}{2\pi RC}$$

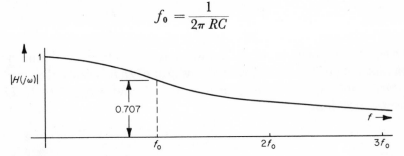

Fig. 4.31   *The magnitude of the frequency response of the* RC *network as a function of frequency.*

The *phase* or angle of the frequency response is the angle by which the output sinusoid leads the input signal. For this circuit

$$\text{Angle } H(j\omega) = - \arctan\left(\frac{f}{f_0}\right)$$

showing that the output always lags the input. Angle $H(j\omega)$ is plotted versus frequency in Fig. 4.32.

The half-power frequency, f_0, is defined as the frequency at which the output signal has a magnitude of $1/\sqrt{2}$ times its maximum value. Since power is proportional to the square of either current or voltage, then this implies that the power is down by a factor of $\frac{1}{2}$. Actually no

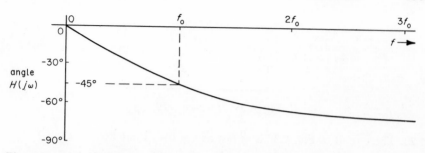

Fig. 4.32 *The angle of the frequency response of the RC network as a function of frequency.*

power as such is really being taken from the circuit at the output, so the expression tends to be misleading. Since db is defined by

$$db = 20 \log_{10} \frac{V_{out}}{V_{out\ max}}$$

then, with $V_{out}/V_{out\ max} = 1/\sqrt{2}$

$$db = 20 \log_{10} (1/\sqrt{2}) = -20 \log_{10} 2^{1/2}$$
$$= -10 \log_{10} 2 = -3.0103$$
$$\doteq -3.0$$

For this reason the frequency f_0 is also referred to as the 3-db frequency.

PROBLEMS

4.17. For the circuit of Fig. 4.33: (*a*) Write the single mesh equation for the network, transform it, and solve for $I(s)$. Use $I(s)$ to determine $V_c(s)$. (*b*) Obtain $V_c(s)$ using one nodal equation. What value of γ makes $I(s) = 0$? What is $V_c(s)$ for this value of γ?

4.18. In the circuit of Fig. 4.34 there is no energy stored at $t = 0-$. E is a constant. Find $V(s) = \mathcal{L}[v(t)]$.

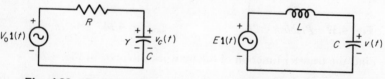

Fig. 4.33 *Problem 4.17.*   **Fig. 4.34** *Problem 4.18.*

4.19. In the circuit of Fig. 4.35 find $I(s)$, the transform of the current $i(t)$. Assume that $i(0) = 0$.

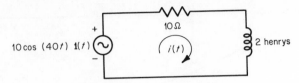

Fig. 4.35   *Problem 4.19.*

4.20. The circuit in Fig. 4.36 is at rest at $t = 0-$. Find $V(s) = \mathscr{L}[v(t)]$.

$$Answer:\ V(s) = \frac{2 \times 10^8 s}{(s^2 + 10^6)^2}$$

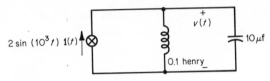

Fig. 4.36   *Problem 4.20.*

4.21. Find the transfer function and impulse response of the network pictured in Fig. 4.37.

4.22. Find the transfer function and impulse response of the network pictured in Fig. 4.38.

$$Answer:\ h(t) = \delta(t) - \frac{1}{RC} e^{-t/RC} \mathbf{1}(t)$$

This circuit is sometimes called a differentiating circuit. If it were truly a differentiating circuit in which the output was the derivative of the input, what would its transfer function be? What conditions must be placed on R and C to make this transfer function approximate the ideal differentiator?

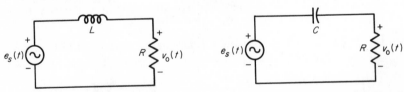

Fig. 4.37   *Problem 4.21.*   **Fig. 4.38**   *Problem 4.22.*

4.23. Find the transfer function of the network pictured in Fig. 4.39.

4.24. Find the transfer function for the circuit shown in Fig. 4.40. Note that the input here is a current.

$$Answer:\ H(s) = \frac{1/(LC)^2}{s^3 + (1/RC)s^2 + (2/LC)s + 1/(RLC^2)}$$

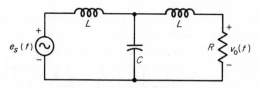

Fig. 4.39   *Problem 4.23.*

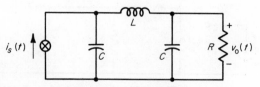

Fig. 4.40   *Problem 4.24.*

4.25. Find the transfer function for the circuit in Fig. 4.41.

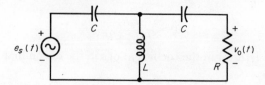

Fig. 4.41   *Problem 4.25.*

4.26. Find the transfer function for the circuit in Fig. 4.42. The output signal is the capacitance current $i_0(t)$.

$$Answer: \frac{(R_1/L)s}{s^2 + [(1/R_2C) + (R_1/L)]s + [1 + (R_1/R_2)]/LC}$$

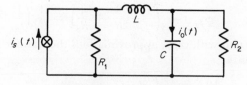

Fig. 4.42   *Problem 4.26.*

4.27. Find the transfer function for the circuit in Fig. 4.43. Find the frequency response of the circuit and plot its magnitude and phase versus frequency.

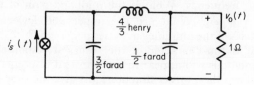

Fig. 4.43   *Problem 4.27.*

4.28. The equivalent circuit for an R-C coupled amplifier is shown in Fig. 4.44. Find the transfer function $V_0(s)/E_g(s)$.

$$\text{Answer: } H(s) = \frac{-\mu s/(r_p C_p)}{s^2 + \left[\dfrac{1}{C_p}\left(\dfrac{1}{r_p}+\dfrac{1}{R_L}+\dfrac{1}{R_g}\right)+\dfrac{1}{R_g C_c}\right]s + \dfrac{r_p + R_L}{R_g R_L r_p C_c C_p}}$$

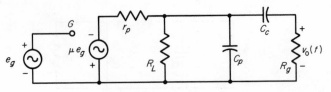

Fig. 4.44   *Problem 4.28.*

4.29. If the parallel combination of r_p and R_L is small compared to R_g in Prob. 4.28

$$1 + \frac{r_p R_L}{R_g(r_p+R_L)} \doteq 1$$

Replace $1/(R_g C_c)$ in the coefficient of s in the denominator of $H(s)$ by

$$\frac{1}{R_g C_c} \cdot \frac{1}{1 + r_p R_L/[R_g(r_p+R_L)]}$$

The denominator can be easily factored into

$$(s+\omega_1)(s+\omega_2)$$

where

$$\omega_1 = \frac{1}{C_c\,[R_g+r_p R_L/(r_p+R_L)]} \doteq \frac{1}{(R_g C_c)}$$

and

$$\omega_2 = \frac{1}{C_p}\left(\frac{1}{r_p}+\frac{1}{R_L}+\frac{1}{R_g}\right) \doteq \frac{1}{C_p}\left(\frac{1}{r_p}+\frac{1}{R_L}\right)$$

(a)   Show that with these approximations the transfer function can be written as

$$H(s) = \frac{-\mu R_L}{r_p + R_L} \cdot \frac{1}{(1 + \omega_1/s)(1 + s/\omega_2)}$$

(b)   Substitute $C_p = 20 \times 10^{-12} f$, $\mu = 18$, $r_p = 2K$, $\omega_1 = 400$, and $\omega_2 = 10^7$ in the last expression and obtain the frequency response by setting $s = j\omega$. Plot the magnitude and phase of this response versus frequency. What is the midband gain of the amplifier at $\omega = \sqrt{\omega_1 \omega_2}$? What are the upper and lower half-power frequencies of the amplifier in cycles per second?

(c)   What is the character of the transient response; that is, what exponentials will appear in the transient response? Do not inverse transform the transfer function; just give the time-constants of the exponentials.

4.30. Find the transfer function of the single-tuned bandpass amplifier whose equivalent circuit appears in Fig. 4.45. Let $\omega_0 = 1/\sqrt{LC}$ and $Q = \omega_0 CR$, and eliminate C and R by using ω_0 and Q. ω_0 is the resonant (radian per second) frequency; Q, called the quality of the circuit, is the ratio of the center frequency to the half-power bandwidth.

$$\textit{Answer: } H(s) = \frac{-g_m\,\omega_0\,Ls}{s^2 + \dfrac{\omega_0}{Q}s + \omega_0^2}$$

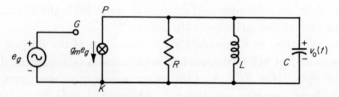

Fig. 4.45 *Problem 4.30.*

4.31. Show that the frequency response of the circuit of Fig. 4.45 can be expressed as

$$H(j\omega) = \frac{-g_m R}{1 + jQ(\omega/\omega_0 - \omega_0/\omega)}$$

$$\doteq \frac{-g_m R}{1 + j\,2Q(\omega - \omega_0)/\omega_0}$$

where the last expression is obtained by expanding $(\omega/\omega_0) - (\omega_0/\omega)$ in a Taylor series about $\omega = \omega_0$ and retaining only the first term.

From the second expression for $H(j\omega)$ (the approximation), show that the 3-db or half-power points occur at $\omega = \omega_0 \pm \omega_0/(2Q)$, making the 3-db bandwidth $B = (\omega_0/Q)$rad/sec and making $Q = \omega_0/B$.

4.32. If $Q = 10$ in Prob. 4.30, what is the character of the transient response? Sketch at least four cycles of the transient response.

4.5 Factoring

No method of solving simultaneous differential equations has yet been discovered that avoids the factoring of a polynomial. As will be seen, the next step in the solution of transient problems with the Laplace transform is the factoring of the denominator polynomial.

A factor of s in the denominator is obvious, and if the denominator is a quadratic such as

$$s^2 + bs + c$$

the roots are easily obtained by the quadratic formula:

$$s = -\frac{b}{2} \pm \sqrt{\left(\frac{b}{2}\right)^2 - c}$$

One note of caution should be observed: the transform of the output variable will always be the sum of the products of the transfer functions and the transforms of the input voltage sources, current sources, and/or initial conditions. All the signal transforms will then have in their denominators a factor that arises from the *circuit*, and a factor or factors that arise from the *sources*.

For example, in Example 4.7 the transform of the output voltage $V_2(s)$ consisted of five terms, each of which had a factor in the denominator of $s^3 + 2s^2 + 2s + 1$. This factor came from the circuit itself. Since the letter s enters a problem only when associated with an inductive or capacitive element, the degree of this factor of the denominator will generally be equal to the total number of inductances and capacitances in the network. The circuit of Example 4.7 has three such elements, one inductance, and two capacitances. Thus s enters the equations as Ls (or Γ/s) or as Cs, but in no other way except in the transforms of the sources and initial conditions.

Of course, two inductances in series can be combined into one equivalent inductance, so the rule of thumb given does not always work. The degree of the denominator polynomial to be factored then will be less than or equal to the number of energy storage elements in the circuit. It is a good idea to keep this in mind as an additional check on the transforms. There have been instances where the factor of the denominator that arises from the source has been multiplied through with the factor arising from the circuit, making the denominator one large polynomial. There is nothing fundamentally wrong with this except that ultimately, the denominator has to be factored and hence the procedure wastes time and effort. (Furthermore, there are instances in which both the circuit factor and the source factor are quadratics and hence easy to factor. Their product would be a quartic. In one such instance a student multiplied the quadratics together and was then unable to factor the resultant quartic.)

Horner's Method

One of the more convenient methods for extracting real roots of equations is *Horner's method*. A polynomial of degree n has n roots. This is called the *fundamental theorem of algebra.* If the coefficients in the polynomial are all real, and if any complex or imaginary roots exist, then the roots appear in conjugate pairs. Thus if the polynomial is of odd degree, it must have at least one real root. Horner's method coupled with synthetic division is useful in finding the real roots.

EXAMPLE 4.10. Find the real root of the quintic

$$s^5 + 140s^4 + 6000s^3 + 1.3 \times 10^5 s^2 + 1.18 \times 10^6 s + 5 \times 10^6$$

Solution: The coefficients can be made smaller by replacing s by $10x$ and dividing through by 10^5:

$$x^5 + 14x^4 + 60x^3 + 130x^2 + 118x + 50$$

First guess: Take the last two terms, set them equal to zero, and solve for x:

$$118x + 50 = 0$$

$$x = -50/118 = -0.423$$

A real root *might* be near this value of x. Substitute 0 and -1 in the equation and see if the polynomial changes sign. For $x = -1$, by synthetic division

1	14	60	130	118	50	$\underline{|-1}$
	-1	-13	-47	-83	-35	
1	13	47	83	35	$\boxed{15}$	

the polynomial is seen to have the value of $+15$. But at $x = 0$ the polynomial is just the constant term, or $+50$. It appears that there is no root between 0 and -1, or else there are two roots. Looking at the synthetic division above it is clear that trying a number between 0 and -1 will not produce a negative remainder since the signs on the second line never changed. As x approaches $-\infty$, however, the polynomial goes to $-\infty$, since it is of odd degree, so the real root must be more negative than -1. Try -2.

1	14	60	130	118	50	$\underline{|-2}$
	-2	-24	-72	-116	-4	
1	12	36	58	2	$\boxed{46}$	

The value of the polynomial is seen to be positive again. Again the signs on the second line never changed, so it is not likely that a root exists between -1 and -2. Trying -3, the polynomial has a value of 137; at -5 it has a value of 835; at -10 it has a value of -8130. This means that the root is somewhere between -5 and -10. At $x = -8$ the polynomial has the value 1282, and at -9 it has a value of -1417, so the root must be near -8.5.

Instead of continuing to try values between 8 and 9, Horner's method provides a way in which a new polynomial can be found that has the same roots as the original polynomial but that differ in that the real parts of the new roots are greater by a given number. In this example, if the new polynomial is to have a root that lies between 0 and -1, say, the roots of the polynomial in x should be increased by 8. This really means a substitution of $y - 8$ for x. This can be done by synthetic division.

1	14	60	130	118	50	$\rvert -8$
	-8	-48	-96	-272	1232	
1	6	12	34	-154	$\boxed{1282}$	
	-8	16	-224	1520		
1	-2	28	-190	$\boxed{1366}$		
	-8	80	-864			
1	-10	108	$\boxed{-1054}$			
	-8	144				
1	-18	$\boxed{252}$				
	-8					
$\boxed{1 \quad -26}$						

yielding the polynomial

$$y^5 - 26y^4 + 252y^3 - 1054y^2 + 1366y + 1282$$

which must have a root between 0 and -1.

Setting only the last two terms equal to zero

$$1366y = -1282$$

$$y = -0.938$$

so try -0.9.

1	-26	252	-1054	1366	1282	$\lfloor -0.9$
	-0.9	24.2	249	1172	-2280	
1	-26.9	276.2	-1303	2538	$\boxed{-998}$	

where only slide rule multiplication was used. It appears that the root is actually less than 0.9 (in magnitude). In fact, judging from the last set of numbers, the value of -0.6 looks better.

1	-26	252	-1054	1366	1282	$\lfloor -0.6$
	-0.6	15.96	-160.8	728.9	-1256.9	
1	-26.6	267.96	-1214.8	2094.9	$\boxed{25.1}$	
	-0.6	16.32	-170.6	831.2		
1	-27.2	284.28	-1385.4	$\boxed{2926.1}$		

Because the remainder of 25.1 was so small, the roots of the equation are reduced by 0.6, but the work was not completed since the next estimate will be found by $-25.1/2926 \doteq -0.0086$, so the y-root must be very near -0.609, and the x-root very near -8.609. Substituting this value of x in the original polynomial gives

1	14	60	130	118	50	$\lfloor -8.609$
	-8.61	-46.41	-116.99	-112	-51.6	
1	5.39	13.59	13.01	6	$\boxed{-1.6}$	

The remainder is sufficiently small that the remaining numbers in the last line may be considered to be the coefficients of the quartic that remains after the quintic is divided by $x + 8.609$:

$$x^4 + 5.39x^3 + 13.59x^2 + 13.01x + 6$$

This will be factored by Lin's method.

Lin's Method*

When a polynomial is of even degree, there is no assurance that any of the roots are real. Lin's method factors these polynomials into quadratics, and then the quadratic formula can be used.

The last three terms of the polynomial are chosen as a trial quadratic factor, and from the results of dividing this factor into the original polynomial a new trial quadratic is obtained.

EXAMPLE 4.11. Find the remaining roots of the quintic of Example 4.10.

Solution: The problem is reduced to finding the roots of the quartic

$$x^4 + 5.39x^3 + 13.59x^2 + 13.01x + 6$$

First trial quadratic: $13.59x^2 + 13.01x + 6 = 13.59(x^2+0.96x+0.44)$
By long division

1	0.96	0.44)	1	5.39	13.59	13.01	6
			1	.96	.44		
				4.43	13.15	13.01	
				4.43	4.25	1.95	
					8.90	11.06	6
					8.90	8.55	4.75

The remainder is not zero, so try as a new trial quadratic the three numbers in the next to last line of the long division:

$8.90x^2 + 11.06x + 6 = 8.9(x^2+1.24x+0.675)$

1	1.24	0.675)	1	5.39	13.59	13.01	6
			1	1.24	.68		
				4.15	12.91	13.01	
				4.15	5.15	2.8	
					7.76	10.21	6
					7.76	9.62	5.24

*S. LIN. "A Method of Successive Approximations for Evaluating the Real and Complex Roots of Cubic and Higher Order Equations." *Journal of Math. and Physics*, **20**, No. 3, August 1941.

The remainder is seen to be smaller than before, so try $7.76x^2 + 10.21x + 6 = 7.76(x^2+1.315x+0.773)$. The process is repeated until the trial quadratic $x^2 + 1.305x + 0.808$ is obtained.

1	1.305	0.808	) 1	5.39	13.59	13.01	6
			$\boxed{1}$	1.305	.808		
				4.085	12.78	13.01	
				$\boxed{4.085}$	5.34	3.31	
					7.44	9.70	6
					$\boxed{7.44}$	9.71	6.01

This is very close. The terms in the rectangles are the coefficients of the other quadratic factor:

$$x^2 + 4.085x + 7.44$$

Using the quadratic formula on $x^2 + 1.305x + 0.808$ yields the roots $-0.652 \pm j0.618$, and using the quadratic formula on $x^2 + 4.085x + 7.44$ yields the roots $-2.043 \pm j1.81$.

The roots of the original equation in s

$$s^5 + 140s^4 + 6000s^3 + 1.3 \times 10^5 s^2 + 1.18 \times 10^6 s + 5 \times 10^6 = 0$$

are ten times the roots of the polynomial in x; hence they are

$$s = -86.09 \quad -6.52 \pm j6.18 \quad -20.43 \pm j18.1$$

The coefficient of s^4 should be the negative sum of the roots. This is $-86.09 - 13.04 - 40.86 = -139.99$, which is very close to -140. The roots are probably accurate to three places.

In factored form then, the polynomial is

$$(s+86.09)\,(s+6.52-j6.18)\,(s+6.52+j6.18)\,(s+20.43-j18.1)$$
$$(s+20.43+j18.1)$$

It is clear from this example that factoring a polynomial is an enormous chore. Lin's method does not always converge as it did here, but a judicious choice of trial quadratics can usually be deduced when the method diverges.

Sometimes the circuit itself gives some indication as to possible roots. It can be shown that if all the storage elements are of one type, and the circuit does not have dependent sources in it (that is, it is a passive circuit), the roots will all be negative real. Only when both L and C appear will the roots be complex.

In many of the examples given in the chapter problems that follow the roots are integers. This is not the case in the problems below, but it will be true in many of the problems in succeeding chapters. This is done because the task of factoring is excessively tedious. In practice the use of digital computers for this purpose is so efficient and rapid that we are rarely called upon to factor polynomials of degree four or higher. However, it is still essential that we know how to do it.

PROBLEMS

4.33. Use Horner's method to find the real roots of the following cubic polynomials, and express the polynomial as a product of three factors.

(a) $s^3 + 15s^2 + 600s + 1500$

(b) $s^3 + 2s^2 + 64s + 220$

(c) $s^3 + 21s^2 + 3s + 32$

(d) $4s^3 + 8s^2 + 240s + 4000$

4.34. Use Lin's method to factor the following quartics into quadratics, and then solve for the roots of the quadratics. Write the polynomials in factored form. If Lin's method diverges, look for real roots.

(a) $s^4 + 4s^3 + 16s^2 + 32s + 33$

(b) $s^4 + 12s^3 + 30s^2 + 120s + 200$

(c) $s^4 + 5s^3 + 46s^2 + 100s + 300$

(d) $s^4 + 12s^3 + 30s^2 + 60s + 20$

CHAPTER PROBLEMS

4.35. Find the transfer function for each of the networks in Fig. 4.46. The source labelled with IN as a subscript is to be chosen as the input variable, and the variable with O as a subscript is to be chosen as the output variable. Express the transfer functions as a ratio of polynomials, the denominator of which is written in factored form, with unity as the coefficient of the highest power of s. All elements are given in ohms, henrys, and farads.

Answer to (d): $\dfrac{-10^8}{s + 5.31 \times 10^6}$

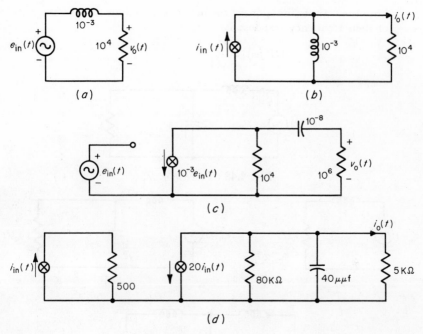

(a)   (b)

(c)

(d)

Fig. 4.46 *Problem 4.35.*

4.36. Find the transfer function $H(s) = V_0(s)/I_{in}(s)$ for the circuit of Fig. 4.47. Factor the denominator. This transfer function is called the *driving-point impedance* of the circuit, since it is the ratio of the transforms of the voltage and current at one terminal pair.

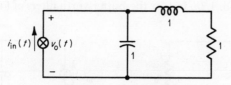

Fig. 4.47 *Problem 4.36.*

4.37. Find the transfer function $I_0(s)/E_{in}(s)$ for the circuit of Fig. 4.48 and factor the denominator. This transfer function is called the *driving-point admittance*, since it relates a current to a voltage at one terminal-pair.

Answer: $$\frac{s + 1}{[s + 1/2 - j\sqrt{3}/2]\,[s + 1/2 + j\sqrt{3}/2]}$$

4.38. The circuits pictured in Fig. 4.49 are called Butterworth low-pass filters of order n. (n is the number of reactive elements in the filter.)

Find the transfer functions of the networks and show that the magnitude of their frequency response is

$$|H(j\omega)| = \frac{1}{\sqrt{1 + \omega^{2n}}}$$

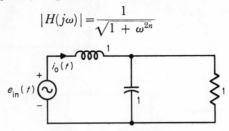

Fig. 4.48 *Problem 4.37.*

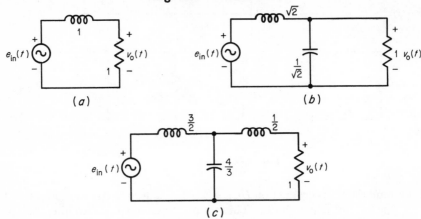

Fig. 4.49 *Problem 4.38.*

4.39. Repeat Prob. 4.38, but for the Butterworth filters of Fig. 4.50.

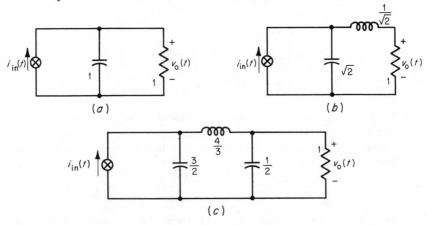

Fig. 4.50 *Problem 4.39.*

4.40. Repeat Prob. 4.38, but for the Butterworth filters of Fig. 4.51.

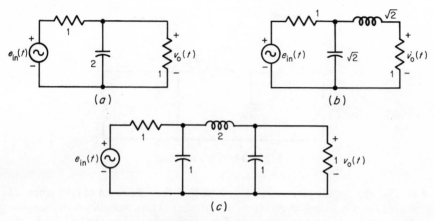

Fig. 4.51 *Problem 4.40.*

4.41. Find the transfer function (also called a transfer impedance, since it is the ratio of voltage to current but not at one terminal pair) of the network of Fig. 4.52. Factor the denominator.

$$Answer: \frac{(s^2 + 1)^2}{(s + 1)^4}$$

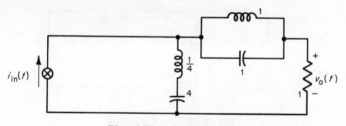

Fig. 4.52 *Problem 4.41.*

4.42. Find the transfer function of the circuit in Fig. 4.53 and factor the denominator.

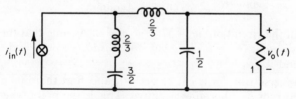

Fig. 4.53 *Problem 4.42.*

4.43. Find the transfer function of the circuit in Fig. 4.54 and factor the denominator.

$$Answer: \quad \frac{3}{(s + 1.634)\,(s + 3.366)}$$

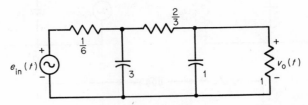

Fig. 4.54 *Problem 4.43.*

4.44. For the circuit pictured in Fig. 4.55 find the transform of $i_L(t)$ when all initial conditions and sources are present. Thus, actually transform the sources and get one large transform as the ratio of two polynomials, the coefficient of the highest-order term in the denominator being unity. Factor the denominator. Check with the initial value theorem to see if $\lim_{s\to\infty} sI_L(s) = 2.$

$$Answer: \quad \frac{2s^3 + 51.25s^2 + 211.25s + 5500}{(s - j10)\,(s + j10)\,(s + 0.502)\,(s + 24.9)}$$

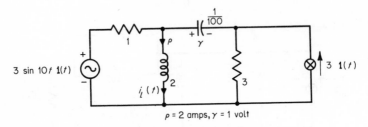

$p = 2$ amps, $\gamma = 1$ volt

Fig. 4.55 *Problem 4.44.*

4.45. Find the transform of $i_L(t)$ in the circuit of Fig. 4.56 as one fraction, as instructed in Prob. 4.44. Factor the denominator.

$$Answer: \quad \frac{0.5\,s^2 + 70\,s + 3 \times 10^5}{s(s + 150.5)\,(s + 3989.5)}$$

4.46. (a) In the circuit of Fig. 4.57, $\gamma = \rho = 0$. Assume that the ideal diode is absent (that is, represent it by a short-circuit) and solve for $I(s)$ and $V_0(s)$.

(b) Inverse transform $I(s)$ to get $i(t)$, and find the time at which the current first becomes negative. This is the point where the diode interrupts the current and will appear as an open circuit so long as the voltage across it is maintained more positive on the right than on the left.

(c) Inverse transform $V_0(s)$ by finding C_1 and C_2 such that

$$V_0(s) = \frac{C_1}{s} + \frac{C_2 s}{s^2 + \beta^2}$$

(d) Plot $v_0(t)$ up to the time the current first goes to zero. With the diode present will the diode ever conduct again? Plot $v_0(t)$ for $t > 0$ when the diode is present.

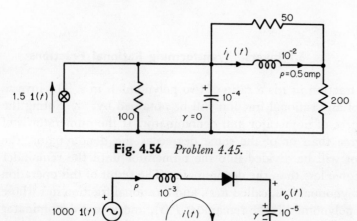

Fig. 4.56 *Problem 4.45.*

Fig. 4.57 *Problem 4.46.*

chapter

5

The Inverse Transform

5.1 Inverse Transforming Rational Fractions

A rational fraction in s is a ratio of two polynomials in s. The inverse transform of any rational fraction will be obtained by: (1) Noting the relative degree of numerator and denominator. If the numerator is of higher degree than or of the same degree as the denominator, the denominator will be divided into the numerator until the remainder is of one degree less than the denominator. The result of this operation will be a polynomial in s, called $R(s)$, and a rational fraction in s whose numerator polynomial is the remainder $P_r(s)$, and whose denominator polynomial is $Q(s)$. Thus

$$F(s) = R(s) + \frac{P_r(s)}{Q(s)}$$

EXAMPLE 5.1. Find $R(s)$, $P_r(s)$, and $Q(s)$ when

$$F(s) = \frac{0.5\ (s^4+6s^3+15s^2+22s+14)}{s^3+4s^2+5s+2}$$

Solution: By long division

$$
\begin{array}{r}
1 \quad 4 \quad 5 \quad 2\ \overline{)}\ 1 \quad\ 6 \quad\ 15 \quad\ 22 \quad\ 14 \\[4pt]
1^* \quad 4 \quad\ 5 \quad\ 2 \\[4pt]
\hline
2 \quad\ 10 \quad\ 20 \quad\ 14 \\[4pt]
2^* \quad\ 8 \quad\ 10 \quad\ 4 \\[4pt]
\hline
2 \quad\ 10 \quad\ 10
\end{array}
$$

The result of the division shows that

$$R(s) = \frac{1}{2}(s+2) = \frac{s}{2} + 1$$

since the factor of 0.5 was left out of the division,

$$P_r(s) = \frac{1}{2}(2s^2 + 10s + 10) = s^2 + 5s + 5$$

which is the remainder polynomial, and, of course,

$$Q(s) = s^3 + 4s^2 + 5s + 2$$

Thus

$$F(s) = \frac{s}{2} + 1 + \frac{s^2 + 5s + 5}{s^3 + 4s^2 + 5s + 2}$$

(2) The rational fraction that remains after the polynomial $R(s)$ is removed must now be expanded into a sum of terms of the type

$$\frac{A}{(s+\alpha)^n}$$

or

$$\frac{A}{(s+\alpha-j\beta)^n}$$

and the inverse transform of the function can then be obtained by inverse transforming term by term, using key pairs (1) and (2) of Table 3.2.

The Polynomial R(s), The Partial Fraction Expansion

The inverse transform of a constant is a delta function, or impulse, whose area is given by the constant. Since multiplication by s is equivalent to differentiation, the inverse transform of a constant times s is the derivative of an impulse with area equal to that constant. Similarly, s^2 is the transform of the second derivative of the impulse, s^3 the third derivative, and so on.

The derivative of the unit impulse is called the unit doublet; this was encountered in Prob. 2.39. The derivative of the unit doublet is called the unit triplet. It is rare indeed that a doublet will appear, and the author has *never* encountered a triplet. For the very unlikely situation of a doublet appearing, the unit doublet will be denoted by $\delta_1(t)$, and defined as

$$\delta_1(t) = \frac{d\delta(t)}{dt} \tag{5.1}$$

This function will have a Laplace transform of s and will be assumed to be the limit (as $\epsilon \to 0$) of a rectangular pulse starting at $t = -\epsilon$, having a height $1/\epsilon^2$, and ending at $t = 0$; followed by a negative pulse starting at $t = 0$, having a height $-1/\epsilon^2$, and ending at $t = \epsilon$.

Thus it is seen that it will be rare that the degree of the numerator of a fraction will exceed the degree of the denominator by more than one unit. Usually the numerator will be of equal or smaller degree than the denominator. If they are of equal degree, long division is not necessary, for the constant term is simply

$$\lim_{s \to \infty} F(s)$$

nor will it be necessary to perform the long division to obtain the remainder, as will be seen in Example 5.2.

Assuming that the polynomial $R(s)$ has been obtained, the denominator must now be factored and its roots obtained. Suppose the roots are $s_1, s_2, \ldots s_n$. If the denominator is of degree n, there will be at most n numbers for which the denominator will vanish. The polynomial $Q(s)$ may have duplicate factors—for example

$$Q(s) = s^2 + 2s + 1 = (s+1)^2$$

and hence fewer distinct roots than the degree of the polynomial indicates.

In general, $F(s)$ may be written as

$$F(s) = \frac{P(s)}{(s-s_1)^{n_1} (s-s_2)^{n_2} \ldots (s-s_k)^{n_k}}$$

and may be expanded into

$$F(s) = R(s) + \frac{a_1}{(s-s_1)^{n_1}} + \frac{a_2}{(s-s_1)^{n_1-1}} + \ldots + \frac{a_{n_1}}{s-s_1}$$

$$+ \frac{b_1}{(s-s_2)^{n_2}} + \frac{b_2}{(s-s_2)^{n_2-1}} + \ldots + \frac{b_{n_2}}{s-s_2}$$

$$+ \ldots + \frac{k_1}{(s-s_k)^{n_k}} + \ldots + \frac{k_{n_k}}{s-s_k}$$

which development is known as the *partial fraction expansion* of $F(s)$.

It will be seen that each term in the expansion is a special case of key pair (1) (Table 3.2) when the s_k terms are real, and of key pair (2) when the s_k terms are complex. In the subsections that follow, the partial fraction expansion will be broken down into five parts: (1) all the roots of the denominator are real and distinct, (2) all the roots are real, but some may be of second order; that is, duplications may occur, (3) all the roots are distinct, but conjugate complex roots are present, (4) second-order conjugate complex roots occur, and (5) multiple-order real or complex roots may appear.

Roots Real and Distinct

If all the roots of $Q(s)$ are real and distinct, and the roots are $-\alpha_1$, $-\alpha_2, \ldots -\alpha_n$, then

$$Q(s) = (s+\alpha_1)(s+\alpha_2) \ldots (s+\alpha_n)$$

where it is assumed, of course, that the coefficient of the highest power of s in $Q(s)$ has been set equal to unity. Then if $F(s) = P(s)/Q(s)$

$$F(s) = R(s) + \frac{a_1}{s+\alpha_1} + \frac{a_2}{s+\alpha_2} + \ldots + \frac{a_n}{s+\alpha_n} \tag{5.2}$$

where $a_1, a_2, \ldots a_n$ are constants to be determined.

The constants a_k in Eq. (5.2) can be determined in any number of ways, but the easiest is as follows.

To determine a_k for example, multiply both sides of the equation by $(s+\alpha_k)$ and evaluate $(s+\alpha_k)F(s)$ when $s = -\alpha_k$. The result will be a_k.

Proof:

$$(s+\alpha_k)F(s) = \frac{(s+\alpha_k)P(s)}{(s+\alpha_1) \ldots (s+\alpha_k) \ldots (s+\alpha_n)}$$

$$= (s+\alpha_k)R(s) + \frac{(s+\alpha_k)a_1}{s+\alpha_1} + \ldots + a_k +$$

$$\ldots + \frac{(s+\alpha_k)a_n}{s+\alpha_n}$$

Clearly the right-hand side of the latter expression reduces to a_k when we set $s = -\alpha_k$, since every term has a factor $(s+\alpha_k)$ in it except the a_k term. The left-hand side of the expression, however, is an indeterminate form, since factors of $(s+\alpha_k)$ appear in both the numerator and the denominator. If these are cancelled out, and s is set equal to $-\alpha_k$

$$a_k = \frac{P(-\alpha_k)}{(\alpha_1-\alpha_k) \ldots (\alpha_{k-1}-\alpha_k)(\alpha_{k+1}-\alpha_k) \ldots (\alpha_n-\alpha_k)}$$

If all the a_k terms are determined in this manner, the inverse transform can be written by inspection, for it is known that the inverse transform of $A/(s+\alpha)$ is simply $Ae^{-\alpha t}\mathbf{1}(t)$.

EXAMPLE 5.2. Find the inverse transform of

$$F(s) = \frac{3s^3 + 2s - 5}{s^3 + 6s^2 + 11s + 6}$$

Solution: Evidently $F(s)$ approaches 3 as s becomes infinite, so $R(s) = 3$. The denominator has roots at -1, -2, and -3, so

$$F(s) = 3 + \frac{a_1}{s+1} + \frac{a_2}{s+2} + \frac{a_3}{s+3} = \frac{3s^3 + 2s - 5}{(s+1)(s+2)(s+3)}$$

If we cover up the factor $(s+1)$ in the denominator of the right-hand side of the equation, [the same as multiplying by $(s+1)$] and then let $s = -1$

$$a_1 = \frac{3(-1)^3 + 2(-1) - 5}{(-1+2)(-1+3)} = \frac{-10}{2} = -5$$

In like manner, covering up the factor $(s+2)$ and letting $s = -2$

$$a_2 = \frac{3(-2)^3 + 2(-2) - 5}{(-2+1)(-2+3)} = \frac{-33}{-1} = 33$$

It can be verified that $a_3 = -46$, so

$$F(s) = 3 - \frac{5}{s+1} + \frac{33}{s+2} - \frac{46}{s+3}$$

and the inverse transform can be obtained directly as

$$f(t) = 3\delta(t) + (-5e^{-t} + 33e^{-2t} - 46e^{-3t})\, \mathbf{1}(t)$$

The initial-value theorem is a very handy check, but in this example it is made useless by the delta function. If, however, we divide the denominator of the original transform into the numerator just enough to find the first term of the remainder

$$s^3 + 6s^2 + 11s + 6 \,\overline{\big)\, 3s^3 \qquad\qquad + 2s - 5}$$
$$\underline{3s^3 + 18s^2}$$
$$- 18s^2$$

then

$$F(s) = 3 + \frac{-18s^2 \text{ etc.}}{s^3 + \text{ etc.}}$$

The limit of the fraction times s, as s becomes infinite, is -18, and this is the initial value of the inverse transform without the delta function.

Going back to our inverse transform it is seen that the coefficient of $\mathbf{1}(t)$ at $t = 0$ is $-5 + 33 - 46 = -18$. (*Check*).

EXAMPLE 5.3. Inverse transform

$$F(s) = \frac{2s^2 - 3s + 4}{s^3 + 3s^2 + 2.75s + 0.75}$$

Solution: Here the denominator is of higher degree than the numerator, so $R(s) = 0$. Furthermore the initial value of the solution must be $+2$. The denominator can be factored into

$$\left(s + \frac{1}{2}\right)(s+1)\left(s + \frac{3}{2}\right)$$

so

$$a_1 = \frac{2(-1/2)^2 - 3(-1/2) + 4}{(-1/2+1)(-1/2+3/2)} = 12$$

$$a_2 = \frac{2(-1)^2 - 3(-1) + 4}{(-1+1/2)(-1+3/2)} = -36$$

$$a_3 = \frac{2(-3/2)^2 - 3(-3/2) + 4}{(-3/2+1/2)(-3/2+1)} = 26$$

making

$$F(s) = \frac{12}{s+1/2} - \frac{36}{s+1} + \frac{26}{s+3/2}$$

$$f(t) = (12e^{-t/2} - 36e^{-t} + 26e^{-3t/2})\mathbf{1}(t)$$

which has an initial value of $12 - 36 + 26 = 2$. (*Check.*)

PROBLEMS

Find the inverse transforms of the functions given, and check results using the initial-value theorem.

5.1. (a) $\dfrac{s^2 + 2}{s + 1}$ (b) $\dfrac{s + 2}{s + 1}$ (c) $\dfrac{2}{s + 1}$

Answer: (a) $\delta_1(t) - \delta(t) + 3e^{-t}\mathbf{1}(t)$

5.2. (a) $\dfrac{s^2 + 2}{s(s+1)}$ (b) $\dfrac{s + 2}{s(s+1)}$ (c) $\dfrac{4}{s(s+1)}$

5.3. (a) $\dfrac{s^3 + 2s^2 + 6}{s(s+1)(s+2)}$ (b) $\dfrac{-s^2 + 2s + 2}{s(s+1)(s+2)}$ (c) $\dfrac{3s - 4}{s(s+1)(s+2)}$

Answer: (c) $[7e^{-t} - 2 - 5e^{-2t}]\mathbf{1}(t)$

5.4. (a) $\dfrac{2s^3 + s^2 + 2s + 3}{s(s+1)\ (s+2)\ (s+3)}$ (b) $\dfrac{s^4 - 1}{s(s+1)\ (s+2)\ (s+3)}$

5.5. (a) $\dfrac{s^2 + 3s + 2}{(s-3)\ (s+2)\ (s+3)}$ (b) $\dfrac{s^3 - 4s + 10}{s(s-1)\ (s+1)\ (s+2)}$

$$\text{\textit{Answer:} (b)} \quad \left[-5 + \frac{7}{6}e^t + 6.5e^{-t} - \frac{5}{3}e^{-2t} \right]\mathbf{1}(t)$$

Second-Order Real Roots

If the denominator of the transform has double real factors, we can expand the transform so that two terms appear with this factor in the denominator, one to the second degree, and one to the first. Thus

$$F(s) = \frac{P(s)}{(s+\alpha_1)^2(s+\alpha_2)^2(s+\alpha_3)}$$

$$= \frac{a_1}{(s+\alpha_1)^2} + \frac{a_2}{(s+\alpha_1)} + \frac{b_1}{(s+\alpha_2)^2} + \frac{b_2}{(s+\alpha_2)} + \frac{c}{(s+\alpha_3)}$$

has two roots of second order and one of first order. The reason for the expansion is that the result can be easily inverse transformed since the inverse transform of $A/(s+\alpha)^2$ is $Ate^{-\alpha t}\mathbf{1}(t)$. In general, all five terms are needed. There may be some tendency to doubt that the first-degree terms are required and to leave them out. The proof that they are required will not be given here. Let it suffice to say that $P(s)$ may be a quartic [since $R(s) = 0$ above], so five coefficients are needed for $P(s)$, some of which may be zero. If the partial fraction expansion contained only three terms, and if the fractions were combined with a least common denominator, only three constants would be available to determine five coefficients in $P(s)$. It is clear that this cannot always be done and that five constants are actually required. Thus the first-degree terms will generally be present. An example will be given to demonstrate that they are required.

The constants that go into the numerators of the several fractions are not as easy to evaluate as they were with first-order roots. In particular, the constants that are associated with the first-degree factors are the most difficult to obtain.

EXAMPLE 5.4. Inverse transform

$$F(s) = \frac{0.5(s^4+6s^3+15s^2+22s+14)}{s^3+4s^2+5s+2}$$

Solution: This function was first discussed early in this section, and $R(s)$

was found to be $s/2 + 1$. The denominator can be factored into $(s+1)^2$ $(s+2)$, so

$$\frac{0.5(s^4+6s^3+15s^2+22s+14)}{(s+1)^2(s+2)} = \frac{s}{2}+1+\frac{a_1}{(s+1)^2}+\frac{a_2}{s+1}+\frac{b}{s+2}$$

If both sides are multiplied by $(s+1)^2$

$$\frac{0.5(s^4+6s^3+15s^2+22s+14)}{s+2} = \frac{s(s+1)^2}{2}+(s+1)^2+a_1+a_2(s+1)$$

$$+b\frac{(s+1)^2}{s+2}$$

and it can be seen that when $s = -1$

$$\frac{0.5(1-6+15-22+14)}{1} = 1 = a_1$$

Furthermore, if we differentiate the last equation with respect to s

$$\frac{1}{2}\cdot\frac{(s+2)(4s^3+18s^2+30s+22)-(s^4+6s^3+15s^2+22s+14)}{(s+2)^2}$$

$$=\frac{s(2)(s+1)+(s+1)^2}{2}+2(s+1)+0+a_2+$$

$$b\cdot\frac{(s+2)2(s+1)-(s+1)^2}{(s+2)^2}$$

But every term on the right has a factor $(s+1)$ except a_2, so setting $s = -1$

$$\frac{1}{2}\cdot\frac{(1)(-4+18-30+22)-(1-6+15-22+14)}{(1)^2} = 2 = a_2$$

b can be determined as before by covering up $(s+2)$ in $F(s)$ and letting $s = -2$

$$b = \frac{0.5\,(16-48+60-44+14)}{(-1)^2} = -1$$

so

$$F(s) = \frac{s}{2}+1+\frac{1}{(s+1)^2}+\frac{2}{s+1}-\frac{1}{s+2}$$

$$f(t) = \frac{1}{2}\delta_1(t)+\delta(t)+(te^{-t}+2e^{-t}-e^{-2t})\mathbf{1}(t)$$

The initial-value theorem cannot be used on $F(s)$ directly, because of the doublet and impulse. But earlier in this section the remainder after long division was $s^2 + 5s + 5$, so

$$\lim_{s \to \infty} s \times \frac{s^2 + \text{etc.}}{s^3 + \text{etc.}} = 1$$

At $t = 0+$, that part of $f(t)$ that does not contain the doublet and impulse also has the value $+1$, so it checks.

If the $2/(s+1)$ term were not included in the partial fraction expansion, then

$$\frac{s}{2} + 1 + \frac{1}{(s+1)^2} + \frac{-1}{s+2} = \frac{0.5(s^4 + 6s^3 + 11s^2 + 10s + 6)}{(s+1)^2(s+2)}$$

which is seen to be different from $F(s)$. If, however, $2/(s+1)$ is added to the result above, then $F(s)$ will be obtained.

EXAMPLE 5.5. Find the inverse transform of

$$F(s) = \frac{1}{s^2(s+1)^2(s+2)^2}$$

Solution: $\quad F(s) = \frac{a_1}{s^2} + \frac{a_2}{s} + \frac{b_1}{(s+1)^2} + \frac{b_2}{(s+1)} + \frac{c_1}{(s+2)^2} + \frac{c_2}{(s+2)}$

(a) $\quad s^2 F(s) = \frac{1}{(s+1)^2(s+2)^2}$

$$s^2 F(s) \Big|_{s=0} = a_1 = \frac{1}{4}$$

$$\frac{d}{ds} s^2 F(s) \Big|_{s=0} = \frac{-2(s+1)(s+2)^2 - 2(s+1)^2(s+2)}{(s+1)^4(s+2)^4} \Big|_{s=0}$$

$$= \frac{-3}{4} = a_2$$

(b) $\quad (s+1)^2 F(s) = \frac{1}{s^2(s+2)^2}$

$$(s+1)^2 F(s) \Big|_{s=-1} = 1 = b_1$$

$$\frac{d}{ds} (s+1)^2 F(s) \Big|_{s=-1} = \frac{-2s(s+2)^2 - 2(s+2)s^2}{s^4(s+2)^4} \Big|_{s=-1} = b_2 = 0$$

Here is a situation where the first-degree term was not required, but there is no way of knowing this in advance.

(c) $(s+2)^2F(s) = \dfrac{1}{s^2(s+1)^2}$

$(s+2)^2F(s)\big|_{s=-2} = \dfrac{1}{4} = c_1$

$\dfrac{d}{ds}(s+2)^2F(s)\bigg|_{s=-2} = \dfrac{-2s(s+1)^2-2s^2(s+1)}{s^4(s+1)^4}\bigg|_{s=-2} = \dfrac{3}{4} = c_2$

Thus

$$F(s) = \dfrac{1/4}{s^2} + \dfrac{-3/4}{s} + \dfrac{1}{(s+1)^2} + \dfrac{1/4}{(s+2)^2} + \dfrac{3/4}{s+2}$$

$$f(t) = \left[\dfrac{t}{4} - \dfrac{3}{4} + te^{-t} + \dfrac{1}{4}te^{-2t} + \dfrac{3}{4}e^{-2t}\right]\mathbf{1}(t)$$

From the initial-value theorem, $f(0+) = 0$. Setting $t = 0+$ in the last expression yields

$$f(0+) = \left(0 - \dfrac{3}{4} + 0 + 0 + \dfrac{3}{4}\right) = 0 \quad (Check)$$

PROBLEMS

Find the inverse transforms of the functions below and check the results with the initial-value theorem.

5.6. (a) $\dfrac{s^2+3s+4}{s^2(s+1)}$ (b) $\dfrac{s+2}{s(s+1)^2}$ (c) $\dfrac{6}{s^2}$

Answer to (b): $[2 - te^{-t} - 2e^{-t}]\mathbf{1}(t)$

5.7. (a) $\dfrac{1}{s(s+1)^2}$ (b) $\dfrac{s}{(s+1)(s+2)^2}$ (c) $\dfrac{s+3}{(s+1)^2(s+2)}$

Answer to (c): $[2te^{-t} - e^{-t} + e^{-2t}]\mathbf{1}(t)$

5.8. (a) $\dfrac{1}{(s-1)^2(s+1)^2}$ (b) $\dfrac{s-5}{(s-4)(s+2)^2}$ (c) $\dfrac{s^2+4s+1}{s(s+4)^2}$

Answer to (a): $\frac{1}{2}(t\cosh t - \sinh t)\mathbf{1}(t)$

5.9. (a) $\dfrac{1}{s^2\left(s+\dfrac{1}{2}\right)^2(s+2)}$ (b) $\dfrac{1-s}{s\left(s+\dfrac{1}{2}\right)^2(s+1)^2}$

Answer to (b): $[4 - 12te^{-t/2} + 32e^{-t/2} - 8te^{-t} - 36e^{-t}]\mathbf{1}(t)$

5.10. (a) $\dfrac{4s+2}{s^3+2s^2+s}$ (b) $\dfrac{3s+4}{(s^2+3s+2)^2}$

Answer to (b): $[te^{-t} + e^{-t} - 2te^{-2t} - e^{-2t}]\mathbf{1}(t)$

First-Order Complex Roots

The inverse transformation of complex roots follows the same pattern as those of real roots, with the exception that complex arithmetic is used. Since all physical transforms will be real when s is real, all complex roots will appear in conjugate pairs.

The key pair to use after the partial fraction expansion is

$$\mathscr{L}^{-1}\left[\frac{A\underline{/\theta}}{s+\alpha-j\beta} + \frac{A\underline{/-\theta}}{s+\alpha+j\beta}\right] = 2Ae^{-\alpha t}\cos(\beta t+\theta)\,\mathbf{1}(t)$$

Note that the second term in the transform above contains no information that is not contained in the first term. This will be used to advantage, and only the constant that goes with the denominator factor that has the negative imaginary part (the *root* has a positive imaginary part) will have to be found. In writing the partial fraction expansion, we will not even write the conjugate term.

EXAMPLE 5.6. Find the inverse transform of

$$F(s) = \frac{s^2 - 3s + 2}{s(s+1)(s^2+1)(s^2+2s+2)}$$

Solution: The partial fraction expansion is now determined. Note that $f(0+) = 0$, $s^2 + 1 = (s-j)(s+j)$, $s^2 + 2s + 2 = (s+1-j)(s+1+j)$, and $R(s) = 0$, since the numerator is of smaller degree than the denominator.

$$F(s) = \frac{s^2 - 3s + 2}{s(s+1)(s-j)(s+j)(s+1-j)(s+1+j)}$$

$$= \frac{a}{s} + \frac{b}{s+1} + \frac{A}{s-j} + \frac{B}{s+1-j} + \text{conjugates}*$$

where A and B are complex. Note that the latter equation is incomplete since $A*/(s+j)$ and $B*/(s+1+j)$ should be present. The fact that they are not really needed is emphasized by leaving them out.

It is easier to use the original expression for $F(s)$ to get a and b: cover up the s in the denominator of the original $F(s)$ and let $s = 0$

$$\frac{2}{(1)(1)(2)} = 1 = a$$

---

*The missing terms are not really the conjugates of those present unless s is considered to be real. Thus, strictly speaking

$$\text{conjugate}\left[\frac{A}{s-j}\right] = \frac{A*}{s* + j}$$

Covering up the $(s+1)$ factor in the original expression of $F(s)$ and letting $s = -1$ gives

$$\frac{(-1)^2 - 3(-1) + 2}{(-1)(1+1)(1-2+2)} = -3 = b$$

Now go to the factored form of $F(s)$, cover the $(s-j)$ factor in the denominator, and set $s = j$.

$$\frac{(j)^2 - 3(j) + 2}{(j)(j+1)(j+j)(j+1-j)(j+1+j)} = \frac{1-3j}{2-6j} = \frac{1}{2}\underline{/0°} = A$$

The fact that A is real is mere chance, for in general it will be complex.

Going finally to the factored form of $F(s)$, covering the $(s+1-j)$ factor in the denominator, and letting $s = -1+j$, we have

$$B = \frac{(-1+j)^2 - 3(-1+j) + 2}{(-1+j)(j)(-1)(-1+2j)(2j)} = \frac{5-5j}{-2-6j} = 1.118\underline{/63.44°}$$

Then

$$F(s) = \frac{1}{s} - \frac{3}{s+1} + \frac{1/2}{s-j} + \frac{1.118\underline{/63.44°}}{s+1-j} + \text{conjugates}$$

$$f(t) = [1 - 3e^{-t} + \cos t + 2.236\, e^{-t} \cos (t+63.44°)]\, \mathbf{1}(t)$$

At $t = 0+$

$$f(0+) = 1 - 3 + 1 + 2.236 \cos (63.44°)$$

$$= 0. \quad (Check)$$

EXAMPLE 5.7. Find the inverse transform of

$$F(s) = \frac{4.5s^3 + 65s^2 + 516s + 1208}{(s^2+4s+104)(s^2+8s+16)}$$

Solution: The denominator can be factored into $(s+2-j10)\,(s+2+j10)$ and $(s+4)^2$, so

$$F(s) = \frac{A}{s+2-j10} + \frac{b_1}{(s+4)^2} + \frac{b_2}{s+4} + \text{conjugate}$$

b_1 is easily determined by covering up $(s+4)^2$ in the denominator

$$(s+4)^2 F(s) = \frac{4.5s^3 + 65s^2 + 516s + 1208}{s^2+4s+104}$$

and setting $s = -4$. Then

$$b_1 = \frac{4.5(-4)^3 + 65(-4)^2 + 516(-4) + 1208}{(-4)^2 + 4(-4) + 104} = -1$$

Differentiating $(s+4)^2 F(s)$ with respect to s and substituting $s = -4$ into the result gives

$$\frac{(s^2+4s+104)(13.5s^2+130s+516) - (4.5s^3+65s^2+516s+1208)(2s+4)}{(s^2+4s+104)^2}\bigg|_{s=-4}$$

$$= \frac{104 \times 212 + 104 \times (-4)}{104^2} = 2 = b_2$$

Finally, writing $(s+2-j10)\, F(s)$, and letting $s = -2+j10$

$$A = \frac{4.5s^3+65s^2+516s+1208}{(s+4)^2(s+2+j10)}\bigg|_{s=-2+j10} = \frac{3400+j1400}{800+j1920} = \frac{5\sqrt{2}}{4}\underline{/-45^\circ}$$

Thus

$$f(t) = \left[(2-t)e^{-4t} + \frac{5\sqrt{2}}{2}\, e^{-2t} \cos{(10t-45^\circ)}\right]\mathbf{1}(t)$$

At $t = 0+$, the initial value theorem gives 4.5 and the time expression gives

$$f(0+) = 2 + \frac{5\sqrt{2}}{2} \cos{(-45^\circ)} = 4.5. \qquad (Check)$$

PROBLEMS

Find the inverse transforms of the following functions and check your results with the initial-value theorem.

5.11. (a) $\dfrac{s+4}{s^2+4}$ (b) $\dfrac{1}{s(s^2+4)}$ (c) $\dfrac{1}{s(s^2+2s+10)}$

Answer to (c): $\dfrac{1}{10}$ $[1 + 1.055\, e^{-t} \cos{(3t + 161.56^\circ)}]\mathbf{1}(t)$

5.12. (a) $\dfrac{s+2}{s(s^2+4)}$ (b) $\dfrac{s-5}{(s-1)(s^2+16)}$ (c) $\dfrac{1}{s^2(s^2+6s+13)}$

Answer to (c): $\left[\dfrac{t}{13} - \dfrac{6}{169} + \dfrac{1}{26}\, e^{-3t} \cos{(2t - 22.6^\circ)}\right]\mathbf{1}(t)$

5.13. (a) $\dfrac{s^2+3}{(s+1)^2(s^2+2s+2)}$ (b) $\dfrac{s^3-2s+2}{(s+1)(s^2+1)}$

Answer to (b): $\delta(t) + \left[\dfrac{3}{2}\, e^{-t} + \dfrac{\sqrt{26}}{2} \cos{(t+168.7^\circ)}\right]\mathbf{1}(t)$

5.14. (a) $\dfrac{s+2}{(s^2+2s+2)(s^2+s+1)}$ (b) $\dfrac{-s+3}{(s^2+10s+169)(s^2+16)}$

Answer to (a): $\left[\sqrt{2}\ e^{-t}\cos{(t+45°)}\ -\ e^{-t/2}\cos\left(\dfrac{\sqrt{3}}{2}t\right)\right]\mathbf{1}(t)$

5.15. (a) $\dfrac{s^2+2s+4}{s(s+1)\,(s^2+10s+50)}$ (b) $\dfrac{1}{s(s^2-4s+20)}$

Answer to (a): $\left[0.08\ -\ \dfrac{3}{41}\ e^{-t}\ +\ 0.1786\ e^{-5t}\cos{(5t-92.2°)}\right]\mathbf{1}(t)$

Second-Order Complex Roots

To find the inverse transform when the denominator has a second-order complex factor, we follow the same plan that we used with double-order real roots. As with first-order complex roots, only one-half of the terms are required, since

$$\mathscr{L}^{-1}\left[\frac{A/\theta}{(s+\alpha-j\beta)^2}+\frac{A/-\theta}{(s+\alpha+j\beta)^2}\right]=2Ate^{-\alpha t}\cos{(\beta t+\theta)}\ \mathbf{1}(t)$$

and only the constant that goes with the root $-\alpha+j\beta$ is required.

EXAMPLE 5.8. Find the inverse transform of

$$F(s)=\frac{s+2}{s(s^2+4s+8)^2}$$

$$=\frac{s+2}{s(s+2-j2)^2(s+2+j2)^2}$$

$$=\frac{a}{s}+\frac{A_1}{(s+2-j2)^2}+\frac{A_2}{s+2-j2}+\text{conjugates}$$

where the conjugate terms were omitted in the last expression. The usual procedure yields $a=\frac{1}{32}$, and

$$(s+2-j2)^2F(s)=\frac{s+2}{s(s+2+j2)^2}$$

will give A_1 when $s=-2+j2$, and its derivative will give A_2 when s is given the same value.

$$A_1=\frac{j2}{(-2+j2)(j4)^2}=\frac{1}{16\sqrt{2}}\ /135°$$

$$A_2=\frac{s(s+2+j2)^2-(s+2)\ [2s(s+2+j2)+(s+2+j2)^2]}{s^2(s+2+j2)^4}\bigg|_{s=-2+2j}$$

$$=\frac{1}{64}\ /0°$$

Thus the inverse transform is

$$f(t) = \left[\frac{1}{32} + \frac{1}{8\sqrt{2}} \, te^{-2t} \cos{(2t+135°)} + \frac{1}{32} \, e^{-2t} \cos 2t\right]\mathbf{1}(t)$$

and the initial value is zero.

PROBLEMS

Find the inverse transforms of the functions given and check your answers with the initial value Theorem.

5.16. (a) $\dfrac{s}{(s^2+1)^2}$ (b) $\dfrac{1}{s(s^2+4)^2}$ (c) $\dfrac{s}{(s^2+2s+2)^2}$

Answer to (c): $\left[\dfrac{1}{\sqrt{2}} \, te^{-t} \cos{(t-45°)} - \dfrac{1}{2} \, e^{-t} \sin t\right]\mathbf{1}(t)$

5.17. (a) $\dfrac{s^2 + 2}{(s+1)\,(s^2+4)^2}$ (b) $\dfrac{s^2 - 1}{s(s^2+4s+8)^2}$

Answer to (a): $\Big[\dfrac{3}{25} \, e^{-t} + \dfrac{\sqrt{5}}{20} \, t \cos{(2t-63.45°)}$

$$+ \frac{1}{8} \cos{(2t-163.8°)}\Big]\mathbf{1}(t)$$

5.18. (a) $\dfrac{s+5}{s(s^2-4s+8)^2}$ (b) $\dfrac{s^4 + 1}{s^2(s^2+2s+2)^2}$

Answer to (b): $\Big[\dfrac{t}{4} - \dfrac{1}{2} + \dfrac{3}{4} \, te^{-t} \cos{(t + 90°)}$

$$+ 1.346e^{-t} \cos{(t - 68.2°)}\Big]\mathbf{1}(t)$$

5.19. (a) $\dfrac{s}{(s+1)^2\,(s^2+1)^2}$ (b) $\dfrac{s^2 - 2s + 1}{(s-2)\,(s^2+10s + 50)^2}$

Answer to (a): $\dfrac{1}{4}[\sqrt{2} \cos{(t - 45°)} - te^{-t} - e^{-t} - t \cos t]\mathbf{1}(t)$

5.20. (a) $\dfrac{s}{(s^2+4)\,(s^2+2s+2)^2}$ (b) $\dfrac{s + 2}{s(s+1)\,(s^2+1)^2}$

Answer to (a): $[0.05 \cos{(2t+126.9°)} + 0.1582 \, te^{-t} \cos{(t-18.45°)}$

$$+ 0.05 \, e^{-t} \cos{(t+53.1°)}]\mathbf{1}(t)$$

Multiple-Order Roots

Let $F(s)$ have a root of order n at $s = z$. If z is real, the partial fraction expansion of $F(s)$ will contain the terms

$$\frac{a_1}{(s-z)^n} + \frac{a_2}{(s-z)^{n-1}} + \cdots + \frac{a_{n-1}}{(s-z)^2} + \frac{a_n}{s-z}$$

In a manner entirely similar to that used for single- and double-order roots, we formulate

$$(s-z)^n F(s)$$

and differentiate it $n - 1$ times. In each of the n expressions thus obtained we set $s = z$, and

$$a_k = \frac{1}{(k-1)!} \frac{d^{k-1}}{ds^{k-1}} (s-z)^n F(s) \Big|_{s=z}$$

where the zeroth derivative is the function itself and $0! = 1$. Note especially the $(k-1)!$ in the denominator of the expression.

The inverse transform is then obtained using the key pair

$$\mathscr{L}^{-1}\left[\frac{a_k}{(s-z)^{n-k+1}}\right] = \frac{a_k t^{n-k}}{(n-k)!} \, e^{zt} \, \mathbf{1}(t)$$

which is key pair (1) of Table 3.2, with $z = -\alpha$. Note that *two* factorials enter the picture when n is three or greater—one when the a_k is obtained and one in the inverse transform.

EXAMPLE 5.9. Find the inverse transform of

$$F(s) = \frac{s-2}{s(s+1)(s+2)^5}$$

$$= \frac{a}{s} + \frac{b}{s+1} + \frac{c_1}{(s+2)^5} + \frac{c_2}{(s+2)^4}$$

$$+ \frac{c_3}{(s+3)^3} + \frac{c_4}{(s+2)^2} + \frac{c_5}{s+2}$$

Observe that the initial value of $f(t)$ is zero.

Solution: By the usual procedure $a = -\frac{1}{16}$ and $b = 3$. Note at this point that the initial value theorem tells us that $c_5 = -\frac{47}{16}$. Why?

$$(s+2)^5 F(s) = \frac{s-2}{s(s+1)}$$

At $s = -2$, $c_1 = -2$.
First derivative:

$$\frac{d}{ds}(s+2)^5 F(s) = \frac{d}{ds}\frac{s-2}{s(s+1)} = \frac{s(s+1) - (s-2)(2s+1)}{s^2(s+1)^2}$$

$$= \frac{-s^2+4s+2}{s^2(s+1)^2}$$

So $c_2 = -\frac{5}{2}$.

Second derivative

$$\frac{d}{ds}\frac{-s^2+4s+2}{s^2(s+1)^2} = \frac{2(s^3-6s^2-6s-2)}{s^3(s+1)^3}$$

which has a value of $-1\frac{1}{2}$ at $s = -2$. But this is not c_3 but $2!c_3$. Hence $c_3 = -1\frac{1}{4}$.

Third derivative:

$$\frac{d}{ds}\frac{2(s^3-6s^2-6s-2)}{s^3(s+1)^3} = \frac{-6(s^4-8s^3-12s^2-8s-2)}{s^4(s+1)^4}$$

which has a value of $-6\frac{9}{4}$ at $s = -2$. This is $3!c_4$, so $c_4 = -2\frac{3}{8}$.

Fourth derivative:

$$\frac{d}{ds}\frac{-6(s^4-8s^3-12s^2-8s-2)}{s^4(s+1)^4} = \frac{24(s^5-10s^4-20s^3-20s^2-10s-2)}{s^5(s+1)^5}$$

which has a value of $-141\frac{1}{2}$ at $s = -2$. Since this is $4!c_5$, $c_5 = -4\frac{7}{16}$. (*Check.*)

Thus

$$F(s) = \frac{-1/16}{s} + \frac{3}{s+1} - \frac{2}{(s+2)^5} - \frac{5/2}{(s+2)^4} - \frac{11/4}{(s+2)^3} - \frac{23/8}{(s+2)^2} - \frac{47/16}{s+2}$$

and

$$f(t) = \left[-\frac{1}{16} + 3e^{-t} - 2\frac{t^4}{4!}e^{-2t} - \frac{5}{2}\frac{t^3}{3!}e^{-2t} - \frac{11}{4}\frac{t^2}{2!}e^{-2t} - \frac{23}{8}te^{-2t} - \frac{47}{16}e^{-2t} \right]\mathbf{1}(t)$$

$$= \left[-\frac{1}{16} + 3e^{-t} - \frac{1}{12}t^4e^{-2t} - \frac{5}{12}t^3e^{-2t} - \frac{11}{8}t^2e^{-2t} - \frac{23}{8}te^{-2t} - \frac{47}{16}e^{-2t} \right]\mathbf{1}(t)$$

EXAMPLE 5.10. Find the inverse transform of

$$F(s) = \frac{s}{(s^2+2s+2)^3}$$

Solution:

$$F(s) = \frac{A_1}{(s+1-j)^3} + \frac{A_2}{(s+1-j)^2} + \frac{A_3}{s+1-j} + \text{conjugates}$$

$$(s+1-j)^3 F(s) = \frac{s}{(s+1+j)^3}$$

This has a value of $\sqrt{2}/8 \,\underline{/-135°}$ when $s = -1+j$, so this is A_1. The first derivative of the last expression is

$$\frac{-2s+1+j}{(s+1+j)^4}$$

At $s = -1 + j$ this has a value of $\sqrt{2}/16\ \underline{/-45°}$, and this is A_2.
The second derivative is

$$\frac{6(s-1-j)}{(s+1+j)^5}$$

and this has a value of $\frac{3}{8}\ \underline{/90°}$ at $s = -1 + j$. This, however, is not A_3, but twice A_3—that is, $A_3 = \frac{3}{16}\ \underline{/90°}$.
Then

$$f(t) = \left[\frac{\sqrt{2}}{4}\frac{t^2}{2!}e^{-t}\cos(t-135°) + \frac{\sqrt{2}}{8}te^{-t}\cos(t-45°)\right.$$

$$\left. + \frac{3}{8}e^{-t}\cos(t+90°)\right]\mathbf{1}(t)$$

and this checks with the initial-value theorem.

The method for evaluating the constants in the partial fraction expansion was stated without proof. A proof of the method is now given.

LEMMA 5.1. Let $G(s)$ be a function of s such that $G(s)$ and its first n derivatives are finite at $s = -a$. Then $G(s)(s+a)^n$ and its first $n - 1$ derivatives vanish at $s = -a$.

Proof: Obviously $G(s)(s+a)^n$ vanishes at $s = -a$. The derivative of this function is

$$G'(s)(s+a)^n + n(s+a)^{n-1}G(s)$$

where $G'(s) = dG(s)/ds$. This expression also vanishes at $s = -a$.
The second derivative

$$G''(s)(s+a)^n + 2G'(s)n(s+a)^{n-1} + G(s)n(n-1)(s+a)^{n-2}$$

is also seen to vanish at $s = -a$ (for n greater than 2). In fact, it is clear that for a derivative not to vanish we must keep differentiating until the last term on the right has no factor $(s+a)$. After $n - 1$ differentiations, the last term—the one with the factor $(s+a)$ to the lowest power—will be

$$n!(s+a)G(s)$$

and it can be seen that one more differentiation will yield a term $n!G(s)$ which in general will not vanish at $s = -a$. Thus the values of the function and its first $n - 1$ derivatives are zero, and the nth derivative has the value $n!G(-a)$.

THEOREM 5.1. Let $F(s)$ have a factor $(s+a)^n$ in its denominator. Then

$$F(s) = G(s) + \frac{a_1}{(s+a)^n} + \frac{a_2}{(s+a)^{n-1}} + \cdots + \frac{a_n}{s+a}$$

where $G(s)$ is the sum of all the other terms in the partial fraction expansion of $F(s)$. Then a_k is given by

$$a_k = \frac{1}{(k-1)!} \frac{d^{k-1}}{ds^{k-1}} (s+a)^n F(s)$$

Proof:

$$(s+a)^n F(s) = (s+a)^n G(s) + a_1 + a_2(s+a) + a_3(s+a)^2$$
$$+ a_4(s+a)^3 + \cdots + a_j(s+a)^{j-1}$$
$$+ \cdots + a_n(s+a)^{n-1}$$
$$= \sum_{j=1}^{n} a_j(s+a)^{j-1} + (s+a)^n G(s)$$

The first $n - 1$ derivatives of $G(s)(s+a)^n$ vanish (by Lemma 5.1) so for $k < n$

$$\frac{d^{k-1}}{ds^{k-1}} (s+a)^n F(s) \bigg|_{s=-a} = \sum_{j=1}^{n} a_j(j-1)(j-2) \cdots (j-k+1)(s+a)^{j-k} \bigg|_{s=-a}$$
$$= a_k (k-1)!$$

since only when $j = k$ will the factor $(s+a)^{j-k}$ be different from zero for $j \geq k$, and since the coefficient $(j-1)(j-2)$ and so on will vanish for $j < k$.

There is nothing in the proof which restricts a or the constants a_k to being real; hence the proof holds for complex numbers.

PROBLEMS

Find the inverse transforms of the following functions and check your results using the initial-value theorem.

5.21. (a) $\dfrac{s+1}{s(s+2)^3}$ (b) $\dfrac{s+1}{s^3(s^2+2s+2)}$

Answers: (a) $\dfrac{1}{8} [1 + 2t^2e^{-2t} - 2te^{-2t} - e^{-t}]\mathbf{1}(t)$

(b) $\dfrac{1}{4} [t^2 - 1 + \sqrt{2}\, e^{-t} \cos (t-45°)]\mathbf{1}(t)$

5.22. (a) $\dfrac{s}{(s+3)^5}$ (b) $\dfrac{s}{(s^2+4s+8)^3}$

$\qquad$ *Answers:* (a) $\dfrac{t^3 e^{-3t}}{6} \left[1 - \dfrac{3}{4} t \right] \mathbf{1}(t)$

$\qquad$ (b) $\dfrac{1}{128} [4\sqrt{2}\, t^2 e^{-2t} \cos\ (2t-135°)$

$\qquad\qquad + 2\sqrt{10}\, te^{-2t} \cos\ (2t-18.44°) - 3e^{-2t} \sin\ 2t] \mathbf{1}(t)$

5.23. (a) $\dfrac{5s+3}{s(s+1)^5}$ (b) $\dfrac{s+1}{(s^2+1)^4}$

$\qquad$ *Answer to* (a): $\left[3 + \dfrac{t^4}{12} e^{-t} - \dfrac{t^3}{2} e^{-t} - \dfrac{3t^2}{2} e^{-t} - 3te^{-t} - 3e^{-t} \right] \mathbf{1}(t)$

5.24. (a) $\dfrac{1}{s(s+10)^3}$ (b) $\dfrac{1}{s(s^2+4)^3}$

$\qquad$ *Answer to* (b): $\dfrac{1}{64} \left[1 + \dfrac{t^2}{2} \cos 2t - \dfrac{5t}{2} \sin 2t - \cos 2t \right] \mathbf{1}(t)$

5.25. (a) $\dfrac{s^2+2}{s^2(s+1)^3}$ (b) $\dfrac{-4}{(s^2+1)^3}$

$\qquad$ *Answer to* (b): $\dfrac{1}{2} [t^2 \sin t + 3t \cos t - 3 \sin t] \mathbf{1}(t)$

5.2. Inverse Transformation of Functions Containing e⁻ᵃˢ

As a consequence of the real translation theorem, many signals used in engineering have transforms that contain e^{-as} in both numerators and denominators of fractions. There are three approaches to finding the inverse transforms of such functions, and they lead to three different ways in which the inverse transform can be expressed. In the three subsections to follow, each technique will be discussed separately.

The Real Translation Theorem in Reverse

Probably the most obvious method of finding the inverse transform of functions containing e^{-as} is to separate the transform into a product of a rational fraction and a series in e^{-as} and to use the fact that $F(s)e^{-as}$ has an inverse transform that is $f(t)$, the inverse transform of $F(s)$ shifted to the right a units, that is, $f(t-a)$.

EXAMPLE 5.11. Find the inverse transform of

$$F(s) = \frac{(1-e^{-2s})(1+e^{-3s})}{s}$$

Solution: (*a*) The rational fraction in this example is $1/s$, which is known to be the transform of the step function. If the numerator factor is multiplied out

$$F(s) = \frac{1}{s}(1 - e^{-2s} + e^{-3s} - e^{-5s})$$

and this must be the transform of a step function at $t = 0$, followed by a negative step at $t = 2$, a positive step at $t = 3$, and finally a negative step at $t = 5$. Two rectangular pulses result; they are shown in Fig. 5.1.

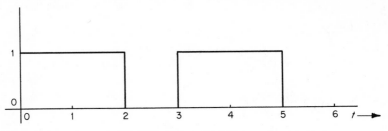

Fig. 5.1 *Example 5.11.*

(*b*) The inverse transform could have been obtained by taking $\frac{1}{s}(1 - e^{-2s})$ and inverse transforming this to obtain a step at $t = 0$ followed by a negative step at $t = 2$. This would give the first pulse only. The factor $(1 + e^{-3s})$ then states that the inverse transform of the whole function is the first pulse just obtained plus this first pulse shifted to the right three units. Evidently this leads to the same result.

EXAMPLE 5.12. Find the inverse transform of

$$F(s) = \frac{1 - e^{-s}}{s(s+1)(1+e^{-s})}$$

Solution: It was shown in Probs. 3.29 and 3.30 that factors in the denominator of $(1 - e^{-as})$ and $(1 + e^{-as})$ cause the inverse transform to be periodic; the former expression makes the inverse transform of the function it multiplies repeat every a sec, and the latter causes it to invert alternately as it is repeated. This factor will be ignored for the moment then, and the inverse transform of

$$P(s) = \frac{1 - e^{-s}}{s(s+1)}$$

will be sought.

With the factor $(1-e^{-s})$ also ignored, we have

$$\frac{1}{s(s+1)} = \frac{1}{s} - \frac{1}{s+1}$$

is seen to be the transform of $(1-e^{-t})\mathbf{1}(t)$. This function is plotted in Fig. 5.2(*a*). The factor $(1-e^{-s})$ in the numerator evidently requires this function again, shifted to the right and with opposite sign. The inverse transforms of both $1/[s(s+1)]$ and $-e^{-s}/[s(s+1)]$ are shown in Fig. 5.2(*b*), and Fig. 5.2(*c*) shows the sum of the two, that is, the inverse transform of $P(s)$.

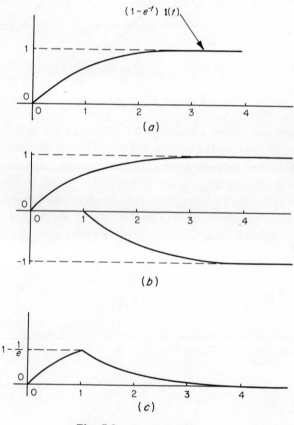

Fig. 5.2 *Example 5.12.*

Notice that $p(t)$, the function in Fig. 5.2(*c*), does not end at $t = 1$; in fact it does not end for any finite time. Figure 5.3(*a*) shows this function repeated every second, with every other term inverted. Figure 5.3(*b*) shows the sum of all these, and hence the inverse transform of $F(s)$.

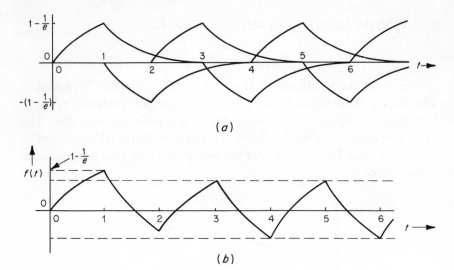

Fig. 5.3 *Example 5.12.*

Though the above solution is adequate for the understanding of the *nature* of the inverse transform, it is not easy to calculate values of the signal after a few periods have elapsed. A more efficient method for finding the inverse transform of this function is given in Example 5.13. Nevertheless, this technique proves valuable in many practical situations where only the waveform of the signal is desired and where it will not be necessary at some future time to calculate accurately the amplitude of the signal.

PROBLEMS

Find the inverse transforms of the following functions. Give your answers as careful sketches, sufficiently long that the behavior of the function can be seen.

5.26. (a) $\dfrac{1 - e^{-s/2}}{s(s+2)}$ (b) $\dfrac{1 - e^{-s/2} + e^{-s}}{s+2}$

5.27. (a) $\dfrac{\beta}{s^2 + \beta^2}(1 + e^{-2\pi s/\beta})$ (b) $\dfrac{\beta}{s^2 + \beta^2}(1 + e^{-\pi s/\beta})$

(c) $\dfrac{\beta}{s^2 + \beta^2}(1 - e^{-\pi s/\beta})$

5.28. (a) $\dfrac{1}{s(1-e^{-s})}$ (b) $\dfrac{1}{s(1+e^{-s})}$ (c) $\dfrac{1}{(s+1)(1-e^{-s})}$

5.29. (a) $\dfrac{2}{s^2}(1-e^{-s}) - \dfrac{2}{s}e^{-2s}$ (b) $\dfrac{1+e^{-\pi s}}{(s^2+1)(1-e^{-2\pi s})}$

5.30. (a) $\dfrac{1+e^{-s}}{s(1+e^{-3s})}$ (b) $\dfrac{1-se^{-s}}{s(s+2)}$

The Transient and Steady State

Those values of s for which the denominator of a transform goes to zero and the numerator is not zero are called the *poles* of the transform. The origin of the name can be demonstrated from a plot of the magnitude M of the transform $1/s$

$$M = \left| \frac{1}{s} \right| = \left| \frac{1}{\sigma+j\omega} \right| = \frac{1}{\sqrt{\sigma^2+\omega^2}}$$

versus σ and ω in three dimensions. Such a plot appears in Fig. 5.4.

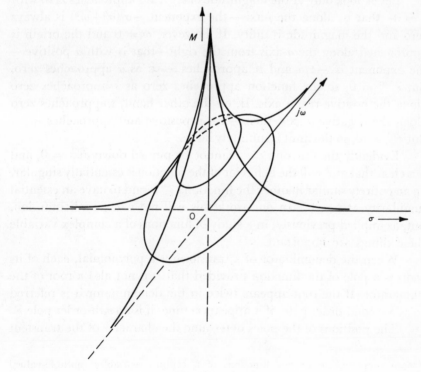

Fig. 5.4 *A pole.*

M is seen to be a surface that goes to infinity at $\sigma = 0$ and $\omega = 0$ and that looks something like a tent with a pole in the center.

In the theory of functions of a complex variable, the definition of a pole requires that the magnitude of the function become large as the pole is approached from any direction.

In the language of function theory, the pole is known as a *singularity*. Functions of a complex variable* may have one other type of singularity, called an *essential* singularity. It is not necessary to discuss this type in detail, since it is only encountered at infinity in our work, but it is well to give an example.

The function $e^{-1/s}$ has an essential singularity at $s = 0$. If $1/s$ is written in rectangular form in terms of σ and ω

$$\frac{1}{s} = \frac{1}{\sigma + j\omega} = \frac{\sigma}{\sigma^2 + \omega^2} - j\,\frac{\omega}{\sigma^2 + \omega^2}$$

then

$$e^{-1/s} = e^{-\sigma/(\sigma^2 + \omega^2)}\big/\!-\omega/(\sigma^2 + \omega^2)$$

Let us look only at the magnitude of $e^{-1/s}$. If s approaches zero with $\sigma = 0$—that is, along the j-axis—the exponent $-\sigma/(\sigma^2 + \omega^2)$ is always zero and the magnitude is unity. If, however, $\omega = 0$ and the origin is approached along the σ-axis from the right—that is with σ positive—the exponent is $-1/\sigma$ and it approaches $-\infty$ as σ approaches zero. But $e^{-\infty} = 0$, so the function approaches zero as s approaches zero along the positive real σ axis. If, on the other hand, s approaches zero along the negative σ axis, then $-1/\sigma$ is positive and approaches $+\infty$. But $e^{\infty} = \infty$, so the limit is infinitely large.

Evidently the function $e^{-1/s}$ cannot be pinned down at $s = 0$, and it is clear that at $s = 0$ the behavior of the function is essentially singular. In an entirely similar manner the function e^{-as} is said to have an essential singularity at $s = \infty$. In our work this will not cause any confusion, but, as implied previously, in a study of functions of a complex variable these things are important.

When the denominator of a transform is a polynomial, each of its roots is a pole of the function provided that it is not also a root of the numerator. If the root appears twice in the denominator it is referred to as a second-order pole; if it appears m times it is an mth-order pole.

The positions of the poles determine the character of the transient

---

*More properly, *single-valued* functions of a complex variable; multiple-valued functions also have singularities, which are called *branch points*. (See Prob. 8.35).

and steady-state responses. If a pole is on the negative real axis and of order n, the inverse transform will contain the terms

$$\frac{t^{k-1}}{(k-1)!} \, e^{-bt} \, \mathbf{1}(t) \qquad \text{with } k = 1,2,\ldots n$$

and each of these expressions will go to zero as t becomes infinite (see Probs. 2.68 and 2.69). Thus any pole on the negative real axis leads to a *transient* term in the inverse transform; that is, the expression will disappear in time.

All poles in the left-half s-plane that are not on the negative σ-axis must occur in conjugate pairs. For each pair of order n, the inverse transform will contain the terms

$$\frac{t^{k-1}}{(k-1)!} \, e^{-\alpha t} \cos{(\beta t + \theta)} \, \mathbf{1}(t) \qquad \text{with } k = 1,2,\ldots n$$

Each of these terms also goes to zero as t becomes infinite, since the magnitude is bounded by the expression obtained when the cosine function is absent, the cosine oscillating between $+1$ and -1. The magnitude is similar to that of a pole on the negative real axis with the same abscissa $\sigma = -\alpha$. Hence *all* poles in the left-hand s-plane lead to *transient* terms—terms that will ultimately go to zero as t becomes infinite.

The *time constant* associated with these transient terms is the reciprocal of the real part of the pole position, and since the transient dies out in about five time constants, then the nearer the pole is to the j-axis the longer the transient will last.

In the case of the complex root, the imaginary part is the radian frequency with which the transients oscillate as they die out.

If the poles are on the j-axis, the inverse transform corresponding to these poles is called the steady state *if* these poles are of first order. First-order j-axis poles lead to terms of the type $\cos{(\beta t + \theta)}$, which is a constant-amplitude sinusoid. A first-order pole at the origin leads to a constant (or d-c) term. If the poles on the j axis are of second order or higher, the inverse transform includes terms such as $t^n \cos{\beta t} \mathbf{1}(t)$ or $t^n \mathbf{1}(t)$, which go to infinity as t becomes infinite. Although these are acceptable mathematical functions, they do not depict actual physical time signals, for nothing in the natural world goes to infinity.

Similarly, if poles occur in the right-half s plane, the inverse transforms are constants or sinusoids that are multiplied by e^{at}, where a is positive. These terms go to infinity even faster than the multiple-order poles on the j axis. If these functions represented actual physical signals an explosion would result.

The following ideas should be memorized.

1. Poles in the left-half plane, real part $-\alpha$, imaginary part β: these are transient terms with time constant $1/\alpha$ and frequency $f = \beta /2\pi$ cps.

2. First-order poles on the j axis, imaginary part β: these are the steady-state terms, each pair giving a sinusoid with frequency $\beta /2\pi$ cps. $f = 0$ is interpreted as d-c.

3. Poles of second order or higher on the j axis, or poles in the right-half plane: the response will grow with time. See Fig. 5.5.

Fig. 5.5   *"But sir, according to my calculations the poles were in the* left *half plane!"*

When a function of a complex variable, such as the Laplace transform of a function of time, has poles only in the finite s-plane, the function is called *meromorphic*, whether or not it has an essential singularity at infinity. Usually the term meromorphic is applied only to those functions that do have an essential singularity at infinity, and this includes the transforms that have e^{-as} in them. Thus the transforms of this section will be distinguished from rational fractions by referring to them as meromorphic functions.

When a meromorphic function is inverse transformed by means of the real translation theorem in reverse, it often happens that the transient and steady-state terms are mixed together as in Example 5.12. It is possible to separate the transient from the steady state in such problems.

EXAMPLE 5.13. Separate the transforms of the transient and the steady state for

$$F(s) = \frac{1 - e^{-s}}{s(s+1)(1+e^{-s})}$$

and inverse transform each term separately.

Solution: The poles of the function are those values of s for which the denominator vanishes, providing that the numerator does not go to zero at the respective points. Apparently there are poles at $s = 0, -1$, and $jk\pi$, where k is a positive or negative odd integer, since $e^{jk\pi} = (\cos k\pi + j \sin k\pi) = -1$ whenever k is an odd integer. (See Prob. 2.73).

All the poles are on the j-axis except the one at $s = -1$, so the transient is determined as before from

$$\lim_{s \to -1} (s+1)F(s) = \frac{1-e^{-s}}{s(1+e^{-s})}\bigg|_{s=-1}$$

$$= \frac{e-1}{e+1} \doteq 0.462$$

If for the moment we set $c = (e-1)/(e+1) \doteq 0.462$, the transform of the transient must be

$$F_{tr}(s) = \frac{c}{s+1}$$

which has an inverse transform of $ce^{-t}\mathbf{1}(t) \doteq 0.462\, e^{-t}\mathbf{1}(t)$.

To find the transform of the steady state, simply subtract the transform of the transient from the original transform.

$$F_{ss}(s) = \frac{1-e^{-s}}{s(s+1)(1+e^{-s})} - \frac{c}{(s+1)}$$

Combining these into one fraction, we have

$$F_{ss}(s) = \frac{(1-cs) - e^{-s}(1+cs)}{s(s+1)(1+e^{-s})}$$

The factor $(1+e^{-s})$ is a repetition factor, so drop it temporarily and inverse transform

$$\frac{1-cs}{s(s+1)} - \frac{1+cs}{s(s+1)} e^{-s} = \left[\frac{1}{s} - \frac{1+c}{s+1}\right] - \left[\frac{1}{s} - \frac{1-c}{s+1}\right] e^{-s}$$

Since $1 + c = 1 + (e-1)/(e+1) = 2e/(e+1)$, and $1 - c = 2/(e+1)$, the inverse transform of the first term on the right of the last equation is

$$\left[1 - \frac{2e}{e+1}\, e^{-t}\right] \mathbf{1}(t)$$

and the inverse transform of the last term on the right is

$$-\left[1 - \frac{2}{e+1}\, e^{-t}\right] \mathbf{1}(t)$$

but shifted to the *right* one unit. These are shown in Fig. 5.6(a) and their sum in Fig. 5.6(b). Notice that the inverse transform of the first function has a value of $-c$ at $t = 0$, and at $t = 1$ it has the value $+c$.

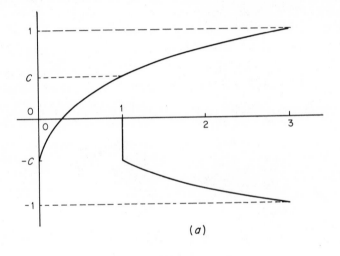

(a)

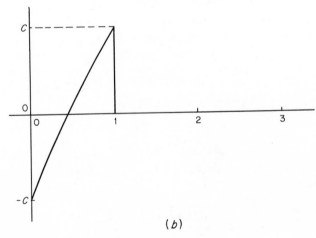

(b)

Fig. 5.6   *Example 5.13.*

The second function has a value of $-c$ at $t = 0$ (really at $t = 1$, since it has to be shifted to the right one unit), and beyond that point the second function when translated one unit seems to cancel out the first function beyond $t = 1$. This is the case, for with $t > 1$ the complete inverse transform is

$$1 - \frac{2e}{e+1} e^{-t} - 1 + \frac{2}{e+1} e^{-(t-1)} = 0$$

Since the inverse transform is zero for $t > 1$, and according to Prob. 3.4, the transform must exist for *all* values of s—that is, it must have *no* poles in the finite s-plane, the transform

$$\frac{(1 - cs) - (1 + cs) e^{-s}}{s(s+1)}$$

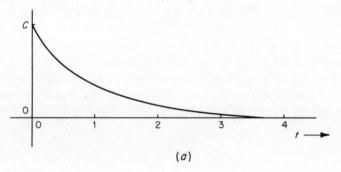

(a)

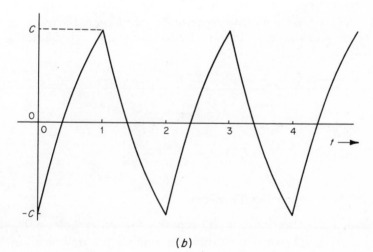

(b)

Fig. 5.7 *The transient and the steady state.*

must not have poles at $s = 0$ or -1. It does not have a pole at -1, since the transient was removed, but this can be checked by

$$\lim_{s \to -1} (s+1) \frac{(1-cs) - (1+cs)e^{-s}}{s(s+1)}$$

$$= \frac{(1+c) - (1-c)e}{-1} = 0$$

since $c = (e-1)/(e+1)$.

It is not clear that the function does not have a pole at $s = 0$, but

$$\lim_{s \to 0} s \frac{(1-cs) - (1+cs)e^{-s}}{s(s+1)} = \frac{1-e^0}{1} = 0$$

shows that the numerator also goes to zero at $s = 0$, so there is really no pole at all at $s = 0$. This indicates that the original $F(s)$ has no pole at $s = 0$ either, so the inverse transform can have no d-c term in it. Thus the original guess as to a pole at $s = 0$ was incorrect, since the factor $(1-e^{-s})$ vanishes at $s = 0$.

The factor $(1+e^{-s})$ in the denominator merely means that the pulse of Fig. 5.6(b) is repeated every second, and it is alternately right side up and upside down. Figure 5.7(a) depicts the transient and Fig. 5.7(b) the steady state. The sum of the two is the result shown previously in Fig. 5.3(b).

PROBLEMS

In each of the problems below separate the transform of the transient from that of the steady state, and inverse transform each. Sketch the steady state carefully.

5.31. $\dfrac{1}{(s+1)(1-e^{-s})}$

5.33. $\dfrac{1 - e^{-s}}{(s+1)(1+e^{-s})}$

5.32. $\dfrac{1}{(s+2)(1+e^{-s})}$

5.34. $\dfrac{(1-e^{-s})^2}{(s+1)(1-e^{-2s})}$

5.35. $\dfrac{s}{(s+2)(1-e^{-s})}$

The Laplace Expansion Theorem

When the transform of $f(t)$ contains first-order poles only, there exists a straightforward procedure for finding the inverse transform. The only real objection to the use of this procedure, called the *Laplace expansion theorem*, is that the answer obtained is entirely in the form of exponentials and as such is nearly useless except for the case of poles on the negative real axis. It is nevertheless interesting, and can have the desirable effect of helping to make transforms and the *s*-plane vital.

THEOREM 5.2. Let $F(s)$ be the transform of $f(t)$, and let the only singularities of $F(s)$—in the finite *s*-plane—be first-order poles. Furthermore, let $F(s)$ be expressed as a fraction, the numerator and denominator of which may be polynomials, functions of e^{-s}, or a mixture of both. Let the numerator of the fraction be $N(s)$ and the denominator be $D(s)$. Let the poles of $F(s)$ be at $s_1, s_2, \ldots s_k, \ldots$. The possibility of an infinite number of poles will not be ruled out. Note that the poles of $F(s)$ are zeros of $D(s)$, but that all zeros of $D(s)$ are not necessarily poles. Clearly $D(s_k) = 0$ for all k.

Then if $D'(s)$ is $dD(s)/ds$

$$f(t) = p(t) + \sum_k \frac{N(s_k)\, e^{s_k t}}{D'(s_k)}\, \mathbf{1}(t)$$

where $p(t)$ is some function of t that vanishes for $t < 0$ *and* $t > T$, with T some finite positive number.

The Laplace transform of $p(t)$, $P(s)$, can have no poles in the finite *s*-plane (see Prob. 3.4). Furthermore since $F(s)$ has only first-order poles $D'(s_k) \neq 0$. It should also be clear that $f(t)$ must be zero for $t < 0$. If it is not, multiplication of the transform by e^{-as} with a sufficiently large will insure that the transform does indeed correspond to a function that is zero for $t < 0$.

Proof: The proof of this theorem when there are infinitely many poles requires the result of the *Mittag-Leffler theorem*[*], which states, in effect, that it is legitimate to expand a meromorphic function into a partial fraction expansion with infinitely many terms. This result will be assumed here, so it is correct to write

$$F(s) = P(s) + \sum_k \left[\frac{a_k}{(s - s_k)} - g_k(s) \right]$$

where the $g_k(s)$ are polynomials in s and are required in the general case to assure the convergence of the series. From a physical standpoint it should be clear that the $g_k(s) = 0$ for all k, since the inverse transform of a polynomial consists of impulses, doublets, and so on, which could have been included in $P(s)$. For realistic transforms, then, the last equation could have been written

---

[*]K. KNOPP. *Theory of Functions*, New York: Dover Press (1947), Part II, pp. 34–57.

$$F(s) = P(s) + \sum_k \frac{a_k}{s - s_k}$$

But the constants a_k can be determined as before by multiplying both sides by $(s - s_j)$ and taking the limit as $s \to s_j$.

$$\lim_{s \to s_j} \left[(s - s_j)P(s) + (s - s_j)\frac{N(s)}{D(s)} \right] = \lim_{s \to s_j} \sum_k \frac{a_k(s - s_j)}{(s - s_k)}$$

or

$$\lim_{s \to s_j} (s - s_j)\frac{N(s)}{D(s)} = a_j$$

But $(s - s_j)N(s)/D(s)$ is indeterminate at $s = s_j$, so, using L'Hôpital's rule

$$\lim_{s \to s_j} \frac{(s - s_j)N(s)}{D(s)} = \lim_{s \to s_j} \frac{(s - s_j)N'(s) + N(s)}{D'(s)}$$

$$= \frac{N(s_j)}{D'(s_j)} = a_j$$

or, writing k for j

$$a_k = \frac{N(s_k)}{D'(s_k)}$$

Then

$$F(s) = P(s) + \sum_k \frac{N(s_k)}{D'(s_k)} \cdot \frac{1}{(s - s_k)}$$

and inverse transforming term by term yields

$$f(t) = p(t) + \sum_k \frac{N(s_k)}{D'(s_k)} e^{s_k t} \mathbf{1}(t) \qquad \text{Q.E.D.}$$

Note that nothing is mentioned about $p(t)$ or $P(s)$. In general these are difficult functions to find. When $F(s)$ is a ratio of polynomials in s, $P(s)$ is easily found [see the first part of Sec. 5.1; $P(s)$ corresponds to $R(s)$]. When $F(s)$ is meromorphic—that is, when it has an infinite number of poles, $p(t)$ can very often be deduced by using the real translation theorem in reverse and comparing $f(t)$ thus obtained with the series

$$\sum_k \frac{N(s_k)}{D'(s_k)} e^{s_k t} \mathbf{1}(t)$$

General rules can be stated for determining from $F(s)$ itself whether $P(s) = 0$, but this is beyond the scope of this book.*

EXAMPLE 5.14. Use the Laplace expansion theorem to find the inverse transform of

$$F(s) = \frac{\beta(1+e^{-\pi s/\beta})}{(s^2+\beta^2)(1-e^{-\pi s/\beta})}$$

Solution: Poles apparently exist at $s = \pm j\beta$, and at $\pi s/\beta = j2k\pi$, with k a positive or negative integer, or zero, since $e^{j2k\pi} = 1$. Note that if we were to find the inverse transform of this function by using the real translation theorem in reverse, we would get Fig. 3.13 (Prob. 3.31) the rectified full-wave sinusoid with $\beta = \pi/T$. Actually it will turn out that the function does not have poles at $s = \pm j\beta$, but we need not worry about this, because it will all be taken care of by the algebra.

Evidently

$$N(s) = \beta(1+e^{-\pi s/\beta})$$

so $N(j\beta) = \beta(1+e^{-j\pi}) = 0$. Similarly $N(-j\beta) = 0$, and hence there are no poles at $\pm j\beta$, as asserted. For the poles at $s = j2k\beta$

$$N(j2k\beta) = \beta(1+e^{j2k\pi}) = 2\beta$$

for all k, positive, negative, and zero.

Since

$$D(s) = (s^2+\beta^2)(1-e^{-\pi s/\beta})$$

then

$$D'(s) = (s^2+\beta^2)(\pi/\beta)(e^{-\pi s/\beta}) + 2s(1-e^{-\pi s/\beta})$$

and

$$D'(j2k\beta) = (-4k^2\beta^2+\beta^2)(\pi/\beta)$$
$$= -\pi\beta(4k^2-1)$$

Then, from the theorem

$$f(t) = p(t) - \frac{2}{\pi}\sum_{-\infty}^{\infty}\frac{e^{j2k\beta t}}{(4k^2-1)}\mathbf{1}(t)$$

But what good is this answer? As it stands it is probably meaningless. It can be made meaningful by breaking the summation over both

---

*G. DOETSCH. *Einfuehrung in Theorie und Andwendung der Laplace-Transformation.* Basel und Stuttgart: Birkhaeuser Verlag (1958), pp. 165–173. *See also* E. G. PHILLIPS, *Functions of a Complex Variable with Applications.* Edinburgh and London: Oliver and Boyd (1949), pp. 131–133.

positive and negative k into a summation over positive integers only. If k is set equal to zero, the summation yields $2/\pi$. If k is set equal to $+1$ *and* -1

$$-\frac{2}{\pi}\left[\frac{e^{j2\beta t}}{3}+\frac{e^{-j2\beta t}}{3}\right]$$

But this is seen to be

$$-\frac{4}{3\pi}\frac{(e^{j2\beta t}+e^{-j2\beta t})}{2}=-\frac{4}{3\pi}\cos 2\beta t$$

(instantly? see Eq. 2.49(a) and the remarks that follow it).

If for each positive k the corresponding negative integer is used, the function $f(t)$ can be written as

$$f(t)=p(t)+\frac{2}{\pi}\mathbf{1}(t)\left[1-\frac{2}{3}\cos 2\beta t-\frac{2}{15}\cos 4\beta t-\cdots\right.$$

$$\left.-\frac{2}{(4k^2-1)}\cos 2k\beta t-\cdots\right]$$

$$=p(t)+\frac{2}{\pi}\mathbf{1}(t)\left[1-2\sum_{k=1}^{\infty}\frac{\cos 2k\beta t}{(4k^2-1)}\right]$$

But what does this tell us? That a rectified sine wave can be represented by a series of sinusoids and a constant term? Either this is acceptable, or the expansion theorem is incorrect.

The series of cosines that represent $f(t)$ is known as its Fourier series. The irregularly shaped curve, the full-wave rectified sinusoid with period π/β and hence (fundamental) frequency β/π cps, can evidently be expressed in terms of a constant or d-c term, its average value, and a sum of *pure* sinusoidal frequencies each related to the fundamental by having a frequency that is an integral multiple of the fundamental or base frequency.

From this point on, the word frequency will be reserved for the sinusoid. If a waveform is nonsinusoidal, but is periodic, it will be said to have a fundamental frequency and *harmonics*, the harmonic frequencies being integral multiples of the fundamental.

The technique described here for obtaining the Fourier series is not the simplest we can devise; better techniques are discussed in Chapter 7. The value of the result is that it shows that even for infinitely many j-axis poles, the inverse transform can be interpreted in terms of infinitely many sinusoids, and conversely, if a periodic function has infinitely many harmonics, as does the rectified sine wave of Example 5.14, its transform will have infinitely many poles on the j-axis.

Since the use of the real translation theorem in reverse told us that the function $f(t)$ was periodic, and since the Fourier series just obtained is indeed periodic, then one can deduce that $P(s) = p(t) = 0$.

EXAMPLE 5.15. Find the inverse transform of

$$F(s) = \frac{2 - e^{-2s}}{s(1 + e^{-s})}$$

and express it as an infinite series of exponentials.

Solution: The denominator vanishes at $s = 0$ and at $s = jk\pi$, with k odd (positive or negative). $N(s) = 1$ at each of these poles. Since $D'(s) = -se^{-s} + 1 + e^{-s}$, $D'(0) = 2$ and $D'(jk\pi) = jk\pi$ with k odd.

Then

$$f(t) = p(t) + 1(t)\left[\frac{1}{2} + \sum_{k \text{ odd}} \frac{e^{jk\pi t}}{jk\pi}\right]$$

$$= p(t) + 1(t)\left[\frac{1}{2} + \frac{2}{\pi}\sum_{k=1,3,5}^{\infty} \frac{e^{jk\pi t}}{2jk} + \frac{e^{-jk\pi t}}{-2jk}\right]$$

$$= p(t) + 1(t)\left[\frac{1}{2} + \frac{2}{\pi}\sum_{k=1,3,5}^{\infty} \frac{\sin(k\pi t)}{k}\right]$$

Again it is seen that the j-axis poles lead to a periodic function with average value ½. If $F(s)$ is inverse transformed by means of the real

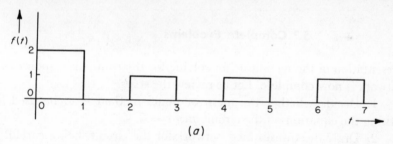

(a)

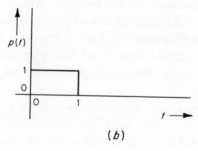

(b)

Fig. 5.8 *Example 5.15.*

translation theorem in reverse, we obtain the function pictured in Fig. 5.8(a). This is seen to be the sum of a periodic function and the rectangular pulse of Fig. 5.8(b). Then $p(t)$ must be this rectangular pulse and $P(s) = (1-e^{-s})/s$. The reader may verify for himself that the function $1/[s(1+e^{-s})]$ has the same partial fraction expansion as the $F(s)$ of this example, and if added to $P(s)$ it will yield $F(s)$.

PROBLEMS

Use the Laplace expansion theorem to find the inverse transforms of the following functions. For those cases where infinite series result, combine the positive and negative exponents and obtain the Fourier series. Use the real translation theorem in reverse to see what the function is whose series is thus obtained.

5.36.
$$\frac{s^2 - 4}{s^3 + 6s^2 + 11s + 6}$$

5.37.
$$\frac{1 - e^{-s}}{s(1+e^{-s})}$$

$$\text{Answer: } f(t) = \frac{4}{\pi} \mathbf{1}(t) \sum_{1,3,5}^{\infty} \frac{\sin (k\pi t)}{k}$$

5.3 Complete Problems

Presentation of the technique for solving for the transient response of a network is now complete. Let us review the steps.

1. Decide whether the mesh or nodal method is to be used for writing the equations of the circuit *after* $t = 0$.

2. Draw the transformed network for the circuit, being careful to use admittances for the nodal method, impedances for the mesh method.

3. Write the equations for the network, collect coefficients of like variables, and make the coefficients of the diagonal elements polynomials, with the coefficient of the highest-powered term in s as unity. The right-hand side should contain all source information and should be expressed as fractions, with the highest-powered term in s in each denominator as unity.

4. Solve the equations by Cramer's rule or an elimination procedure. Express the transforms of the desired variables as ratios of polynomials in s (or e^{-as} if required) and set the coefficient of the highest-powered term in s in the denominator(s) equal to unity.

5. Factor the denominator and make a partial fraction expansion of the transform or transforms.

6. Inverse transform the result.

EXAMPLE 5.16. In the circuit pictured in Fig. 5.9, the switch has been open for a long time and it is closed at $t = 0$. Find the voltage $v_0(t)$ across the capacitance for $t > 0$.

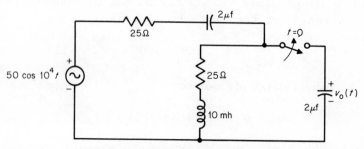

Fig. 5.9 *The circuit of Example 5.16.*

Solution: Observe that no initial conditions are given directly. There must be current in the coil at $t = 0-$, since it has been under the excitation of the sinusoidal source for a long time. For the same reason, the top 2-μf capacitance must have a voltage across it at $t = 0-$. The output capacitance may or may not have a voltage across it; nothing in the problem states or implies the condition of this capacitance at $t = 0-$. Since nothing is said about it, we shall assume it is uncharged at $t = 0-$.

The circuit *before* $t = 0$ is in the sinusoidal steady state, so ordinary complex circuit methods can be used to determine the initial conditions. Figure 5.10 shows the circuit at $\omega = 10^4$ rad/sec; note that the reference phasor is a cosine—that is, 50 cos $(10^4 t)$—and that it is abbreviated to $50\underline{/0^\circ}$. $j\omega L = j10^4 \times 10^{-2} = j100$, and $1/(j\omega C) = -j/(10^4 \times 2 \times 10^{-6}) = -j50$. Since the switch is open for negative t, the other capacitance is not even drawn in the circuit.

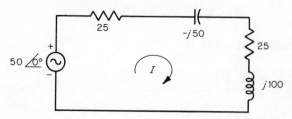

Fig. 5.10 *The steady-state circuit of Fig. 5.9 for $t < 0$.*

The total impedance is $50 + j50 = 50\sqrt{2}\underline{/45°}$, so the complex current I is $1/\sqrt{2}\ \underline{/-45°}$, and the expression for this current must be

$$i(t) = \frac{1}{\sqrt{2}}\cos(10^4t - 45°)$$

for $t < 0$. Then the current at $t = 0-$ is $1/\sqrt{2}\cos(-45°) = \frac{1}{2}$ amp, and this is ρ, the initial value of the current in the inductance. To get the initial voltage across the top capacitance, the complex voltage must be obtained first. The voltage, from left to right, is

$$V_c = \frac{1}{\sqrt{2}}\ \underline{/-45°}\ \times\ 50\ \underline{/-90°} = \frac{50}{\sqrt{2}}\ \underline{/-135°}$$

so its expression in terms of t must be

$$v_c(t) = \frac{50}{\sqrt{2}}\cos(10^4t - 135°)$$

At $t = 0-$ this has a value of -25 volts, so $\gamma = -25$ (because γ is defined as plus on the left; $+25$ would be used if γ were defined as plus on the right).

After the switch is closed there will be three nodes and two meshes, so the mesh method will be used. Figure 5.11 shows the transformed network for $t > 0$ set up for the mesh method.

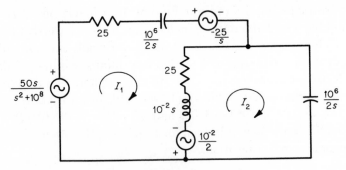

Fig. 5.11   *The transformed network.*

The mesh equations are

$$\left[10^{-2}s + 50 + \frac{10^6}{2s}\right]I_1 - (10^{-2}s + 25)I_2 = \frac{50s}{s^2+10^8} + \frac{25}{s} + \frac{10^{-2}}{2}$$

$$-(10^{-2}s + 25)I_1 + \left[10^{-2}s + 25 + \frac{10^6}{2s}\right]I_2 = -\frac{10^{-2}}{2}$$

Collecting terms and multiplying each equation by $100s$ gives

$$(s^2+5000s+50 \times 10^6)I_1 - s(s+2500)I_2$$
$$= \frac{0.5(s^3+15000s^2+10^8s+5 \times 10^{11})}{s^2+10^8}$$

$$-s(s+2500)I_1 + (s^2+2500s+50 \times 10^6)I_2 = -\frac{s}{2}$$

The coefficients are so large that a great saving can be effected at this point by making a change of scale. If s is replaced by $10^4 s_1$, $I_1(s)$ by $10^4 I_1(10^4 s_1) = 10^4 \tilde{I}_1(s_1)$, $I_2(s)$ by $10^4 \tilde{I}_2(s_1)$, and the equations divided by 10^4, they become

$$(s_1^2+0.5s_1+0.5)\tilde{I}_1 - s_1(s_1+0.25)\tilde{I}_2 = \frac{0.5(s_1^3+1.5s_1^2+s_1+0.5)}{s_1^2+1}$$

$$- s_1(s_1+0.25)I_1 + (s_1^2+0.25s_1+0.5)I_2 = - 0.5s_1$$

This change of scale amounts to decreasing the coefficients of all but the highest power of s in any given polynomial by 10^4, 10^8, 10^{12}, and so on, depending on whether the degree of s is 1, 2, 3, ... less than the largest in the given polynomial. If any term contained a polynomial

$$s^5 + 2 \times 10^4 s^4 + 2 \times 10^{12} s^2 + 10^{21}$$

for example, the result would be

$$s_1^5 + 2s_1^4 + 2s_1^2 + 10$$

after the change of scale. The rule we have followed here is easier to remember than

$$I_1(s) \text{ is replaced by } aI_1(as_1) = a\tilde{I}_1(s_1)$$

The new unit of time is now $100 \,\mu\text{sec}$ or 10^{-4} sec.

Since $V_0(s)$ is sought, we do not want either $I_1(s)$ or $I_2(s)$, but rather

$$V_0(s) = \frac{I_2(s)}{Cs} + \frac{\gamma}{s}$$

for the output capacitance. Since γ is zero for this capacitance, and $C = 2 \times 10^{-6}$, we really want

$$V_0(s) = \frac{10^6 I_2(s)}{2s}$$

Using the change of scale, we get

$$10^4 \tilde{V}_0(s_1) = 10^4 V_0(10^4 s_1) = \frac{10^4 \times 10^6 I_2(10^4 s_1)}{2 \times 10^4 \, s_1}$$

$$\tilde{V}_0 = \frac{10^6 \tilde{I}_2(s_1)}{2 \times 10^4 s_1} = \frac{50}{s_1} \tilde{I}_2$$

Thus it can be seen that if I_2 is obtained, V_0 can be obtained by simply multiplying by $50/s_1$. Using Cramer's rule

$$\tilde{I}_2(s_1) = \frac{\begin{vmatrix} (s_1^2 + 0.5 s_1 + 0.5) & \dfrac{0.5(s_1^3 + 1.5 s_1^2 + s_1 + 0.5)}{s_1^2 + 1} \\ -s_1(s_1 + 0.25) & -0.5 s_1 \end{vmatrix}}{\begin{vmatrix} (s_1^2 + 0.5 s_1 + 0.5) & -s_1(s_1 + 0.25) \\ -s_1(s_1 + 0.25) & (s_1^2 + 0.25 s_1 + 0.5) \end{vmatrix}}$$

$$= \frac{0.625 s_1 \, (s_1^3 - 0.1 s_1^2 + 0.2 s_1 - 0.3)}{0.25 \left(s_1^3 + \dfrac{17}{4} s_1^2 + \dfrac{3}{2} s_1 + 1\right)(s_1^2 + 1)}$$

so

$$\tilde{V}_2(s_1) = \frac{50}{s_1} \tilde{I}_2(s_1) = \frac{125(s_1^3 - 0.1 s_1^2 + 0.2 s_1 - 0.3)}{\left(s_1^3 + \dfrac{17}{4} s_1^2 + \dfrac{3}{2} s_1 + 1\right)(s_1^2 + 1)}$$

Expanding this in a partial-fraction expansion requires the roots of the denominator, which can be shown to be

$$s_1 = \pm j \qquad -3.933 \qquad -0.1585 \pm j 0.4776$$

Thus

$$\tilde{V}_2(s_1) = \frac{A}{s - j} + \frac{B}{s + 0.1585 - j 0.4776} + \frac{c}{s + 3.933} + \text{conjugates}$$

By the usual procedure

$$A = 50 \sqrt{\frac{17}{173}} \, \underline{/\tan^{-1} 4 - \tan^{-1} 6.5}$$

$$= 15.7 \, \underline{/-5.28°}$$

$$B = 8.96 \, \underline{/84.2°}$$

and

$$c = -33.2$$

making

$$v_0(t) = [31.4 \cos(10^4 t - 5.28°) + 17.92\, e^{-1585t} \cos(4776t + 84.2°)$$
$$- 33.2\, e^{39330t}]\, 1(t)$$

At $t = 0$ the solution gives -0.06 volt; it should be zero, so the answer is correct to three significant figures.

By this time we may well imagine the amount of work that is left out of the solution above and the enormous amount of algebra involved in a complete solution. The number of storage elements, even more than the number of equations, is responsible. When many storage elements are present, we must ask ourselves, "Is a complete solution essential?" If only the first, or steady-state, term is needed, then the problem is a very simple one. Figure 5.12 shows the steady-state equivalent circuit, and it can be treated as a voltage divider. The equivalent impedance of the $-j50$-ohm reactance in parallel with the $(25+j100)$-ohm impedance is easily shown to be $20 - j90$, so

$$V_0(j\omega) = \frac{20 - j90}{45 - j140} \times 50\, \underline{/0°}$$

$$= 31.4\, \underline{/-5.28°}$$

which leads to the expression $31.4 \cos(10^4 t - 5.28°)$ for the steady state.

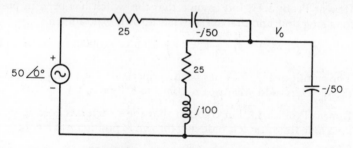

Fig. 5.12 *The steady-state circuit.*

If only the form of the transient were required, then only the roots of the determinant of the coefficients of the I terms would have to be found. The purely exponential decay has a time-constant of $\frac{1}{39,330}$ sec, so the transient due to this term will disappear in about $\frac{1}{10}$ millisec. The oscillatory transient will have a time-constant of $\frac{1}{1585}$ sec and will require almost 3 millisec to disappear.

It often happens that information such as the foregoing is sufficient for solving a problem, in which case we would not attempt to use a tool as powerful as the Laplace transform to obtain a complete solution. If the complete solution *is* required, there is at least a straightforward, though tedious, algebraic approach to the problem.

PROBLEMS

In the following problems, complete solutions are required. If the essential initial conditions are not given explicitly, it should be possible to calculate them by observing the circuit before the switching operation occurs.

5.41. The switch in Fig. 5.13 has been in position a for a long time. At $t = 0$ it is thrown to position b. Find $i(t)$ and $v_0(t)$ for $t > 0$.

$$Answer: \quad i(t) = 0.0192 \, e^{-1000t} 1(t)$$
$$v_0(t) = -19.2 \, e^{-1000t} \, 1(t)$$

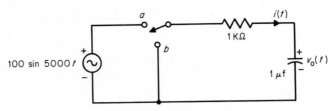

Fig. 5.13   *Problems 5.41 and 5.42.*

5.42. Repeat Prob. 5.41, but assume that the switch has been in position b for a long time and that at $t = 0$ it is thrown to position a.

$$Answer: \quad v_0(t) = \left[\frac{250}{13} e^{-1000t} + 19.6 \cos (5000t - 168.7°) \right] 1(t)$$

5.43. The circuit of Fig. 5.14 has been in operation for a long time. At $t = 0$ the switch is suddenly thrown from a to b. Find $v_0(t)$ for $t > 0$.

5.44. Repeat Prob. 5.43, but consider that the switch has been in position b for a long time and it is suddenly thrown to position a at $t = 0$.

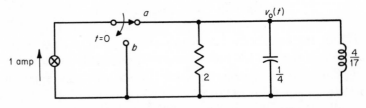

Fig. 5.14   *Problems 5.43 and 5.44.*

5.45. In the circuit shown in Fig. 5.15, the switch has been open a long time and it is closed at $t = 0$. Find $v_c(t)$ for $t > 0$.

Answer: $v_c(t) = \dfrac{10}{3}\,[1 + \sqrt{3}\,e^{-t}\cos(\sqrt{2}\,t - 125.3°)]\,\mathbf{1}(t)$

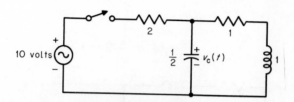

Fig. 5.15 *Problem 5.45.*

5.46. In the circuit of Fig. 5.16, the switch is closed at $t = 0$. The capacitance is initially charged to 10 volts. Find $v_c(t)$ for $t > 0$.

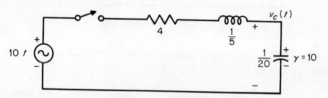

Fig. 5.16 *Problem 5.46.*

5.47. In the circuit in Fig. 5.17, find $i(t)$.

Answer: $(\sqrt{2}/2)\,e^{-600t}\cos(800t - 45°)\,\mathbf{1}(t)$

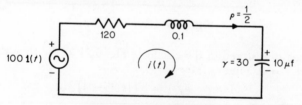

Fig. 5.17 *Problem 5.47.*

5.48. Find $v_0(t)$ in the circuit of Fig. 5.18 if there is no energy stored in the circuit at $t = 0-$. $\delta(t)$ is the unit impulse.

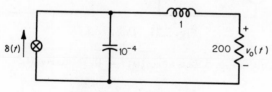

Fig. 5.18 *Problem 5.48.*

5.49. In the circuit of Fig. 5.19, assume that the switch has been open for a long time and that it is suddenly closed at $t = 0$. Find $i(t)$ and $v_0(t)$.

$$\text{Answer: } i(t) = \frac{2}{5}[6 - e^{-2.4t}] \, \mathbf{1}(t)$$

$$v_0(t) = -2 e^{-t} \, \mathbf{1}(t)$$

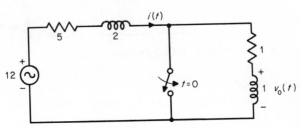

Fig. 5.19 *Problem 5.49*

5.50. In Fig. 5.20, no energy is stored in the circuit at $t = 0$. The switch is closed at $t = 0$. Find $v_c(t)$ for $t > 0$.

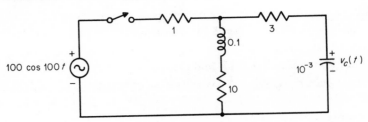

Fig. 5.20 *Problem 5.50.*

5.51. No energy is stored in the circuit of Fig. 5.21 at the time the switch is closed, $t = 0$. Find $v_0(t)$ for $t > 0$.

$$\text{Answer: } v_0(t) = 50 \, [e^{-2t} - 1] \, \mathbf{1}(t)$$

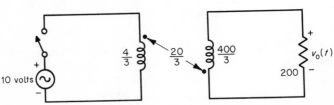

Fig. 5.21 *Problem 5.51.*

5.52. The circuit of Fig. 5.22 is at rest at $t = 0$. What is $v_0(t)$?

$$\text{Answer: } v_0(t) = 5\left[1 - e^{-2 \times 10^4 t} - \frac{2}{\sqrt{3}} e^{-10^4 t} \sin{(\sqrt{3} \times 10^4 t)}\right]\mathbf{1}(t)$$

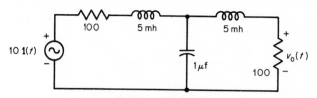

Fig. 5.22 *Problem 5.52.*

5.4 The s Plane

In Chapter 4 it was shown that the frequency response of a network could be obtained from the Laplace transform by setting $s = j\omega$. Another demonstration of this is possible using a partial fraction expansion involving the transfer function $H(s)$. If $s_0(t)$ is the output signal (a current or a voltage) and $s_{in}(t)$ is the input signal, with $S_0(s)$ and $S_{in}(s)$ their respective transforms, then

$$\frac{S_{in}(s)}{S_0(s)} = H(s)$$

or

$$S_0(s) = S_{in}(s)H(s)$$

Now suppose the input signal is a sinusoid of frequency ω, that is

$$s_{in}(t) = A \cos(\omega t + \theta)$$

with A and θ real constants. Then

$$S_{in}(s) = \frac{As \cos \theta - A\omega \sin \theta}{s^2 + \omega^2}$$

and

$$S_0(s) = \frac{H(s)A(s \cos \theta - \omega \sin \theta)}{s^2 + \omega^2}$$

A partial fraction expansion of $S_0(s)$ will contain terms arising from the poles of $H(s)$ plus a term

$$\frac{B}{s - j\omega}$$

and its conjugate. The poles of $H(s)$ will yield the transient terms, but B will determine the steady-state portion of $s_0(t)$. To obtain B we multiply $S_0(s)$ by $(s - j\omega)$ and let $s = j\omega$ according to the usual procedure; hence

$$B = \frac{H(s)A(s\cos\theta - \omega\sin\theta)}{s+j\omega}\Bigg|_{s=jw}$$

$$= \frac{H(j\omega)A(j\omega\cos\theta - \omega\sin\theta)}{2j\omega}$$

$$= \frac{H(j\omega)A(\cos\theta + j\sin\theta)}{2}$$

$$= \frac{H(j\omega)}{2}\ A\underline{/\theta}$$

This makes the sinusoidal portion of the output signal

$$A\ |H(j\omega)\ |\cos[\omega t + \theta + \text{angle of } H(j\omega)]$$

But $A\underline{/\theta}$ is the standard form for the complex amplitude of the input sinusoid, so the complex form of the output sinusoid is simply

$$A\ |H(j\omega)\ |\ \underline{/\theta + \text{angle of } H(j\omega)}$$

making the *ratio* of the complex amplitude of the output to the complex amplitude of the input simply

$$|\ H(j\omega)\ |\ \underline{/\text{angle of } H(j\omega)} = H(j\omega)$$

Since the positions of the poles of the transfer function determine its transient response, it is worthwhile at this point to show how the poles affect the frequency response.

It will be recalled that s is a complex variable, equal to $\sigma + j\omega$. Setting $s = j\omega$ is the same as setting $\sigma = 0$. In the terminology involved in discussing frequency response, ω is the radian frequency of the source or driving sinusoid; hence, this sinusoid can be envisioned as a *point* on the j axis in the s plane. As frequency is varied from 0 to ∞, this point moves from the origin along the positive ω axis towards infinity The distance between the point representing the source and the point or points representing the poles of the transfer function will determine to a large extent the frequency response of the system.

EXAMPLE 5.17. Consider the circuit of Fig. 5.23(a). This is a standard circuit for a single-tuned bandpass amplifier found in nearly every radio and TV receiver. The equivalent circuit for small input signals (e_g small) is shown in Fig. 5.23(b). The response will be the output voltage, $v_0(t)$. Note that the capacitances C_k, C_s, and C_c do not appear in the equivalent circuit. Understanding this requires knowledge of the design of vacuum-tube circuits, but for our purposes these capacitances should be sufficiently large that the actual circuit behaves in the same way as the circuit of Fig. 5.23(b). Find the transient and frequency response of the circuit.

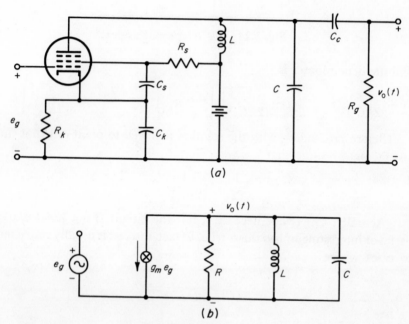

Fig. 5.23 (a) *A single-tuned amplifier stage.* (b) *Its equivalent circuit.*

Solution (The Transient): The transformed equivalent circuit with zero initial conditions is shown in Fig. 5.24. Writing the single-node equation gives

$$V_0(s)\left[Cs + \frac{1}{R} + \frac{1}{Ls}\right] = -g_m E_g(s)$$

so

$$H(s) = \frac{V_0(s)}{E_g(s)} = \frac{-g_m s/C}{s^2 + \dfrac{1}{RC}s + \dfrac{1}{LC}}$$

The inverse transform of the transfer function is the impulse response, that is, the response $v_0(t)$ that would occur if $e_g(t) = \delta(t)$. This will give the character of the transient.

Factoring the denominator yields

$$s = -\frac{1}{2RC} \pm \sqrt{\frac{1}{(2RC)^2} - \frac{1}{LC}}$$

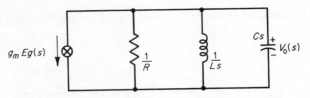

Fig. 5.24   *The transformed network.*

and the denominator is

$$\left[s + \frac{1}{2RC} - j\sqrt{\frac{1}{LC} - \frac{1}{(2RC)^2}}\right]\left[s + \frac{1}{2RC} + j\sqrt{\frac{1}{LC} - \frac{1}{(2RC)^2}}\right]$$

Before proceeding with the solution it is well to point out that the last factors presume that

$$\frac{1}{LC} > \frac{1}{(2RC)^2}$$

Actually, this is not necessary, but the circuit is not particularly useful or interesting unless this is true. In fact, interest is usually restricted to cases where

$$\frac{1}{LC} \geq \frac{82.4}{(2RC)^2}$$

so

$$\frac{0.994}{\sqrt{LC}} < \sqrt{\frac{1}{LC} - \frac{1}{(2RC)^2}} < \frac{1}{\sqrt{LC}}$$

or

$$\sqrt{\frac{1}{LC} - \frac{1}{(2RC)^2}} \doteq \frac{1}{\sqrt{LC}}$$

The choice of 82.4 is arbitrary, because any number that is large enough to make the imaginary part of the root equal to $1/\sqrt{LC}$ would do. It can be seen that this choice makes the error in the imaginary part less than 1 percent, and it will also have the effect, when the equals sign holds, that is, when

$$\frac{1}{LC} = \frac{82.4}{(2RC)^2}$$

of making the "half-life" of the transient equal to one period of oscillation of the transient. Such circuits are called *high-Q* resonant circuits, where Q (or Q_0 as it is used below) means quality.

Restricting ourselves to this condition, and defining

$$\omega_0 = 1/\sqrt{LC}$$

$$Q_0 = R\sqrt{\frac{C}{L}}$$

then

$$\frac{1}{2RC} = \frac{1}{2CQ_0}\sqrt{\frac{C}{L}} = \frac{\omega_0}{2Q_0}$$

and the roots are

$$s = \omega_0\left[-\frac{1}{2Q_0} \pm j\right]$$

and

$$\frac{V_0(s)}{E_g(s)} = \frac{-g_m s/C}{[s+(\omega_0/2Q_0)-j\omega_0]\,[s+\omega_0/2Q_0+j\omega_0]}$$

$$= \frac{-[1+(j/2Q_0)]\,[g_m/2C]}{s+(\omega_0/2Q_0)-j\omega_0} + \text{conjugate}$$

But

$$1+j\frac{1}{2Q_0} = \sqrt{1+\frac{1}{4Q_0^2}}\ \underline{/\tan^{-1} 1/(2Q_0)}$$

and if

$$\frac{1}{LC} \geq \frac{82.4}{(2RC)^2}$$

$$\frac{R^2C^2}{LC} \geq 20.6$$

$$R\sqrt{\frac{C}{L}} = Q_0 \geq \sqrt{20.6} = 4.54$$

Then

$$\sqrt{1+\frac{1}{4Q_0^2}} \doteq 1$$

and $\tan^{-1} 1/(2Q_0) \doteq 1/(2Q_0)$ rad $= 28.65/Q_0$ deg.

Then $h(t)$ is

$$h(t) \doteq -\frac{g_m}{C} e^{-\omega_0 t/(2Q_0)} \cos\left(\omega_0 t + \frac{28.65°}{Q_0}\right)$$

which is a slowly decaying sinusoid of frequency

$$f_0 = \frac{\omega_0}{2\pi} = \frac{1}{2\pi\sqrt{LC}} \text{ cps}$$

and time-constant

$$\tau = \frac{2Q_0}{\omega_0} \text{ sec}$$

If the period of oscillation is $T_0 = 1/f_0 = 2\pi/\omega_0$, the amplitude will, after one period, have fallen to

$$e^{-\pi/Q_0} \geq e^{-\pi/4.54} = e^{-0.693} = \frac{1}{2}$$

Thus, when $Q_0 = 4.54$, the amplitude will have fallen to one half its value at $t = 0$, and one period is the same as the half-life of the transient. For Q_0 larger than 4.54, the half-life extends for more than one period, the number of cycles in the half-life being $Q_0/4.54$ and the number of cycles in one time-constant being Q_0/π.

The circuit, then, will ring whenever any change in its condition begins. It is like a pendulum which, no matter how it is displaced, will oscillate at some frequency determined primarily by its length.

This has led to the use of the term *natural frequency* (or *natural frequencies*) for the pole positions. Even if the transfer function is $1/(s+5)$, $s = -5$ is often referred to as the natural (complex-radian) frequency of the system, though in the time domain nothing is oscillating in the ordinary sense. In the example given above, the natural frequencies are $\omega_0[-1/(2Q_0) \pm j]$, though in the time domain the "frequency" portion is simply the imaginary part ω_0.

It is well known that many systems have oscillatory behavior. Long hollow pipes will oscillate in the transient state, emitting musical sounds. This has led to such musical instruments as the woodwinds and brasses, as well as the pipe organ. It can be concluded that each of these devices has poles near the j axis. In fact, the positions of the poles for brass instruments are such that the imaginary parts are harmonically related to one another. The fundamental (the pedal tone), and consequently the harmonics, depend on the length of the pipe.

The term Q, or Q_0 as it is used here, is applied to any system that has oscillatory transient behavior. In addition to determining the half-life of the transient, Q_0 has a very interesting interpretation in connection with the frequency response.

Solution (The Frequency Response): If $e_g(t)$ is a constant-amplitude sinusoid with radian frequency ω, the ratio of the complex output to the complex input as ω goes from 0 to ∞ is its frequency response $H(j\omega)$. Since

$$H(s) \doteq \frac{-g_m s/C}{[s+\omega_0/(2Q_0)-j\omega_0] \, [s+\omega_0/(2Q_0)+j\omega_0]}$$

$H(s) = 0$ at $s = 0$. Figure 5.25 shows the s plane; the poles are shown with crosses and the zero with a circle. The excitation ω is shown as a small square. This excitation moves along the positive ω-axis from 0 to ∞.

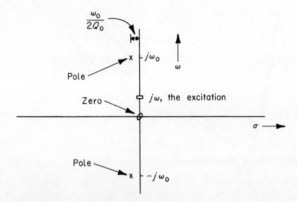

Fig. 5.25 *The poles and zero of the tuned amplifier.*

Figure 5.26 shows a three-dimensional plot of $|H(s)|$ versus σ and ω; a plane that is normal to the s plane cutting through the j axis intersects the surface $|H(s)|$, the intersection being the magnitude of the frequency response $|H(j\omega)| = |V_0(j\omega)/E_g(j\omega)|$.

Notice that the frequency response is *selective*, the output for a given magnitude input being much higher when ω is near ω_0. There is another graphical way of seeing this. Since

$$H(j\omega) = \frac{-jg_m\omega/C}{[\omega_0/(2Q_0)+j(\omega-\omega_0)] \, [\omega_0/(2Q_0)+j(\omega+\omega_0)]}$$

the first factor in the denominator is small when ω is near ω_0. The factor $j\omega$ in the numerator can be thought of as the phasor drawn from the zero at $s = 0$ to the point $s = j\omega$, the factor $\omega_0/(2Q_0)+j(\omega-\omega_0)$ as a phasor drawn from the upper pole to $j\omega$, and the factor $\omega_0/(2Q_0)+j(\omega+\omega_0)$ as the phasor drawn to $j\omega$ from the lower pole. This is shown in Fig. 5.27.

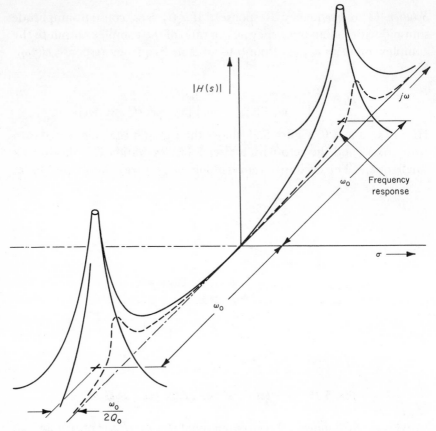

Fig. 5.26 *A three-dimensional view of* $|H(s)|$ *versus s, with the dashed line showing the intersection of the plane* $\sigma = 0$ *and the surface* $|H(s)|$, *thus placing the frequency response in evidence.*

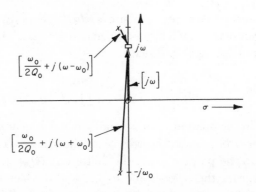

Fig. 5.27 *The factors of* $H(j\omega)$ *shown in the s plane as phasors (complex vectors).*

It should be pointed out that no matter what $H(s)$ is, if it had poles at $s_1, s_3, s_5, \ldots$ and zeros at $s_0, s_2, s_4, \ldots$, $H(s)$ could be written in factored form as

$$H(s) = A \frac{(s-s_0)\ (s-s_2)\ (s-s_4)\ \cdots}{(s-s_1)\ (s-s_3)\ (s-s_5)\ \cdots}$$

where A is some real constant. Then when $s = j\omega$, the numerator and denominator can be thought of as a collection of phasors, and $H(j\omega)$ is the product of the numerator phasors divided by the product of the denominator phasors (and multiplied by the constant A).

This particular view is not especially helpful in general, except when $H(j\omega)$ has poles near the j axis and the response is to be evaluated near the pole, as in this example. When this occurs, some very convenient approximations can be made which simplify the form of the transfer function. This can be seen with a numerical example. Suppose we wanted the frequency response of a network near $\omega = 100$, say for $98 < \omega < 102$, and the transfer function $H(s)$ were

$$H(s) = 5 \frac{(s+10)s}{(s+1-j100)\ (s+1+j100)}$$

Then

$$H(j\omega) = 5 \frac{(10+j\omega)j\omega}{[1+j(\omega-100)]\ [1+j(\omega+100)]}$$

Now as ω goes from 98 to 102, the first numerator factor goes from $10 + j98$ to $10 + j102$, and is never very different from $10 + j100 \doteq 100/84.3°$. The second factor in the numerator, $j\omega$, is always within 2 percent of $j100 = 100/90°$. Within a few percent then, the numerator is about $10^4/174.3°$ for all ω in the vicinity of 100.

In a similar manner the second factor in the denominator is never far from $1 + j200 \doteq 200/90°$ for ω in the same range. But the first factor in the denominator changes rapidly as ω goes from 98 to 102. At $\omega = 98$ this factor is $1 - j2$, at $\omega = 100$ it is 1, and at $\omega = 102$ it is $1 + j2$. Both its magnitude and angle change rapidly, so it appears that it is legitimate to replace s by $j100$ in all factors whose roots are far removed from $j100$, but we must replace s by $j\omega$ in any factor or factors whose roots are near 100.

Going back to the example of the tuned amplifier and Fig. 5.27, it is clear that in the vicinity of $s = j\omega_0$ the only phasor that changes rapidly is the one drawn to $s = j\omega$ from the upper pole. Then for $Q_0 \geq 4.54$ and ω near ω_0, the $j\omega$ in the numerator may be replaced by $j\omega_0$ and the factor arising from the lower pole can be approximated by

$$\frac{\omega_0}{2Q_0} + j(\omega+\omega_0) \doteq 2j\omega_0$$

so

$$H(j\omega) \doteq \frac{-(jg_m\omega_0/C)}{[\omega_0/(2Q_0) + j(\omega - \omega_0)]\,(2j\omega_0)}$$

$$= \frac{-g_m/(2C)}{\omega_0/(2Q_0) + j(\omega - \omega_0)}$$

Notice that when $\omega = \omega_0$ the transfer function has a maximum value of

$$H(j\omega_0) = -\frac{g_m 2Q_0}{2\omega_0 C} = -g_m R$$

so

$$H(j\omega) \doteq \frac{-(g_m R)}{1 + j(2Q_0/\omega_0)\,(\omega - \omega_0)}$$

When $\omega - \omega_0 = \omega_0/2Q_0$

$$H(j\omega) = \frac{-(g_m R)}{1+j} = -\frac{g_m R}{\sqrt{2}}\,\underline{/-45^\circ}$$

or the response has fallen 3 db. Similarly, for $\omega - \omega_0 = -\omega_0/2Q_0$

$$H(j\omega) = \frac{-(g_m R)}{1-j} = -\frac{g_m R}{\sqrt{2}}\,\underline{/45^\circ}$$

showing that the response is again down 3 db.

Then

$$\omega_L = \omega_0 - \frac{\omega_0}{2Q_0}$$

is the lower half-power frequency, and

$$\omega_H = \omega_0 + \frac{\omega_0}{2Q_0}$$

is the upper half-power frequency. The bandwidth B is defined as the difference between half-power frequencies in cps, so

$$B = \frac{\omega_H - \omega_L}{2\pi} = \frac{\omega_0/Q_0}{2\pi} = \frac{f_0}{Q_0}$$

so

$$Q_0 = f_0/B$$

Thus Q_0 in addition to determining the number of cycles for the half-life of the transient, is the ratio of center-frequency to bandwidth in the frequency response. It is this latter property—that is, the narrow-band frequency response—that makes this circuit so valuable for radio-frequency (r-f) and intermediate-frequency (i-f) amplifiers.

Actually the two results make sense, for the frequency response indicates that only frequencies near f_0 will be passed with any degree of amplitude, and the transient response proves this, for no matter what the input signal, the circuit itself always responds with its "favorite" frequency f_0.

The magnitude of the frequency response is shown in Fig. 5.28(a) and the angle is shown in Fig. 5.28(b).

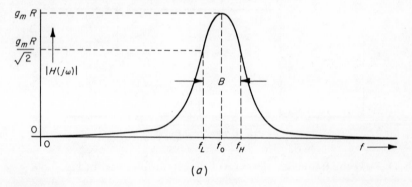

(a)

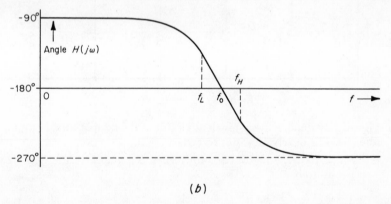

(b)

Fig. 5.28 *The magnitude and phase of the frequency response of the single-tuned amplifier of Fig. 5.23.*

PROBLEMS

In the following problems the poles of the transfer functions are assumed to be near the j axis (high Q_0). Find the transfer functions and plot the poles in the s plane. If, say, the frequency response near a pole at radian frequency

ω_1 is sought, set $s = j\omega_1$ in all the factors of $H(s)$ *except* the one or ones near ω_1. In the latter factors set $s = j\omega$. Find the approximate frequency response, and plot its magnitude and phase versus frequency.

5.53. Find the frequency response of the circuit pictured in Fig. 5.29.

  Note: $pf = $ picofarad $= \mu\mu f = $ micro-microfarad $= $ farad $\times 10^{-12}$.

$$\text{Answer: } H(j\omega) \doteq \frac{-80}{1 + j25.33\left(\dfrac{f}{f_0} - 1\right)} \text{ with } f_0 = 1.01 \text{ megacycles}$$

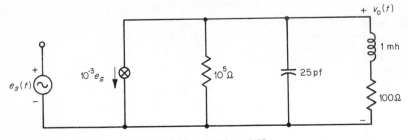

Fig. 5.29   *Problem 5.53.*

5.54. Find the frequency response of the circuit pictured in Fig. 5.30.

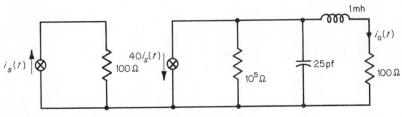

Fig. 5.30   *Problem 5.54.*

5.55. Figure 5.31 depicts the equivalent circuit of the double-tuned bandpass filter used in nearly all radio receivers.

  (a)   Show that the nodal equations for the network in the figure can be written

$$\left[\left(\frac{s}{\omega_0}\right)^2 + \frac{1}{Q_0}\left(\frac{s}{\omega_0}\right) + \frac{1}{1 - k^2}\right]V_1 - \frac{k}{1 - k^2}\,V_0 = \sqrt{\frac{L}{C}}\left(\frac{s}{\omega_0}\right)I_{in}$$

$$-\frac{k}{1 - k^2}\,V_1 + \left[\left(\frac{s}{\omega_0}\right)^2 + \frac{1}{Q_0}\left(\frac{s}{\omega_0}\right) + \frac{1}{1 - k^2}\right]V_0 = 0$$

  where

$$Q_0 = R\sqrt{\frac{C}{L}} \qquad \omega_0 = \frac{1}{\sqrt{LC}} \qquad \text{and} \qquad k = \frac{M}{L}$$

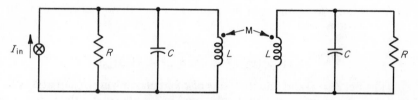

Fig. 5.31 *Problem 5.55.*

is the coefficient of coupling of the coils.

(b) Let $x = s/\omega_0$ and show that the transfer function $H(s) = V_0/I_{in}$ can be written as

$$H(s) = \frac{\dfrac{k}{1-k^2}\sqrt{\dfrac{L}{C}}\,x}{x^4 + \dfrac{2}{Q_0}x^3 + \left[\dfrac{2}{1-k^2} + \dfrac{1}{Q_0^2}\right]x^2 + \dfrac{2}{Q_0(1-k^2)}x + \dfrac{1}{1-k^2}}$$

$$H(s) = \frac{\dfrac{k}{1-k^2}\sqrt{\dfrac{L}{C}}\,x}{\left[x^2 + \dfrac{1}{Q_0}x + \dfrac{1}{1-k}\right]\left[x^2 + \dfrac{1}{Q_0}x + \dfrac{1}{1+k}\right]}$$

(c) Assume that $Q_0 >> 1$ and k is small. Show that the factors of the denominator are very nearly

$$\left[x + \frac{1}{2Q_0} \pm j\left(1 \pm \frac{k}{2}\right)\right]$$

Note: Use the binomial theorem to obtain

$$\frac{1}{\sqrt{1-k}} = (1-k)^{-1/2} \doteq 1 + \frac{k}{2} \quad \text{(and so on)}$$

(d) Let $s = j\omega$ so $x = j(\omega/\omega_0) = j(f/f_0)$, and set $\Delta = \dfrac{f}{f_0} - 1$

This makes $x = j(1+\Delta)$, where Δ is the percentage of f_0 by which the frequency f deviates from f_0. Replace x by $j(1+\Delta)$ and show that $H(j\omega)$ can be written as

$$H(j\omega) \doteq \frac{-j\dfrac{k}{4}\sqrt{\dfrac{L}{C}}(1+\Delta)}{\left[\dfrac{1}{2Q_0} + j\left(\Delta - \dfrac{k}{2}\right)\right]\left[\dfrac{1}{2Q_0} + j\left(\Delta + \dfrac{k}{2}\right)\right]}$$

where the approximation $1 - k^2 \doteq 1$ has been used in the numerator and Δ, k, and $1/Q_0$ are assumed small compared to unity in the other two denominator factors.

(e) Throw away the Δ in the numerator and show that $H(j\omega)$ can be written as

$$H(j\omega) \doteq \frac{-jRkQ_0}{1 + (kQ_0)^2 - 4(\Delta Q_0)^2 + j4(\Delta Q_0)}$$

(f) Set $\Delta = 0$ and find the value of k that maximizes $|H(j\omega)|$ at $\Delta = 0$.

(g) Set k equal to the value obtained in (f) above and show that the magnitude of the transfer function is down by 3 db (0.707) when $\Delta = \pm 1/(\sqrt{2}\,Q_0)$. Choose $Q_0 = 35.35$ and sketch $2\,|H(j\omega)|/R$ versus Δ for $-0.05 < \Delta < 0.05$.

CHAPTER PROBLEMS

5.56. The impulse response of a certain circuit is
$$h(t) = 10^3 e^{-1000t} \mathbf{1}(t)$$

(a) If the input signal is a voltage source and the output a voltage, then what is the circuit?

(b) If the input signal is a current source and the output signal a voltage, then what is the circuit?

5.57. Find the transfer function and impulse response for the network pictured in Fig. 5.32. Note that it is simplest if C is eliminated by $C = 16L/(3R^2)$.

$$\text{Answer: } h(t) = \frac{3R}{8L}\,[e^{-Rt/4L} - e^{-3Rt/4L}]\mathbf{1}(t)$$

5.58. In the circuit of Fig. 5.33 find $i(t)$, given that $\rho = \frac{1}{3}, \gamma = 1$.

$$\text{Answer: } i(t) = \left[\frac{7t}{15}\,e^{-t} - \frac{76}{75}\,e^{-t} + 2.436 \cos{(2t - 46.35°)}\right]\mathbf{1}(t)$$

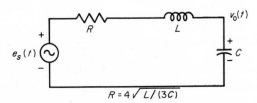

$$R = 4\sqrt{L/(3C)}$$

Fig. 5.32 *Problem 5.57.*

5.59. The d-c separately excited shunt motor in Fig. 5.34(a) is characterized by the equivalent circuit of Fig. 5.34(b). It is known that the moment of inertia of the motor and load is J kg-m² and that the load is such that its torque-speed characteristic is a straight line whose equation is

$$T_L = B\omega,$$

where T_L is the torque required to overcome the load (exclusive of its

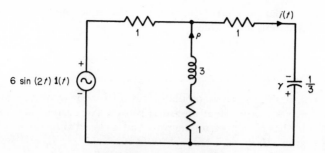

Fig. 5.33 *Problem 5.58.*

inertia) in newton-meters and ω_r is the angular velocity of the motor shaft in radians per second. It is also known that

$$e_g(t) = 0.6\omega_r \text{ volts}$$

and that the total electromagnetic torque $T(t)$ produced is

$$T(t) = 0.6\,i(t) \text{ newton-meters}$$

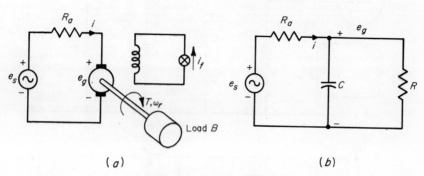

Fig. 5.34 *Problem 5.59.*

Since the difference in the torque available $T(t)$ and the load torque T_L is the torque available for accelerating the rotor

$$T(t) = T_L + \mathcal{J}\frac{d\omega_r}{dt}$$

(a) Express C in terms of $\mathcal{J}$.

(b) Express R in terms of B.

(c) If $\mathcal{J} = 3.96\text{kg-m}^2$, $B = 0.036$ newton-meters-sec, $R_a = 1\Omega$, and $e_s = 120\,\mathbf{1}(t)$, what is the angular velocity $\omega_r(t)$ for $t > 0$ if the motor is at rest at $t = 0$? What is the time-constant of the transient and what is the steady-state speed in rpm?

Answer to last part of (c): Steady-state speed = 1734 rpm

5.60. A servomechanism is being tested for use on an automatic gunsight for USAF bomber. The input signal $\theta_s(t)$ is the angular position of the remote gunsight relative to the tail-nose axis of the airplane, and $\theta_0(t)$

is the angular position of the guns that the sight controls. Analysis of the control system shows that

$$H(s) = \frac{\theta_0(s)}{\theta_s(s)} = \frac{4s^2 + 5s + 37}{s^3 + 3s^2 + 39s + 37}$$

Let $\theta_s(t) = \mathbf{1}(t)$. Find $\theta_0(t)$. Would you accept this system for use?

5.61. In Fig. 5.35(a) a triode oscillator circuit is shown, and in Fig. 5.35(b) its linear a-c equivalent circuit is shown. No current can exist in L_g. Switch k has been open a long time and is closed at $t = 0$. $\rho = 10$ ma $= 0.01$ amp. If $R_{eq} = 5$ k$\Omega = 5000\Omega$, $C = 0.1$ μf, $L_p = 10$ mh, $M = 2$ mh, and $L_g = 40$ mh, what *must* g_m be so that $V_0(s)$ will have a pair of j axis poles? What is $v_0(t)$ and the frequency of oscillation in cps for this value of g_m?

   Answer: $g_m = 10^{-3}$ $v_0(t) = \sqrt{10} \sin (31600t)\mathbf{1}(t)$ $f = 5.03$ kc

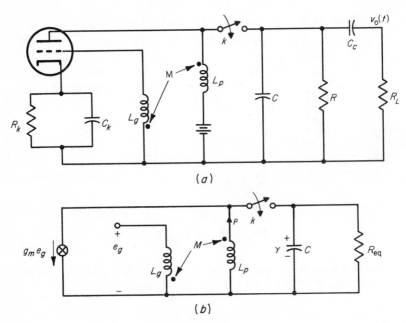

Fig. 5.35 *Problem 5.61.*

5.62. (a) Find the impulse response of the amplifier stage in Fig. 5.36 and sketch it carefully as a function of time. Assume that $g_m/C = 10^3$ sec^{-1} and $R_eC = 10^{-2}$ sec.

   (b) If the output v_0 is the input of a second identical stage in cascade, what is the over-all impulse response of the two stages? Sketch this as before, finding the numerical value of the peak voltage at the output.

   Answer to (b): $h(t) = 10^6 t \, e^{-100t} \, \mathbf{1}(t)$

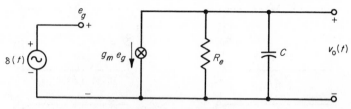

Fig. 5.36 *Problem 5.62.*

5.63. A particular amplifier circuit has a transfer function

$$H(s) = \frac{1}{s^2 + s + 4} = \frac{V_0(s)}{E_s(s)}$$

(a) What is its impulse response $h(t)$? Is the amplifier stable; that is, do its transients die out?

(b) The amplifier is used in the servomechanism shown in Fig. 5.37. Over-all negative feedback through an integration network is used, the transfer function for the integrator being k/s, with k a constant. The overall transfer function $H_f(s)$, which includes the feedback, is related to $H(s)$ by

$$H_f(s) = \frac{H(s)}{1 + kH(s)/s}$$

Find the impulse response with feedback $h_f(t)$ when $k = 4$. Is the amplifier stable?

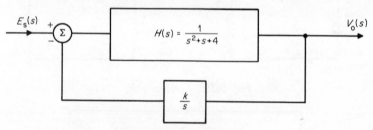

Fig. 5.37 *Problem 5.63.*

5.64. Find the responses of the networks in Fig. 5.38 when the input is a unit step function. Do *not* use the Laplace transform and do *not* use differential equations. Merely use the fact that the current in an inductance and the voltage across a capacitance cannot change suddenly, and the fact that the time-constants of R-C and R-L networks are RC and L/R respectively. Assume that no energy is stored at $t = 0$.

5.65. Solve for $v_1(t)$, $v_2(t)$, and $v_3(t)$ in the circuit of Fig. 5.39 when $i_s(t) = 1(t)$ and $R = \sqrt{L/C}$. Use the Laplace transform to get the transfer function V_3/I_s, but after doing so, obtain v_1 and v_2 by physical reasoning only.

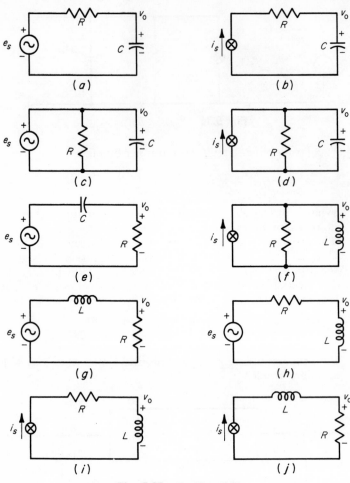

Fig. 5.38   *Problem 5.64.*

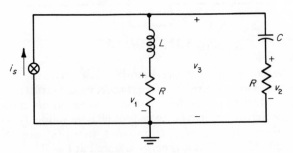

Fig. 5.39   *Problem 5.65.*

chapter

6

Matrix Analysis of Networks

6.1 Matrix Algebra

It is clear that evaluating the transient and steady-state responses of a network is a straightforward but nevertheless complicated process. It is the intent of this chapter to summarize what has been accomplished in the language of *matrices*. In this chapter, nothing really new will be added to our knowledge of these responses except a more commanding point of view; however, this will be well worthwhile.

A matrix is a rectangular array of elements. These elements may be numbers, functions of time, functions of s, or functions of several variables. A matrix will be denoted simply by a single script letter as

$$\mathscr{A} = \begin{bmatrix} a_{11} & a_{12} & a_{13} \\ a_{21} & a_{22} & a_{23} \\ a_{31} & a_{32} & a_{33} \\ a_{41} & a_{42} & a_{43} \end{bmatrix}$$

The letters with double subscripts are the elements of the matrix, the first subscript representing the *row* in which the element appears and the second subscript the *column* in which the element appears. Thus a_{ij} is the element in the ith row and jth column. The matrix $\mathscr{A}$ is called a four-by-three or 4×3 matrix, indicating that it contains four rows and three columns.

The matrix consisting of one column is called a *column matrix* or *vector*. The notion of a vector is borrowed from geometry. Thus the vector

$$\mathbf{x} = \begin{bmatrix} x_1 \\ x_2 \\ x_3 \end{bmatrix}$$

is the directed line joining the origin $(0,0,0)$ and (x_1, x_2, x_3). Though the human mind can visualize only three dimensions, it is mathematically a routine matter to write a vector consisting of forty elements (a vector in forty-dimensional space).

Addition and Subtraction

Only matrices that have the same number of rows and columns may be added. If a_{ij} is the i-jth element of $\mathscr{A}$, and b_{ij} the i-jth element of $\mathscr{B}$, then the i-jth element of $\mathscr{A} + \mathscr{B}$ is simply $(a_{ij}+b_{ij})$. In like manner, the i-jth element of $\mathscr{A} - \mathscr{B}$ is $(a_{ij}-b_{ij})$.

Two matrices are said to be equal if *all* corresponding elements are equal. Thus, if $\mathscr{A} = \mathscr{B}$, then $\mathscr{A} - \mathscr{B} = \mathcal{O}$, where $\mathcal{O}$ is a matrix with the same number of rows and columns as $\mathscr{A}$ or $\mathscr{B}$, but with every element a zero. $\mathcal{O}$ is called the *null* matrix.

EXAMPLE 6.1.

$$\begin{bmatrix} 2 & -1 & 3 \\ 0 & 4 & 7 \end{bmatrix} + \begin{bmatrix} -2 & 6 & -4 \\ 5 & 1 & 4 \end{bmatrix} = \begin{bmatrix} 0 & 5 & -1 \\ 5 & 5 & 11 \end{bmatrix}$$

Multiplication by a Scalar

A matrix is multiplied by a scalar if *all* its elements are multiplied by the scalar. This differs from the multiplication of determinants by scalars, since in the latter case only one row or one column is multiplied by the scalar. Note that brackets are used to enclose matrices to help distinguish them from determinants. Even without brackets, there would be no confusion between the two except for square matrices—those having equal numbers of rows and columns—since all determinants are square.

If the elements of a matrix are functions of time, the derivative of the matrix with respect to time is the matrix of the derivatives of the elements. Similarly, the Laplace transform of a matrix will be the matrix of Laplace transforms of the elements and the integral with respect to time of the matrix will be the matrix of the integrals of the elements.

EXAMPLE 6.2. If

$$\mathscr{A} = \begin{bmatrix} \mathbf{1}(t) & e^{-t}\mathbf{1}(t) \\ 0 & t\mathbf{1}(t) \end{bmatrix}$$

then

$$4\mathscr{A} = \begin{bmatrix} 4\,\mathbf{1}(t) & 4\,e^{-t}\mathbf{1}(t) \\ 0 & 4t\mathbf{1}(t) \end{bmatrix} \qquad \frac{d}{dt}\mathscr{A} = \begin{bmatrix} \delta(t) & \delta(t) - e^{-t}\mathbf{1}(t) \\ 0 & \mathbf{1}(t) \end{bmatrix}$$

$$\mathscr{L}\,[\mathscr{A}] = \begin{bmatrix} 1/s & 1/(s+1) \\ 0 & 1/s^2 \end{bmatrix}$$

The Transposed Matrix

If the rows and columns of a matrix $\mathcal{B}$ are interchanged, the result is known as the *transpose* of $\mathcal{B}$ and is denoted by $\mathcal{B}^T$ (read $\mathcal{B}$-transpose).

EXAMPLE 6.3.

$$\mathcal{B} = \begin{bmatrix} 5 & -2 & 4 \\ 2 & -1 & 3 \end{bmatrix} \qquad \mathcal{B}^T = \begin{bmatrix} 5 & 2 \\ -2 & -1 \\ 4 & 3 \end{bmatrix}$$

If a matrix is *square*—that is, if it has the same number of rows and columns—it may be that the matrix and its transpose are identical (equal). Such a matrix is called a *symmetric* matrix.

A *skew-symmetric* matrix is a matrix that is the negative of its transpose. (It would have to be a square matrix.)

Scalar Product of Vectors

The scalar product of two vectors, sometimes called the *dot* product, is defined as the sum of the products of corresponding elements. In matrix algebra this will always be expressed as the product of a transposed vector (or a *row* matrix) and another vector, the transposed vector being always written *first*.

EXAMPLE 6.4. Given that

$$\mathbf{x} = \begin{bmatrix} x_1 \\ x_2 \\ x_3 \end{bmatrix} \quad \text{and} \quad \mathbf{y} = \begin{bmatrix} y_1 \\ y_2 \\ y_3 \end{bmatrix}$$

the scalar product of $\mathbf{x}$ and $\mathbf{y}$ can be written as

$$\mathbf{x}^T\mathbf{y} = [x_1\ x_2\ x_3] \begin{bmatrix} y_1 \\ y_2 \\ y_3 \end{bmatrix} = (x_1 y_1 + x_2 y_2 + x_3 y_3)$$

Observe that the scalar product can also be written as

$$\mathbf{y}^T\mathbf{x} = [y_1\ y_2\ y_3] \begin{bmatrix} x_1 \\ x_2 \\ x_3 \end{bmatrix} = (x_1 y_1 + x_2 y_2 + x_3 y_3)$$

Multiplication of Matrices

A noncolumn or nonrow matrix will be thought of as a double vector set. If $\mathcal{A}$ is an $N \times M$ (N rows, M columns) matrix, it may be imagined to be a set of N M-dimensional vectors transposed (the rows), or a set of M N-dimensional vectors (the columns). Let $\mathbf{v}_1^T$ be the first row of the matrix $\mathscr{A}$ and $\mathbf{v}_i^T$ the ith row. Let $\mathbf{u}_j$ be the jth column of another matrix $\mathscr{B}$. If these vectors have the same number of elements— that is, if the number of columns of $\mathscr{A}$ is equal to the number of rows of $\mathscr{B}$—then, *by definition*, the i-jth element of the product $\mathscr{A}\mathscr{B}$ will be the scalar product $\mathbf{v}_i^T\mathbf{u}_j$. Thus the elements of the product of two matrices are obtained by taking the scalar products of the rows of the first with the columns of the second. The matrix representing the product will have the same number of rows as the first and the same number of columns as the second. Thus an $M \times L$ matrix times an $L \times N$ matrix yields an $M \times N$ matrix. Thus if

$$\mathscr{A} = \begin{bmatrix} \mathbf{v}_1^T \\ \mathbf{v}_2^T \\ \mathbf{v}_3^T \end{bmatrix} \quad \text{and} \quad \mathscr{B} = [\mathbf{u}_1 \, \mathbf{u}_2 \, \mathbf{u}_3 \, \mathbf{u}_4]$$

then

$$\mathscr{A}\mathscr{B} = \begin{bmatrix} \mathbf{v}_1^T\mathbf{u}_1 & \mathbf{v}_1^T\mathbf{u}_2 & \mathbf{v}_1^T\mathbf{u}_3 & \mathbf{v}_1^T\mathbf{u}_4 \\ \mathbf{v}_2^T\mathbf{u}_1 & \mathbf{v}_2^T\mathbf{u}_2 & \mathbf{v}_2^T\mathbf{u}_3 & \mathbf{v}_2^T\mathbf{u}_4 \\ \mathbf{v}_3^T\mathbf{u}_1 & \mathbf{v}_3^T\mathbf{u}_2 & \mathbf{v}_3^T\mathbf{u}_3 & \mathbf{v}_3^T\mathbf{u}_4 \end{bmatrix}$$

It must be pointed out that multiplication of matrices depends on the order in which they appear, and that the product $\mathscr{A}\mathscr{B}$ will not in general be equal to $\mathscr{B}\mathscr{A}$; in fact, one product may not even exist. For example, if $\mathscr{A}$ is a 3×4 matrix and $\mathscr{B}$ is a 5×3 matrix, $\mathscr{A}\mathscr{B}$ is meaningless but $\mathscr{B}\mathscr{A}$ exists.

When speaking of a product such as $\mathscr{A}\mathscr{B}$, we refer to the order in which the matrices appear by saying that $\mathscr{A}$ *premultiplies* $\mathscr{B}$ or that $\mathscr{B}$ *postmultiplies* $\mathscr{A}$.

EXAMPLE 6.5.

$$[1 \quad -2] \begin{bmatrix} 1 \\ 2 \end{bmatrix} = [(1 \cdot 1 - 2 \cdot 2)] = [-3]$$

$$\begin{bmatrix} 1 \\ 2 \end{bmatrix} [1 \quad -2] = \begin{bmatrix} 1 \cdot 1 & 1 \cdot (-2) \\ 2 \cdot 1 & (-2) \cdot 2 \end{bmatrix} = \begin{bmatrix} 1 & -2 \\ 2 & -4 \end{bmatrix}$$

EXAMPLE 6.6.

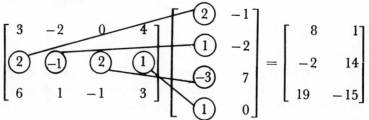

In Example 6.6, the elements of row 2 of the first matrix and the elements of column 1 of the second matrix are encircled. Thus the 2–1 element of the product is

$$2 \cdot 2 + (-1) \cdot (1) + 2 \cdot (-3) + 1 \cdot 1 = -2$$

One rule that will prove useful is that the transpose of a product of matrices is the product of the transposed matrices in the reverse order; that is

$$(\mathscr{A}\mathscr{B}\mathscr{C}\mathscr{D})^T = \mathscr{D}^T\mathscr{C}^T\mathscr{B}^T\mathscr{A}^T$$

Square Matrices

If a matrix has the same number of rows and columns, it is called a *square* matrix. The *order* of a square matrix is the number of rows or columns of the matrix.

The *diagonal* (or principal diagonal) of a square matrix is the diagonal from the upper left to the lower right.

A *diagonal matrix* is a square matrix, all of whose elements are zero except those on the diagonal. The *unit matrix* $\mathscr{U}$ is a diagonal matrix (of any order) whose principal diagonal consists solely of ones (1). The unit matrix has the property of unity in any algebra; that is

$$\mathscr{U}\mathscr{A} = \mathscr{A}\mathscr{U} = \mathscr{A}$$

A square matrix possesses a *determinant;* for matrix $\mathscr{A}$, for example, this will be denoted $\mathscr{A}_{det}$. A square matrix is said to be *singular* if its determinant is zero. Conversely, if the determinant of a matrix is not zero, the matrix is said to be *nonsingular*.

The Inverse Matrix

A square nonsingular matrix $\mathscr{A}$ always has an inverse matrix $\mathscr{A}^{-1}$ (read $\mathscr{A}$-inverse) such that

$$\mathscr{A}^{-1}\mathscr{A} = \mathscr{A}\mathscr{A}^{-1} = \mathscr{U}$$

where $\mathscr{U}$ is the unit matrix of the same order as $\mathscr{A}$. It is interesting to note that as with the transposed matrices, the inverse of a product of nonsingular square matrices is the product of the inverse matrices in the reverse order:

$$(\mathscr{A}\mathscr{B}\mathscr{C}\mathscr{D})^{-1} = \mathscr{D}^{-1}\mathscr{C}^{-1}\mathscr{B}^{-1}\mathscr{A}^{-1}$$

The evaluation of the inverse matrix is a large task, and should the order exceed six, the evaluation might take a week or so. Finding the inverse of matrices of order four or less is not unduly difficult. For orders higher than this, digital computers should be used.

Let $\mathscr{A}$ be a square matrix whose inverse $\mathscr{A}^{-1}$ is sought. Let a_{ij} be the element in the ith row and jth column of $\mathscr{A}$, and let α_{ij} be the cofactor of that element (see "Determinants," Chap. 4). Then the j-ith element (note the reversed order) of $\mathscr{A}^{-1}$ is $\alpha_{ij}/\mathscr{A}_{\det}$.

The best procedure for computing the inverse is as follows.

1. Write $\mathscr{A}^T$.
2. Evaluate $\mathscr{A}_{\det} = \mathscr{A}^T_{\det}$.
3. Evaluate in turn all the cofactors of the elements of $\mathscr{A}^T$ and construct a matrix by writing the value of each cofactor in the position corresponding to the element of $\mathscr{A}^T$ to which it is related. (The result is called the *adjoint* of $\mathscr{A}$.)
4. Divide the matrix thus obtained (that is, divide every element) by $\mathscr{A}_{\det}$. The result is $\mathscr{A}^{-1}$.

EXAMPLE 6.7. Find the inverse of

$$\mathscr{A} = \begin{bmatrix} 2 & 1 & -1 \\ 0 & 2 & 4 \\ -2 & 3 & 1 \end{bmatrix}$$

and check your result by showing that $\mathscr{A}\mathscr{A}^{-1} = \mathscr{A}^{-1}\mathscr{A} = \mathscr{U}$.
Solution: (1)

$$\mathscr{A}^T = \begin{bmatrix} 2 & 0 & -2 \\ 1 & 2 & 3 \\ -1 & 4 & 1 \end{bmatrix}$$

(2) $$\mathscr{A}_{\det} = \mathscr{A}^T_{\det} = -32$$

(3) Constructing the matrix of the cofactors of $\mathscr{A}^T$, we have

$$\begin{bmatrix} -10 & -4 & 6 \\ -8 & 0 & -8 \\ 4 & -8 & 4 \end{bmatrix}$$

(4) Dividing every element by -32, we have

$$\mathscr{A}^{-1} = \begin{bmatrix} 5/16 & 1/8 & -3/16 \\ 1/4 & 0 & 1/4 \\ -1/8 & 1/4 & -1/8 \end{bmatrix}$$

$$\mathscr{A}\mathscr{A}^{-1} = \begin{bmatrix} 2 & 1 & -1 \\ 0 & 2 & 4 \\ -2 & 3 & 1 \end{bmatrix} \begin{bmatrix} 5/16 & 1/8 & -3/16 \\ 1/4 & 0 & 1/4 \\ -1/8 & 1/4 & -1/8 \end{bmatrix} = \begin{bmatrix} 1 & 0 & 0 \\ 0 & 1 & 0 \\ 0 & 0 & 1 \end{bmatrix}$$

$$\mathcal{A}^{-1}\mathcal{A} = \begin{bmatrix} 5/16 & 1/8 & -3/16 \\ 1/4 & 0 & 1/4 \\ -1/8 & 1/4 & -1/8 \end{bmatrix} \begin{bmatrix} 2 & 1 & -1 \\ 0 & 2 & 4 \\ -2 & 3 & 1 \end{bmatrix} = \begin{bmatrix} 1 & 0 & 0 \\ 0 & 1 & 0 \\ 0 & 0 & 1 \end{bmatrix}$$

It can be demonstrated that the determinant of the matrix is the reciprocal of the determinant of the inverse matrix, and that the determinant of a product of square matrices is the product of the determinants of these matrices. The proof of these statements can be found elsewhere.* Occasionally they prove to be helpful checks on numerical work.

Quadratic Forms

If $\mathbf{x}$ is an unknown (variable) vector and $\mathcal{A}$ any square matrix (whose order must equal the number of rows of $\mathbf{x}$), the product $\mathbf{x}^T\mathcal{A}\mathbf{x}$ is known as a *quadratic form*. Since this is the multiplication of a $1 \times N$ by an $N \times N$ by an $N \times 1$ matrix, the product is a 1×1 matrix or a scalar. Therefore the quadratic form, *must* be symmetric and hence equal to its transpose.

$$\mathbf{x}^T\mathcal{A}\mathbf{x} = (\mathbf{x}^T\mathcal{A}\mathbf{x})^T = \mathbf{x}^T\mathcal{A}^T\mathbf{x}$$

since the transpose of a transpose is the matrix itself.

PROBLEMS

6.1. Given the matrices

$$\mathcal{A} = \begin{bmatrix} 2 & 1 \\ 3 & -2 \\ 4 & 6 \end{bmatrix} \quad \mathcal{B} = \begin{bmatrix} 1 & 3 \\ -6 & 4 \\ 2 & 0 \end{bmatrix} \quad \text{and} \quad \mathcal{C} = \begin{bmatrix} 0 & 1 & -1 \\ 2 & -1 & -3 \end{bmatrix}$$

Perform each of the following operations *if* they are possible. If they are not possible, so state. Evaluate

(a) $\mathcal{A} + \mathcal{B}$ (b) $\mathcal{B}^T + \mathcal{C}$ (c) $\mathcal{A} + \mathcal{B} - 2\mathcal{C}^T$ (d) $\mathcal{A} + \mathcal{C}$

6.2. Find the matrix $\mathcal{A}$ if

$$\mathcal{B} = \begin{bmatrix} 2 & 0 & 1 \\ 1 & 1 & -1 \\ 5 & -2 & 2 \end{bmatrix} \quad \mathcal{C} = \begin{bmatrix} 6 & 2 & 1 \\ -2 & 0 & 3 \\ 1 & -4 & -2 \end{bmatrix}$$

and $4\mathcal{A} - \mathcal{B} = -2\mathcal{C}$

---

*See, for example, GUILLEMIN (3).

6.3. Find the Laplace transform of the matrix $\mathscr{P}$, with

$$\mathscr{P} = \begin{bmatrix} t^2 & 1 & e^t \\ 0 & \sin t & 0 \\ -1 & 0 & \cosh t \end{bmatrix} \mathbf{1}(t)$$

6.4. Given the matrix

$$\mathscr{F} = \begin{bmatrix} f_{11}(t) & f_{12}(t) \\ f_{21}(t) & f_{22}(t) \end{bmatrix}$$

and the fact that at $t = 0$, $\mathscr{F} = \mathcal{O}$ (the null matrix), what must $\mathscr{F}$ be for $t > 0$ if it is known that it must satisfy the following matrix differential equation?

$$\frac{d}{dt}\mathscr{F} + 2\mathscr{F} = \mathscr{U}$$

Answer: $\mathscr{F} = \frac{1}{2}(1 - e^{-2t})\mathbf{1}(t)\,\mathscr{U}$

6.5. Let $\mathscr{A}$ be a square matrix, let $\mathscr{B}$ be a symmetric matrix of the same order as $\mathscr{A}$, and let $\mathscr{S}$ be a skew-symmetric matrix of that order. What must $\mathscr{B}$ and $\mathscr{S}$ be to give

$$\mathscr{A} = \mathscr{B} + \mathscr{S}$$

6.6. Prove that the diagonal elements of a skew-symmetric matrix must all be zero.

6.7. A constant force given by the vector $\mathbf{f}$ acts on a body moving with velocity $\mathbf{v}$. What power in watts is being supplied to the body by the force $\mathbf{f}$ if it is known that

$$\mathbf{f} = \begin{bmatrix} 6 \\ 3 \\ -2 \end{bmatrix} \text{ newtons} \quad \text{and} \quad \mathbf{v} = \begin{bmatrix} 50 \\ -20 \\ 10 \end{bmatrix} \text{ meters per sec}$$

6.8. Given are

$$\mathbf{x} = \begin{bmatrix} 1 \\ 2 \\ -3 \end{bmatrix} \quad \mathbf{y} = \begin{bmatrix} -2 \\ -4 \\ 6 \end{bmatrix} \quad \mathbf{z} = \begin{bmatrix} -1 \\ 5/4 \\ 1/2 \end{bmatrix} \quad \mathbf{p} = \begin{bmatrix} 6 \\ -1 \\ 2 \end{bmatrix} \quad \mathbf{q} = \begin{bmatrix} -5 \\ 1 \\ -1 \end{bmatrix}$$

(a) Which vector(s) is (are) normal to $\mathbf{x}$?
(b) Which vector(s) is (are) parallel to $\mathbf{x}$?
(c) What is the length of vector $\mathbf{y}$?

6.9. Given are the matrices

$$\mathscr{A} = \begin{bmatrix} 2 & 0 & -1 \\ 4 & 2 & 3 \\ -3 & -2 & 1 \end{bmatrix} \quad \text{and} \quad \mathbf{x} = \begin{bmatrix} 5 \\ 2 \\ 1 \end{bmatrix}$$

Evaluate: (a) $\mathscr{A}\mathbf{x}$ (b) $\mathscr{A}^T\mathbf{x}$ (c) $\mathbf{x}^T\mathscr{A}\mathbf{x}$
(d) $\mathbf{x}^T\mathscr{A}^T\mathbf{x}$ (e) $\mathbf{x}^T\mathbf{x}$ (f) $\mathbf{x}\mathbf{x}^T$

6.10. (a) Evaluate $\mathscr{A}\mathscr{B}$ and $\mathscr{B}\mathscr{A}$ if

$$\mathscr{A} = \begin{bmatrix} 4 & -2 \\ -2 & 6 \end{bmatrix} \qquad \mathscr{B} = \begin{bmatrix} 6 & 2 \\ 2 & 3 \end{bmatrix}$$

(b) Is the following statement true or false? If $\mathscr{A}$ and $\mathscr{B}$ are symmetric matrices, $\mathscr{A}\mathscr{B}$ must be symmetric also.

6.11. Prove that if $\mathscr{A}$, $\mathscr{B}$, and $\mathscr{C}$ are symmetric, $\mathscr{A}\mathscr{B}\mathscr{C}$ is the transpose of $\mathscr{C}\mathscr{B}\mathscr{A}$.

6.12. Given are

$$\mathscr{A} = \begin{bmatrix} 3 & -2 & -1 \\ -2 & 4 & -2 \\ -1 & -2 & 7 \end{bmatrix} \qquad \mathbf{x} = \begin{bmatrix} x_1 \\ x_2 \\ x_3 \end{bmatrix} \qquad \mathbf{y} = \begin{bmatrix} 5 \\ -6 \\ 1 \end{bmatrix}$$

If $\mathbf{y} = \mathscr{A}\mathbf{x}$, what is $\mathbf{x}$?

6.13. Find the products $\mathscr{A}\mathscr{B}$, $\mathscr{B}^T\mathscr{A}^T$, $\mathscr{A}^T\mathscr{B}$, if

$$\mathscr{A} = \begin{bmatrix} 2 & 1 & -1 \\ 3 & 2 & 0 \\ 0 & -1 & 4 \end{bmatrix} \quad \text{and} \quad \mathscr{B} = \begin{bmatrix} -1 & -2 & -3 \\ 3 & 2 & 1 \\ 0 & 1 & 2 \end{bmatrix}$$

$$\textit{Answer: } \mathscr{A}^T\mathscr{B} = \begin{bmatrix} 7 & 2 & -3 \\ 5 & 1 & -3 \\ 1 & 6 & 11 \end{bmatrix}$$

6.14. Find $\mathscr{C}^{-1}$ if

$$\mathscr{C} = \begin{bmatrix} 6 & 4 \\ 1 & -2 \end{bmatrix}$$

and check your answer by showing that $\mathscr{C}\mathscr{C}^{-1} = \mathscr{C}^{-1}\mathscr{C} = \mathscr{U}$.

6.15. Find $\mathscr{A}^{-1}$ if

$$\mathscr{A} = \begin{bmatrix} 2 & -1 & 1 \\ -1 & 2 & 0 \\ 1 & 3 & -2 \end{bmatrix}$$

Check your answer by showing that $\mathscr{A}\mathscr{A}^{-1} = \mathscr{A}^{-1}\mathscr{A} = \mathscr{U}$.

6.16. Find $\mathscr{B}^{-1}$ if

$$\mathscr{B} = \begin{bmatrix} 4 & 0 & -1 \\ 0 & 6 & -4 \\ -1 & -4 & 8 \end{bmatrix}$$

Check your answer by showing that $\mathscr{B}\mathscr{B}^{-1} = \mathscr{B}^{-1}\mathscr{B} = \mathscr{U}$.

$$\textit{Answer: } \mathscr{B}^{-1} = \begin{bmatrix} \dfrac{16}{61} & \dfrac{2}{61} & \dfrac{3}{61} \\[2mm] \dfrac{2}{61} & \dfrac{31}{122} & \dfrac{8}{61} \\[2mm] \dfrac{3}{61} & \dfrac{8}{61} & \dfrac{12}{61} \end{bmatrix}$$

6.17. Let $\mathscr{A}$, $\mathscr{B}$, $\mathscr{C}$, and $\mathscr{D}$ be nonsingular square matrices of equal orders. Solve for $\mathscr{B}$ in terms of $\mathscr{A}$ or $\mathscr{A}^{-1}$, $\mathscr{C}$ or $\mathscr{C}^{-1}$, and $\mathscr{D}$ or $\mathscr{D}^{-1}$ if

$$\mathscr{A}\mathscr{B}\mathscr{C} = \mathscr{D}$$

6.18. If

$$\mathscr{A} = \begin{bmatrix} 4 & -1 \\ -1 & 7 \end{bmatrix} \qquad \mathbf{y} = \begin{bmatrix} 2 \\ 4 \end{bmatrix}$$

(a) Find $\mathscr{A}^{-1}$ (b) Evaluate $\mathscr{A}^{-1}\mathbf{y}$ (c) Show that if $\mathbf{x} = \mathscr{A}^{-1}\mathbf{y}$, then $\mathscr{A}\mathbf{x} = \mathbf{y}$ by direct substitution of the elements of $\mathbf{x}$ into the simultaneous equations

$$\begin{aligned} 4x_1 - x_2 &= 2 \\ -x_1 + 7x_2 &= 4 \end{aligned}$$

6.19. Let $\mathscr{D}$ be a diagonal matrix whose diagonal elements are d_{kk}, $k = 1, 2, 3, \ldots n$. Prove that $\mathscr{D}^{-1}$ is a diagonal matrix whose $k - k$ element is $1/d_{kk}$ for all $k = 1, 2, \ldots n$.

6.20. Given that

$$v_1 = L_1 \frac{di_1}{dt} + M \frac{di_2}{dt}$$

$$v_2 = M \frac{di_1}{dt} + L_2 \frac{di_2}{dt}$$

let

$$\mathbf{v} = \begin{bmatrix} v_1 \\ v_2 \end{bmatrix} \qquad \mathbf{i} = \begin{bmatrix} i_1 \\ i_2 \end{bmatrix}$$

Write a matrix equation relating $\mathbf{v}$ to $\mathbf{i}$.

6.21. Write out the simultaneous equations represented by the matrix equation $\mathscr{A}\mathbf{x} = \mathbf{y}$, if

$$\mathscr{A} = \begin{bmatrix} 2 & 0 & 1 & -1 \\ 3 & 2 & -1 & 0 \\ 4 & 1 & -3 & 0 \\ 1 & 2 & 1 & 2 \end{bmatrix} \qquad \mathbf{x} = \begin{bmatrix} x_1 \\ x_2 \\ x_3 \\ x_4 \end{bmatrix} \qquad \mathbf{y} = \begin{bmatrix} 2 \\ 0 \\ 1 \\ =2 \end{bmatrix}$$

6.22. Given is the matrix

$$\mathscr{L} = \begin{bmatrix} a & b \\ c & d \end{bmatrix}$$

It is known that $\mathscr{L}_{\det} = 1$, and that $\mathscr{L}^T = \mathscr{L}^{-1}$.

(a) Set $a = r \cos \theta$ and $b = r \sin \theta$, with r a constant, and express c and d in terms of r and θ. Can you evaluate r?

(b) Let

$$\mathbf{x}_0 = \begin{bmatrix} x \\ y \end{bmatrix} \qquad \mathbf{x}_1 = \begin{bmatrix} x' \\ y' \end{bmatrix}$$

Show that if $r = 1$, then $\mathbf{x}_1 = \mathscr{L}\mathbf{x}_0$ are the equations for rotating the x-y coordinate axes through an angle θ into the x'-y' coordinate axes. Because multiplication by $\mathscr{L}$ rotates orthogonal axes into other orthogonal axes, $\mathscr{L}$ is called an *orthogonal matrix*.

6.23. The symbol $\mathscr{A}^2 = \mathscr{A}\mathscr{A}$, $\mathscr{A}^3 = \mathscr{A}\mathscr{A}\mathscr{A}$, and so on. Thus $\mathscr{A}^3 - 2\mathscr{A} + 5\mathscr{U} = \mathscr{A}\mathscr{A}\mathscr{A} - 2\mathscr{A} + 5\mathscr{U}$.

(a) Let λ be a complex variable, and

$$\mathscr{A} = \begin{bmatrix} 2 & -1 \\ -1 & 3 \end{bmatrix}$$

Evaluate $P(\lambda) = det\,[\mathscr{A} - \lambda\mathscr{U}]$

Answer: $P(\lambda) = \lambda^2 - 5\lambda + 5$

(b) $P(\lambda) = 0$ is known as the characteristic equation of the matrix $\mathscr{A}$. Show that $\mathscr{A}$ satisfies its own characteristic equation; that is, that

$$P(\mathscr{A}) = \mathscr{O}$$

This is true in general; it is known as the *Cayley-Hamilton theorem*.

6.24. Find $\mathscr{A}^{-1}$ if

(a) $\mathscr{A} = \begin{bmatrix} (s+2) & -s \\ -s & (2s+1) \end{bmatrix}$ (b) $\mathscr{A} = \begin{bmatrix} (s+1)^2 & -4 \\ -4 & (s+3) \end{bmatrix}$

6.2 Matrix Analysis of Networks

Since the solution of networks involves the use of simultaneous linear equations, and since matrix algebra affords a very compact notation for such equations, it is possible to discuss the analysis of networks in terms of matrices.

The use of digital computers has eliminated the drudgery of this type of computation, and no new concepts are introduced in this section (with the possible exception of the notion of reciprocal mutual inductances). In view of this, we may well ask, "Why bother with an analysis of circuits using matrix algebra?"

There are two reasons for introducing this study of matrix methods: The concentration until now has been upon individual aspects of network analysis, whereas matrix algebra presents an over-all view of the field. Also, a thorough understanding of matrix methods provides a greater sense of power and confidence than can be gained from any other approach.

The Generalized Branch

Generalized networks will be studied first by dissection: it will be shown that all networks can be broken down into a collection of three different types of branch—the R-branch, the C-branch, and the L-branch. Since sources are not mentioned, each of the branches will be supplied with a current source and a voltage source; one or both of these sources may be zero, depending upon whether or not the appropriate passive element—R, C, or L—in the network happens to be associated with no source, one source, or both sources.

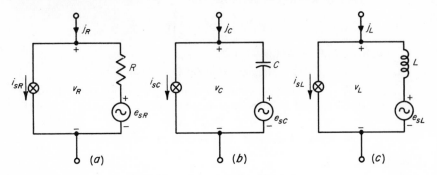

Fig. 6.1   *The generalized branches.*

The generalized branches appear in Fig. 6.1(a), (b), and (c). Although in some cases one or more of the sources may be zero or absent, in *no event* will any section of a network be considered a branch if R, C, or L vanish.

The generalized branches of Fig. 6.1 suggest that we are confining our attention to circuits in which the voltage sources are in series with at least one element and the current sources are in parallel with at least one element. It is possible to draw networks for which this is not true, and for these exceptional cases it will not be possible to break the networks down into collections of branches identical to those of Fig. 6.1. With slight alteration of the circuits, however, these exceptional cases can be made equivalent to circuits that *can* be broken down into branches of the type of Fig. 6.1. These exceptional cases and the methods for handling them are discussed in "Exceptional Cases," at the end of this subsection.

It is important to note that it will be very rare indeed when a branch in a network actually has *two* sources associated with it, but if it does, it will not matter how the sources are connected so long as the voltage source is in series with the element and the current source is in parallel with the element. Consider, for example, the two resistive branches of Fig. 6.2. The volt-ampere relation for either one of them is

$$v_R = e_{sR} + (j_R - i_{sR})R$$

so either configuration leads to the same generalized branch.

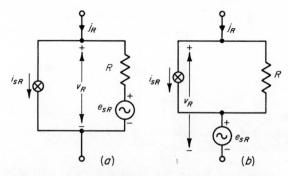

Fig. 6.2 *Two equivalent forms of the generalized resistance branch.*

EXAMPLE 6.8. In the circuit of Fig. 6.3, dissect the network into branches of the type shown in Fig. 6.1 or their equivalents.

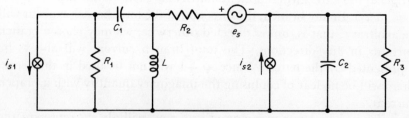

Fig. 6.3 *A network to be dissected.*

Solution: Since the storage elements may have initial conditions, these elements will, in general, always have one source associated with them. As a matter of convenience it will always be assumed that an inductance will have zero initial current and that it will be in parallel with a current source of ρ amp. Similarly all capacitances will be represented by an uncharged capacitance in series with a constant voltage source of γ volts. If there are other sources present, they will simply be added to the initial-condition sources.

Notice that the current source on the right in Fig. 6.3 is in parallel with a capacitance and a resistance. It could be associated with either element. We choose to associate it with the capacitance. The dissected network appears in Fig. 6.4.

Notice that the directions and polarities of the initial conditions and sources were not supplied in Fig. 6.4. The reasons for this are contained in the rules listed below. It is advisable to learn the rules; this should not prove difficult, since most of them are consistent with the notations already used in this text.

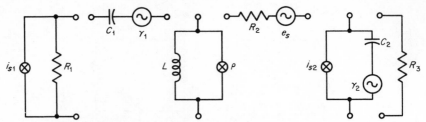

Fig. 6.4 *The result of dissecting the network of Fig. 6.3. Note that the initial conditions are included as sources.*

Rule 1. Lower-case letters, such as j, i, or e, will always refer to functions of time t. If the lower-case letter is in **bold face** form, it will represent a matrix of such functions.

Rule 2. Capital letters will always refer to the Laplace transform of the variable; thus E will be the Laplace transform of e, and so on. *Script* capital letters will represent matrices of such transforms.

Rule 3. In any branch, the direction of the total branch current will be arbitrary; that is, unless directed otherwise, we may choose branch currents in any directions. The total branch current will always be represented by the letter j. Since $\sqrt{-1}$ will not be used in this work, there will be no fear of confusing the imaginary quantity with a branch current.

Rule 4. The letter v, in any of its forms, will always represent the voltage drop across a branch (including associated sources, if present) from *plus to minus* in the direction chosen for the branch current.

Rule 5. The letter e will be reserved for voltage sources. Previously in the text, the symbol e_s has been used, but in the interest of economy in writing, the s subscript will be dropped. The polarity of the voltage source must be from *plus to minus* in the direction of the branch current. If the direction of a branch current is not consistent with the polarity of the source as given in a circuit, the polarity marks on that source should be changed as well as the algebraic sign of the source.

Rule 6. The letter i will be reserved for current sources. Again this will enable us to drop the subscript s for source. The direction of the current source in any branch must be the same as that of the branch current.

Rule 7. The Greek letters γ and ρ will be reserved, as always, for the initial capacitance voltage and initial inductance current, respectively, but their directions will always be such that they are consistent with the directions of the other sources as given in rules 5 and 6. γ will have the same direction as v and ρ the same direction as j.

THE RESISTANCE BRANCH

The volt-ampere relation for the resistance branch in Fig. 6.1(a) is

$$v_R = e_R + (j_R - i_R)R \tag{6.1}$$

Suppose we had a network with μ resistances in it. Then the volt-ampere relations for all μ resistances would be

$$v_{Rk} = e_{Rk} + (j_{Rk} - i_{Rk})R_k$$

with $k = 1, 2, \ldots \mu$.

But this is just a set of simultaneous equations, and hence it can be written more compactly in matrix form. To this end we define

$$
\mathbf{v}_R = \begin{bmatrix} v_{R1} \\ v_{R2} \\ \cdot \\ \cdot \\ \cdot \\ v_{R\mu} \end{bmatrix}
\quad
\mathbf{e}_R = \begin{bmatrix} e_{R1} \\ e_{R2} \\ \cdot \\ \cdot \\ \cdot \\ e_{R\mu} \end{bmatrix}
\quad
\mathbf{i}_R = \begin{bmatrix} i_{R1} \\ i_{R2} \\ \cdot \\ \cdot \\ \cdot \\ i_{R\mu} \end{bmatrix}
\quad
\mathbf{j}_R = \begin{bmatrix} j_{R1} \\ j_{R2} \\ \cdot \\ \cdot \\ \cdot \\ j_{R\mu} \end{bmatrix}
$$

and

$$
\mathscr{R} = \begin{bmatrix}
R_1 & 0 & 0 & \cdot & \cdot & \cdot & 0 \\
0 & R_2 & 0 & \cdot & \cdot & \cdot & 0 \\
0 & 0 & R_3 & \cdot & \cdot & \cdot & 0 \\
\cdot & \cdot & \cdot & \cdot & & & \cdot \\
\cdot & \cdot & \cdot & & \cdot & & \cdot \\
\cdot & \cdot & \cdot & & & \cdot & \cdot \\
0 & 0 & 0 & \cdot & \cdot & \cdot & R_\mu
\end{bmatrix}
$$

Observe that each of these matrices is simply a *list* of variables and functions, with $\mathscr{R}$ a diagonal matrix of the resistances, $\mathbf{e}_R$ and $\mathbf{i}_R$ column matrices of the sources. Usually most of the elements of $\mathbf{e}_R$ and $\mathbf{i}_R$ are zero, since only rarely are there many sources in a circuit.

All μ volt-ampere relations can be written with one matrix equation

$$\mathbf{v}_R = \mathbf{e}_R + \mathscr{R}(\mathbf{j}_R - \mathbf{i}_R) \tag{6.2}$$

Compare Eqs. (6.1) and (6.2). With the exception that $\mathscr{R}$ must precede $(\mathbf{j}_R - \mathbf{i}_R)$, the equations are identical. Then writing *one* branch equation is substantially the same as writing all such equations if the variables are thought of as matrices.

Note that since $\mathscr{R}$ is a diagonal matrix, $\mathscr{R}^{-1}$ is easily calculated, since it is simply

$$\mathscr{R}^{-1} = \begin{bmatrix} 1/R_1 & 0 & \cdot & \cdot & \cdot & 0 \\ 0 & 1/R_2 & \cdot & \cdot & \cdot & 0 \\ \cdot & \cdot & \cdot & & & \cdot \\ \cdot & \cdot & & \cdot & & \cdot \\ \cdot & \cdot & & & \cdot & \cdot \\ 0 & 0 & \cdot & \cdot & \cdot & 1/R_\mu \end{bmatrix}$$

If Eq. (6.2) is premultiplied by $\mathscr{R}^{-1}$ and solved for $\mathbf{j}_R$, then

$$\mathbf{j}_R = \mathscr{R}^{-1}\mathbf{v}_R + \mathbf{i}_R - \mathscr{R}^{-1}\mathbf{e}_R \qquad (6.3)$$

EXAMPLE 6.9. For the resistance circuit of Fig. 6.5, choose branch currents and directions and write out the matrices $\mathbf{e}_R$, $\mathbf{i}_R$, $\mathscr{R}$, and $\mathscr{R}^{-1}$. *Solution:* The current directions (j) are shown in Fig. 6.6. This automatically orders the elements 1, 2, 3, 4, 5, 6.

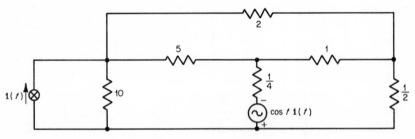

Fig. 6.5   *A resistance network.*

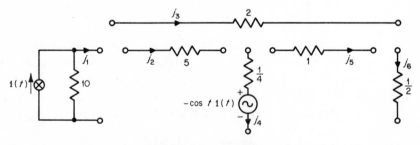

Fig. 6.6   *The dissected network showing an arbitrary choice of branch currents.*

Note that the current source $\mathbf{1}(t)$ in branch 1 happens to be in the direction of j_1, so its sign and direction are not changed. But the voltage source in branch 4 does not conform to the choice of the branch current j_4, so the polarity marks and the sign are changed so that it does conform in Fig. 6.6. Then

$$\mathbf{e}_R = \begin{bmatrix} 0 \\ 0 \\ 0 \\ -\cos t\mathbf{1}(t) \\ 0 \\ 0 \end{bmatrix} \qquad \mathbf{i}_R = \begin{bmatrix} \mathbf{1}(t) \\ 0 \\ 0 \\ 0 \\ 0 \\ 0 \end{bmatrix} \qquad \mathscr{R} = \begin{bmatrix} 10 & & & & & \\ & 5 & & & & \\ & & 2 & & & \\ & & & 1/4 & & \\ & & & & 1 & \\ & & & & & 1/2 \end{bmatrix}$$

and

$$\mathscr{R}^{-1} = \begin{bmatrix} 1/10 & & & & & \\ & 1/5 & & & & \\ & & 1/2 & & & \\ & & & 4 & & \\ & & & & 1 & \\ & & & & & 2 \end{bmatrix}$$

where the zeros have been omitted.

THE CAPACITANCE BRANCH

In a manner analogous to the resistance branch, the volt–ampere relation can be seen from Fig. 6.1(*b*) to be

$$v_C = e_C + \frac{1}{Cp}(j_C - i_C) + \gamma \tag{6.4}$$

Defining

$$\mathscr{C} = \begin{bmatrix} C_1 & 0 & \cdot & \cdot & \cdot & 0 \\ 0 & C_2 & \cdot & \cdot & \cdot & 0 \\ \cdot & & \cdot & & & \cdot \\ \cdot & & & \cdot & & \cdot \\ \cdot & & & & \cdot & \cdot \\ 0 & 0 & \cdot & \cdot & \cdot & C_\nu \end{bmatrix} \qquad \mathscr{C}^{-1} = \begin{bmatrix} 1/C_1 & 0 & \cdot & \cdot & \cdot & 0 \\ 0 & 1/C_2 & \cdot & & \cdot & 0 \\ \cdot & & \cdot & & & \cdot \\ \cdot & & & \cdot & & \cdot \\ \cdot & & & & \cdot & \cdot \\ 0 & 0 & \cdot & \cdot & \cdot & 1/C_\nu \end{bmatrix}$$

$$\mathbf{v}_C = \begin{bmatrix} v_{C1} \\ v_{C2} \\ \cdot \\ \cdot \\ \cdot \\ v_{C\nu} \end{bmatrix} \qquad \mathbf{j}_C = \begin{bmatrix} j_{C1} \\ j_{C2} \\ \cdot \\ \cdot \\ \cdot \\ j_{C\nu} \end{bmatrix} \qquad \mathbf{e}_C = \begin{bmatrix} e_{C1} \\ e_{C2} \\ \cdot \\ \cdot \\ \cdot \\ e_{C\nu} \end{bmatrix} \qquad \mathbf{i}_C = \begin{bmatrix} i_{C1} \\ i_{C2} \\ \cdot \\ \cdot \\ \cdot \\ i_{C\nu} \end{bmatrix} \qquad \boldsymbol{\gamma} = \begin{bmatrix} \gamma_1 \\ \gamma_2 \\ \cdot \\ \cdot \\ \cdot \\ \gamma_\nu \end{bmatrix}$$

the volt–ampere relations for ν capacitances can be written in matrix form by

$$\mathbf{v}_C = \mathbf{e}_C + \frac{\mathscr{C}^{-1}}{p}(\mathbf{j}_C - \mathbf{i}_C) + \boldsymbol{\gamma} \tag{6.5}$$

Equation (6.5) can be premultiplied by $\mathscr{C}$, multiplied through (or rather operated upon by) p, and solved for $\mathbf{j}_C$:

$$\mathbf{j}_C = p\mathscr{C}\mathbf{v}_C + \mathbf{i}_C - p\mathscr{C}\mathbf{e}_C \qquad (6.6)$$

Since the Laplace transform has been so useful to us in the past, it is more convenient at this time to write the volt-ampere relations in terms of the transforms and impedances or admittances. In fact, since the matrices are nothing but lists of variables, sources, and elements, why not take the R and C terms together? This can be done in an orderly manner if, when numbering the branches, the resistances are numbered first and the capacitances second. Each capacitance initial voltage can be drawn (transformed) as a voltage source of γ/s volts/cps in series with the capacitance, and hence can be included in the source matrix **e**. The subscripts R and C are no longer needed, since the branch number will identify the type of branch.

Instead of using diagonal $\mathscr{R}$ and $\mathscr{C}$ matrices, we can now define an impedance or admittance matrix, with the R terms representing (as before) the impedances of the resistance branches, but with the $1/(Cs)$ terms representing the impedances of the capacitance branches. Similarly, the admittance matrix has $1/R$ terms and Cs terms on the principal diagonal. The symbol $\mathscr{Z}$ will be used for the impedance matrix, and $\mathscr{Y} = \mathscr{Z}^{-1}$ will be used for the admittance matrix.

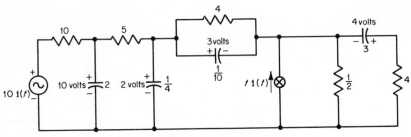

Fig. 6.7   *An R-C network.*

EXAMPLE 6.10. In the circuit of Fig. 6.7, number the resistance branches first and the capacitance branches second. Dissect the network and choose branch-current directions. For each capacitance, include the appropriate initial condition as a voltage source in the dissected network and write the impedance next to the element. Write out the impedance matrix $\mathscr{Z}$, the admittance matrix $\mathscr{Y}$, and the source matrices $\mathscr{E}$ and $\mathscr{I}$. By defining the branch current matrix $\mathscr{J}$ and the branch voltage matrix $\mathscr{V}$, write the matrix equation that represents the transformed volt-ampere relations for all the branches.

Solution: The transformed network in dissected form appears in Fig. 6.8.

In this figure, the choice of branch current directions is clearly shown, and the numbering of the branches corresponds to the subscripts used in the branch currents. All the sources, including those that arise from initial conditions, have their polarities and directions altered to conform to the chosen directions of the branch currents. Where directions of sources have been altered, compensation is made by altering the signs of the sources.

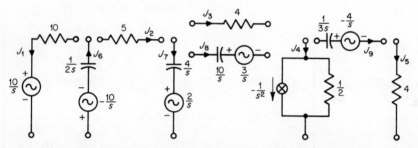

Fig. 6.8   *The R-C network of Fig. 6.7 dissected and transformed.*

Notice that every branch receives its own branch current and number even though two or more branch currents may be equal; for example, j_5 and j_9 are obviously equal in Fig. 6.7.

Let

$$\mathscr{J} = \begin{bmatrix} \mathscr{J}_1 \\ \mathscr{J}_2 \\ \mathscr{J}_3 \\ \mathscr{J}_4 \\ \mathscr{J}_5 \\ \mathscr{J}_6 \\ \mathscr{J}_7 \\ \mathscr{J}_8 \\ \mathscr{J}_9 \end{bmatrix} \quad \mathscr{V} = \begin{bmatrix} V_1 \\ V_2 \\ V_3 \\ V_4 \\ V_5 \\ V_6 \\ V_7 \\ V_8 \\ V_9 \end{bmatrix} \quad \mathscr{E} = \begin{bmatrix} 10/s \\ 0 \\ 0 \\ 0 \\ 0 \\ -10/s \\ 2/s \\ 3/s \\ -4/s \end{bmatrix} \quad \mathscr{I} = \begin{bmatrix} 0 \\ 0 \\ 0 \\ -1/s^2 \\ 0 \\ 0 \\ 0 \\ 0 \\ 0 \end{bmatrix}$$

These can be seen to be nothing but listings of the variables and the transforms of the sources and initial conditions, the row numbers indicating the branches to which they belong.

Finally, the $\mathscr{Z}$ matrix is a diagonal list of the branch impedances, and its inverse, $\mathscr{Y}$, is a diagonal list of the branch admittances:

$$
\mathscr{Z} = \begin{bmatrix}
10 \\
& 5 \\
&& 4 \\
&&& 1/2 \\
&&&& 4 \\
&&&&& 1/2s \\
&&&&&& 4/s \\
&&&&&&& 10/s \\
&&&&&&&& 1/3s
\end{bmatrix}
$$

and

$$
\mathscr{Z}^{-1} = \mathscr{Y} = \begin{bmatrix}
1/10 \\
& 1/5 \\
&& 1/4 \\
&&& 2 \\
&&&& 1/4 \\
&&&&& 2s \\
&&&&&& s/4 \\
&&&&&&& s/10 \\
&&&&&&&& 3s
\end{bmatrix}
$$

The matrix equations relating all these quantities can be obtained simply by drawing one representative branch, such as is done in Fig. 6.9, writing its volt-ampere equation

$$V = Z(J - I) + E \tag{6.7}$$

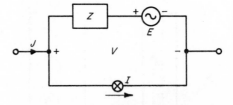

Fig. 6.9 *A representative branch.*

and replacing the quantities in the equation by the corresponding matrices:

$$\mathscr{V} = \mathscr{Z}\mathscr{J} - \mathscr{Z}\mathscr{I} + \mathscr{E} \tag{6.8}$$

By premultiplying Eq. (6.8) by $\mathscr{Y} = \mathscr{Z}^{-1}$ and rearranging terms we get

$$\mathscr{J} = \mathscr{Y}\mathscr{V} - \mathscr{Y}\mathscr{E} + \mathscr{I} \tag{6.9}$$

So long as a little care is exercised in numbering the branches and correcting source directions so all conform to a general scheme, the procedures outlined are completely straightforward and will apply to any network. Before generalizing completely, we will look into the inductance branch.

THE INDUCTANCE BRANCH

As with R and C, we can write the volt-ampere relation for one branch containing an inductance; if the variables are interpreted or replaced by the corresponding matrices, we have automatically written the volt-ampere relations for all inductance branches. There is a difference here, however. The inductance matrix, because of the possibility of mutual inductance, will not always be a diagonal matrix.*

The inductance parameters are *defined* by the relations

$$v_1 = L_1 p j_1 + M_{12} p j_2 + \cdots + M_{1\lambda} p j_\lambda$$
$$v_2 = M_{12} p j_1 + L_2 p j_2 + \cdots + M_{2\lambda} p j_\lambda$$
$$\vdots$$
$$v_\lambda = M_{1\lambda} p j_1 + M_{2\lambda} p j_2 + \cdots + L_\lambda p j_\lambda$$

where, for the moment, the sources associated with the inductance branches are assumed to be zero. The signs of the mutual terms are determined using the technique discussed in Probs. 2.27 and 2.29(1). If this set of equations is written in matrix notation, we must define the vectors $\mathscr{V}$ and $\mathscr{J}$ as before, and the inductance matrix by

$$\mathscr{L} = \begin{bmatrix} L_1 & M_{12} & M_{13} & \cdots & M_{1\lambda} \\ M_{12} & L_2 & M_{23} & \cdots & M_{2\lambda} \\ M_{13} & M_{23} & L_3 & \cdots & M_{3\lambda} \\ \vdots & & & & \\ M_{1\lambda} & M_{2\lambda} & M_{3\lambda} & \cdots & L_\lambda \end{bmatrix}$$

where it is assumed that there is a total of λ inductances. Obviously all M terms need not be present, but notice that the matrix is symmetric.

---

*Actually there is such a thing as mutual capacitance. This is discussed in RAMO and WHINNERY (10), pp. 262–269. It causes the $\mathscr{C}$ matrix to possess off-diagonal terms. Since most capacitor manufacturers shield their products, this effect is not usually important and hence has been ignored.

The proof of this, as indicated previously, is beyond the scope of this text.*

The equations relating v and i, or the transforms V and I, can now be written for the general case. Since in the generalized branch of Fig. 6.1(c) the current in the inductance is $j - i$, the matrix equations are

$$\mathbf{v} = \mathscr{L}p\,(\mathbf{j}-\mathbf{i}) + \mathbf{e}$$

and the transformed matrix equation becomes

$$\mathbf{v} = \mathscr{L}s\,(\mathscr{J}-\mathscr{I}) + \mathscr{E} - \mathscr{L}\boldsymbol{\rho}$$

where $\boldsymbol{\rho}$ is the matrix of the initial inductance currents. As with the initial voltages across the capacitances, these currents will be considered part of the source currents and included in the matrix $\mathscr{I}$.

In dissecting a circuit containing inductances, we shall consider the initial currents in the inductances to be current sources of ρ/s amp/cps (when transformed) in parallel with the branch. The matrix equation for the transformed inductance branches then becomes

$$\mathbf{v} = \mathscr{L}s\mathscr{J} - \mathscr{L}s\mathscr{I} + \mathscr{E} \tag{6.10}$$

Premultiplying by $\mathscr{L}^{-1}$, dividing through by s, and rearranging terms, we obtain

$$\mathscr{J} = \frac{\mathscr{L}^{-1}}{s}\,\mathscr{V} - \frac{\mathscr{L}^{-1}}{s}\,\mathscr{E} + \mathscr{I} \tag{6.11}$$

$\mathscr{L}^{-1}$ must be the matrix of the Γ terms, the reciprocal inductances. This is the reason why general formulas for the Γ terms in terms of the inductances were not given in Chapter 2. General formulas for the inverse of a matrix are not available; they are too complicated to remember for orders higher than two.

The reasons for the qualifications made in Prob. 2.29(2) may be apparent now. If the rule of signs for the reciprocal inductances given in that problem were always true, it would have to be true that the reciprocal mutual inductance terms off the main diagonal would *always* have signs opposite those of the corresponding mutual inductance terms. This is simply not true. Thus, in discussing mutual inductance, the parameters are always given for the inductances, and the dots refer only to these. To obtain the reciprocal equivalents (and their signs) it is necessary to perform a matrix inversion.

---

*The simplest proof that M_{ij} is the same as M_{ji} can be found in RAMO and WHINNERY (10).

We are now in a position to generalize completely. The impedance matrix will now be enlarged to include the matrix $\mathscr{L}s$. The branches will be numbered, with inductances first, resistances second, and capacitances last. The steps in the procedure are as follows.

1. Redraw the network in dissected form and number the branches by assigning numbers first to the inductances, second to the resistances, and then to the capacitances. Choose the directions of the branch currents and number them consecutively to correspond to the appropriate branches.

2. Write the impedances of all the elements and mutual terms on the diagram.

3. Draw in all initial-condition and other sources and take care to assign directions that are consistent with those chosen for the branch currents. Alter the signs of those sources whose directions were changed. Label the sources with their transforms. (Remember ρ/s and γ/s for the initial conditions.)

4. Write out the $\mathscr{E}$, $\mathscr{I}$, and $\mathscr{L}$ matrices by listing the sources in columns by type and by listing the impedances, with the upper left-hand corner of the $\mathscr{L}$ matrix the inductance submatrix multiplied by s, and the diagonal resistance and capacitance matrices below this and on the principal diagonal. The $\mathscr{L}$ matrix will appear like this:

$$\mathscr{Z} = \begin{bmatrix} L_1 s & M_{12}s & M_{13}s & & & & \\ M_{12}s & L_2 s & M_{23}s & & & & \\ M_{13}s & M_{23}s & L_3 s & & & & \\ & & & R_1 & & & \\ & & & & R_2 & & \\ & & & & & 1/(C_1 s) & \\ & & & & & & 1/(C_2 s) \end{bmatrix}$$

5. With $\mathscr{V}$ and $\mathscr{J}$ as column matrices of the branch voltages and branch currents, listed in numerical order, the volt-ampere relations for all the branches are contained in the one matrix equation

$$\mathscr{V} = \mathscr{Z}\mathscr{J} - \mathscr{Z}\mathscr{I} + \mathscr{E}$$

which is Eq. (6.8).

6. Alternatively, the admittance matrix can be obtained by inverting the $\mathscr{Z}$ matrix. It can be shown that this does not require as much labor as it might seem to at first. The individual $\mathscr{L}$, $\mathscr{R}$, and $\mathscr{C}^{-1}$ matrices can be inverted separately and arranged in a manner analogous to the impedance matrix. Inversion of the $\mathscr{R}$ and $\mathscr{C}^{-1}$ matrices is trivial, so the

labor is concentrated in the task of calculating $\mathcal{L}^{-1}$. When inverted, the admittance matrix will appear this way:

$$\mathscr{Y} = \begin{bmatrix} \Gamma_{11}/s & \Gamma_{12}/s & \Gamma_{13}/s & & & & \\ \Gamma_{12}/s & \Gamma_{22}/s & \Gamma_{23}/s & & & & \\ \Gamma_{13}/s & \Gamma_{23}/s & \Gamma_{33}/s & & & & \\ & & & 1/R_1 & & & \\ & & & & 1/R_2 & & \\ & & & & & C_1 s & \\ & & & & & & C_2 s \end{bmatrix}$$

The matrix equation relating these quantities is then

$$\mathscr{J} = \mathscr{Y}\mathscr{V} - \mathscr{Y}\mathscr{E} + \mathscr{I}$$

which is Eq. (6.9).

EXAMPLE 6.11. Dissect the circuit appearing in Fig. 6.10 and write the $\mathscr{E}$, $\mathscr{I}$, $\mathscr{Z}$, and $\mathscr{Y}$ matrices of the network.

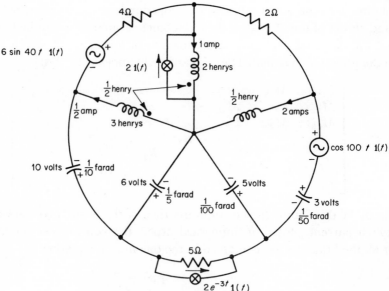

Fig. 6.10   *An L-R-C network to be dissected.*

Solution: The dissected network appears in Fig. 6.11. Study the two carefully and note in particular these points: (1) In branch 10 (marked $\mathscr{J}_{10}$), the transformed source includes the $3/s$ resulting from the initial voltage on the capacitance as well as the transform of the source, cos

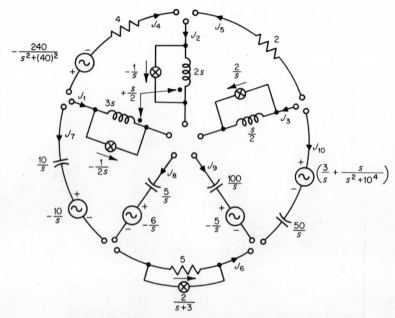

Fig. 6.11 *The network of Fig. 6.10 dissected.*

$(100t)\mathbf{1}(t)$. (2) In branch 2 the current source includes the 2-amp source (negative down) and the initial current ($+1$ amp down) to give a total of -1 amp down. The transform is then $-1/s$. (3) The mutual impedance term is $+s/2$ since branch currents $\mathcal{J}_1$ and $\mathcal{J}_2$ both leave the dotted ends of the coil.

The appropriate matrices are

$$\mathcal{E} = \begin{bmatrix} 0 \\ 0 \\ 0 \\ -240/(s^2+1600) \\ 0 \\ 0 \\ -10/s \\ -6/s \\ -5/s \\ 3/s + s/(s^2+10^4) \end{bmatrix} \qquad \mathcal{I} = \begin{bmatrix} -1/(2s) \\ -1/s \\ 2/s \\ 0 \\ 0 \\ 2/(s+3) \\ 0 \\ 0 \\ 0 \\ 0 \end{bmatrix}$$

The inductance matrix and its inverse are calculated to be

$$\mathcal{L} = \begin{bmatrix} 3 & 1/2 & 0 \\ 1/2 & 2 & 0 \\ 0 & 0 & 1/2 \end{bmatrix} \quad \text{and} \quad \mathcal{L}^{-1} = \begin{bmatrix} 8/23 & -2/23 & 0 \\ -2/23 & 12/23 & 0 \\ 0 & 0 & 2 \end{bmatrix}$$

so the $\mathscr{Z}$ and $\mathscr{Y}$ matrices are

$$\mathscr{Z} = \begin{bmatrix} 3s & s/2 \\ s/2 & 2s \\ & & s/2 \\ & & & 4 \\ & & & & 2 \\ & & & & & 5 \\ & & & & & & 10/s \\ & & & & & & & 5/s \\ & & & & & & & & 100/s \\ & & & & & & & & & 50/s \end{bmatrix}$$

$$\mathscr{Y} = \begin{bmatrix} 8/(23s) & -2/(23s) \\ -2/(23s) & 12/(23s) \\ & & 2/s \\ & & & 1/4 \\ & & & & 1/2 \\ & & & & & 1/5 \\ & & & & & & s/10 \\ & & & & & & & s/5 \\ & & & & & & & & s/100 \\ & & & & & & & & & s/50 \end{bmatrix}$$

PROBLEMS

In each of the problems below, dissect the circuit, choose branch current directions, and label the network with the transformed *impedances* and sources. Be certain to include in the latter the initial conditions for the L and C terms. Write the matrices $\mathscr{E}$, $\mathscr{I}$, $\mathscr{Z}$, $\mathscr{Y}$.

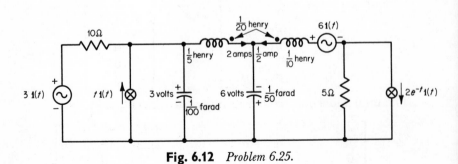

Fig. 6.12 *Problem 6.25.*

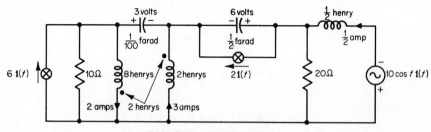

Fig. 6.13 *Problem 6.26.*

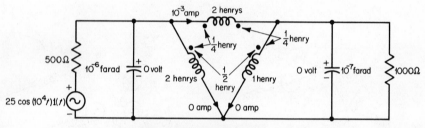

Fig. 6.14 *Problem 6.27.*

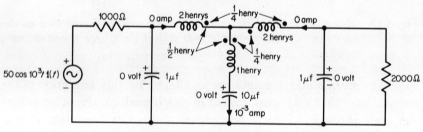

Fig. 6.15 *Problem 6.28.*

EXCEPTIONAL CASES

One of the restrictions placed on our general network was that a voltage source had to be in series with an R, L, or C, and a current source had to be in parallel with an R, L, or C. The following two artifices will be used to insure that this can be made to occur in any case.

In Fig. 6.16 nodes a and b are not independent because

$$v_a - v_b = e_s(t)$$

The voltage source can be moved through either node a, as in Fig. 6.17(a), or through node b, as in Fig. 6.17(b). In Fig. 6.17(a) points a_1 and a_2 are at the same potential as point a in Fig. 6.16; hence the branch currents and element voltages must be the same. In Fig. 6.17(b), points b_1, b_2, and b_3 are at the same potential as point b in Fig. 6.16; hence the

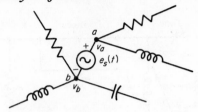

Fig. 6.16 *A situation in which a voltage source is not in series with any single element.*

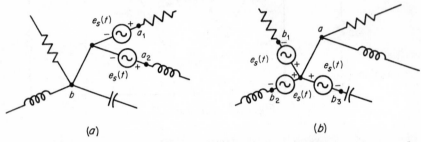

(a) (b)

Fig. 6.17 *Two methods by which a voltage source in series with more than one element can be moved through a node so that the voltage sources are now, individually, in series with but one element.*

element currents and voltages are unaltered by this alteration of the circuit. Note that $e_s(t)$ must appear in *each* branch on the other side of the node through which it was moved; hence at least two sources equivalent to the original are required.

Fig. 6.18 *A current source in parallel with more than one element.*

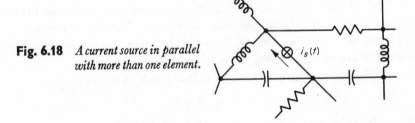

Figure 6.18 depicts a situation in which a current source is in parallel with more than one element. The current source can be moved through a mesh or loop using either of the two methods shown in Figs. 6.19(a) and (b). Note that the element currents will be unchanged by

the presence of the extra sources; at the intermediate nodes where no current had been injected, the source current into the node equals exactly the source current out, so no additional current is added in Figs. 6.19(a) and (b).

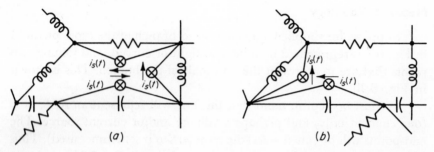

Fig. 6.19 *Two methods for moving a current source through a loop so that the resulting current sources are in parallel with no more than one element.*

Note that these network transformations change the individual branches, since originally no source was associated with some elements, and after the transformation sources do appear with these elements. In the rest of this chapter it will be assumed that these transformations, if necessary, will be made before any analysis is started.

It is well to note here that power and energy are in no way affected by the transformations discussed in this section. The energy supplied by the multiple sources used to replace the original is exactly the same for the group as the energy supplied by the original source.

The Primitive Network

It must have been noted that the preceding sections ignored completely the manner in which the branches were connected. In fact, all the previous matrix equations could have been written if instead of a network, a basketful of generalized branches had been emptied on a table with all the elements separated from one another— that is, unsoldered—but with each branch having its own source or sources.

The matrices $\mathscr{V}$, $\mathscr{J}$, $\mathscr{E}$, $\mathscr{I}$, $\mathscr{Z}$, and $\mathscr{Y}$ define the *primitive network*,* the network before any connections between branches are made, or at least before any information is given on the way in which the branches are connected.

---

*G. KRON (4). (rhymes with *own*)

It will be the objective of the next three subsections to describe how the connections of the branches can be viewed from the standpoints of network topology and matrix algebra.

Network Topology

Suppose, for simplicity, a generalized branch of the types pictured in Fig. 6.1 is represented by a line, straight or curved, and joining two points that are to represent the terminals of the branch. This is shown in Fig. 6.20.

It must be kept in mind that this line will represent an R, L, or C (one element only) and perhaps a voltage and/or current source. The end-points will be called *nodes* (the term *vertices* is sometimes used). Thus the network of Fig. 6.10 can be drawn as shown in Fig. 6.21.

Fig. 6.20   *A line representation of a generalized branch.*

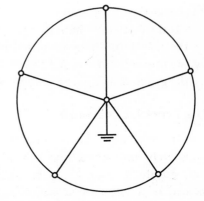

Fig. 6.21   *The graph of the network of Fig. 6.10.*

If b represents the *number* of branches in the network, and n_t the total number of nodes, then in Fig. 6.21 there are $b = 10$ branches and $n_t = 6$ nodes. The sketch of a network using the line representation for the branches is known as the *graph* of the network. Care must be used in drawing graphs to avoid representing impedanceless connecting wires by lines, as has been done in all the circuit schematics up to this point, since such a line in a graph represents an element.

Since it is known that voltages or potential differences are measured relative to the potential of some point in the network, then the potential of one of the n_t nodes may be defined as zero and used as the reference or *datum* node. In Fig. 6.21 the center node is chosen as datum or *ground*, this choice being quite arbitrary.

If a network consists of separate parts coupled by mutual inductance, but not by conductors, we shall choose a datum node for each, and when drawing the graph we shall connect the datum nodes and call them one node. This is demonstrated in Fig. 6.22, where the letters representing the elements are written on the graph for clarity. A careful drawing of the graph next to the circuit it represents will usually make it unnecessary to label the branches on the graph. The total number of *independent* nodes n is one less than n_t; that is

$$n = n_t - 1 \tag{6.12}$$

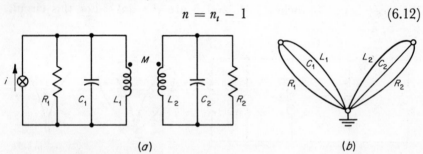

(a)   (b)

Fig. 6.22 (a) *A network with two separate parts* (b) *Its graph.*

The *fewest* number of branches that can be drawn that will join all the nodes of a network is $n = n_t - 1$. This can be seen by imagining that we begin at a node and draw a line to another node. If we proceed from this node to another, and so on, never returning to a node that we have already visited, we will require n such lines. It is also clear that the path of these n branches will contain no closed loops.

If n branches are chosen to connect all n_t nodes of a network together, and no closed loops are formed, these branches form a *tree* of the network. In general, a network will have many trees. The network of Fig. 6.22 has nine trees; these are shown in Fig. 6.23.

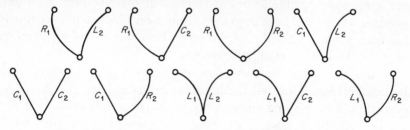

Fig. 6.23 *The nine trees of the graph of Fig. 6.22(b).*

The branches of the original graph that do not appear in a specific tree are called the *links* of that tree. Since there are b branches in a network and n branches in a tree, there must be

$$l = b - n \tag{6.13}$$

links in any graph.

Link Currents and Loop Equations

Consider a network graph with all the links of one tree removed. In Fig. 6.24, for example, the branches are numbered with L terms first, R terms second, and C terms last. Branches 1 and 2 are chosen for the tree; hence branches 3, 4, and 5 are the links. For this circuit, $b = 5$, $n = 2$, and $l = 3$.

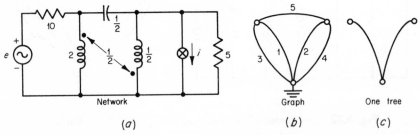

Fig. 6.24 (*a*) *A network.* (*b*) *Its graph.* (*c*) *One tree of that graph.*

Suppose branch 3 is replaced. Its presence completes a loop or circuit and allows current to exist in that loop. Similarly, with the replacement of branch 4, another loop is created with this branch and the tree branches. Thus the links give life to the circuit, for in their absence all the branch currents must be zero. Then there are as many *independent* currents as there are links.

The choice of any l branch currents as *independent* variables will suffice if the l branches are the links of some tree. Mesh currents are not always identifiable as link currents, but these constitute an independent set also and have been the variables on which so much emphasis has been placed. They do not, however, have any singular advantages over the choice of a set of link currents.

Note that there are b branches, and hence b branch voltages and b branch currents. Once all the branches are connected together, however, these voltages and currents are subjected to *constraints*, that is, to the two Kirchhoff laws. These constraints are easily handled by the *connection matrices* (tensors) $\mathscr{C}$ and $\mathscr{B}$, to be described.

Choose the l variables, link currents, mesh currents, or loop currents that are to be used as the unknowns in writing the circuit equations. Using Kirchhoff's current law, write the b equations that relate all the branch currents $j_1, j_2, \ldots j_b$ to these variables. Defining **j** as the matrix of the branch currents, as done previously, and defining $\mathbf{i}_l$ as the matrix of the independent current variables, write the matrix $\mathscr{C}$ so that

$$\mathbf{j} = \mathscr{C}\mathbf{i}_l$$

or, in the case of the transformed variables

$$\mathscr{J} = \mathscr{C}\mathscr{I}_l \tag{6.14}$$

EXAMPLE 6.12. For the network of Fig. 6.24(a), draw the graph, and on it label the branch currents and indicate their directions. This is done in Fig. 6.25(a). Choose the links of some tree as the independent variables, and write the matrix $\mathscr{C}$. Also choose the mesh-currents as the independent currents, and write the matrix $\mathscr{C}$ for this situation.

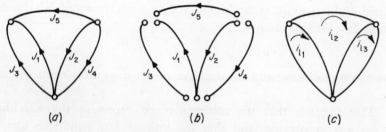

(a)   (b)   (c)

Fig. 6.25 *The graph of Fig. 6.24(b), in which: (a) the branch currents are defined, (b) the tree and links are shown, (c) the mesh current variables are defined.*

Solution: Figure 6.25(b) shows the tree chosen, and hence branches 3, 4, and 5 are the links. From the graph in Fig. 6.25(a) it can be seen that Kirchhoff's current law leads to the relations

$$
\begin{aligned}
\mathscr{J}_1 &= -\mathscr{J}_3 && -\mathscr{J}_5 \\
\mathscr{J}_2 &= && -\mathscr{J}_4 - \mathscr{J}_5 \\
\mathscr{J}_3 &= \mathscr{J}_3 \\
\mathscr{J}_4 &= && \mathscr{J}_4 \\
\mathscr{J}_5 &= && \mathscr{J}_5
\end{aligned}
$$

and, with

$$
\mathscr{J} = \begin{bmatrix} \mathscr{J}_1 \\ \mathscr{J}_2 \\ \mathscr{J}_3 \\ \mathscr{J}_4 \\ \mathscr{J}_5 \end{bmatrix}
\qquad
\mathscr{C} = \begin{matrix} \\ 1 \\ 2 \\ 3 \\ 4 \\ 5 \end{matrix}
\begin{matrix} 3 & 4 & 5 \end{matrix}
\begin{bmatrix} -1 & 0 & -1 \\ 0 & -1 & -1 \\ 1 & 0 & 0 \\ 0 & 1 & 0 \\ 0 & 0 & 1 \end{bmatrix}
\qquad
\mathscr{I}_l = \begin{bmatrix} \mathscr{J}_3 \\ \mathscr{J}_4 \\ \mathscr{J}_5 \end{bmatrix}
$$

the set of equations can be written in matrix form as

$$\mathscr{J} = \mathscr{C}\mathscr{I}_l$$

Evidently the matrix $\mathscr{C}$ has b rows and l columns and consists of elements that are either 0, 1, or -1. Without actually writing the equations, the matrix can be constructed easily by rows in answering the question: $\mathscr{J}_k$ is equal to what combination of link currents?

The matrix $\mathscr{C}$ is called the *connection tensor* by G. Kron (4), and $\mathscr{C}^T$ is called the *tie-set schedule* by E. Guillemin (2). The columns of $\mathscr{C}$ are as interesting as the rows. Look at column 3, for example. It has a -1 for branch 1, a -1 for branch 2, and a 1 for branch 5. Referring to the graph in Fig. 6.25(a), this defines the center mesh, since it is made up of branches 1, 2, and 5. Notice that if we move around this mesh in a clockwise fashion, we move with the arrows defining the branch currents in branches 1 and 2 and against the arrow defining $\mathscr{J}_5$. Since branch voltages are always defined as plus to minus in the direction of the branch current, Kirchhoff's voltage law for this mesh is

$$V_1 + V_2 - V_5 = 0$$

if we move clockwise, and the negative of this if we move counterclockwise.

This suggests that the columns of $\mathscr{C}$ represent the Kirchhoff voltage law constraints and that the voltage law equations can be written in matrix form as

$$\mathscr{C}^T\mathscr{V} = \mathscr{O} \tag{6.15}$$

This is indeed the case, and it can be verified in the example by investigating the other two columns of $\mathscr{C}$.

Another connection-matrix $\mathscr{C}$ can be written for the mesh current variables defined in Fig. 6.25(c). This time the rows of the matrix will be written without actually writing the equations; for example, *branch-current 1 is mesh-current 2 less mesh-current 1*. The first row of $\mathscr{C}$ will then have -1 in column 1, $+1$ in column 2, and 0 in column 3. Taking each branch current in turn and constructing $\mathscr{C}$ by rows leads to

$$
\mathscr{C} =
\begin{array}{c}
1 \\ 2 \\ 3 \\ 4 \\ 5
\end{array}
\begin{array}{ccc}
i_{l1} & i_{l2} & i_{l3} \\
\left[\begin{array}{ccc}
-1 & 1 & 0 \\
0 & 1 & -1 \\
1 & 0 & 0 \\
0 & 0 & 1 \\
0 & -1 & 0
\end{array}\right]
\end{array}
$$

It is seen that the columns in turn again represent the voltage equations for meshes 1, 2, 3, in that order.

Suppose we now go back to Eqs. (6.8) and (6.9) and rewrite them for the primitive network. We then have

$$\mathscr{V} = \mathscr{Z}\mathscr{J} - \mathscr{Z}\mathscr{I} + \mathscr{E}$$

$$\mathscr{J} = \mathscr{Y}\mathscr{V} - \mathscr{Y}\mathscr{E} + \mathscr{I}$$

The act of connecting the branches of the primitive network together can be summarized again in Eqs. (6.14) and (6.15):

$$\mathscr{J} = \mathscr{C}\mathscr{I}_l$$

$$\mathscr{C}^T\mathscr{V} = 0$$

Substituting Eq. (6.14) into Eq. (6.8) and premultiplying by $\mathscr{C}^T$ gives

$$\mathscr{C}^T\mathscr{V} = \mathscr{C}^T\mathscr{Z}\,\mathscr{C}\mathscr{I}_l - \mathscr{C}^T(\mathscr{Z}\mathscr{I} - \mathscr{E})$$

But the left-hand side vanishes according to Eq. (6.15), so

$$\mathscr{C}^T(\mathscr{Z}\mathscr{I} - \mathscr{E}) = \mathscr{C}^T\mathscr{Z}\mathscr{C}\mathscr{I}_l \qquad (6.16)$$

is the matrix form of the network equations. Notice that everything on the left-hand side is known, and that $\mathscr{I}_l$ on the right-hand side is the matrix of the unknowns. $\mathscr{C}^T\mathscr{Z}\,\mathscr{C}$ can be thought of as the *connected* impedance matrix $\mathscr{Z}_c$, which must be the matrix of the coefficients of the mesh (or link) equations discussed in Chapter 2.

$$\mathscr{E}_s = \mathscr{C}^T(\mathscr{Z}\mathscr{I} - \mathscr{E}) \qquad (6.17)$$

must be the column matrix of the elements on the right-hand side of the mesh-current (link-current) equations. With

$$\mathscr{Z}_c = \mathscr{C}^T\mathscr{Z}\mathscr{C} \qquad (6.18)$$

Eq. (6.16) can be written

$$\mathscr{E}_s = \mathscr{Z}_c\mathscr{I}_l \qquad (6.19)$$

which is Ohm's law in matrix form for the entire network.

EXAMPLE 6.13. In the circuit of Fig. 6.24(*a*), write the mesh-current equations by writing out the matrices of the primitive network and operating on them with the connection-matrix $\mathscr{C}$.

Solution:

$$\mathscr{J} = \begin{bmatrix} \mathscr{J}_1 \\ \mathscr{J}_2 \\ \mathscr{J}_3 \\ \mathscr{J}_4 \\ \mathscr{J}_5 \end{bmatrix} \quad \mathscr{V} = \begin{bmatrix} V_1 \\ V_2 \\ V_3 \\ V_4 \\ V_5 \end{bmatrix} \quad \mathscr{E} = \begin{bmatrix} 0 \\ 0 \\ -E \\ 0 \\ 0 \end{bmatrix} \quad \mathscr{I} = \begin{bmatrix} 0 \\ I \\ 0 \\ 0 \\ 0 \end{bmatrix}$$

$$\mathscr{Z} = \begin{bmatrix} 2s & s/2 & & & \\ s/2 & s/2 & & & \\ & & 10 & & \\ & & & 5 & \\ & & & & 2/s \end{bmatrix}$$

These are derived using the ordinary rules of the earlier sections and assuming that the initial conditions are all zero. E represents the transform of the source in branch 3, and the current source i is associated with the ½-henry coil.

From the previous example, $\mathscr{C}$ was found to be

$$\mathscr{C} = \begin{array}{c} \\ 1 \\ 2 \\ 3 \\ 4 \\ 5 \end{array} \overset{\displaystyle i_{l1} \quad i_{l2} \quad i_{l3}}{\begin{bmatrix} -1 & 1 & 0 \\ 0 & 1 & -1 \\ 1 & 0 & 0 \\ 0 & 0 & 1 \\ 0 & -1 & 0 \end{bmatrix}}$$

Since $\mathscr{C}^T\mathscr{Z}$ appears in both $\mathscr{Z}_c$ and $\mathscr{E}_s$, it will be calculated first:

$$\mathscr{C}^T\mathscr{Z} = \begin{bmatrix} -1 & 0 & 1 & 0 & 0 \\ 1 & 1 & 0 & 0 & -1 \\ 0 & -1 & 0 & 1 & 0 \end{bmatrix} \begin{bmatrix} 2s & s/2 & & & \\ s/2 & s/2 & & & \\ & & 10 & & \\ & & & 5 & \\ & & & & 2/s \end{bmatrix}$$

$$= \begin{bmatrix} -2s & -s/2 & 10 & 0 & 0 \\ 5s/2 & s & 0 & 0 & -2/s \\ -s/2 & -s/2 & 0 & 5 & 0 \end{bmatrix}$$

so

$$\mathscr{Z}_c = \mathscr{C}^T\mathscr{Z}\mathscr{C} = \begin{bmatrix} -2s & -s/2 & 10 & 0 & 0 \\ 5s/2 & s & 0 & 0 & -2/s \\ -s/2 & -s/2 & 0 & 5 & 0 \end{bmatrix} \begin{bmatrix} -1 & 1 & 0 \\ 0 & 1 & -1 \\ 1 & 0 & 0 \\ 0 & 0 & 1 \\ 0 & -1 & 0 \end{bmatrix}$$

$$= \begin{bmatrix} 2s+10 & -5s/2 & s/2 \\ -5s/2 & 7s/2+2/s & -s \\ s/2 & -s & s/2+5 \end{bmatrix}$$

For $\mathscr{E}_s$:

$$\mathscr{C}^T\mathscr{Z}\mathscr{I} = \begin{bmatrix} -2s & -s/2 & 10 & 0 & 0 \\ 5s/2 & s & 0 & 0 & -2/s \\ -s/2 & -s/2 & 0 & 5 & 0 \end{bmatrix} \begin{bmatrix} 0 \\ I \\ 0 \\ 0 \\ 0 \end{bmatrix} = \begin{bmatrix} -sI/2 \\ sI \\ -sI/2 \end{bmatrix}$$

so

$$\mathcal{E}_s = \mathcal{C}^T \mathcal{Z} \mathcal{I} - \mathcal{C}^T \mathcal{E} = \begin{bmatrix} E - sI/2 \\ sI \\ -sI/2 \end{bmatrix}$$

If the matrix equations are written out in standard form, we have

$$(2s+10)I_{l1} \qquad -\frac{5s}{2}I_{l2} \qquad +\frac{s}{2}I_{l3} = E - \frac{sI}{2}$$

$$-\frac{5s}{2}I_{l1} + \left(\frac{7s}{2}+\frac{2}{s}\right)I_{l2} \qquad - sI_{l3} = sI$$

$$\frac{s}{2}I_{l1} \qquad - sI_{l2} \qquad + \left(\frac{s}{2}+5\right)I_{l3} = -\frac{sI}{2}$$

The complete solution of the equations can be indicated in matrix form, since

$$\mathcal{Z}_c \mathcal{I}_l = \mathcal{E}_s \qquad\qquad (6.19)$$

Premultiplication by $\mathcal{Z}_c^{-1}$ yields

$$\mathcal{I}_l = \mathcal{Z}_c^{-1}\mathcal{E}_s \qquad\qquad (6.20)$$

from which the branch currents can be obtained with premultiplication by $\mathcal{C}$. Finally, if the branch voltages are desired, a final premultiplication by $\mathcal{Z}$ will yield them. Thus

$$\mathcal{I} = \mathcal{C}\mathcal{Z}_c^{-1}\mathcal{E}_s \qquad\qquad (6.21)$$

and

$$\mathcal{V} = \mathcal{Z}\mathcal{C}\mathcal{Z}_c^{-1}\mathcal{E}_s - \mathcal{Z}\mathcal{I} + \mathcal{E} \qquad\qquad (6.22)$$

The power of the matrix method lies not in that it now permits you to do something you could not do already (probably faster), but that by following a few rigid rules, you will find no linear lumped parameter circuit impossible to solve, even a circuit with 100 branches, 75 elements of which are energy-storage devices all with initial conditions. Of course, no one would seriously consider solving such a problem without the aid of a digital computer, yet it should be clear at this point that the problem is entirely straightforward. Computer programs have been written to solve matrix equations of any order (so long as the machine can store all the elements of the matrix).

In this connection the matrix $\mathcal{Z}_c = \mathcal{C}^T \mathcal{Z} \mathcal{C}$ warrants more discussion. Since the transpose of a product of matrices is the product of the transposed matrices in the reverse order

$$\mathcal{Z}_c^T = (\mathcal{C}^T \mathcal{Z} \mathcal{C})^T = \mathcal{C}^T \mathcal{Z}^T \mathcal{C}$$

But the primitive impedance matrix $\mathcal{Z}$ is symmetric, so $\mathcal{Z}^T = \mathcal{Z}$, and hence $\mathscr{Z}_c^T = \mathscr{Z}_c$. Thus the matrix of coefficients of the variables is also symmetric. This is not only a convenient check when making pencil-and-paper calculations, but also an invaluable aid in computer work; in many cases, because of duplications of the off-diagonal elements, not all the matrix need be stored.

If another set of loop-current variables is chosen and it is not obvious from physical reasoning that these currents constitute an independent set, the independence of the set can be ascertained mathematically. If all the branches were 1-ohm resistances, the $\mathscr{Z}$ matrix would be the unit matrix and $\mathscr{Z}_c = \mathscr{C}^T \mathscr{C}$. For a unique solution, $\mathscr{Z}_c^{-1}$ has to exist, so $[\mathscr{C}^T \mathscr{C}]_{\text{det}} \neq 0$. This is the condition for the independence of the current variables.

It can be shown that the total number of trees of a network is numerically equal to $[\mathscr{C}^T \mathscr{C}]_{\text{det}}$.* Since the number of trees is fixed for any network, $[\mathscr{C}^T \mathscr{C}]_{\text{det}}$ is always the same no matter which link- or loop-currents are chosen.

EXAMPLE 6.14. Find and draw the trees of the network whose graph appears in Fig. 6.26.

Solution: Choosing the links to be branches 4 and 5, we find that

$$
\mathscr{C} = \begin{matrix} & & 4 & 5 \\ 1 & \Bigg[& 1 & 0 \\ 2 & & -1 & 1 \\ 3 & & 0 & -1 \\ 4 & & 1 & 0 \\ 5 & & 0 & 1 \Bigg] \end{matrix}
$$

from which

$$
\mathscr{C}^T \mathscr{C} = \begin{bmatrix} 3 & -1 \\ -1 & 3 \end{bmatrix}
$$

and $[\mathscr{C}^T \mathscr{C}]_{\text{det}} = 8$. There must be eight trees. (These are shown in Fig. 6.27).

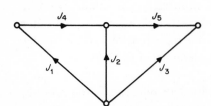

Fig. 6.26 *A graph of a network.*

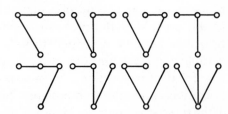

Fig. 6.27 *The eight trees of the graph of Fig. 6.26.*

*See WEINBERG (5).

Tree-Branch Voltages, the Nodal Method

The branch voltages of any tree in a network form an independent set of variables. This can be seen physically, since if all these voltages were set equal to zero, *all* branch voltages would equal zero. In fact the voltages from the n nodes to the datum node also form an independent set, since reducing all of these voltages to zero (by shorting the nodes to ground) causes all branch voltages to become zero.

In the nodal approach it is usual to choose as variables the voltages from each node to ground. This is not necessary, however, since the branch voltages of any tree of the network will do just as well.

As in the case of link currents, a set of tree-branch voltages is chosen as the independent variables, and all of the b branch voltages are expressed in terms of these by defining a matrix $\mathscr{B}$ where

$$\mathscr{V} = \mathscr{B}\mathscr{V}_n \tag{6.23}$$

with $\mathscr{V}_n$ as the matrix of the n-nodal or tree-branch voltages. $\mathscr{B}$ is called a *connection matrix* (in this text) and a *tensor* [G. Kron (4)]. $\mathscr{B}^T$ is called a *cut-set schedule* [E. Guillemin (2)] and an *incidence matrix* (in the literature).

$\mathscr{B}$ is constructed in much the same manner as was $\mathscr{C}$. Its elements consist of 1, -1, or 0, and we construct the matrix by rows, answering the question: V_k is equal to what combination of the independent variables?

As we might suspect, since Kirchhoff's voltage law is used to construct $\mathscr{B}$, the equation

$$\mathscr{B}^T \mathscr{J} = \mathscr{0} \tag{6.24}$$

might represent the equations that the branch currents must obey to satisfy Kirchhoff's current law. This is indeed the case, so the entire nodal or tree-branch voltage method can be summed up by

$$\mathscr{V} = \mathscr{B}\mathscr{V}_n$$

$$\mathscr{J} = \mathscr{Y}\mathscr{V} - \mathscr{Y}\mathscr{E} + \mathscr{I}$$

$$\mathscr{B}^T \mathscr{J} = \mathscr{B}^T \mathscr{Y} \mathscr{B}\mathscr{V}_n - \mathscr{B}^T(\mathscr{Y}\mathscr{E} - \mathscr{I})$$

$$= \mathscr{0}$$

or

$$\mathscr{B}^T \mathscr{Y} \mathscr{B}\mathscr{V}_n = \mathscr{B}^T (\mathscr{Y}\mathscr{E} - \mathscr{I}) \tag{6.25}$$

Defining $\mathscr{Y}_b = \mathscr{B}^T \mathscr{Y} \mathscr{B}$ and $\mathscr{I}_s = \mathscr{B}^T (\mathscr{Y} \mathscr{E} - \mathscr{I})$, Eq. (6.25) becomes

$$\mathscr{Y}_b \mathscr{V}_n = \mathscr{I}_s \tag{6.26}$$

$$\mathscr{V}_n = \mathscr{Y}_b^{-1} \mathscr{I}_s \tag{6.27}$$

$$\mathscr{V} = \mathscr{B} \mathscr{Y}_b^{-1} \mathscr{I}_s \tag{6.28}$$

and

$$\mathscr{I} = \mathscr{Y} \mathscr{B} \mathscr{Y}_b^{-1} \mathscr{I}_s - \mathscr{Y} \mathscr{E} + \mathscr{I} \tag{6.29}$$

As with $\mathscr{C}$, the condition for the independence of the voltage variables is $[\mathscr{B}^T \mathscr{B}]_{\text{det}} \neq 0$, and once again $[\mathscr{B}^T \mathscr{B}]_{\text{det}}$ is equal to the number of trees of the graph.

EXAMPLE 6.15. For the network of Fig. 6.24, write the connection matrix for two cases: (1) the voltages of some tree as independent variables; (2) the node-to-ground voltages as independent variables.
Solution: The graph of the network appears in Fig. 6.28(a). Arbitrarily, the branch currents are chosen just as they were when the link-current method was used. In Fig. 6.28(b), the tree is chosen, and the branches and links are now labeled with the voltages; in each case the polarity marks are plus to minus in the direction of the branch currents shown in Fig. 6.28(a). In Fig. 6.28(c), the nodal voltages are chosen.

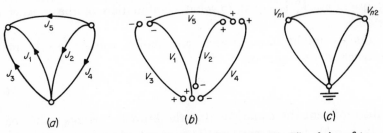

(a)   (b)   (c)

Fig. 6.28 *The graph of the network of Fig. 6.24. (b) The choice of tree. (c) The nodal voltages defined.*

The two matrices $\mathscr{B}$ are then (1) with V_1 and V_5 as tree voltages

$$\mathscr{B} = \begin{array}{c} \\ 1 \\ 2 \\ 3 \\ 4 \\ 5 \end{array} \begin{array}{cc} V_1 & V_5 \\ \left[\begin{array}{cc} 1 & 0 \\ -1 & 1 \\ 1 & 0 \\ -1 & 1 \\ 0 & 1 \end{array}\right] \end{array}$$

(2) with V_{n1} and V_{n2} as independent variables

$$\mathscr{B} = \begin{matrix} 1 \\ 2 \\ 3 \\ 4 \\ 5 \end{matrix} \begin{bmatrix} \overset{V_{n1}}{-1} & \overset{V_{n2}}{0} \\ 0 & 1 \\ -1 & 0 \\ 0 & 1 \\ -1 & 1 \end{bmatrix}$$

CHAPTER PROBLEMS

For the networks in Probs. 6.29 through 6.44, (1) draw the graph of each network and on it define the branch-current directions. If the graph is given, use the branch currents as defined thereon, (2) write out the matrices $\mathscr{E}$, $\mathscr{I}$, $\mathscr{Z}$, and $\mathscr{Y}$. (3) follow any additional instructions given in each problem.

6.29. Write the connection matrices $\mathscr{C}$ and $\mathscr{B}$ for the network of Fig. 6.29, using the link currents of one tree and the branch voltages of another tree for the independent variables.

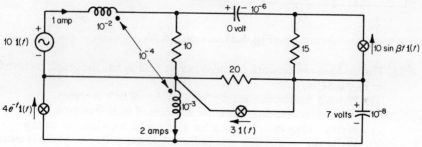

Fig. 6.29 *Problem 6.29.*

6.30. Write the connection matrices $\mathscr{C}$ and $\mathscr{B}$ for the network pictured in Fig. 6.30 for
 (a) one choice of link currents
 (b) one choice of mesh (or loop) currents
 (c) one choice of tree-branch voltages
 (d) the node voltages to ground.

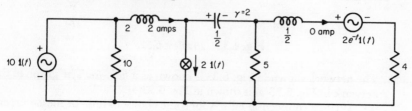

Fig. 6.30 *Problem 6.30.*

For the networks in Probs. 6.29 through 6.44, (1) draw the graph of each network and on it define the branch-current directions. If the graph is given, use the branch currents as defined thereon, (2) write out the matrices $\mathscr{E}$, $\mathscr{I},\mathscr{Z}$, and $\mathscr{Y}$, (3) follow any additional instructions given in each problem.

6.31. For the network of Fig. 6.31(a) and its graph in Fig. 6.31(b)

  (a) choose branches 1, 2, and 3 as links, and write the connection matrix $\mathscr{C}$ relating the branch currents to these link currents.

  (b) choose branches 4, 6, 7, and 5 as the tree, and write the connection matrix $\mathscr{B}$ relating all branch voltages to these tree-branch voltages.

  (c) How many trees does the network have?

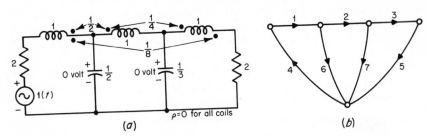

(a)   (b)

Fig. 6.31   *Problem 6.31.*

6.32. The bridged-tee network pictured in Fig. 6.32(a) has the graph pictured in Fig. 6.32(b).

  (a) Write a connection matrix for a choice of link currents.

  (b) Write a connection matrix for a choice of mesh currents.

  (c) Write a connection matrix for a choice of tree-branch voltages.

  (d) Write the connection matrix for the nodal voltages. Make it clear what the independent variables are.

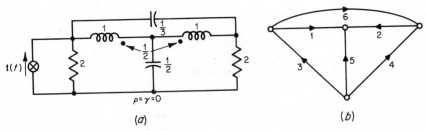

(a)   (b)

Fig. 6.32   *Problem 6.32.*

6.33. The network shown in Fig. 6.33 is known as a *twin-tee*. The graph of the network in Fig. 6.33(a) is shown in Fig. 6.33(b).

  (a) Write a connection matrix for some choice of link- or mesh-current variables.

For the networks in Probs. 6.29 through 6.44, (1) draw the graph of each network and on it define the branch-current directions. If the graph is given, use the branch currents as defined thereon, (2) write out the matrices $\mathscr{E}$, $\mathscr{I}, \mathscr{Z}$, and $\mathscr{Y}$, (3) follow any additional instructions given in each problem.

(b) Write a connection matrix for some choice of tree-branch or node voltages.

(c) How many trees does the graph have?

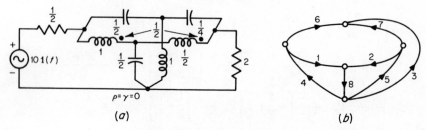

(a)   (b)

Fig. 6.33 *Problem 6.33.*

6.34. For the circuit pictured in Fig. 6.34, choose an independent set of *loop* currents (note that the network is not mappable and hence mesh currents as such cannot be chosen) and write the connection matrix $\mathscr{C}$. Write the matrix $\mathscr{B}$ for the node-voltages and draw one tree for the network.

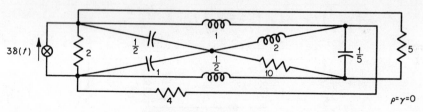

Fig. 6.34 *Problem 6.34.*

6.35. For the circuit of Fig. 6.35, write the matrix $\mathscr{C}$ for a choice of mesh currents and calculate $\mathscr{Z}_c = \mathscr{C}^T \mathscr{Z} \mathscr{C}$ and $\mathscr{E}_s = \mathscr{C}^T (\mathscr{Z} \mathscr{I} - \mathscr{E})$. Write out the mesh-current equations for the network.

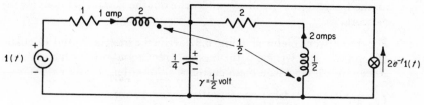

Fig. 6.35 *Problems 6.35 and 6.36.*

For the networks in Probs. 6.29 through 6.44, (1) draw the graph of each network and on it define the branch-current directions. If the graph is given, use the branch currents as defined thereon, (2) write out the matrices $\mathscr{E}$, $\mathscr{I}, \mathscr{Z}$, and $\mathscr{Y}$, (3) follow any additional instructions given in each problem.

6.36. Repeat Prob. 6.35, but write the matrix $\mathscr{B}$ and calculate $\mathscr{Y}_b = \mathscr{B}^T \mathscr{Y} \mathscr{B}$ and $\mathscr{I}_s = \mathscr{B}^T (\mathscr{Y} \mathscr{E} - \mathscr{I})$. Write out the nodal equations for the network.

   Answer: Choosing nodes: V_a, V_b, and V_c from left to right

$$\left[1+\frac{2}{3s}\right]V_a \quad - \quad \frac{2}{3s}V_b \quad - \quad \frac{2}{3s}V_c \quad = 0$$

$$-\frac{2}{3s}V_a \; + \; \left[\frac{s}{4}+\frac{1}{2}+\frac{2}{3s}\right]V_b \; + \; \left[-\frac{1}{2}+\frac{2}{3s}\right]V_c \quad = \frac{s^2+25s+8}{8s(s+1)}$$

$$-\frac{2}{3s}V_a \; + \; \left[-\frac{1}{2}+\frac{2}{3s}\right]V_b \; + \; \left[\frac{1}{2}+\frac{8}{3s}\right]V_c \quad = \frac{2}{s}$$

6.37. For the network pictured in Fig. 6.36, write the connection matrix $\mathscr{C}$ and calculate $\mathscr{Z}_c = \mathscr{C}^T \mathscr{Z} \mathscr{C}$ and $\mathscr{E}_s = \mathscr{C}^T (\mathscr{Z} \mathscr{I} - \mathscr{E})$. Write out the mesh equations for the network.

   Answer: With clockwise mesh currents i_1 and i_2

$$\left(2s+2+\frac{2}{s}\right)I_1 \quad + \quad \left(\frac{s}{2}-\frac{2}{s}\right)I_2 \quad = \quad \frac{9s^3-8s^2+21s-8}{4s(s^2+1)}$$

$$\left(\frac{s}{2}-\frac{2}{s}\right)I_1 \quad + \quad \left(\frac{s}{2}+5+\frac{2}{s}\right)I_2 \quad = \quad \frac{3s+8}{4s}$$

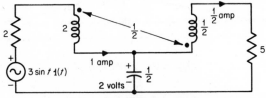

Fig. 6.36   *Problems 6.37 and 6.38.*

6.38. Repeat Prob. 6.37, but this time write the matrix $\mathscr{B}$ for the nodal method, calculate $\mathscr{Y}_b$ and $\mathscr{I}_s$, and write out the nodal equations for the network.

6.39. For the network pictured in Fig. 6.37, write the matrix $\mathscr{C}$ and calculate $\mathscr{Z}_c$ and $\mathscr{E}_s$, and write out the mesh-current equations for the network.

   Answer: With clockwise mesh currents, i_1 lower left, i_3 lower right

$$\left(s+5+\frac{10}{s}\right)I_1 - \frac{19}{20}sI_2 + \left(\frac{s}{5}-\frac{10}{s}\right)I_3 \quad = \frac{10}{s^2}$$

For the networks in Probs. 6.29 through 6.44, (1) draw the graph of each network and on it define the branch-current directions. If the graph is given, use the branch currents as defined thereon, (2) write out the matrices $\mathscr{E}$, $\mathscr{I}$, $\mathscr{Z}$ and $\mathscr{Y}$, (3) follow any additional instructions given in each problem.

$$-\frac{19}{20}sI_1 + \frac{49}{10}sI_2 \quad - \quad \frac{17}{10}sI_3 = 0$$

$$\left(\frac{s}{5}-\frac{10}{s}\right)I_1 - \frac{17}{10}sI_2 + \left(s+5+\frac{10}{s}\right)I_3 = 0$$

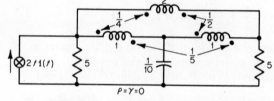

$P = \gamma = 0$

Fig. 6.37 *Problems 6.39 and 6.40.*

6.40. For the network of Fig. 6.37, write the matrix $\mathscr{B}$, calculate $\mathscr{Y}_b$ and $\mathscr{I}_s$, and write out the nodal equations for the network.

Answer: With node voltages a, b, c from left to right

$$\left[\frac{1}{5}+\frac{804}{623s}\right]V_a \quad - \quad \frac{550}{623s}V_b \quad - \quad \frac{254}{623s}V_c = \frac{2}{s^2}$$

$$-\frac{550}{623s}V_a + \left[\frac{s}{10}+\frac{1895}{623s}\right]V_b \quad - \quad \frac{1345}{623s}V_c = 0$$

$$-\frac{254}{623s}V_a \quad - \quad \frac{1345}{623s}V_b + \left[\frac{1}{5}+\frac{1599}{623s}\right]V_c = 0$$

6.41. For the network of Fig. 6.38, write out the connection matrix $\mathscr{C}$ and the matrices $\mathscr{Z}_c$ and $\mathscr{E}_s$. Write out the mesh equations for the network.

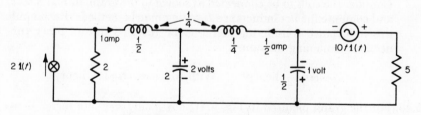

Fig. 6.38 *Problems 6.41 and 6.42.*

6.42. For the network in Fig. 6.38, write the matrix $\mathscr{B}$, the matrices $\mathscr{Y}_b$ and $\mathscr{I}_s$, and write out the nodal equations for the network.

For the networks in Probs. 6.29 through 6.44, (1) draw the graph of each network and on it define the branch-current directions. If the graph is given, use the branch currents as defined thereon, (2) write out the matrices $\mathscr{E}$, $\mathscr{I}$, $\mathscr{Z}$, and $\mathscr{Y}$, (3) follow any additional instructions given in each problem.

6.43. For the network pictured in Fig. 6.39, write the matrices $\mathscr{C}$, $\mathscr{Z}_c$, and $\mathscr{E}_s$. Write out the mesh equations for the network.

Answer: With clockwise mesh currents i_1 and i_2, left to right

$$\left(s+\frac{2}{s}\right)I_1 \quad - \quad \frac{s}{2}I_2 \quad = \quad \frac{-s^2+10s+20}{2s(s+2)}$$

$$-\frac{s}{2}I_1 + (2s+3)I_2 = -\frac{5s+7}{s+2}$$

6.44. For the network in Fig. 6.39, write out the matrices $\mathscr{B}$, $\mathscr{Y}_b$ and $\mathscr{I}_s$. Write out the nodal equations of the network.

Answer: With V_a and V_b defined left to right

$$\left(\frac{s}{2}+\frac{1}{3}+\frac{8}{7s}\right)V_a - \left(\frac{1}{3}+\frac{2}{7s}\right)V_b = \frac{5s-2}{2s}$$

$$-\left(\frac{1}{3}+\frac{2}{7s}\right)V_a + \left(\frac{1}{3}+\frac{4}{7s}\right)V_b = \frac{3s+4}{s(s+2)}$$

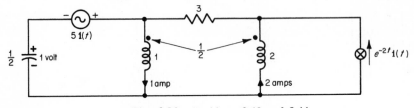

Fig. 6.39   *Problems 6.43 and 6.44.*

6.45. Each coil in the network of Fig. 6.40(a) has a self-inductance of 2 henrys, and the mutual inductance between coils is $\frac{1}{2}$ henry for all coil pairs. Consider the coils to be connected as shown in the graph in Fig. 6.40(b) and compute the net inductance L_{ab} using matrix methods. Recompute this inductance considering coil 1 to be reversed but all other connections remaining the same.

Answer: $\frac{23}{4}$ henrys   With coil 1 reversed: $\frac{7}{4}$ henrys.

6.46. For the graph pictured in Fig. 6.41, how many trees are there? Draw *all* the trees of the network.

6.47. For the network pictured in Fig. 6.42
   (a) draw all the trees for the network when terminals *a—b* are open-circuited.

(b) draw all the trees of the network that results when terminals *a—b* are short-circuited. Note that Y_1 is discarded here since it is short-circuited.

(c) If the Y terms are the reciprocals of the impedances of the branches, show that the input impedance Z is given by

$$Z = \frac{\text{sum of the products of tree admittances, } a\text{—}b \text{ shorted}}{\text{sum of the products of tree admittances, } a\text{—}b \text{ open}}$$

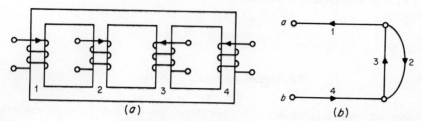

(a)   (b)

Fig. 6.40 *Problem 6.45.*

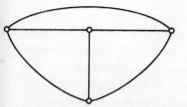

Fig. 6.41 *Problem 6.46.*

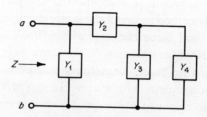

Fig. 6.42 *Problem 6.47.*

chapter

7

The Fourier Series

7.1 Signal Analysis

Chapter 6 was a summary of network analysis. We use the word *analysis* to mean the division or separation of the subject analyzed into the parts of which it is composed. Chapter 6 not only dissected networks but described in detail the methods by which the parts were put together. The final three chapters of this book are concerned with the *frequency analysis* of time signals. As the name suggests, the signals are to be broken down into more elementary components called *frequencies*. Since this sometimes proves to be a novel concept, the understanding of the *frequency domain* may not come quickly. However, these concepts can be useful; most of the ideas behind communication channels and modulation are based upon them.

The word *frequency* suggests, "How often does it happen?" Meals are taken three times a day, winter comes once a year. The word suggests that some act or situation recurs in a periodic fashion.

In the world of mathematics, a function of time $f(t)$ is said to be *periodic* if there exists a number T such that

$$f(t) = f(t-T) \qquad (7.1)$$

This means that if the function $f(t)$ is translated to the right T units, it will equal identically the original function. More precisely, if a portion of $f(t)$ were chosen from any arbitrary time t_0 to the time $t_0 + T$, then the entire function $f(t)$ could be obtained by placing this portion and reproductions thereof end to end, *ad infinitum*. For example, consider the periodic function $f(t)$ pictured in Fig. 7.1. Figure 7.2 shows a cutout of $f(t)$. If several copies (an infinite number, in fact) of these cutouts were made and placed end to end, the sum would reproduce the periodic function.

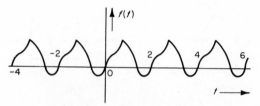

Fig. 7.1 *A periodic function.*

Notice that the cutout of Fig. 7.2 is longer than is actually necessary. Figure 7.3 shows the smallest length of cutout that could, by being placed end to end, reproduce the original signal. It would not be surprising, then, if the section appearing in Fig. 7.3 contained all the information in the function.

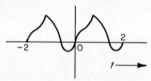 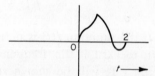

Fig. 7.2 *A cutout of the periodic function of Fig. 7.1, which can be used to construct the original function.*

Fig. 7.3 *A period of the periodic function of Fig. 7.1.*

The *period* T of a periodic function is defined as the *smallest* length of time into which the signal can be cut and still have the original signal reproducible by a continuous translation of this portion of the signal. If $f(t)$ is periodic with period T,

$$p(t) = f(t) \left[\mathbf{1}(t - t_0) - \mathbf{1}(t - t_0 - T) \right]$$

represents one period of $f(t)$; t_0 is completely arbitrary, since it merely identifies the time at which the period begins. Referring back to Fig. 7.1, note that any portion of the wave two units long would do as well as that of Fig. 7.3. (Two other examples of periods of $f(t)$ are given in Figures 7.4(a) and (b).)

Frequency is usually defined quantitatively as the reciprocal of T. This definition will not be used here, although it will be clear later on that frequency is very closely related to this value. Instead, frequency will be defined by the *variable f*, and the building block on which frequency (or harmonic) analysis is based is the function $e^{j2\pi ft}$.

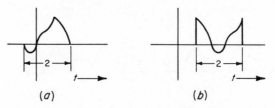

Fig. 7.4 *Two other examples of a period of the wave of Fig. 7.1.*

Let B_k, with k any positive or negative integer, be a set of complex constants, and let f_k be a set of real constants, the frequencies. It is then the objective of frequency analysis to demonstrate that a function of time $f(t)$ can be represented by the sum

$$f(t) = \sum_k B_k\, e^{j2\pi f_k t} \tag{7.2}$$

If the function $f(t)$ is periodic, the summation of Eq. (7.2) will be shown to exist if the frequencies are given by $f_k = k/T$, $k = 0, \pm1, \pm2, \ldots$. It will be shown subsequently that if $f(t)$ is not periodic, either the frequencies f_k are not integral multiples of a single constant $1/T$ or Eq. (7.2) becomes an integral (which, it will be recalled, is a sum of infinitesimals) and f_k becomes a continuous variable f assuming any value from $-\infty$ to $+\infty$.

7.2 The Fourier Series

Let $f(t)$ be a periodic function with period T, as defined in Eq. (7.1). Fourier asserts that $f(t)$ can be represented by the trigonometric series

$$f(t) = \frac{c_0}{T} + \frac{2c_1}{T}\cos\left(\frac{2\pi t}{T} + \theta_1\right) + \frac{2c_2}{T}\cos\left(\frac{4\pi t}{T} + \theta_2\right)$$

$$+ \cdots + \frac{2c_k}{T}\cos\left(\frac{2\pi k t}{T} + \theta_k\right) + \cdots \tag{7.3}$$

where there may or may not be infinitely many terms in the series. Equation (7.3) can be expressed more compactly by using summation notation:

$$f(t) = \frac{c_0}{T} + \frac{2}{T}\sum_{k=1}^{\infty} c_k \cos\left(\frac{2\pi k t}{T} + \theta_k\right) \tag{7.4}$$

is simply a shorthand representation of Eq. (7.3).

Suppose for the time being we take Fourier's word for the validity of Eq. (7.4). (We shall derive it later in Sec. 7.4.) How can Eq. (7.4) be expressed in the form of Eq. (7.2)?

Section 2.11 presented relations by which sinusoids could be written in terms of exponentials. Using the relation for the cosine, we have

$$\cos\left(\frac{2\pi kt}{T}+\theta_k\right) = \frac{e^{j(2\pi kt/T+\theta_k)} + e^{-j(2\pi kt/T+\theta_k)}}{2}$$

$$= \frac{e^{j\theta_k}\,e^{j2\pi kt/T} + e^{-j\theta_k}\,e^{-j2\pi kt/T}}{2} \tag{7.5}$$

If we define

$$C_k = c_k e^{j\theta_k} = c_k\underline{/\theta_k}$$

and

$$C_{-k} = C_k^* = c_k e^{-j\theta_k} = c_k\underline{/-\theta_k} \tag{7.6}$$

where the asterisk denotes the conjugate, then

$$2c_k \cos\left(\frac{2\pi kt}{T}+\theta_k\right) = C_k e^{j2\pi kt/T} + C_{-k}e^{-j2\pi kt/T} \tag{7.7}$$

Since for $k = 0$, $\exp(j2\pi kt/T) = e^0 = 1$, Eq. (7.4) can be written as

$$f(t) = \frac{1}{T}\sum_{k=-\infty}^{\infty} C_k e^{j2\pi kt/T} \tag{7.8}$$

Comparison of Eq. (7.8) with Eq. (7.2) shows that for a periodic function

$$B_k = \frac{C_k}{T} \tag{7.9}$$

which is, we must admit, neat. Comparison with Eq. (7.4) indicates that the magnitudes of the cosine harmonics are not really hidden by Eq. (7.8), inasmuch as the amplitude of the kth harmonic is simply $2\,|C_k|/T = 2\,|B_k|$ and its phase angle is the angle of C_k, where k is positive. This is really not inconsistent with the conventional notation for a sinusoid in complex form as normally used in a-c circuit theory. The factor of 2 is used to make Eq. (7.8) as compact and easy to remember as possible, and the factor of $1/T$ is used to make the connection between the Laplace transform and the Fourier series as simple as possible. This will be brought out in Sec. 7.4.

Since *frequency* is reserved for the exponential, Eq. (7.8) tells us that the frequencies contained in a periodic function are $f = 0,\ 1/T,$

$-1/T$, $2/T$, $-2/T$, ... cps, or, stated more generally, $f = k/T$ cps, with $k = 0$, ± 1, ± 2, ... Notice that corresponding positive and negative values of k lead to one positive *sinusoidal frequency*. The frequency $1/T$ is called the *fundamental* frequency, and all the others are called *harmonics*, because these frequencies are integral multiples of the fundamental frequency. The constants B_k need not be different from zero, for if $f(t) = 10 \cos 40\pi t$, then $B_0 = 0$ (no zero frequency or d-c), $B_1 = 5$, and $B_{-1} = 5$. The period is $T = \frac{1}{20}$ sec, and the fundamental frequency is 20 cps. Thus only the frequencies ± 20 cps are present, and all the rest are zero.

Clearly B_k (or $C_k = TB_k$) indicates the *amount* of the kth harmonic present in $f(t)$. It is important to note that the lowest frequency (other than zero frequency) contained in a signal is not necessarily the fundamental. For example, if

$$f(t) = 10 \cos 40\pi t + 5 \sin 60\pi t$$

then, since $\cos (x - 90°) = \sin x$

$$f(t) = 10 \cos 40\pi t + 5 \cos (60\pi t - 90°)$$

But the period now is not $\frac{1}{20}$ sec, since the frequencies of the first term are ± 20 and that of the second term are ± 30. These are multiples not of 20, but of 10, so the fundamental frequency is 10 cps. With $T = \frac{1}{10}$

$$B_0 = 0$$
$$B_1 = 0$$
$$B_2 = 5\underline{/0°}$$
$$B_3 = \frac{5}{2}\underline{/-90°}$$

then

$$f(t) = 5e^{j40\pi t} + 5e^{-j40\pi t} + \frac{5}{2}\underline{/-90°}\, e^{j60\pi t} + \frac{5}{2}\underline{/90°}\, e^{-j60\pi t}$$

In this example $f(t)$ contains no terms involving the fundamental frequency.

If two functions are periodic, but the ratio of their periods is not a rational number, then the sum of these functions is not periodic. They can, however, be expressed in exponential form. Since the frequencies are not harmonically related, the fundamental frequency as such does not exist. An example of this is easy to construct. Consider

$$f(t) = 10 \cos 40\pi t + 5 \cos 220t$$

The frequencies of the first sinusoid are ± 20 cps, but that of the second are $\pm 110/\pi \doteq \pm 35^-$ cps. There is no mathematically exact least common divisor for these frequencies, though five comes fairly close. If the function were plotted, it would appear to have a period of $\frac{1}{5}$ sec for several cycles, but in time the wave would change and its non-periodic nature would become apparent. Such a function is often referred to as an *almost periodic* function. Clearly, whether it is periodic or not, the function can be expressed in exponential form; that is,

$$f(t) = 5\,e^{j40\pi t} + 5\,e^{-j40\pi t} + \frac{5}{2}\,e^{j220t} + \frac{5}{2}\,e^{-j220t}$$

PROBLEMS

In Probs. 7.1 through 7.5, determine whether $f(t)$ is periodic. If it is, find its period and its fundamental frequency. Whether it is periodic or not, write the function in exponential form and list all the frequencies in cycles per second, both positive and negative, contained within the function.

7.1. $f(t) = 5 + 7\,\cos\,(20\pi t + 35°) + 2\,\cos\,(200\pi t - 30°)$

$$\text{Answer: } f(t) = 5 + \frac{7}{2}\underline{/35°}\,e^{j20\pi t} + \frac{7}{2}\underline{/-35°}\,e^{-j20\pi t}$$

$$+ 1\underline{/-30°}\,e^{j200\pi t} + 1\underline{/30°}\,e^{-j200\pi t}$$

Frequencies are 0, ± 10, ± 100 cps

7.2. $f(t) = 30 + 60\,\sin\,2\pi t + 120\,\sin\,3\pi t + 240\,\sin\,5\pi t$

7.3. $f(t) = (10\,\cos\,10\pi t)^2$

7.4. $f(t) = (2\,\cos\,10t + \sin\,20t)^2$

$$\text{Answer: } f(t) = 2.5 + 1\underline{/-90°}\,e^{j10t} + 1\underline{/90°}\,e^{-j10t} + e^{j20t}$$

$$+ e^{-j20t} + 1\underline{/-90°}\,e^{j30t} + 1\underline{/90°}\,e^{-j30t}$$

$$- \frac{1}{4}\,e^{j40t} - \frac{1}{4}\,e^{-j40t}$$

7.5. $f(t) = 3 + \cos\,20t + \frac{1}{2}\,\cos\,(20\pi t + 30°)$

7.6. Given that

$$f(t) = \frac{1}{T}\left[c_0 + 2\sum_{k=1}^{\infty} c_k \cos\left(\frac{2\pi k t}{T} + \theta_k\right)\right]$$

express a_k and b_k in terms of c_k and θ_k if

$$f(t) = a_0 + \sum_{k=1}^{\infty} \left(a_k \cos \frac{2\pi kt}{T} + b_k \sin \frac{2\pi kt}{T} \right)$$

7.7. Given the Fourier series in exponential form

$$f(t) = 4 \sum_{k=-\infty}^{\infty} \frac{e^{j20\pi kt}}{4k^2 - 1}$$

write out the first five terms of the series in cosine form, starting with the *d-c* term and proceeding to the fourth harmonic.

$$\textit{Answer:} \; -4 + \frac{8}{3} \cos 20\pi t + \frac{8}{15} \cos 40\pi t$$

$$+ \frac{8}{35} \cos 60\pi t + \frac{8}{63} \cos 80\pi t$$

7.8. Repeat Prob. 7.7 for

$$f(t) = 10 \sum_{k=-\infty}^{\infty} \frac{\sin \, (k\pi/2)}{k} e^{j42\pi kt}$$

Note that at $k = 0$, $[\sin \, (k\pi/2)] \, /k$ is indeterminate. Assume that the expression means to take the limit of $[\sin \, (k\pi/2)]/k$ as k approaches zero.

7.3 Frequency and the Exponential

No really telling argument has yet been given for relating frequency to the exponential only. The arguments given thus far involved the neat appearance of this form of the Fourier series and the fact that it is really not too difficult to obtain the cosine series from the exponential form if we remember to combine in pairs the positive and negative frequencies. In fact the factor of 2 in the expression $2|C_k|/T$ is really not difficult to remember, since *two* exponential frequencies make a real sinusoid.

Most of the arguments can be summed up by saying that the exponential form is not *bad*, but it is legitimate to ask, "What *good* is it?"

Recall the process by which functions with poles on the *j* axis in the *s* plane were inverse transformed. The transforms of both $\sin \beta t$ and $\cos \beta t$ have poles at $s = \pm j\beta$, so the notion of negative exponential frequencies is not really new. Without so stating, the exponential frequency was the basis of the technique by which all functions with complex poles were inverse transformed. In this sense, at least, the plus and minus frequency has already filtered into our work in a very natural way.

Even more important, however, is the ease with which exponentials can be manipulated mathematically. When exponentials are multiplied the exponents simply add together; when they are differentiated, the result is the exponential multiplied by the coefficient of t in the exponent. Division of exponentials results in the subtraction of exponents, and integration results in division by the coefficient of t in the exponent. The position of the harmonic analyst is this:

Since the exponential form of the Fourier series tells us just as much as the cosine form, and since the writing of the cosine form from the exponential form is trivial, then the advantages mathematically of using the exponential form are well worth the small price of remembering that real sinusoids are made up of two exponential frequencies, and that the (complex) amplitude of a negative frequency must be the conjugate of the amplitude of the corresponding positive frequency.

The mathematical advantages of the exponential form have not been demonstrated. One such advantage is the *orthogonal* property of two such functions that are harmonically related.

THEOREM 7.1. Given two exponential functions of unity amplitude and frequencies mf and nf, where m and n are integers, the average of the product of these two functions over the period $T = 1/f$ is (a) zero if $m \neq -n$ and (b) 1 if $m = -n$.

Proof: Let $f_1(t) = e^{j2\pi mft}$ and $f_2(t) = e^{j2\pi nft}$. The average of the product over the interval $T = 1/f$ is

$$\text{Average} = \frac{1}{T}\int_{t_0}^{t_0+T} (f_1 f_2)\,dt = \frac{1}{T}\int_{t_0}^{t_0+T} e^{j2\pi(m+n)t/T}\,dt \qquad (7.10)$$

(a) If $m \neq -n$, then $n + n \neq 0$ and the integral is

$$\text{Average} = \frac{T}{T\,[j2\pi(m+n)]}\, e^{j2\pi(m+n)t/T}\Big|_{t_0}^{t_0+T}$$

$$= \frac{1}{j2\pi(m+n)}\,\left[e^{j2\pi(m+n)(t_0+T)/T} - e^{j2\pi(m+n)t_0/T}\right]$$

But the first exponential can be written as the product of two exponentials; that is

$$e^{j2\pi(m+n)(t_0+T)/T} = e^{j2\pi(m+n)t_0/T}\, e^{j2\pi(m+n)}$$

But $e^{j2\pi(m+n)} = 1$, since m and n are both integers, so the exponentials are identically equal and the average of the product is zero; that is,

$$\text{Average} = 0$$

(*b*) If $m = -n$, then $m + n = 0$ and the integrand of Eq. (7.10) is simply unity. The indefinite integral is t then, and the value of the integral becomes

$$\text{Average} = \frac{1}{T}(t_0 + T - t_0) = 1 \qquad \text{Q.E.D.}$$

The theorem just proved will be used to derive Fourier's theorem, but it has another important application. It can be used to lend an important physical picture to the frequency domain and place on a firm mathematical basis the notion of a *frequency spectrum*.

Consider, for example, two voltage sources connected in series across a 1-ohm resistance. Let one source have an emf of $10 \cos 2\pi t$ and the other an emf of $5 \cos 20t$. Together, it will be observed, these two voltages do not make a periodic function.

If the power dissipated in the resistance at any moment is to be calculated, we have, from Eq. (2.10)

$$p(t) = \frac{v^2(t)}{R} = v^2 = (10 \cos 2\pi t + 5 \cos 20t)^2$$

$$= 100 \cos^2 2\pi t + 100 \cos 2\pi t \cos 20t + 25 \cos^2 20t$$

But the two trigonometric identities

$$\cos^2 x = \frac{1}{2}(1 + \cos 2x)$$

and

$$\cos x \cos y = \frac{1}{2}[\cos (x+y) + \cos (x-y)]$$

allow the power $p(t)$ to be written

$$p(t) = 50 + 12.5 + 50 \cos 4\pi t + 12.5 \cos 40t + 50 \cos (2\pi + 20)t$$
$$+ 50 \cos (2\pi - 20)t$$

However, 50 is the *average* power that would be dissipated in the load if the 1-cps source acted alone, and 12.5 is the average power in the load that would be dissipated if the $10/\pi$-cps source acted alone. The total *average* power when both sources are present is the *sum* of the averages for both sources acting alone. The instantaneous power $p(t)$, as can be seen from the last equation, is not the sum of the instantaneous powers that would exist if the sources acted alone, but has in addition a cross-product pair of terms

$$50 \cos (2\pi + 20)t + 50 \cos (2\pi - 20)t$$

Since these are simply sinusoids, however, they have zero average value. The other double-frequency terms in the expression for $p(t)$ also have zero average value.

Although it is still true that the square of a sum is not equal to the sum of the squares—that is, $(x+y)^2 \neq x^2 + y^2$—the total *average power* associated with a signal containing many sinusoids can be thought of as the sum of the average powers contained in the individual sinusoids. This is true no matter how many sinusoids are contained in a voltage or current, and whether or not the function is periodic.

When we discuss individual exponential functions of the form e^{jat}, where a is a constant, we cannot discuss power, since the exponential function without its mate e^{-jat} does not represent anything physical. Nevertheless, it will prove to be very convenient to *imagine* that half of the average power in any sinusoid is actually associated with the negative frequency and half is associated with the positive frequency. In a Fourier series, for example, the kth sinusoidal harmonic is

$$2c_k/T \cos (2\pi kt/T + \theta_k)$$

If this represents a voltage or current, and the resistance level is 1 ohm, the power associated with this function is simply the square of the function, and the average power is one-half the peak value squared, that is, P_{avk} (read P-average-kth harmonic) is simply

$$P_{avk} = \frac{1}{2} \left(\frac{2c_k}{T}\right)^2 = 2 \frac{c_k^2}{T^2} \text{ watts}$$

But the complex amplitude C_k has a magnitude of c_k, so

$$P_{avk} = \frac{2|C_k|^2}{T^2}$$

If, as suggested before, we *imagine* that half of this power is associated with the frequency $+k/T$ and half with the frequency $-k/T$, the average power associated with any one exponential is simply $|C_k|^2/T^2$. In the future, unless stated to the contrary, the expression P_{avk} will be related to the exponential form only and not as indicated above. Thus, by definition,

$$P_{avk} = \frac{|C_k|^2}{T^2} \qquad (7.11a)$$

will be the power associated with the term $C_k/T \; e^{j2\pi kt/T}$, that is, the average power at the frequency k/T. Furthermore, it can be proved in

general (see Prob. 7.16) that whether a function is periodic or almost
periodic, if

$$f(t) = \sum_{-\infty}^{\infty} B_k \, e^{j2\pi f_k t}$$

then

$$P_{\text{av}k} = |B_k|^2 \tag{7.11b}$$

is the average power associated with the frequency f_k. If the *actual*
average power associated with the sinusoidal harmonic is desired, then
Eqs. $(7.11a)$ and $(7.11b)$ must be multiplied by 2.

An interesting question arises at this point: Is the power really
contained in the harmonics? For that matter, we might ask: Are the
harmonics really there? These are legitimate questions, though at the
moment unimportant. At this point all we are trying to say is that,
for calculating the total average power, it is convenient to think of the
power as contained in the harmonics. It will be seen shortly, however,
that if a complicated nonsinusoidal periodic signal is the input to a
narrow-band filter and it is assumed that the signal has only one component of frequency within the pass band of the filter, then not only
will the output of the filter be very nearly a single sinusoid, but the
power associated with the output will be very nearly that given by the
ideas of this section—that is, the power of that one sinusoidal component.
The qualifying terms "very nearly" are required, because—as will
be seen in Chapter 9—no filter can be constructed that will block all
harmonics but one, but the ideal can be approached fairly closely.

The average value of a function $g(t)$ is defined as the area under
the function divided by the duration of the function. For any function
$g(t)$ that is defined for all time t, $\bar{g}$ (the average value of g), is defined as

$$\bar{g} = \lim_{\tau \to \infty} \frac{1}{2\tau} \int_{-\tau}^{\tau} g(t) \, dt \tag{7.12}$$

If $g(t)$ is periodic, then Eq. (7.12) need not be used, since the averaging
need be done over one cycle only; that is,

$$\bar{g} = \frac{1}{T} \int_{t_0}^{t_0 + T} g(t) \, dt \tag{7.13}$$

Equations (7.12) and (7.13) are analogous to computing the average
yearly income of an individual. In that case it would be necessary to sum
(integrate) the income over all the years of employment and divide

this total by the number of years employed, unless the individual's income were known to be periodic—that is, the same each year—in which case it would only be necessary to find the income for one year to compute the average.

The restriction in Theorem 7.1 that the frequencies mf and nf must be integral multiples of the fundamental frequency f could be removed if instead of using Eq. (7.13) we used Eq. (7.12) for computing the average. The proof of this more general form of theorem 7.1 constitutes the solution to Prob. 7.15.

If $f(t)$ is periodic with period T, and

$$f(t) = \frac{1}{T} \sum_{k=-\infty}^{\infty} C_k \, e^{j2\pi kt/T}$$

then it has been asserted that the average power in $f(t)$ (1-ohm level) is given by

$$P_{av} = \frac{1}{T} \int_{t_0}^{t_0+T} f^2(t) \, dt = \sum_{k=-\infty}^{\infty} \frac{|C_k|^2}{T^2} \tag{7.14}$$

Proof: If the Fourier series for $f(t)$

$$f(t) = \frac{1}{T} \sum_{k=-\infty}^{\infty} C_k \, e^{j2\pi kt/T}$$

is squared, it can be written as a double sum

$$f^2(t) = \frac{1}{T^2} \left[\sum_{k=-\infty}^{\infty} C_k \, e^{j2\pi kt/T} \right] \left[\sum_{p=-\infty}^{\infty} C_p \, e^{j2\pi pt/T} \right] \tag{7.15}$$

where k and p are merely indices of the summations, and like the dummy variable of a definite integral can be any letter desired. The summations of Eq. (7.15) can be combined into

$$f^2(t) = \frac{1}{T^2} \sum_{k=-\infty}^{\infty} \sum_{p=-\infty}^{\infty} C_k C_p \, e^{j2\pi(k+p)t/T} \tag{7.16}$$

If Eq. (7.16) is substituted into Eq. (7.13), and if the order of the summations and integration are reversed (legitimate if the series converges uniformly and absolutely in the interval of the integration), then

$$P_{av} = \frac{1}{T^2} \sum_{k=-\infty}^{\infty} \sum_{p=-\infty}^{\infty} C_k C_p \left\{ \frac{1}{T} \int_{t_0}^{t_0+T} e^{j2\pi(k+p)t/T} \, dt \right\}$$

But, according to the theorem above, the expression in the braces vanishes unless $k = -p$, and for this value it has a value of unity. Then

$$P_{av} = \frac{1}{T^2} \sum_{k=-\infty}^{\infty} C_k C_{-k} = \sum_{k=-\infty}^{\infty} \frac{|C_k|^2}{T^2} \qquad \text{Q.E.D.} \qquad (7.17)$$

The averaging in the proof above was done over one period, since $f(t)$ was known to be periodic. Even if the frequencies were not related harmonically, the result would still be the same except that the averaging would have had to be done over an infinite period to complete the proof. (See Prob. 7.16).

The *power spectrum* of a periodic (or almost periodic) function is defined as a plot of points (or vertical lines) whose coordinates are $f = k/T$ (or the different frequencies if almost periodic) and $P_{av} = |C_k|^2/T^2$. Since points are difficult to see on a graph, they are usually made more evident by drawing vertical lines from the abscissa (the frequency axis) to the points. This practice has led to the term *line spectrum*.

EXAMPLE 7.1. The Fourier series for the triangular wave shown in Fig. 7.5 is

$$f(t) = \frac{1}{T} \sum_{k=-\infty}^{\infty} C_k e^{j\pi k t}$$

where $C_0 = 0$ (it is obvious that the wave has no average value or d-c term) and

$$C_k = \left[\frac{\sin (\pi k/2)}{(\pi k/2)}\right]^2 \text{ for } k \neq 0$$

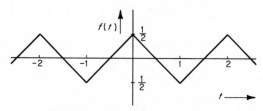

Fig. 7.5   *A triangular wave.*

That this is a correct expression for C_k will be demonstrated in Prob. 7.20. For the present, accept it as true. Write the Fourier series in sinusoidal form and draw the line spectrum of the function.
Solution: Since the C_k are all real, $c_k = C_k$ and $\theta_k = 0$ for all k. Evidently $T = 2$, so $2c_k/T = c_k = C_k$ and hence

$$f(t) = C_1 \cos \pi t + C_2 \cos 2\pi t + C_3 \cos 3\pi t + \dots$$

Substituting integers for k, we find that $\sin^2 (k\pi/2)$ is zero when k

is even (that is, 2, 4, 6, ...) and it is unity when k is odd. C_k can be simplified even further, as follows:

$$C_k = \frac{4}{(\pi k)^2} \text{ for } k = 1, 3, 5, \ldots$$

Then the sinusoidal form of the Fourier series can be written as

$$f(t) = \frac{4}{\pi^2} \left[\cos \pi t + \frac{1}{9} \cos 3\pi t + \frac{1}{25} \cos 5\pi t + \frac{1}{49} \cos 7\pi t + \ldots \right]$$

The line spectrum is obtained by

$$P_{\text{avk}} = \frac{|C_k|^2}{T^2} = \frac{16}{(\pi k)^4 (2)^2} = \frac{4}{\pi^4 k^4} \text{ watts}$$

The line spectrum is plotted in Fig. 7.6. It can be seen that most of the power is contained in the fundamental and its conjugate.

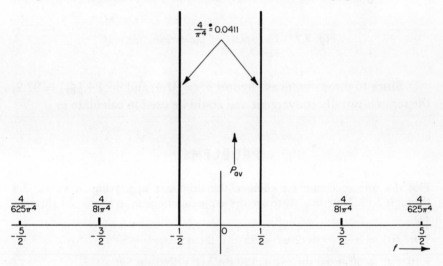

Fig. 7.6 *The line spectrum of the periodic wave of Fig. 7.5.*

A very interesting infinite series can be summed by using the results of this problem. The average power can be calculated by entirely different means: squaring the original function as is done in Fig. 7.7 and finding the average of the result. As can be seen from the figure, the square of a linear rise is parabolic, and the area under a parabolic triangle is $\frac{1}{3}$ the base times the height. (This is an interesting fact, and verifying it is a worthwhile exercise). Since the square of $f(t)$ is periodic with half the original period, the base of any one triangle is 1 sec and the height is $(\frac{1}{2})^2 = \frac{1}{4}$. The average value of $f^2(t)$ must then be $\frac{1}{12}$. But the average value is also the sum of the terms $P_{\text{av}k}$ for all k, so

$$\frac{1}{12} = \frac{8}{\pi^4} + \frac{8}{\pi^4 3^4} + \frac{8}{\pi^4 5^4} + \frac{8}{\pi^4 7^4} + \cdots$$

where the powers of the positive and negative frequencies have been combined. If both sides of the equation are multiplied by $12\pi^4$

$$\pi^4 = 96 \left(1 + \frac{1}{3^4} + \frac{1}{5^4} + \frac{1}{7^4} + \cdots\right)$$

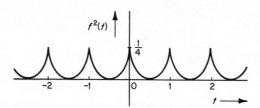

Fig. 7.7   *The square of the periodic wave of Fig. 7.5.*

Since to three significant figures $\pi^4 = 97.4$, and $96(1+\frac{1}{81}) = 97.2$, the series is rapidly convergent and could be used to calculate π.

PROBLEMS

Plot the line spectrum for each of the functions appearing in Probs. 7.9 through 7.13. Note that these are the same functions as in Probs. 7.1 through 7.5.

7.9. $f(t) = 5 + 7 \cos (20\pi t + 35°) + 2 \cos (200\pi t - 30°)$

7.10. $f(t) = 30 + 60 \sin 2\pi t + 120 \sin 3\pi t + 240 \sin 5\pi t$

7.11. $f(t) = (10 \cos 10\pi t)^2$

7.12. $f(t) = (2 \cos 10t + \sin 20t)^2$

7.13. $f(t) = 3 + \cos 20t + \frac{1}{2} \cos (20\pi t + 30°)$

7.14. The Fourier series for the square wave pictured in Fig. 7.8 can be shown to be

$$f(t) = \frac{2A}{\pi} \sum_{\substack{k=-\infty \\ (k \neq 0)}}^{\infty} \frac{\sin (\pi k/2)}{k} e^{j2\pi kt/T}$$

where C_0 is zero, since it is clear from the figure that there is no average value to $f(t)$.

(a) Write out the mathematical expressions in cosine form for the first three nonzero harmonics.

(b) Write a general expression P_{avk} in terms of k and plot the line spectrum of the signal.

$$\textit{Answer:} \quad P_{avk} = \frac{4A^2}{\pi^2 k^2}, \text{ with } k \text{ odd}$$

(c) Find the average power in $f(t)$ by direct methods, and by comparison with the line spectrum, write an infinite series for π^2.

$$\textit{Answer:} \quad \pi^2 = 8\left(1 + \frac{1}{3^2} + \frac{1}{5^2} + \frac{1}{7^2} + \cdots\right)$$

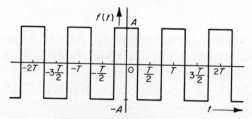

Fig. 7.8 *Problem 7.14.*

7.15. Prove that if frequencies f_1 and f_2 are such that the ratio f_1/f_2 is not a rational number

$$\lim_{\tau \to \infty} \frac{1}{2\tau} \int_{-\tau}^{\tau} e^{j2\pi f_1 t} \, e^{j2\pi f_2 t} \, dt = 0$$

The condition $f_1 = -f_2$ cannot occur, since this would make the ratio of the two frequencies -1, a rational number.)

7.16. Using the results of Prob. 7.15, prove that the average power in

$$f(t) = \sum_{k=-\infty}^{\infty} B_k e^{j2\pi f_k t}$$

is given by

$$P_{av} = \sum_{k=-\infty}^{\infty} |B_k|^2$$

where $B_{-k} = B_k^*$, even though the frequencies f_k may not be harmonically related.

7.4 Derivation of Fourier's Theorem

The material contained in this section is not mathematically rigorous, as it will not be proved that the series converges to the function. This is of course important, but attention should now be directed towards a better understanding and an intuitive feeling for harmonic analysis. The motivation for mathematical rigor will come with understanding. Suffice it to say that if $f(t)$ has in any period a finite number of maxima and minima and a finite number of discontinuities (including impulses), and if $f(t)$ is absolutely integrable over a period, that is

$$\int_{t_0}^{t_0+T} |f(t)| \, dt < \infty$$

then the Fourier series will converge to $f(t)$ for all t. At points where $f(t)$ is discontinuous, the series will approach the average of the values of the function at either side of the discontinuity.

THEOREM 7.2. Let $f(t)$ be periodic with period T. If

$$f(t) = \frac{1}{T} \sum_{k=-\infty}^{\infty} C_k \, e^{j2\pi kt/T} \tag{7.18}$$

then

$$C_k = \int_{t_0}^{t_0+T} f(t) e^{-j2\pi kt/T} \, dt \tag{7.19}$$

where t_0 is completely arbitrary.

Proof: If Eq. (7.18) is multiplied by $e^{-j2\pi mt/T}$, where m is an arbitrary positive or negative integer, and integrated from t_0 to $t_0 + T$

$$\int_{t_0}^{t_0+T} f(t) e^{-j2\pi mt/T} \, dt = \int_{t_0}^{t_0+T} \left\{ \frac{1}{T} \sum_{k=-\infty}^{\infty} C_k e^{j2\pi kt/T} \right\} e^{-j2\pi mt/T} \, dt$$

The series can be integrated term-by-term, yielding

$$\int_{t_0}^{t_0+T} f(t) e^{-j2\pi mt/T} \, dt = \sum_{k=-\infty}^{\infty} C_k \left\{ \frac{1}{T} \int_{t_0}^{t_0+T} e^{j2\pi(k-m)t/T} \, dt \right\}$$

But from Theorem 7.1, the integral under the summation sign is unity if $k = m$ and zero otherwise. The right-hand side then is simply C_m, so

$$C_m = \int\limits_{t_0}^{t_0+T} f(t)e^{-j2\pi mt/T}\, dt$$

which is Eq. (7.19) but with the index m instead of k.

The result of Theorem 7.2 can be remembered in a very simple way: C_k/T was called the *amount* of the frequency k/T contained in $f(t)$. To find this amount, we simply multiply the function $f(t)$ by the frequency $-k/T$—that is, by $e^{-j2\pi kt/T}$—and average the result over one period.

Obviously the constants C_k can be obtained by direct integration, but with proficiency in finding the Laplace transforms of functions, there is an easy way of determining the C_k.

Observe that the expression for the Laplace transform of $f(t)$, if it were transformable,* would be

$$F(s) = \int\limits_{-\infty}^{\infty} f(t)e^{-st}\, dt$$

Notice the similarity between this expression and that for C_k. If we set $s = j2\pi k/T$, the integrands would be identical. The limits of the integration are different, however. This can be easily remedied by defining, as done previously

$$p(t) = f(t)\,[\mathbf{1}(t-t_0) - \mathbf{1}(t-t_0-T)] \tag{7.20}$$

$p(t)$ is simply one period of $f(t)$ and is zero elsewhere. It is transformable, and what is more, its transform exists for all values of s, since its abscissa of exponential order is $-\infty$. (See Prob. 3.4.)

Since $p(t)$ is zero from $-\infty$ to t_0 and zero from $t_0 + T$ to $+\infty$

$$P(s) = \int\limits_{t_0}^{t_0+T} f(t)e^{-st}\, dt$$

so

$$P(j2\pi k/T) = \int\limits_{t_0}^{t_0+T} f(t)e^{-j2\pi kt/T}\, dt \tag{7.21}$$

---

*It is not transformable. Why?

Comparison of Eqs. (7.19) and (7.21) shows that

$$C_k = P(j2\pi k/T) \qquad (7.22)$$

so all the coefficients C_k can be obtained at once by simply transforming one period of the periodic wave. However, make certain that the transform is one that represents a function that is zero for $t > (t_0 + T)$. To stress this point and to demonstrate the procedure, we will give two examples.

EXAMPLE 7.2. Find the complex form of the Fourier series for the periodic function appearing in Fig. 7.9. Write out the first five nonzero terms in the cosine form of the Fourier series.

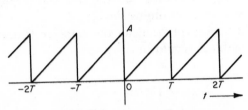

Fig. 7.9　*A sawtooth wave.*

Solution: One period of the wave is shown in Fig. 7.10. Be careful to note that this can be considered a ramp with slope A/T plus a negative ramp of the same magnitude and starting at $t = T$. Don't stop at this point. The result of these two ramps is not one period of $f(t)$, but the function appearing in Fig. 7.11. To get one period only, a negative step of amplitude A must be added at $t = T$. Then

$$p(t) = \frac{A}{T}[t\mathbf{1}(t) - (t-T)\,\mathbf{1}\,(t-T)] - A\,\mathbf{1}\,(t-T)$$

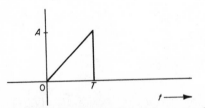

Fig. 7.10　*One period of the sawtooth wave of Fig. 7.9.*

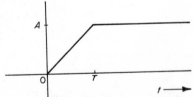

Fig. 7.11　*The result of subtracting a ramp of slope A/T at $t = T$ from a ramp of A/T starting at $t = 0$.*

Since the transform of the ramp with slope A/T is simply $A/(Ts^2)$, the transform of $p(t)$ is

$$P(s) = \frac{A}{Ts^2}(1 - e^{-sT}) - \frac{A}{s}e^{-sT}$$

Setting $s = j2\pi k/T$, we obtain C_k.

$$C_k = \frac{A}{T(j2\pi k/T)^2}(1 - e^{-j2\pi k}) - \frac{A}{j2\pi k/T}e^{-j2\pi k}$$

But $e^{-j2\pi k} = 1$, so

$$C_k = -\frac{A}{j2\pi k/T} = j\frac{AT}{2\pi k} = \frac{AT}{2\pi k}\underline{/90°}$$

Since the amplitude of each frequency component is C_k/T, $C_k/T = A/(2\pi k)\underline{/90°}$ for all k but zero. Obviously $k = 0$ cannot be used in this expression, for that would imply that $C_0 = \infty$; in other words, that the d-c component is infinitely large. A glance at Fig. 7.9 tells us that the average value is $A/2$. What went wrong?

It happens quite frequently that the average value of the wave is not given directly by the transform. Occasionally one of the C_k terms appears to have the value of infinity.

The difficulty here arises because both the numerator and denominator of the transform $P(s)$ vanish for this particular value of s and it happens most frequently at $s = 0$. There are many ways to show that the value of $P(s)$ at $s = 0$ is indeed $AT/2$. One such method is the use of L'Hôpital's rule.

$$P(0) = \lim_{s \to 0} A\left[\frac{1 - e^{-sT}}{Ts^2} - \frac{e^{-sT}}{s}\right] = \lim_{s \to 0}\frac{A(1 - e^{-sT} - Tse^{-sT})}{Ts^2}$$

If the numerator and denominator of the last fraction are differentiated twice, the limit can be shown to be $AT/2$. (Try this as an exercise). Another way of doing this is to use the Maclaurin series for e^{-sT}. Since

$$e^{-sT} = 1 - sT + \frac{(sT)^2}{2!} - \frac{(sT)^3}{3!} + \cdots$$

then

$$1 - e^{-sT} = sT - \frac{(sT)^2}{2} + \frac{(sT)^3}{6} - \cdots$$

$$\frac{1 - e^{-sT}}{Ts^2} = \frac{1}{s} - \frac{T}{2} + \frac{sT^2}{6} - \cdots$$

and

$$-\frac{e^{-sT}}{s} = -\frac{1}{s} + T - \frac{sT^2}{2} + \frac{s^2T^3}{6} - \cdots$$

Then for small s

$$P(s) = A\left[\frac{T}{2} - \frac{sT^2}{3} + \cdots\right]$$

so

$$P(0) = \frac{AT}{2}$$

It becomes clear that the evaluation of the d-c term from the general expression is much more trouble than it is worth. Fortunately, the constant term is the simplest of them all and can often be deduced by inspection. Even so, when a situation such as this arises and the series approach or L'Hôpital's rule looks too much like work, it is always possible to go back to the integral form for the particular C_k and evaluate it separately. For example, since C_0 caused the trouble in this example, calculate it separately, using Eq. (7.19) and setting $k = 0$.

$$C_0 = \int_0^T \frac{At}{T}\,dt = \frac{At^2}{2T}\bigg|_0^T = \frac{AT}{2}$$

The exponential or complex form of the Fourier series is then

$$f(t) = \frac{A}{2} + \frac{A}{2\pi}\sum_{\substack{k=-\infty\\k\neq0}}^{\infty}\frac{je^{j2\pi kt/T}}{k}$$

and the first five terms of the cosine series are

$$f(t) = \frac{A}{2} + \frac{A}{\pi}\left[\cos\left(\frac{2\pi t}{T} + 90°\right) + \frac{1}{2}\cos\left(\frac{4\pi t}{T} + 90°\right)\right.$$
$$\left. + \frac{1}{3}\cos\left(6\pi t + 90°\right) + \frac{1}{4}\cos\left(\frac{8\pi t}{T} + 90°\right) + \cdots\right]$$

EXAMPLE 7.3. In rectifier circuits containing thyratrons and ignitrons, the current waveform is sometimes that shown in Fig. 7.12. Find the complex form of the Fourier series and write out the first five nonzero terms of the cosine series.
Solution: In this example it is fairly obvious what $p(t)$ is. Its transform can be obtained by shifting the pulse to the left $T/4$ sec and noting that

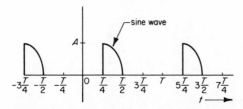

Fig. 7.12 *The output of a controlled rectifier circuit.*

the result can be viewed as the sum of $A \cos 2\pi t/T\mathbf{1}(t)$ and $A \sin 2\pi t/T\mathbf{1}(t)$ shifted to the right $T/4$ sec. This is shown graphically in Fig. 7.13.

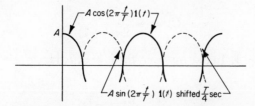

Fig. 7.13 *One period of the wave of Fig. 7.12 constructed by adding a cosine and a translated sine.*

Then

$$P(s) = \left[\frac{As}{s^2 + (2\pi/T)^2} + \frac{(2\pi A/T)e^{-sT/4}}{s^2 + (2\pi/T)^2} \right] e^{-sT/4}$$

$$= \frac{A}{s^2 + (2\pi/T)^2} \left[s + \frac{2\pi}{T} e^{-sT/4} \right] e^{-sT/4}$$

where the final $e^{-sT/4}$ shifts the pulse back to $+T/4$, where it was originally.

Setting $s = j2\pi k/T$ gives

$$C_k = \frac{A}{(2\pi/T)^2(1-k^2)} \left[j\frac{2\pi k}{T} + \frac{2\pi}{T} e^{-j\pi k/2} \right] e^{-j\pi k/2}$$

$$= \frac{AT}{2\pi(1-k^2)} \left[jk + e^{-j\pi k/2} \right] e^{-j\pi k/2}$$

Note that the evaluation of C_1 and C_{-1} will cause trouble. For C_1, by L'Hôpital's rule

$$\lim_{k \to +1} e^{-j\pi k/2} \frac{AT}{2\pi} \left[\frac{e^{-j\pi k/2} + jk}{1 - k^2} \right] = -j \frac{AT}{2\pi} \lim_{k \to +1} \frac{e^{-j\pi k/2} + jk}{1 - k^2}$$

$$= -j\frac{AT}{2\pi} \lim_{k \to +1} \frac{-j(\pi/2)e^{-j\pi k/2} + j}{-2k}$$

$$= j\frac{AT}{2\pi} \left[\frac{-\pi/2 + j}{2}\right] = \frac{AT}{4\pi}(-1 - j\pi/2)$$

$$= \frac{AT}{4\pi}\sqrt{1 + \pi^2/4} \; \underline{/-90° - \tan^{-1}2/\pi}$$

$$\doteq 0.1485\, AT \; \underline{/-122.5°}$$

Observe that when $k = 1, 5, 9, 13$, and so on, $e^{-j\pi k/2} = -j$ and $(jk + e^{-j\pi k/2})(e^{-j\pi k/2}) = k - 1$. Then for $k = 5, 9, 13, \ldots$

$$C_k = -\frac{AT}{2\pi(k+1)}$$

but not for $k = 1$. In like manner, for $k = 3, 7, 11, \ldots e^{-j\pi k/2} = +j$ and

$$C_k = \frac{AT}{2\pi(k-1)}$$

For $k = 2, 6, 10, \ldots$ the exponential is -1 and

$$C_k = -\frac{AT(jk-1)}{2\pi(1-k^2)}$$

For $k = 4, 8, 12, \ldots$

$$C_k = -\frac{AT(1+jk)}{2\pi(k^2-1)}$$

Since $C_0 = AT/2\pi$, the complex Fourier series is

$$f(t) = \frac{A}{2\pi}\left[1 - \frac{1}{2}\left(1 + \frac{j\pi}{2}\right)e^{j2\pi t/T} - \frac{1}{2}\left(1 - \frac{j\pi}{2}\right)e^{-j2\pi t/T}\right.$$

$$+ \sum_{k=\pm 2, \pm 6}\frac{jk-1}{k^2-1}e^{j2\pi kt/T} + \sum_{k=\pm 3, \pm 7}\frac{e^{j2\pi kt/T}}{k-1}$$

$$\left. + \sum_{k=\pm 4, \pm 8}\frac{-(1+jk)}{k^2-1}e^{j2\pi kt/T} + \sum_{k=\pm 5, \pm 9}\frac{-e^{j2\pi kt/T}}{k+1}\right]$$

To write the first five terms of the cosine series, observe that

$$C_0/T = A/2\pi$$

$$2C_1/T = (A/2\pi) \times 1.865 \; \underline{/-122.5°}$$

$$2C_2/T = (A/2\pi) \times 1.49 \underline{/116.6°}$$

$$2C_3/T = A/2\pi$$

$$2C_4/T = (A/2\pi) \times 0.55 \underline{/-104.04°}$$

The series is then

$$f(t) = \frac{A}{2\pi}\left[1 + 1.865 \cos\left(\frac{2\pi t}{T} - 122.5°\right) + 1.49 \cos\left(\frac{4\pi t}{T} + 116.6°\right)\right.$$

$$\left. + \cos\frac{6\pi t}{T} + 0.55 \cos\left(\frac{8\pi t}{T} - 104.04°\right) + \ldots\right]$$

It is apparent that the magnitudes of the terms do not fall off very rapidly and that many more terms would be required to approximate the function accurately.

PROBLEMS

For Probs. 7.17 through 7.23, (*a*) sketch one period of the periodic waves pictured and find its transform $P(s)$, (*b*) set $s = j2\pi k/T$ in each and obtain a general expression for C_k, (*c*) sketch the line spectrum of the signal (at least five lines on either side of the origin), (*d*) write the Fourier series in exponential form, and (*e*) write out the first five nonzero terms of the series in cosine form.

7.17. See Fig. 7.14.

Answers: (*b*) $C_k = \dfrac{AT}{\pi k} \sin\dfrac{\pi k}{3}$

$$(d)\; f(t) = \frac{A}{\pi} \sum_{-\infty}^{\infty} \frac{\sin(\pi k/3)}{k} e^{j2\pi kt/T}$$

$$(e)\; f(t) = \frac{A}{3} + \frac{\sqrt{3}A}{\pi} \cos\frac{2\pi t}{T} + \frac{\sqrt{3}A}{2\pi} \cos\frac{4\pi t}{T}$$

$$- \frac{\sqrt{3}A}{4\pi} \cos\frac{8\pi t}{T} - \frac{\sqrt{3}A}{5\pi} \cos\frac{10\pi t}{T} + \ldots$$

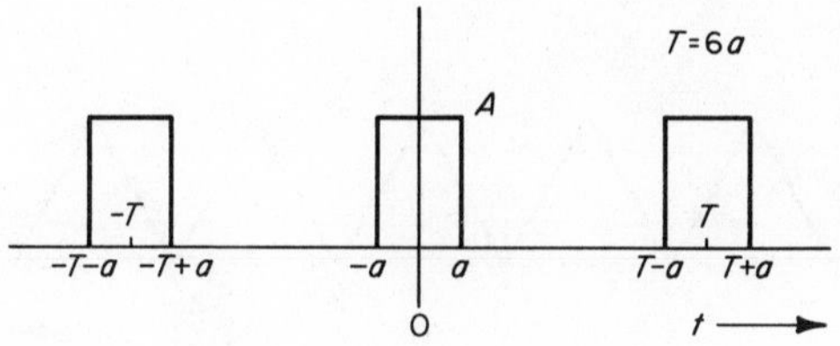

Fig. 7.14 *Problem 7.17.*

7.18. See Fig. 7.15.

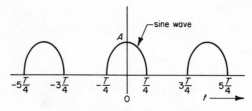

Fig. 7.15   *Problem 7.18.*

7.19. See Fig. 7.16.

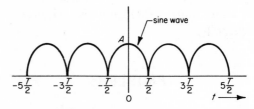

Fig. 7.16   *Problem 7.19.*

Answers: $(b)\ C_k = \dfrac{(-1)^k 2AT}{\pi(1-4k^2)}$

$(d)\ f(t) = \dfrac{2A}{\pi} \sum_{-\infty}^{\infty} \dfrac{(-1)^k}{(1-4k^2)}\ e^{j2\pi kt/T}$

$(e)\ f(t) = \dfrac{2A}{\pi} \left[1 + \dfrac{2}{3} \cos \dfrac{2\pi t}{T} - \dfrac{2}{15} \cos \dfrac{4\pi t}{T} \right.$

$\left. + \dfrac{2}{35} \cos \dfrac{6\pi t}{T} - \dfrac{2}{63} \cos \dfrac{8\pi t}{T} \right.$

$\left. + \dfrac{2}{99} \cos \dfrac{10\pi t}{T} - \cdots \right]$

7.20. See Fig. 7.17.

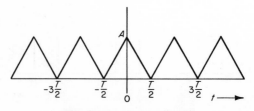

Fig. 7.17   *Problem 7.20.*

7.21. See Fig. 7.18.

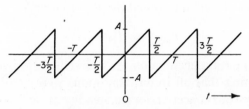

Fig. 7.18 *Problem 7.21.*

7.22. In Fig. 7.19, the curve is an exponential decay with time constant $T/5$.

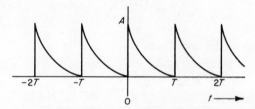

Fig. 7.19 *Problem 7.22.*

$$\text{Answer: } (b) \ C_k = \frac{AT(1-e^{-5})}{5[1+j(2\pi k/5)]}$$

7.23. See Fig. 7.20.

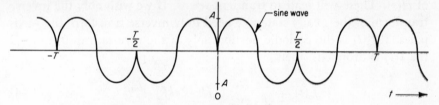

Fig. 7.20 *Problem 7.23.*

$$\text{Answer: } (b) \ C_k = \frac{AT}{\pi(1-k^2/4)} \quad \text{with } k \text{ odd}$$

7.24. Verify the Fourier series given in Prob. 7.14 for the square wave pictured in Fig. 7.8.

7.5 Periodic Signals and Linear Systems

If the input signal to a stable linear network or system is periodic, the steady-state output signal is also periodic with the same period. That this is true can be easily demonstrated by the use of transfer functions.

If a system is linear, the transform of the output signal is related to the transform of the input signal by the equation

$$F_o(s) = H(s)F_{in}(s) \tag{7.23}$$

where $H(s)$ is the transfer function of the system. Observe that $H(s)$ was defined by stating that all initial conditions were zero; this is appropriate here, since our concern is for the steady state and not the transient.

Strictly speaking, $f_{in}(t)$ cannot be periodic if it is to have a Laplace transform, but we can define

$$f_{in}(t) = \frac{1(t)}{T} \sum_{k=-\infty}^{\infty} C_k e^{j2\pi kft}$$

as the input signal. Its transform is

$$F_{in}(s) = \frac{1}{T} \sum_{k=-\infty}^{\infty} \frac{C_k}{(s-j2\pi kf)}$$

With $H(s)$ the transfer function of some linear system then

$$F_o(s) = \frac{1}{T} \sum_{k=-\infty}^{\infty} \frac{C_k H(s)}{(s-j2\pi kf)}$$

$F_o(s)$ will have poles in the left-half plane because of the poles of $H(s)$. These will lead to transient terms. If we wish only the inverse transform of the steady state, we need only inverse transform the j-axis poles. If $f_o(t)$ is the periodic portion only of the inverse transform (and the $1(t)$ is dropped), then

$$f_o(t) = \frac{1}{T} \sum_{k=-\infty}^{\infty} C_k H(j2\pi kf)\, e^{j2\pi kft} \tag{7.24}$$

and the only effect the system has on the series is to alter the amount of each frequency by the transfer function evaluated at that frequency.

The line spectrum of the output signal is given by

$$P_{avk} = \frac{|C_k|^2 |H(j2\pi kf)|^2}{T^2} \tag{7.25}$$

Equations (7.24) and (7.25) represent the principal reasons for the use of the Fourier series in signal analysis. The steady-state effect of a filter on a signal can be seen if we compare the line spectrum of the signal with the frequency response of the filter. Multiplication of the two will produce the spectrum of the output signal.

EXAMPLE 7.4. The rectangular wave of Fig. 7.21 is the input signal (the current i_s) of the *R-L-C* tank circuit pictured in Fig. 7.22. Find the Fourier series of the input and output signals and their line spectra.

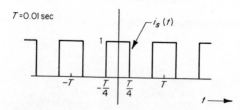

Fig. 7.21 *The square-wave input signal.*

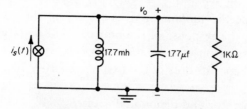

Fig. 7.22 *The bandpass filter.*

Solution: The transform of one period of the input signal is

$$P(s) = \frac{e^{sT/4} - e^{-sT/4}}{s}$$

Setting $s = j2\pi k/T$, we have

$$C_k = \frac{e^{j\pi k/2} - e^{-j\pi k/2}}{2\pi jk/T}$$

$$= T \frac{\sin (\pi k/2)}{\pi k}$$

If we divide by T, the Fourier series of the input signal is

$$i_s(t) = \sum_{k=-\infty}^{\infty} \frac{\sin (\pi k/2)}{\pi k} e^{j2\pi kt/T}$$

Note that for small angles, $\sin x \doteq x$, so for small k, $\sin (\pi k/2) \doteq \pi k/2$, making the d-c term ($k = 0$ term) $= \frac{1}{2}$.

The transfer function of the network is

$$H(s) = \frac{s/C}{s^2 + (1/RC)s + 1/LC}$$

Referring back to the example in Sec. 5.4,* we have

$$Q_o = R \sqrt{\frac{C}{L}} = 1000 \sqrt{\frac{1.77 \times 10^{-6}}{17.7 \times 10^{-3}}} = 10$$

so the roots of the denominator are very nearly

$$s = \frac{1}{\sqrt{LC}} \left(-\frac{1}{20} \pm j\right)$$

$$= 5.65 \times 10^3 \, (-0.05 \pm j)$$

If the frequency response versus frequency is plotted, a sharp resonance will be seen at $f = 900$ cps; at this frequency, $H(s) = R = 1000$. Since the fundamental frequency of the periodic wave is $1/T = 100$ cps, the response of the network will be large at the ninth harmonic. Substitution of even harmonics (k even) will yield zero, so the input signal consists only of the frequencies 100, 300, 500, 700, 900, 1100, ... cps.

If the numerator and denominator of $H(s)$ are multiplied by RC/s, $H(s)$ can be written

$$H(s) = \frac{R}{1 + (RC/s)(s^2 + 1/LC)}$$

and with $s = j2\pi k/T = j200\pi k$

$$H(j200\pi k) = \frac{1000}{1 + (j10/9)(k - 81/k)}$$

Substituting $k = 1, 3, 5, 7, 9, 11$, and computing only the magnitude of $H(s)$, we obtain 11.25, 37.5, 80.5, 193, 1000, and 240, respectively. The circuit is not an ideal bandpass filter, because frequencies other than 900 cps get through, but it certainly shows a "preference" for 900 cps.

The Fourier series of the output is

$$f_o(t) = v_o(t) = \sum_{k=-\infty}^{\infty} \frac{1000 \sin(\pi k/2)}{[1 + (j10/9)(k - 81/k)]\pi k} e^{j200\pi kt}$$

The line spectrum of the input signal is simply a set of lines with

---

*Whenever the Q_o or Q of a resonant circuit is large, the poles are very nearly given by

$$\frac{1}{\sqrt{LC}}\left[-\frac{1}{2Q_o} \pm j\right]$$

height $\frac{1}{4}$ at $f = 0$ and $1/(\pi k)^2$ at the odd harmonics. This is shown in Fig. 7.23. The dashed line in Fig. 7.23 is the magnitude of $H(s)$ squared. Figure 7.24 shows the line spectrum of the output signal. Note that it has no d-c term and that the line at $k = 1$ is $1/\pi^2$ times the square of the magnitude of H at $k = 1$; that is,

$$\frac{(11.25)^2}{\pi^2} \doteq 12.8$$

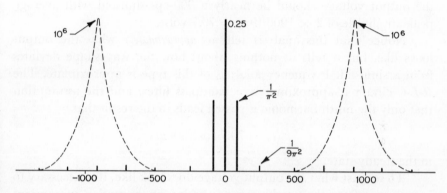

Fig. 7.23 *The line spectrum of the input current and the magnitude squared (dashed line) of the transfer function of the network.*

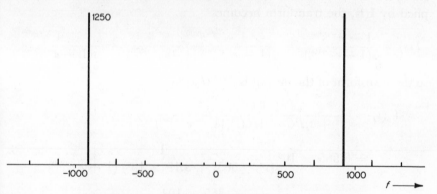

Fig. 7.24 *The line spectrum of the output signal $v_o(t)$.*

Calculating the others in a similar way, we have: $P_{av3} = 15.8$, $P_{av5} = 26.3$, $P_{av7} = 76.7$, $P_{av9} = 1250$, $P_{av11} = 48.1$. If the sum of the power in these harmonics is calculated, the total is 1429.7 watts per ohm (the actual power is one thousandth of this, since $R = 1000$ and $p = v^2/R$), and so about 87.5 percent of the power is in the ninth harmonic. Actually, something less than this value is in the ninth harmonic, since the power in the 13th, 15th, ... harmonics would have to be calculated to obtain the total output power. These are small, however, so 85 percent is probably a good estimate. Note that only the powers in the *positive* frequencies are mentioned above. The powers in the negative frequencies are the same, thus the total sinusoidal power is double that given above for any frequency.

Since the output is a voltage, and the ninth harmonic is dominant, the output voltage should be nearly a 900-cps sinusoid with average peak amplitude of $2 \times 1000/(9\pi) \doteq 70.7$ volts.

Notice that this analysis tells us *approximately* what the output looks like, but it tells us nothing about how the waveshape deviates from a sinusoid. Frequency analysis of this type is approximate. The R-L-C circuit is approximately a bandpass filter, and the assumption that only the ninth harmonic is passed leads to the result that

$$v_o(t) \doteq 70.7 \cos 1800\pi t$$

in the steady state.

To see just what the output voltage does look like, it is necessary to inverse transform the steady state as was done in the section on transient and steady state in Chapter 5. If the input is translated $T/4$ sec to the right, it is easier to transform. When this is done, and the current multiplied by $\mathbf{1}(t)$, the transform becomes

$$I_s(s) = \frac{1 - e^{-s/200}}{s(1 - e^{-s/100})} = \frac{1 - e^{-s/200}}{s(1 - e^{-s/200})(1 + e^{-s/200})} = \frac{1}{s(1 + e^{-s/200})}$$

so the transform of the output is $I_s(s)H(s)$ or

$$V_o(s) = \frac{1/C}{(s^2 + s/RC + 1/LC)(1 + e^{-s/200})}$$

$$= 0.565 \times 10^6 \frac{1}{(s^2 + 565s + 3.19 \times 10^7)(1 + e^{-s/200})}$$

$$= \frac{565 \times 10^3}{(s + 565/2 - j5650)(s + 565/2 + j5650)(1 + e^{-s/200})}$$

Multiplying by $(s+565/2-j5650)$ and setting $s = -565/2+j5650$, we have

$$A = \frac{565 \times 10^3}{j2 \times 5650 \left[1 + e^{(5.65/4 - j9\pi)}\right]}$$

since $5650/200 \doteq 9\pi$. Because $e^{-j9\pi} = -1$

$$A = \frac{50\underline{/90^\circ}}{e^{1.4125} - 1} = \frac{50}{3.11}\underline{/90^\circ} = 16.07\underline{/90^\circ}$$

The transform of the transient, then must be

$$V_{tr} = 16.07 \left[\frac{j}{(s+565/2-j5650)} + \frac{-j}{(s+565/2+j5650)} \right]$$

$$= \frac{-181{,}500}{s^2 + 565s + (5650)^2}$$

If this is now subtracted from the original transform of $v_o(t)$, the result is the transform of the steady state.

$$V_{ss} = 10^3 \frac{746.5 + 181.5\, e^{-s/200}}{[s^2 + 565s + (5650)^2](1 + e^{-s/200})}$$

The factor $(1 + e^{-s/200})$ in the denominator merely indicates the periodic nature of the wave; its polarity is reversed every $1/200$ sec. Dropping this, one-half of one period must have the transform

$$\frac{10^3(746.5 + 181.5\, e^{-s/200})}{s^2 + 565s + (5650)^2}$$

Inverse transforming the first of these terms only; that is,

$$\frac{746.5 \times 10^3}{s^2 + 565s + (5650)^2}$$

gives

$$132.2\, e^{-282.5t} \sin 1800\pi t$$

After $1/200$ sec, the second term—that term with 181.5×10^3—will cancel out this function. The inverse transform of the pulse then lasts for $1800\pi/200 = 9\pi$ rad or $4\frac{1}{2}$ cycles. The pulse is then inverted in polarity and repeated, and so on. The inversion is necessary because the exponential factor discarded had a plus sign in it—that is, $(1 + e^{-s/200})$. The steady state is pictured in Fig. 7.25. Observe also in the figure that the steady state is translated to the left the $T/4$ that it was translated to the right earlier.

The average amplitude of an exponential e^{-at} in the interval $0 < t < b$ is

$$\frac{1}{b} \int_0^b e^{-at}\, dt = \frac{1 - e^{-ab}}{ab}$$

The average amplitude of the sinusoid, then, is 132.2 times the result given with $a = 282.5$ and $b = 1/200$. This is 70.5, which is well within slide-rule accuracy of the 70.7 given previously. Notice again, however, that the frequency analysis gave no hint of the waveshape.

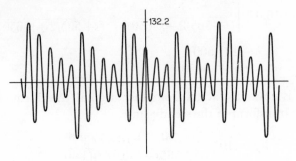

Fig. 7.25   *The actual steady-state output voltage of the circuit depicted in Fig. 7.22.*

7.6 Periodic Signals and Nonlinear Systems

An indication of the behavior of nonlinear systems when excited by periodic signals can be obtained by considering the output signal frequencies when that signal is related to the input signal by a nonlinear equation of the type

$$f_o(t) = [f_{in}(t)]^3$$

or

$$f_o(t) = \tanh [f_{in}(t)]$$

Nonlinear relationships of the type suggested arise from circuits in which nonlinear resistances are present, and the absence of differentials and integrals indicates that there are no storage devices in the network. Most of the discussion that follows will lead to correct results even with storage devices, except in the case of active networks. There are no general techniques for handling nonlinear circuits.

Suppose that a nonlinear resistive circuit is excited by a periodic function, and suppose that the input-output relationship can be expressed by a Maclaurin series of the type

$$f_o = a_0 + a_1 f_{in} + a_2 f_{in}^2 + \cdots \qquad (7.26)$$

Equation (7.26) is about as general a method as can be used to characterize nonlinear circuits, because whatever the functional relationship between input and output, it can usually be approximated arbitrarily closely by a power series. Now if f_{in} is periodic with frequencies kf, what frequencies are contained in $f_{in}^2, f_{in}^3, \ldots$?

Let

$$f_{in}(t) = \frac{1}{T} \sum_{k=-\infty}^{\infty} C_k e^{j2\pi kft}$$

$$= \frac{1}{T} \sum_{k=-\infty}^{\infty} C_p e^{j2\pi pft}$$

since the index of the summation can be any letter or character we choose. Then

$$f_{in}^2 = \frac{1}{T^2} \sum_{k=-\infty}^{\infty} \sum_{p=-\infty}^{\infty} C_k C_p e^{j2\pi(k+p)ft}$$

If we let $r = k + p$, then, as p is summed from $-\infty$ to $+\infty$, r will go from $k - \infty = -\infty$ to $k + \infty = +\infty$. Since $p = r - k$, then p can be eliminated to obtain

$$f_{in}^2 = \frac{1}{T^2} \sum_{r=-\infty}^{\infty} \left\{ \sum_{k=-\infty}^{\infty} C_{r-k} C_k \right\} e^{j2\pi rft}$$

Defining

$$C_r' = \frac{1}{T} \sum_{k=-\infty}^{\infty} C_{r-k} C_k$$

for all r, we have

$$f_{in}^2 = \frac{1}{T} \sum_{r=-\infty}^{\infty} C_r' e^{j2\pi rft}$$

Apparently the square of a periodic function with fundamental frequency f is a new periodic function with the same fundamental frequency. The amount of a particular harmonic is not the square of the amount of the original harmonic, but rather the sum of the products of the C_k terms by pairs divided by the period; each pair of C_k terms is such that the *sum* of the harmonic numbers equals r.

A simple example will clarify this. Suppose we want to know the amount of the fifth harmonic $(+5)$ in the square of $f_{in}(t)$. We would sum the products of $C_m C_n$ for all pairs for which $m + n = 5$. These are $C_0 C_5, C_1 C_4, C_2 C_3, C_3 C_2, C_4 C_1, C_5 C_0, C_6 C_{-1}, C_7 C_{-2}$, and so on, plus $C_{-1} C_6$, $C_{-2} C_7, C_{-3} C_8, \ldots$. Notice that every pair appears twice. When all the products are computed and summed, the new C_5' is this sum divided by T.

Since the cube of a function is simply the function multiplied by the square, the cube of a periodic function will be periodic with the same period. In fact, whatever the nonlinear relationship, the result will be periodic with the same period. Note that sometimes the odd harmonics will disappear and thus the actual period of the result may be half that of the original. The simplest example of this is the function $\cos 2\pi ft$, whose square is $\cos^2 2\pi ft = \frac{1}{2}(1+\cos 4\pi ft)$. The result is a direct current and frequencies of $\pm 2f$. Mathematically speaking, the fundamental is the same, but within the definitions of period and fundamental frequency used in this text we have to say that the new fundamental is $2f$. Another example of this is the full-wave rectified sine wave, whose input is at a frequency f but whose output is periodic with fundamental frequency $2f$.

Although the method outlined above is probably not the simplest method of calculating the spectrum of the output signal for a nonlinear system, it does allow some general conclusions to be drawn. One such conclusion is this: If the output signal is periodic with period T_o, the input signal must have a period of T_o, $2T_o$, or NT_o, where N is a positive integer. Stated in another way: If the output of any passive system, linear or nonlinear, has a fundamental frequency f, the fundamental frequency of the (single) input signal must be f or some fraction thereof.

When two different periodic signals are added and the combination is used as the input to a nonlinear system, some interesting results appear. A device designed for this purpose is called a *mixer*, or sometimes a *converter*. Almost no transmitter or receiver is built today without at least one mixer.

Suppose, for example, the two signals injected into a nonlinear device are sinusoidal with different frequencies, and hence their sum need not be periodic. Suppose further they are added together and used as the input to a square-law device—that is, a device whose output voltage is proportional to the square of the input signal (such as a crystal diode). Then

$$v_o(t) = A(B\cos 2\pi f_1 t + C\cos 2\pi f_2 t)^2$$

If the signals within the parentheses are written in exponential form, then

$$v_o(t) = A\left[\frac{B}{2}e^{j2\pi f_1 t} + \frac{B}{2}e^{-j2\pi f_1 t} + \frac{C}{2}e^{j2\pi f_2 t} + \frac{C}{2}e^{-j2\pi f_2 t}\right]^2$$

Expanding this last expression gives

$$v_0 = \frac{A(B^2+C^2)}{2} + \frac{AB^2}{4}e^{j4\pi f_1 t} + \frac{AB^2}{4}e^{-j4\pi f_1 t} + \frac{AC^2}{4}e^{j4\pi f_2 t}$$

$$+ \frac{AC^2}{4} e^{-j4\pi f_2 t} + \frac{ABC}{2} e^{j2\pi(f_1 + f_2)t} + \frac{ABC}{2} e^{-j2\pi(f_1 + f_2)t}$$

$$+ \frac{ABC}{2} e^{j2\pi(f_2 - f_1)t} + \frac{ABC}{2} e^{-j2\pi(f_2 - f_1)t}$$

from which it can be seen that the new frequencies are 0, $\pm 2f_1$, $\pm 2f_2$, $\pm(f_1 + f_2)$, and $\pm(f_2 - f_1)$.

Interestingly enough, the amplitudes of the sum and difference frequencies depend on the amplitudes of both of the original signals. This principle is used extensively in what is known as *frequency conversion*. The frequency of a signal can be altered by mixing it with another frequency and filtering out all but one of the resulting frequencies. Usually the difference frequency is used in receivers, and this difference frequency is called the *intermediate frequency*. This is discussed in more detail in Chapter 9.

What if the mixer cubes the sum of the input signals? What if the nonlinear relationship is more complicated than the cubic? Clearly a more general approach is called for, because the task of raising the sum of four exponentials to say the tenth power is certainly not desirable. A graphical method, known as *convolution*, is recommended.

Let $f_1(t)$ and $f_2(t)$ be two almost periodic functions; that is, neither need be individually periodic, but what follows is certainly true if either or both *are* periodic. All that is required here is that the functions be expressible in an exponential series. Then the frequencies contained in the product of $f_1(t)$ and $f_2(t)$ and their amounts can be obtained by the following technique.

1. Draw the line spectra of the two signals, and label each with the corresponding complex amplitudes—not with P_{avk}. It will not matter if the lines are to scale; lines of equal heights will probably be easier to work with. Now imagine that one spectrum is drawn on transparent paper. Turn the spectrum on transparent paper face down on top of the other spectrum so that the frequency axes and the origins coincide, but the positive-frequency lines of the transparent spectrum lie over the negative-frequency axis of the fixed spectrum. Thus the transparent spectrum is turned over as are the pages of a book. The "flipped" spectrum now looks as it would if it were held right side up in front of a mirror. The backward lettering is not an insurmountable difficulty.

Consider the two spectra in Fig. 7.26(*a*) and (*b*). The spectrum in Fig. 7.26(*b*) is flipped as described above, and the result of this operation is shown in Fig. 7.27(*a*). Figure 7.27(*a*) is then superimposed on the spectrum of Fig. 7.26(*a*) and the result is shown in Fig. 7.27(*b*). In Fig. 7.27(*b*) the original spectrum lines are shown dashed to facilitate distinguishing the two.

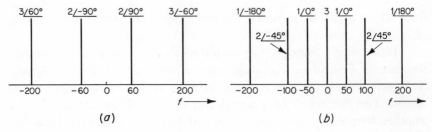

Fig. 7.26   *Two line spectra that represent signals to be mixed. Observe that all lines are labeled with complex amplitudes and not power, and that for simplicity all lines are of the same height.*

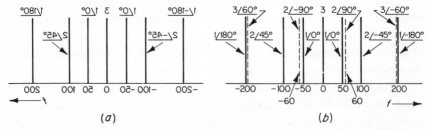

Fig. 7.27   *(a) The spectrum of Fig. 7.26(b) reversed. (b) The superposition of (a) the reversed spectrum (solid lines) on that of Fig. 7.26(a) (dashed lines).*

2. If any two lines in Fig. 7.27(*b*) coincide, the sum of the products of all coincident lines will yield the zero-frequency, or d-c, term of the product of the two signals whose spectra appear in Fig. 7.26(*a*) and (*b*). In Fig. 7.27(*b*) it is clear that the 200-cps and −200-cps lines coincide, so the d-c term must be $1/{-180°} \times 3/{-60°} + 1/180° \times 3/60° = -3$.

3. Now start sliding the transparent spectrum to the right, and continue this until any line on one coincides with any line on the other. In Fig. 7.27(*b*) this will first occur when the solid spectrum is moved 10 cps to the right. At this point the 50-cps line of the solid spectrum coincides with the 60-cps line of the dashed spectrum. Since at this point these are the only lines that coincide, there must be a 10-cps signal in the product with complex amplitude of $1/0° \times 2/90° = 2/90°$. Continue to slide the transparent spectrum, and stop each time a coincidence occurs. Sum the products of the coincident lines; and this

will be the complex amplitude of the frequency of the product that corresponds to the *amount of the shift*.

When the shift is 40 cps, the spectra will appear as in Fig. 7.28, where it is seen that the line that was at -100 has come into contact with the dashed line at -60. The magnitude of the 40-cps term in the product is then $2\underline{/45^\circ} \times 2\underline{/-90^\circ} = 4\underline{/-45^\circ}$. It can be verified that positive and negative frequencies of 60, 100, 110, 140, 150, 160, 200, 250, 260, 300, and 400 will result, in addition to those already mentioned. Note that it is not really necessary to slide the transparent spectrum to the left to obtain the negative frequencies, since every positive frequency must have its negative mate and the amplitude of the negative frequency term must be the conjugate of its mate. Thus the amplitude of the -40-cps term must be $4\underline{/45^\circ}$.

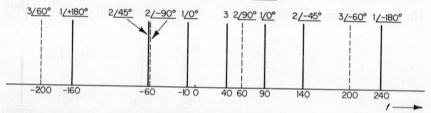

Fig. 7.28 *The composite spectrum of Fig. 7.27(b), but with the solid spectrum translated to the right 40 cps.*

For any two functions that possess line spectra, convolution yields the line spectrum of their product. The operations are, in order: (*a*) flip one spectrum about the $f = 0$ ordinate, (*b*) slide this spectrum to the right for positive frequencies and to the left for negative frequencies (only one need be done, as indicated in the above paragraph), (*c*) whenever a coincidence between any pair of lines occurs, sum the products of the amplitudes of all lines coincident at any given amount of frequency shift. The resultant sum of the products will yield the amplitude in the product of the frequency which corresponds to the shift. Convolution may be remembered by the phrase "flip, slide, multiply, and sum."

The proof of the correctness of the technique just described is trivial, but not necessarily easy to visualize. When any two exponentials are multiplied, the frequency that results is the sum of the two. The process of flipping the spectrum of one requires the process of addition to be changed to subtraction, since in effect the signs of the frequencies of one are changed. The act of translation is equivalent to performing this subtraction.

Since the amplitude of a line at $+f$ is the conjugate of the amplitude of a line at $-f$, the fastest way of convolving two spectra is to draw the spectra and label one with the conjugate amplitudes; this is equivalent to the process of flipping. Then cut one spectrum out so that the translation can be done visually.

EXAMPLE 7.5. Let

$$g(t) = 2\underline{/45°}\, e^{j2\pi f_1 t} + 2\underline{/-45°}\, e^{-j2\pi f_1 t}$$
$$+ 3\underline{/-60°}\, e^{j2\pi f_2 t} + 3\underline{/60°}\, e^{-j2\pi f_2 t}$$

Find the spectrum of $g^2(t)$ by convolution.

Solution: The spectrum of $g(t)$ appears in Fig. 7.29(a), and the flipped spectrum, obtained by repeating the spectrum of $g(t)$ but labeling the amplitudes with the conjugates, appears in Fig. 7.29(b). Notice that the latter is drawn as it might look if it were cut out of paper.

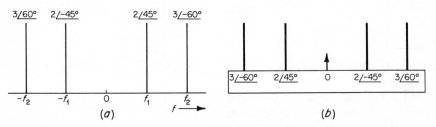

Fig. 7.29   *The spectrum of $g(t)$ and the conjugate or reversed spectrum of $g(t)$.*

In the product there will be

$f = 0$: Origins coincide, all lines coincide. The d-c term is then
$$3\underline{/60°} \times 3\underline{/-60°} + 2\underline{/45°} \times 2\underline{/-45°} + 2\underline{/-45°} \times 2\underline{/45°}$$
$$+ 3\underline{/-60°} \times 3\underline{/60°} = 26$$

$f = f_2 - f_1$: A shift of $f_2 - f_1$ will cause a double coincidence, so the amplitude of this term is
$$3\underline{/-60°} \times 2\underline{/-45°} + 2\underline{/-45°} \times 3\underline{/-60°} = 12\underline{/-105°}$$

$f = 2f_1$: Amplitude will be
$$2\underline{/45°} \times 2\underline{/45°} = 4\underline{/90°}$$

$f = f_1 + f_2$: Amplitude will be
$$3\underline{/-60°} \times 2\underline{/45°} + 2\underline{/45°} \times 3\underline{/-60°} = 12\underline{/-15°}$$

$f = 2f_2$: Amplitude is
$$3\underline{/-60°} \times 3\underline{/-60°} = 9\underline{/-120°}$$

No other coincidences can occur as a result of shifting to the right. The spectrum of $g^2(t)$ appears in Fig. 7.30. To verify the result, square $g(t)$ in the usual fashion.

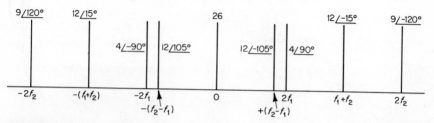

Fig. 7.30   *The spectrum of the square of the function whose spectrum appears in Fig. 7.29(a).*

PROBLEMS

7.25. The current source $i_s(t)$ in Fig. 7.31 is a square wave whose Fourier series is known to be

$$i_s(t) = \sum_{k=-\infty}^{\infty} B_k \, e^{j2\pi kt/T}$$

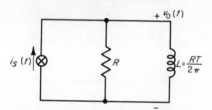

Fig. 7.31   *Problem 7.25.*

with $B_k = 0$ for k even and

$$B_k = A \frac{\sin(\pi k/2)}{\pi k/2}$$

for k odd

(a)   Sketch $i_s(t)$ versus t. (See Prob. 7.14.)

(b)   Find the Fourier series of $v_o(t)$.

Answer: $v_o(t) = \dfrac{2AR}{\pi} \sum_{k \text{ odd}} \dfrac{\sin(\pi k/2)}{k-j} \, e^{j2\pi kt/T}$

(c)   Write the first five nonzero terms of the cosine series for $v_o(t)$.

$$Answer:\ v_0(t) = \frac{2\sqrt{2}AR}{\pi}\left[\cos\left(\frac{2\pi t}{T} + 45°\right) - 0.401\cos\left(\frac{6\pi t}{T} + 18.44°\right)\right.$$

$$+ 0.277\cos\left(\frac{10\pi t}{T} + 11.3°\right) - 0.2\cos\left(\frac{14\pi t}{T} + 8.13°\right)$$

$$\left. + 0.1565\cos\left(\frac{18\pi t}{T} + 6.35°\right) - \cdots\right]$$

(d) Calculate the P_{avk} for $v_0(t)$ if $R = 100$ ohms. Plot the line spectrum.

$$Answer:\ P_{avk} = \frac{400A^2}{\pi^2(1+k^2)}$$

(e) Since the square wave can be thought of as a succession of steps, the steady-state term $v_0(t)$ must be a succession of step responses. Without using the Laplace transform, determine the waveshape of the steady state.

7.26. A sawtooth voltage source whose Fourier series is given by

$$e_s(t) = \sum_{k=-\infty}^{\infty} B_k\,e^{j2\pi kt/T}$$

where $B_0 = 0$ and

$$B_k = j\,\frac{\cos\pi k}{\pi k}$$

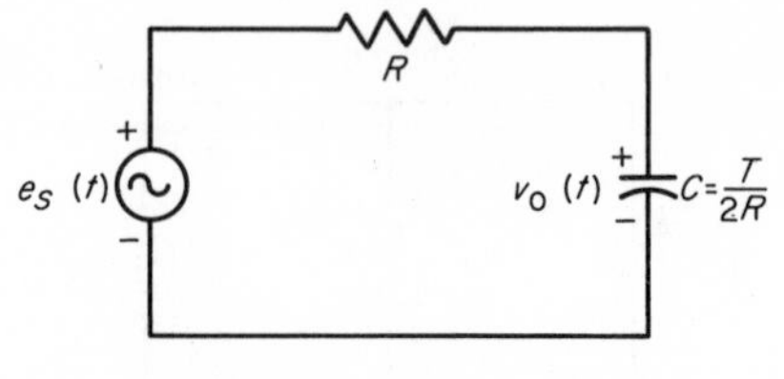

Fig. 7.32 *Problem 7.26.*

for all other k.

(a) Sketch $e_s(t)$ versus t. (See Prob. 7.21.) The voltage source is applied to the circuit of Fig. 7.32 as indicated.

(b) Find the Fourier series for $v_0(t)$.

(c) Write the first five nonzero terms of the cosine series for $v_0(t)$.

(d) Calculate the P_{avk} for $v_0(t)$ if $R = 1$ ohm. Plot the line spectrum of $v_0(t)$.

(e) Since the sawtooth wave can be thought of as a ramp plus a succession of steps, the output should consist of exponentials, but the solution, unlike that of Prob. 7.25, is not so readily seen. Write the transform of $e_s(t)\mathbf{1}(t)$, and from the transfer function of the network, find the transform of $v_0(t)\mathbf{1}(t)$. From this last transform, remove the transient and find the steady state.

Answer:

$$v_0(t) = \begin{cases} 2\dfrac{t}{T} - 1 + \dfrac{2e}{e^2-1}\,e^{-2t/T} & 0 \leqslant t \leqslant \dfrac{T}{2} \\[2mm] 2\dfrac{t}{T} - 3 + \dfrac{2e^3}{e^2-1}\,e^{-2t/T} & \dfrac{T}{2} \leqslant t \leqslant T \end{cases}$$

7.27. The voltage $e_s(t)$ in the circuit of Fig. 7.33(a) is a 1-volt-peak square wave with zero average value and a fundamental frequency of 1 kc. The output voltage has the waveform shown in Fig. 7.33(b).

(a) How must an R and a C be connected within the box to produce this output? What must their element values be?

(b) Sketch carefully the magnitude squared of the transfer function of the box, using the element values obtained in (a), and superimpose it on the line spectrum of $e_s(t)$.

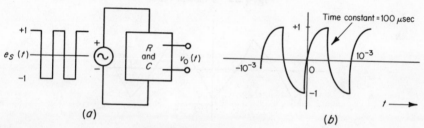

(a)   (b)

Fig. 7.33 *Problem 7.27.*

7.28. Repeat Prob. 7.27 but for the output voltage pictured in Fig. 7.34.

Answers: (a) $RC = 0.002$ sec

(b) $H(j\omega) = \dfrac{1}{1 - j(0.0796/f)}$ f in kc

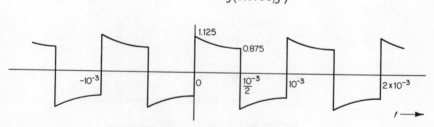

Fig. 7.34 *Problem 7.28.*

7.29. Repeat Prob. 7.27 but for the output voltage pictured in Fig. 7.35. This is called a differentiating circuit. Why?

7.30. Repeat Prob. 7.27, but for the output voltage pictured in Fig. 7.36. This is called an integrating circuit. Why?

Answers: (a) $RC = 0.05$

$$(b)\ H(j\omega) = \frac{1}{1+j314f} \qquad f \text{ in kc}$$

$$H(s) \doteq \frac{20}{s} \qquad \text{for large } s \text{ (or } f)$$

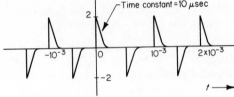

Fig. 7.35   *Problem 7.29.*

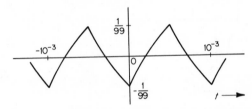

Fig. 7.36   *Problem 7.30.*

7.31. A half-wave rectified sinusoid is produced in the power supply of an inexpensive radio. The Fourier series of $v(t)$ in Fig. 7.37 is given approximately by

$$v(t) = \sum_{k=-\infty}^{\infty} B_k\, e^{j377kt}$$

where

$$B_k = \frac{110\sqrt{2}}{\pi(1-k^2)} \qquad \text{for } k \text{ even}$$

and

$$B_1 = -j27.5\sqrt{2}$$

$$B_k = 0 \qquad \text{for } k \text{ odd and different from } \pm 1$$

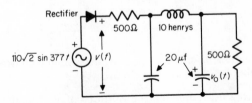

Fig. 7.37   *Problem 7.31.*

The word approximate is used because the expression is correct only if the rectifier is ideal and if the filter network to which it is connected is resistive at all frequencies. In practice, neither of these assumptions is correct, but they are fairly accurate. Find the d-c and 60-cps terms in the output voltage $v_o(t)$. Find the peak value of the 120-cps component in $v_o(t)$.

Answer: $v_o(t) \doteq 24.8 + 0.726 \cos(377t + 30.8°)$

Peak value of second harmonic is 0.0385 volt

7.32. A *harmonic generator* consists of a vacuum tube or transistor operated with a resonant tank (R-L-C) circuit in such a way that for a constant amplitude sinusoidal signal input, only the crest of the input wave is amplified. It is as though only the tops of the input signal are used; a current proportional to these clipped portions, shown in Fig. 7.38(b), is produced. If the current pulses are sufficiently short compared to the time constants of the circuits to which they are to be applied, the current signal can be approximated by a set of impulses having an area a equal to the area of the corresponding current pulses. This type of periodic function is shown in Fig. 7.39.

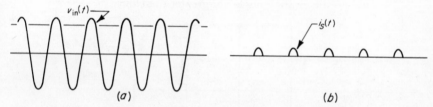

Fig. 7.38   (*a*) *A constant-amplitude sinusoid whose amplitude is clipped by the operation of a transistor or vacuum tube below cutoff. This produces a current, $i_s(t)$, whose waveform is shown in* (*b*).

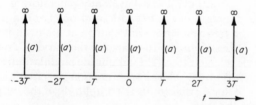

Fig. 7.39   *A periodic train of impulses.*

(*a*) Find the Fourier series of the impulse train in exponential form. Does the following series converge?

$$\sum_{k=-\infty}^{\infty} |C_k|$$

Answer: $i_s(t) = \dfrac{a}{T} \sum_{-\infty}^{\infty} e^{j2\pi kt/T}$

(b) Assume that the Fourier series of $i_s(t)$ is that just obtained, and that this current source is applied to a tank circuit, such as that shown in Fig. 7.40. If this tank circuit is resonant at a frequency of $4/T$, and it has a Q_o of 30, consider that the circuit is an *ideal* bandpass filter with transfer function of R in the frequency range

$$\frac{4}{T} \times \frac{59}{60} < f < \frac{4}{T} \times \frac{61}{60}$$

and zero outside of this range.

Over what range of frequencies can the input sinusoid be varied and still produce an output voltage $v_o(t)$?

$$Answer: \quad \frac{59}{60T} < f < \frac{61}{60T}$$

This device is used in FM (frequency modulation) production, and has the effect, approximately, of multiplying the instantaneous frequency of the input sinusoid by four. Harmonic generators that multiply the input frequency by two and three are also used, but rarely is the multiplying factor greater than four.

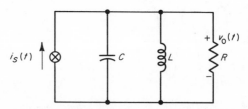

Fig. 7.40   *A harmonic generator.*

(c) Sketch the output of the harmonic generator, using the actual transfer function of the network, and observe that between input pulses the frequency does not change at all, even if the frequency of the pulses changes. In practice, the varying amplitude of the output is referred to as AM (amplitude modulation); for FM transmission it is undesirable. For this reason the circuit is followed by a limiter, a device that limits the amplitude of the output and hence removes the AM.

$$Answer: \quad v_o(t) \doteq \frac{2.91a}{C} e^{-\pi t/(7.5T)} \cos \frac{8\pi t}{T} \quad \text{for } 0 \leqslant t < T$$

7.33. (a) A *converter* or *mixer* adds two signals of different frequencies and operates on the sum in some nonlinear fashion. Assume that the input signals are $g_1(t)$ and $g_2(t)$, and that the output $f_o(t)$ is given by
$f_o(t) = a_0 + a_1(g_1+g_2) + a_2(g_1+g_2)^2 + a_3(g_1+g_2)^3$
It was shown in Sec. 7.6 that if the sum (g_1+g_2) contains the four frequencies $\pm f_1$ and $\pm f_2$, that the output resulting from the

first three terms in the series above contains frequencies of 0, $\pm f_1$, $\pm f_2$, $\pm 2f_1$, $\pm(f_2-f_1)$, $\pm(f_1+f_2)$, and $\pm 2f_2$. What additional frequencies are introduced by the cubic term?

(b) In a conventional i-f (intermediate-frequency) amplifier, all frequencies but $\pm(f_2-f_1)$ are filtered out. In broadcast-band radio receivers, the intermediate frequency is usually set at 455 kc, and the receiver generates its own signal to be mixed with that coming from the antenna. In most receivers the *local oscillator* is operated 455 kc *above* the frequency to which the radio is tuned.

Assume that a certain radio receiver is tuned to 630 kc. Then its local oscillator puts out a signal at $630 + 455 = 1085$ kc. What other signal could be mixed with this local-oscillator frequency to produce an output signal at 455 kc? Does this mean that radio stations in one part of the broadcast band, which goes from 540 kc to 1600 kc, can be heard at two positions on the dial? If so, in what frequency range could this happen? Try it on your radio and suggest what you could do to prevent this from happening.

7.34. Sometimes the process of mixing is used to increase the frequency of a signal, and hence all frequencies but $\pm(f_1+f_2)$ are filtered out. If $f_2 = af_1$, with $a > 1$, what must a be to insure that, with a cube-law mixer as discussed in Prob. 7.33, no frequency component in the output is within f_1 cps of the frequency $f_1 + f_2$? If f_1 is varied and the local-oscillator frequency f_2 is not, notice that the output of the mixer differs from that of the harmonic generator of Prob. 7.32 in that the output changes frequency by the same amount as the input.

7.35. The average *B-H* curve of a power transformer is given by the expression

$$i = 0.1\,(\mathcal{N}\phi) + (\mathcal{N}\phi)^3$$

where i is the exciting current and $\mathcal{N}\phi$ the flux linkages. An emf of

$$e = \frac{d(\mathcal{N}\phi)}{dt} = 110\,\sqrt{2}\,\cos 377t$$

is applied to the primary of the transformer. Find the Fourier series and line spectrum of $i(t)$. Sketch $i(t)$ carefully and write it as a series in cosine form. Plot the inductance L of the transformer (in henrys) versus i, where

$$L = \frac{d(\mathcal{N}\phi)}{di}$$

Partial Answer: $i(t) = 0.0942 \sin 377t - 0.0176 \sin 1131t$

$$L = \frac{10}{1 + 30(\mathcal{N}\phi)^2}\quad\text{henrys}$$

PROBLEMS ON MUSIC*

7.36. It has been well known for years that the human ear is a nonlinear device. If the power in an audio signal is doubled, the ear detects only a small, barely noticeable change in sound level. The ear is something like a "peak clipper," in that high-level sounds are compressed in amplitude before being passed on to the brain.

   If the input signal to the ear is a single sinusoid of frequency $\pm f$ and the response of the ear is an *odd* function (that is, it responds equally well to negative and positive signals), show that the brain receives f, $3f$, $5f$, . . . and their negative mates. This implies that the ear produces only the odd harmonics. Is the assumption that the ear has an odd input-output relation reasonable? (See Prob. 7.38 below.)

7.37. It can be concluded from the previous problem that if a musical note (say middle C) is played softly, the harmonic content produced by the ear will be small. If the instrument used is a flute, which has a waveform that is very nearly sinusoidal, then as the level of the sound is increased, the nonlinearity of the ear should produce the odd harmonics in increasing proportion, though only one frequency enters the ear. The note should *sound* different. If this theory is correct, then since G, an octave-and-a-half above middle C, is the third harmonic, a loud C should have the same quality (timbre) as the combination of C and the higher G, both played softly. Increasing the volume still further should produce a noticeable fifth harmonic. Where is the fifth harmonic of middle C?

7.38. If the ear does not have an odd input-output relationship, then it also produces the even harmonics. Since the second harmonic defines a musical *octave* (an eighth), and is more fundamental to music than the third harmonic, there is good reason to suspect that the even harmonics are produced by the ear.

   Experiment with this notion by playing simultaneously and very softly, middle C, C an octave higher, and the G above that. Play the lower notes more strongly than the high ones. Then play middle C very loudly and compare the effects. The piano is the simplest instrument on which to do this, but the waveform of the signals is not sinusoidal and hence the results are not as good as they would be if three flutes were used. It is also possible to do this with signal generators and an audio amplifier.

7.39. Apparently the ear produces the second and third harmonics in varying degrees even though they may be absent from the original signal.

---

*An extremely interesting and easy-to-read volume on the physics and mathematics of music is *Horns, Strings, and Harmony* by Arthur H. Benade (Garden City, N.Y.: Doubleday and Company, Inc.—Anchor Books, 1960). The engineering student will find this book informative and entertaining.

It should not be surprising then to discover that the entire musical scale has been developed using the numbers 2 and 3.

For example, the first G above middle C must have a fundamental frequency of $\frac{3}{2}$ that of middle C, since it is down an octave from the third harmonic. The interval from C to G is called a *major fifth*, not because of the fifth harmonic content, but because G is the fifth note in the major C scale. The two notes sound well together, and constitute a *chord*.* If middle C is assumed to have a frequency of 260 cps and the G above it a frequency of 390 cps, the ear *mixes* the signals when the two notes are played together. If the ear is cubic, what other frequencies are sent to the brain? (See Prob. 7.33.) What are these notes on the musical scale? Note in particular that the fundamental of these two frequencies, 130 cps, is produced by the ear.

> *Answer:* C_{-1}, C_0, G_0, C_1, E_1, G_1, $B\flat_1$, C_2, D_2 where C_0 means middle C, C_{-1} means an octave below C_0, C_1 an octave above, and so forth.

7.40. If G is the major fifth of C, of what note is C the major fifth? Call this note F. Make a table of the ratios of frequencies of notes, each of which is obtained from the other by going *down* a major fifth. Make all the ratios lie within the range 1–2 by multiplying by 2 (raising an octave) when a ratio falls below unity. For example, letting C = 1, then G = $\frac{3}{2}$. C is $\frac{2}{3}$ of G so F is $\frac{2}{3}$ of C or $\frac{2}{3}$. But this ratio is less than unity, so multiply by 2 and obtain $\frac{4}{3}$ = F. As you move down the scale in this fashion, define the new notes in order as

$$G, C, F, B\flat, E\flat, A\flat, D\flat, G\flat, C\flat, F\flat, B\flat\flat, E\flat\flat, A\flat\flat, D\flat\flat$$

Observe that $D\flat\flat = 2^{20}/3^{12} \doteq 1.9731 \doteq 2$ within 1.5 percent. A good ear can detect a frequency change of this much, but it was decided to stop the scale at this point and define $D\flat\flat = $ C. Thus the scale was cut off at twelve intervals per octave.

7.41. Starting with C, find successively the major fifths of the major fifths, this time dividing by 2 when necessary to keep the ratio between 1 and 2. Name them in order by

$$C, G, D, A, E, B, F\sharp, C\sharp, G\sharp, D\sharp, A\sharp, E\sharp, B\sharp$$

But $B\sharp$ is $3^{12}/2^{19} \doteq 1.0141 \doteq 1$; once again the scale was cut off at twelve intervals per octave.

With $3^{12}/2^{19}$ *assumed* to be unity, show that $D\flat\flat = B\sharp = $ C, $A\flat\flat = $ G, $E\flat\flat = $ D, $B\flat\flat = $ A, $F\flat = $ E, $C\flat = $ B, $E\sharp = $ F, and so forth.

7.42. Tabulate the results of Probs. 7.40 and 7.41 in Tables 7.1 and 7.2 in decimal form, and compare with the *even-tempered* scale given, where the scale is divided into twelve equal frequency intervals, each $2^{1/12} \doteq 1.0595$ times its predecessor.

---

*Strictly speaking, a chord contains at least three notes.

Table 7.1

	C	D♭	E♭♭	E♭	F♭	F
Prob. 7.40	1					
Even Tempered	1	1.0595	1.123	1.189	1.260	1.333
Prob. 7.41	1					
	C	C♯	D	D♯	E	E♯

Table 7.2

	G♭	G	A♭	B♭♭	B♭	C♭	D♭♭
Prob. 7.40		1.500					1.9731
Even Tempered	1.414	1.498	1.588	1.680	1.782	1.885	2.000
Prob. 7.41		1.500					2.0282
	F♯	G	G♯	A	A♯	B	B♯

7.43. Show that the fifth harmonic of C is very nearly E. In the *scientific* or *just* scale, it is exactly E. Show that the seventh harmonic of C falls slightly below B♭. Any combination of C, E, and G constitute the (major) C chord, and any combination of C, E, G, and B♭ is called the C-7 chord.

7.44. If musical instruments all *sound* different, and are readily identifiable, then when they are producing a given note and all produce the same fundamental frequency or *pitch*, their harmonic content must differ. Stated in another way, their waveforms must differ. But if the ear is nonlinear, then it should become increasingly difficult to distinguish instruments by ear as the sound level increases. Comment on this statement. Is there reason to believe that it is correct?

7.45. Almost all major musical instruments are based in design on two principles: the vibrating string and the resonance of a long (cylindrical or conical) air column. Special instruments made of electrical, mechanical, and electro-mechanical resonating systems have been developed, but none so basically simple in construction as the variable-length string or pipe. Since the excitation of a wind instrument is effected by either a vibrating reed or vibrating lips, at what frequency must these vibrate to excite a pipe whose length is tuned for resonance at 440 cps? Specifically, would an excitation of 220 cps have the desired effect? Would an 880-cps excitation produce the 440-cps tone?

chapter

8

The Fourier Transform

8.1 Frequency Analysis and Aperiodic Functions

Since the discovery of electromagnetic radiation, the field of communications has been dominated by the concept of the *frequency domain*.
Electromagnetic radiation is easiest to produce and most effective at
high frequencies—that is, those above 500 kc. The reasons for this depend
partly on the fact that the induced emf in a coil depends on the *rate*
of change of the magnetic field that links the coil. For example, for a
given peak amplitude current in a coil, the higher the frequency of the
current the greater the emf induced in another coil coupled to it. Thus it is
possible, if the frequency is sufficiently high, to induce a detectable
voltage in a loop of wire by varying the current in another loop, even
though the two loops may be separated by several miles.

The phenomenon of electromagnetic radiation is of course not as
elementary as the mutual coupling of two coils; however, for the purposes of this discussion it is necessary only to accept the importance of
the concept of frequency and its relation to communications.

It is well known that a radio is tuned to the *carrier* frequency of the
station desired, and that television channels are defined by frequencies.
Clearly the station using the channel does not send out a single sinusoid, for this would convey no information at all. If we know one period
of a periodic wave, we know everything about it. To send information,
we must alter the sinusoid being transmitted. This alteration is called
modulation, and it will be seen that there are several ways in which a
sinusoid can be modulated. With no modulation, the sinusoid being
transmitted has a single line spectrum. What happens to the spectrum
when the sinusoid is modulated? How wide should channels be to
prevent adjacent channels from interfering with one another?

Radio uses but one medium for the transmission of information:

the atmosphere. Telephones, on the other hand, use wires connecting their transmitters and receivers. Several pairs of telephones can be in operation simultaneously by means of the simple expedient of several sets of wires. But it is possible to send several messages over one pair of wires by using the same techniques that radio broadcasters use with dozens of stations transmitting through the same atmosphere. This is accomplished by modulating several carriers with the voice signals to be transmitted and transmitting them on the same set of wires. At the other end of the line the messages are separated from one another.

With radio, several stations are transmitting energy simultaneously, and each induces a voltage on the antenna of every radio. How then does a radio sort out all these signals and choose only the one desired? The sorting technique is called *filtering*, and the study of communications includes the concepts of modulation (or encoding a carrier), demodulation (decoding a carrier), and filtering.

No practical signal is mathematically periodic. All speeches, music, and audio signals have both beginnings and ends. How then, can the notion of frequency be applied to practical signals?

In Chapter 7, periodic and almost periodic functions were expressed in terms of frequencies by a summation. If C_k/T was the amount of the kth harmonic in $f(t)$, $f(t)$ was expressible as a *sum*

$$f(t) = \sum_{k=-\infty}^{\infty} \frac{C_k}{T} e^{-j2\pi f_k t}$$

where $f_k = k/T$ was the frequency of the kth harmonic. The amount of the kth harmonic was obtained by multiplying $f(t)$ by the conjugate or negative frequency and integrating over one period; thus

$$C_k = \int_{t_0}^{t_0+T} f(t) e^{-j2\pi f_k t} \, dt$$

With practical signals, the notion of a period is meaningless. Nevertheless, the last equation suggests a possible definition for the frequency content of $g(t)$ when $g(t)$ is not periodic:

Define $G(f)$ as the amount of frequency f contained in the signal $g(t)$, where

$$G(f) = \int_{-\infty}^{\infty} g(t) e^{-j2\pi f t} \, dt$$

$$= \int_{-\infty}^{\infty} g(x) e^{-j2\pi f x} \, dx \qquad (8.1)$$

The definition in Eq. (8.1) is consistent with the ideas of the Fourier series, but it remains to be seen whether or not the definition has any practical meaning. For example, we could have multiplied the function $g(t)$ by t^f and integrated over any interval of time and we would have obtained a function of f. Unless some physical meaning can be attached to Eq. (8.1), further study of it is a waste of time.

In Eq. (8.1), $G(f)$ is called the *Fourier transform* of $g(t)$. The limits on the integral are $-\infty$ and $+\infty$ to assure us that all of $g(t)$ is taken into consideration. If $g(t)$ exists in the interval $t_0 < t < t_1$ only, the lower limit should be t_0 and the upper limit t_1.

Keep in mind now that our objective is to transmit faithfully electric signals from one point to another. The channel or system to be used will do just this if the output is a reasonable or acceptable facsimile of the input. Suppose the signal to be transmitted is the single rectangular pulse shown in Fig. 8.1.

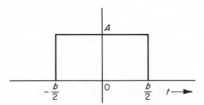

Fig. 8.1   *A rectangular pulse.*

Suppose, for a moment, that a channel transmits this signal exactly. Then the output of the system will look exactly like the input—that is, it will look like the pulse of Fig. 8.1. Suppose we try it again. At some later time the pulse is again transmitted, and unless the channel has been altered in some way, the output will again be the same as the input.

Suppose now we try to send the pulse periodically, with period T (frequency is introduced here), where T is longer than the pulse width b. If the system is in good working order, the pulse train at the output should be exactly the same as that at the input. In fact, it should not make any difference what T is—the output will always be the same as the input.

We know how to find the frequencies in a periodic signal. The frequencies contained in the pulse must be *all* the frequencies contained in any periodic signal constructed by repeating the rectangular pulse $p(t)$ at arbitrary periods T.

EXAMPLE 8.1. In the pulse of Fig. 8.1, find the line spectrum when the period T is b, $2b$, $4b$, $8b$, and $16b$.

Ed. J. Hinman

$$H(s) \, G(s) = \int h(\tau) \, g(t-\tau) \, d\tau$$

Solution: When $T = b$, the pulses are adjacent to each other and become simply a constant A. Thus the spectrum is just one line of height A^2 at $f = 0$. When $T > b$, then

$$C_k = \int_{-b/2}^{b/2} A e^{-j2\pi f_k t} \, dt$$

$$= A \frac{e^{-j2\pi f_k t}}{-j2\pi f_k} \bigg|_{-b/2}^{b/2}$$

$$= A \frac{e^{j\pi f_k b} - e^{-j\pi f_k b}}{\pi f_k (2j)}$$

$$= A \frac{\sin (\pi f_k b)}{(\pi f_k)}$$

But $f_k = k/T$, so

$$\frac{C_k}{T} = A \frac{\sin (\pi k b/T)}{\pi k}$$

with C_0/T given by Ab/T, and obtained by noting that for k small, $\sin (\pi k b/T) \doteq \pi k b/T$.

The line spectrum is obtained by taking the magnitude squared of the last expression, and calculating the P_{avk} for a given T.

$$P_{avk} = A^2 \frac{\sin^2 (\pi k b/T)}{(\pi k)^2}$$

Clearly, the power in the wave for large T will be smaller than that for small T, simply because the pulse occurs more frequently in the latter case. Therefore, so that the line spectra will be large enough to be seen as T gets larger, the line spectra plotted in Fig. 8.2 are really $T^2 P_{avk}$. Notice that by multiplying P_{avk} by T^2, we obtain

$$T^2 P_{avk} = A^2 T^2 \frac{\sin^2 (\pi k b/T)}{(\pi k)^2} = A^2 b^2 \frac{\sin^2 (\pi k b/T)}{(\pi k b/T)^2}$$

and this shows that the spectra will have similar shapes no matter what the choice of T. For example, with $T = 2b$

$$T^2 P_{avk} = A^2 b^2 \frac{\sin^2 (\pi k/2)}{(\pi k/2)^2}$$

and this is tabulated in Table 8.1 for the first seven harmonics. The numbers are all expressed as fractions of $A^2 b^2$. The spectrum appears in Fig. 8.2(*b*).

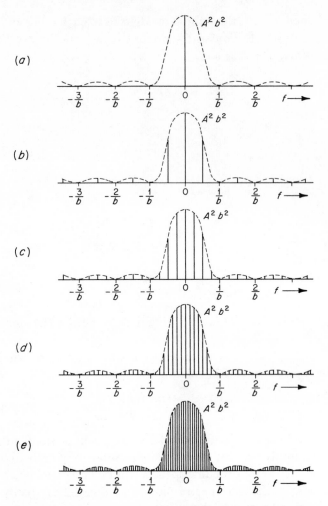

Fig. 8.2   *The line spectra of the periodic waves made from the pulse of Fig. 8.1 with (a) $T=b$, (b) $T=2b$, (c) $T=4b$, (d) $T=8b$, and (e) $T=16b$. The broken line is the envelope of the spectra $(Ab)^2 \sin^2(\pi f b)/(\pi f b)^2$.*

Figures 8.2(c) through (e) are calculated in the same way. For example, with $T = 16b$, $f_k = k/(16b)$ and

$$\frac{T^2 P_{\text{avk}}}{(Ab)^2} = \frac{\sin^2(\pi k/16)}{(\pi k/16)^2}$$

For $k = 16$, $f_{16} = 1/b$ (the same as f_2 when $T = 2b$) and $\sin \pi = 0$. For

$k = 40, f_{40} = 40/(16b) = 5/(2b)$ and the ordinate is 0.016, the same as for $k = 5$ when $T = 2b$.

Table 8.1

k	f_k	$T^2 P_{\text{avk}}/(Ab)^2$
0	0	1.000
1	$1/(2b)$	0.405
2	$1/b$	0
3	$3/(2b)$	0.045
4	$2/b$	0
5	$5/(2b)$	0.016
6	$3/b$	0
7	$7/(2b)$	0.008

Observe that as T gets larger, more and more harmonics appear. This is not really surprising, since as T gets larger the fundamental frequency gets smaller. But no matter what T is, the *envelope* of the spectrum is always the same curve. This curve is simply the squared magnitude of C_k, and

$$C_k = \int_{-b/2}^{b/2} p(t) e^{-j2\pi f_k t}\, dt$$

But this is the Fourier transform, Eq. (8.1), of the pulse $p(t)$ with f replaced by f_k. The Fourier transform has this physical meaning then: The magnitude squared of the Fourier transform of a function of time, $g(t)$, is the *envelope* of all the line spectra of periodic functions that can be constructed by repeating $g(t)$ periodically.

The real utility of the Fourier transform is apparent when the effect of a linear system on the spectrum of a signal is discussed. Observe that the definition of the Fourier transform is very much like that of the Laplace transform, except that the variable is now real. The Fourier transform appears to be nothing but the Laplace transform with s replaced by $j2\pi f$. As will be seen, this is substantially correct, but the next section will make it clear that it is not quite as simple as that.

Nevertheless, if $G_{\text{in}}(f)$ is the transform of the input signal of a linear system whose Laplace transfer function is $H(s)$, the Fourier transform of the output signal $G_0(f)$ is given by

$$G_0(f) = G_{\text{in}}(f) H(j2\pi f)$$

The last equation is fundamental to filter theory, for $H(j2\pi f)$ indeed details the effect of a linear system on the frequencies of a signal.

It will be observed that the new variable f is a continuous real variable when the function is not periodic, and the spectrum $|G(f)|^2$ is no longer a line spectrum, but a *continuous* spectrum. Furthermore, the spectrum $|G(f)|^2$ has units of $sec^2 \times$ watts $(T^2 P_{av})$ = watt-sec per cps = joules per cps. The area under the curve then (that is, the area derived by multiplying dimensionally by cps) is in joules—the measure of energy. It will be shown that $|G(f)|^2$ has an area under it equal exactly to the energy contained in the pulse, and hence the continuous spectrum is called an *energy density spectrum*.

If $G(f)$ is the amount of the frequency f contained in $g(t)$, experience tells us that $g(t)$ must be the sum of all the products of the frequencies and their amounts, divided by the period; that is,

$$f(t) = \sum_{k=-\infty}^{\infty} C_k e^{j2\pi f_k t} \times \frac{1}{T}$$

Since the Fourier transform has been thought of as the limit of the spectrum as T grows large, the continuous counterpart of $1/T = f_1$ must be a differential frequency, for as T grows f_1 shrinks. This leads to the formulation

$$g(t) = \sum_{\text{all } f} G(f) e^{j2\pi f t} \times df$$

or, in more standard mathematical notation

$$g(t) = \int_{-\infty}^{\infty} G(f) e^{j2\pi f t} \, df$$

$$= \int_{-\infty}^{\infty} G(y) e^{j2\pi y t} \, dy \tag{8.2}$$

Although Eq. (8.2) is correct, the steps leading to it should not be considered a proof. A rigorous proof of Eq. (8.2) is beyond the scope of this text.

Comparing Eqs. (8.1) and (8.2), we notice a great similarity, for except for the interchange of $g(t)$ and $G(f)$, and the variables t and f, the equations are almost identical. The question arises, "Which is the transform of which?" The integrals are called Fourier integrals when no physical distinction is made between the variables. In this text the variable f will signify the transform.

8.2 The Fourier Transform

To investigate the Fourier transform we must find those conditions for which the integral

$$\int_{-\infty}^{\infty} g(t)e^{-j2\pi ft}\, dt$$

exists. Since integration can be thought of as "area under the curve of the integrand," $g(t)e^{-j2\pi ft}$ must have a finite area under it. Now the exponential has a magnitude of unity. Since the magnitude of an integral is less than or equal to the integral of the magnitude of the integrand

$$\left| \int_{-\infty}^{\infty} g(t)e^{-j2\pi ft}\, dt \right| \leqslant \int_{-\infty}^{\infty} |g(t)|\, dt$$

tells us that the condition for the existence of the integral is that $|g(t)|$ have a finite area under it. We may conclude that $g(t)$ will have a Fourier transform $G(f)$ given by Eq. (8.1)

$$G(f) = \int_{-\infty}^{\infty} g(x)e^{-j2\pi fx}\, dx$$

if

$$\int_{-\infty}^{\infty} |g(x)|\, dx < \infty \qquad (8.3)$$

Notice that the impulse function is not excluded by Eq. (8.3). For the moment we shall exclude it and discuss it later in Sec. 8.5, since it does present some difficulties.

The definition is rather confining, because no periodic function satisfies Eq. (8.3). Take the sinusoid, for example. If $|\sin \beta t|$ is plotted versus t, it becomes the full-wave rectified sinusoid, which certainly has a nonzero average value. The area under the curve is certainly infinite, since the function is defined for $-\infty < t < \infty$. But the nontransformability of sinusoidal or periodic signals should not distress us, because we already know how to handle these in the frequency domain by using the Fourier series.

The functions $e^{at}\mathbf{1}(t)$ and $e^{\alpha t}\cos \beta t\mathbf{1}(t)$, with a and α positive, are also without Fourier transforms, since these functions grow with time. It appears that almost nothing has a Fourier transform—nothing except practical communication signals. No signal amplitude goes to infinity and no signal lasts forever; therefore, no practical signal can have infinite area under it, and hence all have Fourier transforms.

Note that in the study of the Laplace transform, all signals that did not grow with time or that were not periodic had poles in the left-half s plane. Furthermore, the abscissa of exponential order σ_e was negative, so the Laplace transform certainly existed on the j axis. But on the j axis, $s = j\omega = j2\pi f$, so we can draw two conclusions:

1. If $g(t)$ has a Laplace transform $G'(s)$, which has no poles on the $j\omega$ axis or in the right-half s plane, the Fourier transform of $g(t)$ can be obtained from $G'(s)$ by replacing s by $j2\pi f$. If $G(f)$ is this Fourier transform

$$G(f) = G'(j2\pi f)$$

EXAMPLE 8.2. (*a*) The Laplace transform of $e^{-at}\mathbf{1}(t)$, $a > 0$, is $1/(s+a)$. The pole is in the left-half plane, so

$$\mathscr{F}\left[e^{-at}\mathbf{1}(t)\right] = \frac{1}{j2\pi f + a}$$

(*b*) The Laplace transform of $\mathbf{1}(t)$ is $1/s$. This has a j-axis pole, so the Fourier transform of $\mathbf{1}(t)$ does not exist. Actually, in Sec. 8.5, we will demonstrate (with a little juggling) that it is possible and convenient to define the Fourier transform of the step function, but it will *not* be $1/(j2\pi f)$.

(*c*) The Laplace transform of a rectangular pulse of height A and width b, centered on the origin, is

$$A \frac{e^{sb/2} - e^{-sb/2}}{s}$$

This has no poles, and the abscissa of exponential order is $-\infty$, so the Fourier transform of the pulse is

$$A \frac{e^{j2\pi fb/2} - e^{-j2\pi fb/2}}{j2\pi f} = \frac{A \sin (\pi fb)}{\pi f}$$

2. When the Laplace transform was defined, one of the specified conditions was that the function of time had to be zero for t less than some time t_0. In the definition of the Fourier transform, no such restriction will be imposed. Thus a function such as $e^{at}\mathbf{1}(-t)$, which is zero for positive t and approaches zero as t approaches $-\infty$, will have a Fourier transform though it does *not* have a Laplace transform.

Fourier Transform Theorems

Almost all the Laplace transform theorems are also Fourier transform theorems. Those that are the same will not be proved, but those that are new will be.

1. *Multiplication by a scalar.* If $G(f)$ is the Fourier transform of $g(t)$, $aG(f)$ is the Fourier transform of $ag(t)$.

2. If $G(f)$ and $F(f)$ are Fourier transforms respectively of $g(t)$ and $f(t)$, the Fourier transform of $[g(t)+f(t)]$ is $[G(f)+F(f)]$.

3. If $G(f)$ is the Fourier transform of $g(t)$, the Fourier transform of $e^{j2\pi f_0 t}g(t)$ is $G(f-f_0)$. This is the complex translation theorem of the Laplace transform with $z = j2\pi f_0$. f_0 may be positive or negative real.

4. *Real translation.* If $G(f)$ is the Fourier transform of $g(t)$, the Fourier transform of $g(t-t_0)$ is $e^{-j2\pi f t_0}G(f)$, where t_0 may be positive or negative real.

5. If $G(f)$ is the Fourier transform of $g(t)$, the Fourier transform of $dg(t)/dt$ is $j2\pi f G(f)$. Note that this assumes that $G(f)$ behaves like $1/f^n$, $n \geq 1$, as f becomes large. Actually, Sec. 8.5 will show how $G(f)$ can approach a constant as f becomes infinite.

6. If $G(f)$ is the Fourier transform of $g(t)$, the Fourier transform of $\left\{\int_{-\infty}^{t} g(x)\, dx\right\}$ is $G(f)/(j2\pi f)$, *provided* that this division by f does not produce a pole at $f = 0$. Thus $G(f)$ must vanish at $f = 0$ at least as rapidly as f. More exactly

$$\lim_{f \to 0} \left| \frac{G(f)}{f} \right| < \infty$$

7. If $G(f)$ is the Fourier transform of $g(t)$, the Fourier transform of $tg(t)$ is $(j/2\pi)\, dG(f)/df$.

8. If $G(f)$ is the Fourier transform of $g(t)$, $G(f/a)/a$ is the transform of $g(at)$.

9. If $G(f)$ is the Fourier transform of $g(t)$, $g(-f)$ is the Fourier transform of $G(t)$. This theorem is peculiar to the Fourier transform, and for the first time confuses the use of capital letters for transforms and lower-case letters for functions of time.

Proof: From Eqs. (8.1) and (8.2) we note that

$$G(f) = \int_{-\infty}^{\infty} g(x)e^{-j2\pi fx}\, dx$$

and

$$g(t) = \int_{-\infty}^{\infty} G(y)e^{j2\pi ty}\, dy$$

If, in the second equation, t is replaced by $-f$

$$g(-f) = \int_{-\infty}^{\infty} G(y)e^{-j2\pi fy}\, dy$$

which is seen to be the definition of the transform of $G(t)$.

EXAMPLE 8.3. (*a*) Since

$$\mathscr{F}\left[p(t)\right] = \frac{A \sin \pi fb}{\pi f}$$

where $p(t)$ is a rectangular pulse of height A and width b and centered on the origin, replacing f by t in the transform and t by $-f$ in $p(t)$ gives

$$\mathscr{F}\left(\frac{A \sin \pi bt}{\pi t}\right) = p(-f) = p(f)$$

since the pulse $p(t)$ is symmetric about the $t = 0$ axis. Thus the Fourier transform of $A \sin (\pi bt)/(\pi t)$ is A for $|f| < b$ and 0 for $|f| > b$.

(*b*)   Since

$$\mathscr{F}\left[e^{-at}\mathbf{1}(t)\right] = \frac{1}{j2\pi f + a}$$

then

$$\mathscr{F}\left[\frac{1}{j2\pi t + 1}\right] = e^{af}\mathbf{1}(-f)$$

The theorem actually works both ways, since either t is replaced by $-f$ and f by t or t is replaced by f and f by $-t$. For example, in the last pair above, put t for f on the right and obtain $e^{at}\mathbf{1}(-t)$. Now place $-f$ for t on the left and get the pair

$$\mathscr{F}\left[e^{at}\mathbf{1}(-t)\right] = \frac{1}{-j2\pi f + a}$$

10. If $G(f)$ is the Fourier transform of $g(t)$, the Fourier transform of $g(-t)$ is $G(-f)$. Note that if $g(t)$ is real, the conjugate of $G(f)$, $G^*(f)$, is equal to $G(-f)$.

Proof: Since

$$G(f) = \int_{-\infty}^{\infty} g(x)e^{-j2\pi fx}\, dx$$

then

$$G(-f) = \int_{-\infty}^{\infty} g(x)e^{j2\pi fx}\, dx$$

If the dummy variable of integration is changed to $y = -x$, $dx = -dy$. For $x = -\infty, y = +\infty$. For $x = \infty, y = -\infty$.

$$G(-f) = \int_{\infty}^{-\infty} g(-y)e^{-j2\pi fy}(-dy)$$

The sign of the last integral can be changed if the limits of integration are reversed, so

$$G(-f) = \int_{-\infty}^{\infty} g(-y)e^{-j2\pi fy}\,dy$$

But the last integral is, by definition, the Fourier transform of $g(-t)$. Q.E.D.

EXAMPLE 8.4. (a) Since the Fourier transform of $e^{-at}\mathbf{1}(t)$ is $1/(j2\pi f + a)$, the Fourier transform of $e^{at}\mathbf{1}(-t)$ must be $1/(-j2\pi f + a)$.

(b) The Fourier transform of $e^{-at}\cos\beta t\,\mathbf{1}(t)$ is

$$\frac{s+\alpha}{(s+\alpha)^2+\beta^2}\bigg/_{s=j2\pi f} = \frac{j2\pi f+\alpha}{(j2\pi f+\alpha)^2+\beta^2}$$

and the transform of $e^{at}\cos(-\beta t)\mathbf{1}(-t) = e^{at}\cos\beta t\,\mathbf{1}(-t)$ is simply

$$\frac{-j2\pi f+\alpha}{(-j2\pi f+\alpha)^2+\beta^2}$$

11. If $g(t)$ is a real and even function of t—that is, if $g(t) = g(-t)$—and if $g(t)$ is transformable, its Fourier transform $G(f)$ is real and is an even function of f.

Proof: Let the Fourier transform of $g(t)\mathbf{1}(t)$ be $G'(f)$. Then, by Theorem 10, the transform of $g(-t)\mathbf{1}(-t)$ is $G'(-f)$. But

$$g(t) = g(t)\mathbf{1}(t) + g(t)\mathbf{1}(-t)$$

since $\mathbf{1}(t) + \mathbf{1}(-t) = 1$. The even property of $g(t)$ permits the second $g(t)$ in the last equation to be replaced by $g(-t)$, so

$$g(t) = g(t)\mathbf{1}(t) + g(-t)\mathbf{1}(-t)$$

and

$$G(f) = G'(f) + G'(-f)$$

Clearly, $G(f)$ is even, because if f is replaced by $-f$, the equation does not change. But since $g(t)\mathbf{1}(t)$ is real, $G'(-f) = G'^*(f)$ by Theorem 10. Then

$$G(f) = G'(f) + G'^*(f)$$

But the sum of any complex number and its conjugate is twice the real part of the number, so

$$G(f) = 2 \, \text{Re}[G'(f)]$$

where Re is to be read "Real part of."

Not only has the theorem been proved, but—more important—it also has been proved that if $g(t)$ is an even function of t and has a Fourier transform $G(f)$, the real part of the transform of $g(t)\mathbf{1}(t)$ is $G(f)/2$.

12. If $g(t)$ is a real and odd function of time—that is, if $g(t) = -g(-t)$—the transform of $g(t)$, if it exists, is imaginary and an odd function of f.

Proof: Evidently

$$g(t) = g(t)\mathbf{1}(t) + g(t)\mathbf{1}(-t)$$

and because $g(t)$ is odd

$$g(t) = g(t)\mathbf{1}(t) - g(-t)\mathbf{1}(-t)$$

If $G''(f)$ is the transform of $g(t)\mathbf{1}(t)$, the transform of $g(t)$ is

$$G(f) = G''(f) - G''(-f)$$

which is seen to be odd. The fact that $g(t)\mathbf{1}(t)$ is real means that $G''^*(f) = G''(-f)$, so

$$G(f) = G''(f) - G''^*(f)$$
$$= 2j \, \text{Im}[G''(f)]$$

where Im is to be read "Imaginary part of."

Again there follows the corollary: If $g(t)$ is an odd function of time and $G(f)$ is its transform, the imaginary part of the transform of $g(t)\mathbf{1}(t)$ is $-jG(f)/2$.

Note than any function can be expressed as the sum of an even and an odd function, since for $g(t)$ neither even nor odd

$$g(t) = g_e(t) + g_o(t) \tag{8.4}$$

with

$$g_e(t) = \frac{g(t) + g(-t)}{2} \tag{8.5}$$

and

$$g_o(t) = \frac{g(t) - g(-t)}{2} \tag{8.6}$$

Then Theorems 11 and 12 imply that if $G(f)$ is the Fourier transform of $g(t)$

$$\mathscr{F}[g_e(t)] = \text{Re}[G(f)] \tag{8.7}$$

and

$$\mathscr{F}[g_o(t)] = j\,\text{Im}[G(f)] \tag{8.8}$$

Summary of the Fourier Transform

All the theorems in the preceding section are summarized by the following equations.

Let $g(t)$ and $f(t)$ be transformable with transforms $G(f)$ and $F(f)$ respectively. Then

$$\mathscr{F}[ag(t)] = aG(f) \tag{8.9}$$

$$\mathscr{F}[g(t) + f(t)] = G(f) + F(f) \tag{8.10}$$

$$\mathscr{F}[e^{j2\pi f_o t}\,g(t)] = G(f - f_0) \tag{8.11}$$

$$\mathscr{F}[g(t - t_0)] = e^{-j2\pi t_0 f}G(f) \tag{8.12}$$

$$\mathscr{F}\left[\frac{dg(t)}{dt}\right] = j2\pi f G(f) \tag{8.13}$$

provided that $fG(f)$ is bounded as $f \to \infty$.

$$\mathscr{F}\left[\int_{-\infty}^{t} g(x)\,dx\right] = \frac{G(f)}{j2\pi f} \tag{8.14}$$

provided that $G(f)/f$ is bounded at $f = 0$.

$$\mathscr{F}[tg(t)] = \frac{(j/2\pi)\,dG(f)}{df} \tag{8.15}$$

$$\mathscr{F}[g(at)] = \frac{G(f/a)}{a} \tag{8.16}$$

$$\mathscr{F}[G(t)] = g(-f) \tag{8.17}$$

$$\mathscr{F}[G(-t)] = g(f) \tag{8.18}$$

$$\mathscr{F}[g(-t)] = G(-f) \tag{8.19}$$

$$\mathscr{F}[g_e(t)] = Re[G(f)]$$

$$\mathscr{F}[g_o(t)] = j\,\text{Im}[G(f)]$$

where g_e and g_o are defined by Eqs. (8.5) and (8.6).

The following "flow chart" will prove helpful in sorting out the preceding deluge of theorems and equations.

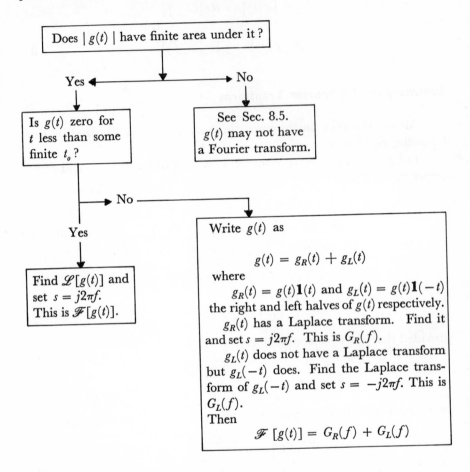

EXAMPLE 8.5. Find the Fourier transform of

$$g(t) = Ae^{-a|t|} \cos \beta t$$

where $|t|$ means the *magnitude of t* and is always positive or zero. Observe that $g(t)$ is an even function of t since the cosine is even. We should expect the transform to be real. Note that the transform should also be twice the real part of the transform of $g_R(t) = g(t)\mathbf{1}(t)$. We shall use this as a check only, since $g(t)$ will not always be even.

Solution: $g(t)$ is pictured in Fig. 8.3(*a*), and g_R and g_L appear in Figs. 8.3(*b*) and (*c*). The flipped g_L—that is, $g_L(-t)$—appears in Fig. 8.3(*d*).

$G(f)$ is the sum of the Laplace transforms of the curve in Fig. 8.3(*b*) with $s = j2\pi f$ and the curve in Fig. 8.3(*d*) with $s = -j2\pi f$.

The Laplace transform of the curve of Fig. 8.3(*b*) is

$$\frac{A(s+\alpha)}{(s+\alpha)^2+\beta^2}$$

and this is the same as the Laplace transform of the curve of Fig. 8.3(*d*). Then

$$G(f) = \frac{A(j2\pi f+\alpha)}{(j2\pi f+\alpha)^2+\beta^2} + \frac{A(-j2\pi f+\alpha)}{(-j2\pi f+\alpha)^2+\beta^2}$$

$$= \frac{A(\alpha+j2\pi f)}{-(2\pi f)^2+\alpha^2+\beta^2+j4\pi\alpha f} + \frac{A(\alpha-j2\pi f)}{-(2\pi f)^2+\alpha^2+\beta^2-j4\pi\alpha f}$$

$$= \frac{2\alpha A[\alpha^2+\beta^2+(2\pi f)^2]}{[\alpha^2+\beta^2-(2\pi f)^2]^2+(4\pi\alpha f)^2}$$

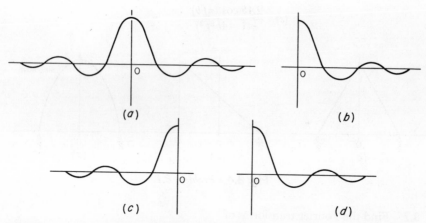

(*a*)　　　　　　　　　　　　(*b*)

(*c*)　　　　　　　　　　　　(*d*)

Fig. 8.3 (*a*) *The function* $Ae^{-\alpha|t|} \cos \beta t$. (*b*). *The right half of this function.* (*c*). *The left half of this function.* (*d*). *The left half of the function when flipped over to the right.*

This last term can be shown to be twice the real part of either term in the preceding equation (which should be obvious, since the second term is the conjugate of the first) by

$$G(f) = 2 \operatorname{Re} \left\{ \frac{A(\alpha+j2\pi f)}{[\alpha^2+\beta^2-(2\pi f)^2+j4\pi\alpha f]} \right\}$$

$$= 2 \operatorname{Re} \left\{ \frac{A(\alpha+j2\pi f)[\alpha^2+\beta^2-(2\pi f)^2-j4\pi\alpha f]}{[\alpha^2+\beta^2-(2\pi f)^2+j4\pi\alpha f] [\alpha^2+\beta^2-(2\pi f)^2-j4\pi\alpha f]} \right\}$$

$$= \frac{2A\{\alpha[\alpha^2+\beta^2-(2\pi f)^2]+(2\pi f)(4\pi\alpha f)\}}{[\alpha^2+\beta^2-(2\pi f)^2]^2+(4\pi\alpha f)^2}$$

$$= \frac{2A\alpha[\alpha^2+\beta^2+(2\pi f)^2]}{[\alpha^2+\beta^2-(2\pi f)^2]^2+(4\pi\alpha f)^2}$$

which is the same answer as before.

PROBLEMS

8.1. Find the Fourier transforms of the functions pictured in Fig. 8.4.

Answers: (a) $\dfrac{Ab}{2}\left[\dfrac{\sin{(\pi fb/2)}}{(\pi fb/2)}\right]^2$

(b) $\dfrac{jA}{2\pi^2f^2b}\left[-\sin{(\pi fb)}+(\pi fb)e^{-j\pi fb}\right]$

(c) $\dfrac{2Ab\cos{(\pi fb)}}{\pi(1-4b^2f^2)}$

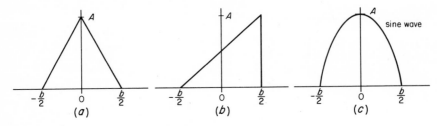

Fig. 8.4 *Problem 8.1.*

8.2. Find the Fourier transforms of

(a) $e^{-a|t|}$

(b) $\sin{(\beta t)}\left[1\left(t+\dfrac{2\pi n}{\beta}\right)-1\left(t-\dfrac{2\pi n}{\beta}\right)\right]$ n is an integer

(c) $te^{-at}1(t)$

Answer to (b): $\dfrac{2j\sin{(4\pi^2 fn/\beta)}}{\beta^2[1-(2\pi f/\beta)^2]}$

8.3. Using the transform of the rectangular pulse and Eq. (8.17), find the Fourier transform of $(\sin{at})/t$.

8.4. Using the transform of the triangular pulse of Fig. 8.4(a) and Eq. (8.17), find the Fourier transform of $(\sin^2{at})/t^2$.

8.5. Find the Fourier transforms of

(a) $e^{-at}\mathbf{1}(t) - e^{at}\mathbf{1}(-t)$

(b) $-e^{at}\sin \beta t\, \mathbf{1}(-t)$

(c) $1/(a^2+t^2)$

$$\text{Answer to }(c)\text{: }\frac{\pi}{a}e^{-2\pi a|f|}$$

8.6. For some transformable functions, the transforms of the integrals of the functions from $-\infty$ to t can be evaluated by division by $j2\pi f$; this is not true for others. Of the functions listed below, which can be used to find the transforms of their integrals and which cannot? You should be able to do this without finding the transforms. How?

(a) $e^{-at}\mathbf{1}(t) - e^{at}\mathbf{1}(-t)$

(b) $\cos \beta t \left[\mathbf{1}\left(t+\dfrac{2\pi}{\beta}\right) - \mathbf{1}\left(t-\dfrac{2\pi}{\beta}\right)\right]$

(c) $\mathbf{1}(t) - \mathbf{1}(t-b)$

8.7. Find the transforms of the functions in Prob. 8.6. Integrate the functions from $-\infty$ to t and express the result in the form of exponentials, sines and/or cosines, and the functions $\mathbf{1}(t)$ and $\mathbf{1}(-t)$.

$$\text{Answer to }(b)\text{: } (1)\ \frac{4\pi f \sin (4\pi^2 f/\beta)}{4\pi^2 f^2 - \beta^2}$$

$$(2)\ \frac{1}{\beta}\sin \beta t \left[\mathbf{1}\left(t+\frac{2\pi}{\beta}\right) - \mathbf{1}\left(t-\frac{2\pi}{\beta}\right)\right]$$

8.8. Find the Fourier transforms of

(a) $e^{-at}\mathbf{1}(t+b)$ a and b are positive

(b) $e^{at}\left[\mathbf{1}(t) - \mathbf{1}(t-b)\right]$

8.9. From Eq. (8.2), setting $t = 0$, we obtain

$$g(0) = \int_{-\infty}^{\infty} G(f)\, df$$

since $e^0 = 1$. Use this relationship and the transforms of the rectangular and triangular pulses [see Fig. 8.1 and Prob. 8.1(a)] to evaluate the definite integrals

(a) $\displaystyle\int_{-\infty}^{\infty} \frac{\sin ax}{x}\, dx$ (b) $\displaystyle\int_{-\infty}^{\infty} \frac{\sin^2 ax}{x^2}\, dx$

$$\text{Answer to }(b)\text{: } a\pi$$

8.10. From Eq. (8.1), setting $f = 0$, we obtain

$$G(0) = \int_{-\infty}^{\infty} g(t) \, dt$$

since $e^0 = 1$. Use this relationship, the transforms of $e^{-a|t|}$, and the cosine pulse of Fig. 8.4(c) to evaluate the definite integrals

(a) $\displaystyle\int_{-\infty}^{\infty} \frac{dt}{a^2+t^2}$ (b) $\displaystyle\int_{-\infty}^{\infty} \frac{\cos(\pi f/2a)}{a^2-f^2} \, df$

Answer to (b): π/a

8.3 The Inverse Fourier Transform of a Rational Function

The inverse transforms of rational functions of the variable f can be found by using a procedure almost exactly like that used for the Laplace transform. If we use the letter $p = j2\pi f$ instead of s, so that the transform is not confused with the Laplace transform (and remember that p is not the operator used in Chapter 2), then $f = -jp/2\pi$, and the Fourier transform can be written as a ratio of polynomials in p.

The inverse transform of the rational function of p is then found by a partial fraction expansion exactly like that used to obtain inverse Laplace transforms of functions of s. In fact, the only new aspects of the procedure are as follows.

1. If there are poles on the j axis of the p plane, the function comes under the class of functions discussed in Sec. 8.5, and caution should be exercised.

2. The inverse transforms of the terms in the partial fraction expansion that have left-half p-plane poles are exactly the same as those in the Laplace transform.

3. The inverse transforms of the terms in the partial fraction expansion that have right-half p-plane poles are also the same functions as those in the Laplace transform, but instead of multiplying them by $\mathbf{1}(t)$, we multiply them by $-\mathbf{1}(-t)$.

EXAMPLE 8.6. Find the inverse Fourier transform of

$$G(f) = \frac{1}{2+4\pi^2 f^2+j2\pi f}$$

Solution: Setting $f = -jp/2\pi$

$$G(f) = \frac{1}{2-p^2+p} = \frac{-1}{(p+1)(p-2)}$$

$$= \frac{1/3}{p+1} - \frac{1/3}{p-2}$$

The first term has a pole in the left-half p plane, so its inverse transform is the same as that obtained from the Laplace transform—that is, $\frac{1}{3} e^{-t}\mathbf{1}(t)$. If the second term were a Laplace transform, its inverse transform would be $-\frac{1}{3} e^{2t}\mathbf{1}(t)$. Since it is a Fourier transform, $\mathbf{1}(t)$ is replaced by $-\mathbf{1}(-t)$, so

$$g(t) = \frac{1}{3}\left[e^{2t}\mathbf{1}(-t) + e^{-t}\mathbf{1}(t)\right]$$

EXAMPLE 8.7. Find the inverse Fourier transform of

$$G(f) = \frac{A}{f^4+a^4}$$

where A and a are real positive constants.
Solution: Replace f by $-jp/(2\pi)$. Then

$$G(f) = \frac{A}{(-jp/2\pi)^4+a^4} = \frac{(2\pi)^4 A}{p^4+(2\pi a)^4}$$

The roots of the denominator are

$$p^4 = -(2\pi a)^4 \qquad p^2 = \pm j(2\pi a)^2$$

Since the square roots of $+j$ are $\pm(1+j)/\sqrt{2}$, and the square roots of $-j$ are $\pm(1-j)/\sqrt{2}$, the four roots are $\sqrt{2}\pi a(1+j)$, $\sqrt{2}\pi a(1-j)$, $\sqrt{2}\,\pi a(-1+j)$, and $\sqrt{2}\,\pi a(-1-j)$. In factored form we have

$$G(f) = \frac{16\pi^4 A}{(p+\sqrt{2}\pi a-j\sqrt{2}\pi a)(p-\sqrt{2}\pi a-j\sqrt{2}\pi a)(p+\sqrt{2}\pi a+j\sqrt{2}\pi a)}$$
$$\overline{(p-\sqrt{2}\pi a+j\sqrt{2}\pi a)}$$

If this is expanded in a partial fraction expansion, only the terms with $-j$ in the factors are required, so

$$G(f) = 16\pi^4 A\left[\frac{1/\!\!-45°/(32\pi^3 a^3)}{p+\sqrt{2}\pi a-j\sqrt{2}\pi a} + \frac{1/\!\!-135°/(32\pi^3 a^3)}{p-\sqrt{2}\pi a-j\sqrt{2}\pi a}\right.$$
$$\left. + \text{conjugates}\right]$$

$$= \frac{\pi A}{2a^3}\left[\frac{1/\!\!-45°}{p+\sqrt{2}\pi a-j\sqrt{2}\pi a} - \frac{1/45°}{p-\sqrt{2}\pi a-j\sqrt{2}\pi a} + \text{conjugates}\right]$$

so

$$g(t) = \frac{\pi A}{a^3} \left[e^{-\sqrt{2}\pi at} \cos\left(\sqrt{2}\pi at - 45°\right) \mathbf{1}(t) \right.$$

$$\left. + e^{\sqrt{2}\pi at} \cos\left(\sqrt{2}\pi at + 45°\right) \mathbf{1}(-t) \right]$$

where it can be seen that the inverse transform of the second term is the same as the one that would be obtained if the expression had been a Laplace transform, except that its sign is changed and $\mathbf{1}(-t)$ appears in place of $\mathbf{1}(t)$.

For negative t the cosine in the second term can be written as $\cos\left(-\sqrt{2}\,\pi a|t| + 45°\right) = \cos\left(\sqrt{2}\,\pi a\,|t| - 45°\right)$, since the cosine is an even function. Then $g(t)$ above may be written as

$$g(t) = \frac{\pi A}{a^3} e^{-\sqrt{2}\pi a|t|} \cos\left(\sqrt{2}\pi a|t| - 45°\right)$$

and it is seen to be an even function of t, as it should be with $G(f)$ being real.

The proof of the technique used on the right-half p-plane poles is now required.

THEOREM 8.1. Let the Laplace transform $F(s)$ of $f(t)\mathbf{1}(t)$ have only right-half s-plane poles. Let $g(t)$ be a function of time whose Fourier transform is exactly the same as $F(s)$, but with s replaced by $j2\pi f$. Then $g(t) = -f(t)\mathbf{1}(-t)$.

Proof: If $F(s)$ has only right-half s-plane poles, its partial fraction expansion will contain a number of terms of the type

$$\frac{A/\theta}{(s - \alpha - j\beta)^n}$$

where α is positive but where β may be positive, zero, or negative.

For any such term the inverse Laplace transform is known to be

$$f(t)\mathbf{1}(t) = \frac{A/\theta \; t^{n-1}}{(n-1)!} e^{\alpha t} e^{j\beta t}\mathbf{1}(t)$$

so $f(t)$ is the expression on the right side without the $\mathbf{1}(t)$.

Given that $g(t)$ is a function whose Fourier transform is

$$\frac{A/\theta}{(j2\pi f - \alpha - j\beta)^n}$$

the theorem will be proved if it can be shown that

$$g(t) = -\frac{A\underline{/\theta}\; t^{n-1}}{(n-1)!}\; e^{\alpha t}\, e^{j\beta t}\mathbf{1}(-t)$$

Whatever $g(t)$ is, Eq. (8.19) tells us that

$$\mathscr{F}[g(-t)] = \frac{A\underline{/\theta}}{(-j2\pi f-\alpha-j\beta)^n}$$

If in this last expression $j2\pi f$ is replaced by s, the right side becomes

$$\frac{A\underline{/\theta}}{(-s-\alpha-j\beta)^n} = \frac{(-1)^n\, A\underline{/\theta}}{(s+\alpha+j\beta)^n}$$

But this is seen to have a left-half s-plane pole of order n, and it is known that its inverse Laplace transform will be identical to $g(-t)$. Then, by Eq. (1) in Table 3.2 and Prob. 3.46 (Chapter 3)

$$g(-t) = \frac{(-1)^n\, A\underline{/\theta}\; t^{n-1}}{(n-1)!}\, e^{-\alpha t}\, e^{-j\beta t}\mathbf{1}(t)$$

$$= -\frac{A\underline{/\theta}\,(-t^{n-1})}{(n-1)!}\, e^{-\alpha t}\, e^{-j\beta t}\mathbf{1}(t)$$

Replacing $-t$ by t, we have

$$g(t) = -\frac{A\underline{/\theta}\; t^{n-1}}{(n-1)!}\, e^{\alpha t}\, e^{j\beta t}\mathbf{1}(-t) \qquad \text{Q.E.D.}$$

PROBLEMS

8.11. Find the inverse Fourier transforms of the following functions.

(a) $\dfrac{B}{f^2+b^2}$ (b) $\dfrac{jBf}{f^2+b^2}$ (c) $\dfrac{p^2-4}{(p+1)\,(p+2)\,(p-3)}$

where B and b are real and $p = j2\pi f$.

Answer to (b): $\pi B[e^{2\pi bt}\mathbf{1}(-t) - e^{-2\pi bt}\mathbf{1}(t)]$

8.12. Find the inverse Fourier transforms of

(a) $\dfrac{1-\pi^2 f^2}{f^4+1.25f^2/\pi^2+0.25/\pi^4}$ (b) $\dfrac{1}{(\pi f+j)^2}$

Answer to (a): $\dfrac{2\pi^4}{3}\,[5e^{-|t|} - 4e^{-2|t|}]$

8.13. Find the inverse Fourier transforms of

(a) $\dfrac{[a/(2\pi)]^2 - f^2}{\{f^2 + [a/(2\pi)]^2\}^2}$ (b) $\dfrac{-jaf/\pi}{\{f^2 + [a/(2\pi)]^2\}^2}$

$\qquad$ *Answers:* (a) $2\pi^2 |t|\; e^{-a|t|}$ (b) $2\pi^2 t e^{-a|t|}$

8.14. Find the inverse Fourier transform of

$$G(f) = \frac{f^2}{(f^2 + a^2)^4}$$

8.15. Find the inverse Fourier transform of

$$G(f) = \frac{f^2 - a^2}{(f^2 + a^2)^4}$$

$$\textit{Answer: } g(t) = -\frac{\pi e^{-|2\pi a t|}}{4a^5}\left[1 + |2\pi a t| + \frac{|2\pi a t|^2}{2} + \frac{|2\pi a t|^3}{6}\right]$$

8.4 Convolution

Suppose that a linear system is excited by an input signal $f_{in}(t)$ such as that shown in Fig. 8.5. Then the output signal $f_0(t)$ will be some function that depends upon the transfer function of the linear system as well as upon the input signal.

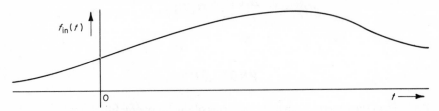

Fig. 8.5 *An arbitrary input signal.*

$\qquad$ Look at Fig. 8.6, in which the input signal is replaced by one that equals the original signal at the times given by kt_0 only, where k is any positive or negative integer, and where this new input signal is a constant in each of the intervals

$$kt_0 < t < (k+1)t_0$$

and has the value $f_{in}(kt_0)$ in each of these intervals. If this chopped version of the input signal is applied to the linear system, would the new output signal resemble the original output signal?

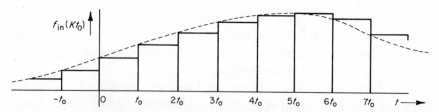

Fig. 8.6 *The signal of Fig. 8.5 approximately by a set of rectangular pulses of length t_0 sec.*

This is a difficult question to answer, but it seems likely that if the intervals t_0 were very small, the outputs in both cases would be very nearly the same. Let us assume that it is possible to choose t_0 small enough that the change in the output signal is negligibly small. Then the input signal can be thought of as a train of rectangular pulses having heights equal to the value of $f_{in}(t)$ at the times $t = kt_0$. Suppose that instead of the train of pulses each t_0 wide, the function $f_{in}(t)$ were replaced by a train of pulses of heights $2f_{in}(kt_0)$ at the times kt_0, as before, but now the pulses are only half as long as they were; that is, they are now only $t_0/2$ sec in length. This is shown in Fig. 8.7. What do you think the output would look like? It is now clear that the input has the character of a

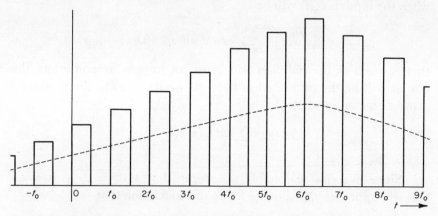

Fig. 8.7 *The signal of Fig. 8.5 approximated by a set of rectangular pulses only half as long as those of Fig. 8.6, but with twice the amplitude of those in Fig. 8.6.*

periodic square wave with fundamental frequency $1/t_0$. If the linear system has resonances at this frequency or at harmonics of this frequency, the output will not look much like the output that results when the signal of Fig. 8.5 is the input. On the other hand, if t_0 is small enough that the response of the linear system to frequencies of $1/t_0$ and higher is negligible, it seems reasonable to assume that the output will be substantially the same whether the signal of Fig. 8.5 or that of Fig. 8.7 is used as the input signal.

If the pulses are made shorter and shorter, and the area is always kept the same, the input approaches a series of impulses each of area $t_0 f_{in}(kt_0)$ and occurring at $t = kt_0$. In effect, it is being stated that as far as the output is concerned, it does not matter whether the input is the function $f_{in}(t)$ or the function

$$f_{in}'(t) = \sum_{k=-\infty}^{\infty} t_0 f_{in}(kt_0) \, \delta \, (t - kt_0)$$

Suppose that the output signal when $f_{in}(t)$ is the input is called $f_0(t)$. Now the output signal when the input is a unit impulse at $t = 0$ is the impulse response $h(t)$, which is the inverse Laplace transform of $H(s)$, the transfer function of the linear system. The output of the network when the impulse has a magnitude of A, for example, would be $Ah(t)$, and if the impulse had a magnitude of A and occurred at $t = t_1$ instead of at the origin, the output would be $Ah(t)$ translated by the amount t_1—that is, $Ah(t - t_1)$. Since the system is linear, the output when the input is $f_{in}'(t)$ will be

$$f_0'(t) = \sum_{k=-\infty}^{\infty} t_0 f_{in} \, (kt_0) h(t - kt_0)$$

that is, each of the impulses will cause an impulse response and the output will be the sum of all of these. If we let $\tau = kt_0$, the preceding expression can be written

$$f_0'(t) = \sum_{\tau=-\infty}^{\infty} \Delta \tau f_{in}(\tau) h(t - \tau)$$

where $\Delta \tau = t_0$.

Since it seems reasonable to assume that as $t_0 = \Delta \tau$ gets small $f_0'(t)$ will approach $f_0(t)$, we are led to the conclusion that

$$f_0(t) = \int_{-\infty}^{\infty} f_{in}(\tau) h(t - \tau) \, d\tau \tag{8.20}$$

The derivation above is referred to as being *heuristic*, which means tending to point out truth. Under no circumstances can it be thought of as a rigorous proof, for a number of unvalidated assumptions were made. Nevertheless, Eq. (8.20) is correct, however casual the arguments leading to it. The integral of the equation is called the *convolution integral*, and the process is exactly the same as the convolution discussed in Chapter 7, wherein we discussed multiplying periodic or almost periodic functions of time. Observe that the integral tells us to take the input and impulse response functions and perform the following operations:

1. Take $h(\tau)$ and flip it—that is, replace τ by $-\tau$.
2. Slide the flipped function to the right (if t is positive) t units; that is, replace τ by $\tau - t$. The result of these two operations yields $h(-\tau)$ and $h(t-\tau)$, respectively.
3. Multiply this result by $f_{in}(\tau)$; this operation yields the integrand.
4. Sum; that is, integrate over all τ.

Probably the most interesting result of Eq. (8.20) is that it now supplies an answer to the questions that must have resulted from the section "Anti-Theorem Number One" in Chapter 3. Since the transform of the output $F_0(s)$ and that of the input $F_{in}(s)$ are related by

$$F_0(s) = F_{in}(s)H(s)$$

Theorem 8.2 must be correct if Eq. (8.20) is correct.

THEOREM 8.2. Let $h(t)$ and $f_{in}(t)$ be Laplace transformable with transforms $H(s)$ and $F_{in}(s)$. The inverse transform of $H(s)F_{in}(s)$ must be

$$f_0(t) = \int_{-\infty}^{\infty} f_{in}(\tau)h(t-\tau)\,d\tau$$

This theorem is quite correct, but its proof will not be supplied. Instead, an entirely similar theorem (8.3) concerning Fourier transforms will be proved.

THEOREM 8.3. Let $g_1(t)$ and $g_2(t)$ be Fourier transformable with transforms $G_1(f)$ and $G_2(f)$ respectively. The Fourier transform of

$$s(t) = \int_{-\infty}^{\infty} g_1(\tau)g_2(t-\tau)\,d\tau$$

is $G_1(f)G_2(f)$.

Proof: By definition, the Fourier transform of $s(t)$ is

$$S(f) = \int_{-\infty}^{\infty} \left\{ \int_{-\infty}^{\infty} g_1(\tau)g_2(x-\tau)\,d\tau \right\} e^{-j2\pi fx}\,dx$$

If the iterated integral is expressed as a double integral

$$S(f) = \int_{-\infty}^{\infty} \int_{-\infty}^{\infty} g_1(\tau)g_2(x-\tau)\,e^{-j2\pi fx}\,dx\,d\tau$$

If the new variable $\zeta = x - \tau$ is substituted for x, then $dx = d\zeta$ and the limits on the x integration become $-\infty - \tau$ and $\infty - \tau$ for the ζ integration. But for fixed τ, this will be the same as $-\infty$ and ∞, so

$$S(f) = \int_{-\infty}^{\infty} \int_{-\infty}^{\infty} g_1(\tau) g_2(\zeta) e^{-j2\pi f(\zeta + \tau)} \, d\zeta \, d\tau$$

But the integrand can now be separated into two functions, one in τ alone and one in ζ alone

$$S(f) = \int_{-\infty}^{\infty} \int_{-\infty}^{\infty} \{g_1(\tau) e^{-j2\pi f\tau} d\tau\} \{g_2(\zeta) e^{-j2\pi f\zeta} d\zeta\}$$

If this is now expressed as an iterated integral

$$S(f) = \left\{ \int_{-\infty}^{\infty} g_1(\tau) \, e^{-j2\pi f\tau} \, d\tau \right\} \left\{ \int_{-\infty}^{\infty} g_2(\zeta) \, e^{-j2\pi f\zeta} \, d\zeta \right\}$$

But this is seen to be nothing but the product of the Fourier transforms of g_1 and g_2, so

$$S(f) = G_1(f)G_2(f) \qquad \text{Q.E.D.}$$

This theorem points out another interesting fact. Since $G_1(f)G_2(f)$ must equal $G_2(f)G_1(f)$, the order in which the functions are chosen is immaterial; that is,

$$\int_{-\infty}^{\infty} g_1(\tau) g_2(t - \tau) \, d\tau = \int_{-\infty}^{\infty} g_2(\tau) g_1(t - \tau) \, d\tau$$

We now recall the similarity between the equation for the inverse Fourier transform and the equation for the direct transform. From this we might guess that there is a similar relation involving transforms.

THEOREM 8.4. If $g_1(t)$ and $g_2(t)$ are Fourier transformable, with transforms $G_1(f)$ and $G_2(f)$ respectively, the Fourier transform of $g_1(t) g_2(t)$ is given by

$$\mathscr{F}\left[g_1(t)g_2(t)\right] = \int_{-\infty}^{\infty} G_1(y) G_2(f - y) \, dy \qquad (8.21)$$

This may be proved in the manner in which the last theorem was proved, or by use of Eq. (8.17).

As techniques for finding transforms and inverse transforms, Eqs. (8.20) and (8.21) leave something to be desired. Very often the integration is difficult, but more often than not the real difficulty comes with the limits of the integration. If either function has step functions in its definition, particular care must be taken with the limits of the integration.

EXAMPLE 8.8. Let $g_1(t) = e^{-t}\mathbf{1}(t)$ and $g_2(t) = e^{-2t}\mathbf{1}(t+2)$. Convolve g_1 and g_2.

Solution: Let $s(t)$ be the result of convolving g_1 and g_2. Then, from Eq. (8.20)

$$s(t) = \int_{-\infty}^{\infty} e^{-\tau}\mathbf{1}(\tau)e^{-2(t-\tau)}\mathbf{1}(t-\tau+2) \, d\tau$$

$$= \int_{-\infty}^{\infty} e^{-\tau}e^{-2t}e^{2\tau}\mathbf{1}(\tau)\mathbf{1}(t-\tau+2) \, d\tau$$

$$= e^{-2t}\int_{-\infty}^{\infty} e^{\tau}\mathbf{1}(\tau)\mathbf{1}(t-\tau+2) \, d\tau$$

since t is independent of the dummy variable of integration τ.

Observe now that the integrand is zero when τ is negative, because of the presence of $\mathbf{1}(\tau)$. Thus the lower limit can be changed to zero. The integrand is also zero when $t - \tau + 2$ is negative—that is, when

$$t - \tau + 2 < 0$$

$$-\tau < -(t+2)$$

or

$$\tau > (t+2)$$

Thus, since the integrand vanishes above $t + 2$, the upper limit can be written as $t + 2$, so

$$s(t) = e^{-2t} \int_{0}^{t+2} e^{\tau} \, d\tau$$

$$= e^{-2t}\left[e^{\tau} \Big/_{0}^{t+2}\right] = e^{-2t}[e^{t+2} - 1]$$

$$= e^{2}e^{-t} - e^{-2t}$$

Observe that the $\mathbf{1}(t)$ terms were not left out of the solution as a result of carelessness, but clearly this answer is not correct for all time, so an oversight must have occurred. Where?

We now do the problem using either the Laplace or Fourier transform; since the Laplace transform is easier, we use it.

$$G_1(s) = \frac{1}{s+1}$$

and

$$G_2(s) = \frac{e^4 e^{2s}}{s+2}$$

The latter is written by using the real translation theorem. Then the transform of $s(t)$ is $e^4 e^{2s}/[(s+1)(s+2)]$, and, by partial fraction expansion,

$$S(s) = e^4 e^{2s} \left[\frac{1}{s+1} - \frac{1}{s+2} \right]$$

for which the inverse transform is $e^4(e^{-t}-e^{-2t})\mathbf{1}(t)$ but translated to the left two units. Setting $t+2$ for t

$$s(t) = [e^2 e^{-t} - e^{-2t}]\, \mathbf{1}(t+2)$$

Comparison of this result with the previous one indicates that the $\mathbf{1}(t+2)$ term is the only thing that was missing. This could have been avoided in the following manner.

$$s(t) = e^{-2t} \int_{-\infty}^{\infty} e^{\tau} \mathbf{1}(\tau)\mathbf{1}(t-\tau+2)\, d\tau$$

Let $y = \tau - 2$ or $\tau = y + 2$, so

$$s(t) = e^{-2t} \int_{-\infty}^{\infty} e^{y+2}\mathbf{1}(y+2)\mathbf{1}(t-y)\, dy$$

$$= e^2 e^{-2t} \int_{-\infty}^{\infty} e^{y}\mathbf{1}(y+2)\mathbf{1}(t-y)\, dy$$

But the integrand is zero for $y > t$, so $\mathbf{1}(t-y)$ can be dropped if the upper limit is changed to t. Then

$$s(t) = e^2 e^{-2t} \int_{-\infty}^{t} e^{y}\mathbf{1}(y+2)\, dy$$

The lower limit may now be changed to -2 if according to Theorem 2.1 in Chapter 2 the step function is brought outside the integral and y replaced by t.

$$s(t) = e^2 e^{-2t}\mathbf{1}(t+2) \int_{-2} e^{y}\, dy$$

This will lead to the correct solution. The generalization of this result is to be found in Prob. 8.16.

Note that the step functions under the integral sign are a nuisance when the convolution integral is evaluated, and unless the integral is to be evaluated by numerical techniques or on a digital computer, the transform approach is generally the more desirable.

The advantages of convolution arise not because it provides an alternative approach to finding inverse transforms, but because it adds additional insight into the concept of the frequency domain. For example, if $f(t)$ is a real transformable function of t, so is $f(-t)$, and the convolution of these two is

$$\phi(t) = \int_{-\infty}^{\infty} f(\tau)f(\tau - t)\, d\tau$$

But if $F(f)$ is the Fourier transform of $f(t)$, $F(-f)$ is the transform of $f(-t)$. The fact that $f(t)$ is real means that $F(-f) = F^*(f)$, so the transform of $\phi(t)$ is $|F(f)|^2$. But this is real and an even function of f, so $\phi(t)$ must also be an even function of t and it must also be true that

$$\phi(t) = \phi(-t) = \int_{-\infty}^{\infty} f(\tau)f(\tau + t)\, d\tau$$

But according to Eq. (8.2), the inverse transform of $|F(f)|^2$ is

$$\phi(t) = \int_{-\infty}^{\infty} |F(f)|^2\, e^{j2\pi ft}\, df$$

so

$$\phi(t) = \int_{-\infty}^{\infty} f(\tau)f(\tau + t)\, d\tau = \int_{-\infty}^{\infty} |F(f)|^2\, e^{j2\pi ft}\, df$$

If we set $t = 0$ in the last equation

$$\phi(0) = \int_{-\infty}^{\infty} f^2(\tau)\, d\tau = \int_{-\infty}^{\infty} |F(f)|^2\, df \qquad (8.22)$$

This equation states that if $f(t)$ is a voltage or a current associated with a 1-ohm resistance, the total energy of the signal is equal to the area under the square of the magnitude of the transform of $f(t)$.

Now if $f(t)$ is the input signal to a filter with transfer function

$H(s) = H(j2\pi f)$, the transform of the output signal $g(t)$ is known to be $F(f)H(j2\pi f)$. The energy of the output signal is then

$$\int_{-\infty}^{\infty} |F(f)|^2 \, |H(j2\pi f)|^2 \, df$$

Now suppose that the transfer function $H(j2\pi f)$ were equal to unity in the interval $f_0 < f < f_0 + \Delta f$ only, and equal to zero elsewhere. Then the energy in the output would be

$$\int_{f_0}^{f_0 + \Delta f} |F(f)|^2 \, df$$

or the *area under the portion of the spectrum that lies between f_0 and $f_0 + \Delta f$.* Then $|F(f)|^2$ is truly an energy density function for the signal $f(t)$.

PROBLEMS

8.16. Prove that if $g_1(t) = 0$ for $t < t_1$ and $g_2(t) = 0$ for $t < t_2$, the convolution of g_1 and g_2 can be written as

$$s(t) = \mathbf{1}(t - t_1 - t_2) \int_{t_1 + t_2}^{t} g_1(y - t_2)g_2(t + t_2 - y) \, dy$$

or, by interchanging subscripts 1 and 2,

$$s(t) = \mathbf{1}(t - t_1 - t_2) \int_{t_1 + t_2}^{t} g_2(y - t_1)g_1(t + t_1 - y) \, dy$$

Note: Set $g_1(t) = g_1(t)\mathbf{1}(t - t_1)$ and $g_2(t) = g_2(t)\mathbf{1}(t - t_2)$, and then change the variable of integration so that the upper limit becomes t. Then use Theorem 2.1 of Chapter 2.

8.17. Use the result of Prob. 8.16 to convolve the functions $e^{-3t}\mathbf{1}(t+2)$ and $e^{2t}\mathbf{1}(t-3)$. Check your result using the Laplace transform.

$$\text{Answer: } \frac{e^{12}}{5} \, [e^{2(t-1)} - e^{-3(t-1)}] \, \mathbf{1}(t-1)$$

8.18. The process of convolution by direct integration is tricky when several step functions appear in the integrand. For example, let $g(t)$ be a rectangular pulse, of height A, and width b that is centered on the origin. Convolve this pulse with itself, and check your result using either the Fourier or Laplace transform.

8.19. Convolve by direct integration, and check by transforms, the functions

(a) $e^{-2t}\mathbf{1}(t)$ and $e^{3t}\mathbf{1}(t)$
(b) $e^{-t}\mathbf{1}(t)$ and $\sin 2t\mathbf{1}(t)$
(c) $e^{t}\mathbf{1}(-t)$ and $e^{-t}\mathbf{1}(t)$

Answer to (b): $\left[\dfrac{2}{5}e^{-t} + \dfrac{1}{5}(\sin 2t - 2\cos 2t)\right]\mathbf{1}(t)$

8.20 Let $f(t)$ be Laplace transformable with transform $F(s)$ and having $\sigma_e = c$. Show that regardless of the sign of c $e^{-bt}f(t)$ has a Fourier transform, provided that $b > c$. Show that this Fourier transform is $F(j2\pi f + b)$.

8.21. If $f_1(t)$ and $f_2(t)$ are Laplace transformable, with transforms $F_1(s)$ and $F_2(s)$, then—from the results of Prob. 8.20—$g_1(t) = e^{-bt}f_1(t)$ and $g_2(t) = e^{-bt}f_2(t)$ are Fourier transformable with transforms $G_1(f) = F_1(j2\pi f + b)$ and $G_2(f) = F_2(j2\pi f + b)$, provided that b is greater than the abscissa of exponential order of either function f_1 or f_2.
But from Eq. (8.21), the Fourier transform of $g_1(t)g_2(t) = e^{-2bt}f_1(t)f_2(t)$ is

$$\mathscr{F}\,[g_1 g_2] = \int\limits_{-\infty}^{\infty} F_1(j2\pi y + b)F_2(j2\pi f - j2\pi y + b)\,dy$$

Set $w = j2\pi y + b$ and $s = j2\pi f$ and show that the Laplace transform of $g_1 g_2$ is given by

$$\mathscr{L}\,[g_1 g_2] = \mathscr{L}\,[e^{-2bt}f_1 f_2] = \frac{1}{2\pi j}\int\limits_{b-j\infty}^{b+j\infty} F_1(w)F_2(s + 2b - w)\,dw$$

8.22. Use the theorem on "Complex Translation" in Chapter 3 and the results of Prob. 8.21 to demonstrate that

$$\mathscr{L}\,[f_1(t)f_2(t)] = \frac{1}{2\pi j}\int\limits_{b-j\infty}^{b+j\infty} F_1(w)F_2(s - w)\,dw$$

provided that b is greater than the abscissa of exponential order of either f_1 or f_2.

8.23. If $f(t)$ is Laplace transformable with transform $F(s)$, then from Prob. 8.20, $g(t) = e^{-bt}f(t)$ with $b > \sigma_e$ is Fourier transformable with transform $G(f) = F(j2\pi f + b)$. Use this relationship and Eq. (8.2) to show that with a substitution as in Prob. 8.21

$$e^{-bt}f(t) = \frac{e^{-bt}}{2\pi j}\int\limits_{b-\infty}^{b+j\infty} F(w)e^{tw}\,dw$$

or that

$$f(t) = \frac{1}{2\pi j} \int_{b-j\infty}^{b+j\infty} F(y)e^{ty}\, dy$$

This is Eq. (3.5).

8.24. The autocorrelation function $\phi(\tau)$ of a function $g(t)$ is defined by

$$\phi(\tau) = \int_{-\infty}^{\infty} g(x)g(x-\tau)\, dx$$

(a) Show that $\phi(\tau)$ is an even function of τ.
(b) Show that $\Phi(f)$, the Fourier transform of $\phi(\tau)$, is $|G(f)|^2$.
(c) Demonstrate that several functions can have the same correlation function. *Hint:* it is necessary to show only that several functions have different transforms but the same $|G(f)|^2$.
(d) Since $|G(f)|^2$ is the transform of $\phi(\tau)$, then, from Eq. (8.2)

$$\phi(\tau) = \int_{-\infty}^{\infty} |G(y)|^2\, e^{j2\pi\tau y}\, dy$$

and

$$\phi(0) = \int_{-\infty}^{\infty} |G(y)|^2\, dy$$

Show that

$$\phi(0) - \phi(\tau) = 2 \int_{-\infty}^{\infty} |G(y)|^2 \sin^2 (\pi\tau y)\, dy$$

by subtracting the two integrals, writing $1 - e^{j2\pi\tau y}$ in rectangular form, and using a well-known trigonometric identity and the fact that $\phi(0) - \phi(\tau)$ must be real. But the last integral cannot be negative, because the integrand is always positive. In fact, unless $|G(f)|^2$ is an impulse or a set of impulses that occur at the zeros of $\sin \pi\tau y$, or unless $G(f)$ is identically zero, the integral must be positive. This proves then that $\phi(\tau)$ is a maximum at $\tau = 0$; that is

$$\phi(\tau) < \phi(0)$$

8.25. Find and sketch versus τ the autocorrelation functions of the following:

(a) $e^{-t}\mathbf{1}(t)$
(b) $e^{t}\mathbf{1}(-t)$
(c) a rectangular pulse of height A, width b, and center at $t = 0$
(d) a rectangular pulse of height A, width b, and center at $t = T$

Answer to (a): $\dfrac{e^{-|\tau|}}{2}$

8.26. Two methods are employed to find the energy density functions of signals. One method employs a variable narrow-band filter and a voltmeter, and the actual energy is measured in the frequency domain in this fashion. Since the inverse transform of the density function is the correlation function, the autocorrelation function can be computed and transformed. The latter technique is usually limited to use with digital computers because of the excessive labor involved.

If the signal $g(t)$ is periodic, or if $|g(t)|$ does not have a finite area under it, its Fourier transform does not exist. Nevertheless the correlation function $\psi(\tau)$ can be defined by the integral

$$\psi(\tau) = \lim_{T \to \infty} \frac{1}{2T} \int_{-T}^{T} g(x)g(x-\tau)\,dx$$

provided, of course, that the limit exists. Find the autocorrelation function of $\cos(\beta t + \theta)$ by performing the integration and limit process described above.

Answer: $\psi(\tau) = \dfrac{1}{2}\cos\beta\tau$

8.27. If $g(t)$ is periodic, with period T, the averaging of $g(x)$ and $g(x-\tau)$ need be done over one cycle only, so the autocorrelation function of Prob. 8.26 can be defined for *periodic* functions as

$$\psi(\tau) = \frac{1}{T} \int_{t_0}^{t_0 + T} g(x)g(x-\tau)\,dx$$

where t_0 is any constant. Using this definition, check the result of Prob. 8.26 by finding the autocorrelation function of $\cos(\beta t + \theta)$.

8.5 Special Fourier Transforms

There are many functions whose Fourier transforms have been evaluated by methods other than those described in this book. Most of these have been evaluated in the past by different mathematicians using widely varying techniques.* In this section we will discuss only those techniques most pertinent to engineering applications.

The Function $\exp[-t^2/2\sigma^2]$

The function $e^{-t^2/2\sigma^2}$ appears constantly in the theory of probability; when divided by $\sqrt{2\pi}\,\sigma$, it is known as the *Gaussian*

---

*The most complete list of these transforms is to be found in Campbell and Foster (6.)

density function. The evaluation of its Fourier transform is based on the definite integral

$$\int_{-\infty}^{\infty} e^{-x^2}\, dx = \sqrt{\pi}$$

This integral is evaluated by what some have termed "the most underhanded scheme in mathematics": Since the integrand is an even function of x

$$\int_{-\infty}^{\infty} e^{-x^2}\, dx = 2 \int_{0}^{\infty} e^{-x^2}\, dx$$

But

$$\int_{0}^{\infty} e^{-x^2}\, dx = \int_{0}^{\infty} e^{-y^2}\, dy$$

so

$$\left\{ \int_{0}^{\infty} e^{-x^2}\, dx \right\}^2 = \left\{ \int_{0}^{\infty} e^{-x^2}\, dx \right\} \left\{ \int_{0}^{\infty} e^{-y^2}\, dy \right\}$$

The last expression on the right is an iterated double integral and can be written as a double integral. Hence

$$\left\{ \int_{0}^{\infty} e^{-x^2}\, dx \right\}^2 = \int_{0}^{\infty} \int_{0}^{\infty} e^{-(x^2+y^2)}\, dx\, dy$$

If the integral is envisioned as an integration over the x-y plane, the integration must be over the first quadrant of that plane. If polar coordinates are used, the differential area $dx\, dy$ becomes $r\, dr\, d\theta$, and $x^2 + y^2$ becomes r^2. The limits for the θ integration are zero and $\pi/2$, and the limits for the r integration are zero and ∞. Then

$$\left\{ \int_{0}^{\infty} e^{-x^2}\, dx \right\}^2 = \int_{0}^{\pi/2} d\theta \int_{0}^{\infty} e^{-r^2} r\, dr = \frac{\pi}{2} \left[\frac{-e^{-r^2}}{2} \right] \Big/_{0}^{\infty} = \frac{\pi}{4}$$

Then

$$\int_{0}^{\infty} e^{-x^2}\, dx = \frac{\sqrt{\pi}}{2}$$

and

$$\int_{-\infty}^{\infty} e^{-x^2} dx = \sqrt{\pi} \tag{8.23}$$

We are now in a position to evaluate the transform of $e^{-t^2/2\sigma^2}$.

$$G(f) = \mathscr{F}[e^{-t^2/2\sigma^2}] = \int_{-\infty}^{\infty} e^{-t^2/(2\sigma^2)} e^{-j2\pi ft} dt$$

The exponents can be combined to yield

$$G(f) = \int_{-\infty}^{\infty} e^{(-t^2/2\sigma^2)-j2\pi ft} dt$$

But the square can be completed in the exponent by adding and subtracting $2\pi^2\sigma^2 f^2$, since

$$-\left[\frac{t}{\sqrt{2}\sigma} + j\sqrt{2}\pi\sigma f\right]^2 - 2\pi^2\sigma^2 f^2 = -\frac{t^2}{2\sigma^2} - j2\pi ft + 2\pi^2\sigma^2 f^2 - 2\pi^2\sigma^2 f^2$$

$$= -\frac{t^2}{2\sigma^2} - j2\pi ft$$

Then

$$G(f) = e^{-2\pi^2\sigma^2 f^2} \int_{-\infty}^{\infty} e^{-[t/(\sqrt{2}\sigma)+j\sqrt{2}\pi\sigma f]^2} dt$$

where $e^{-(2\pi^2\sigma^2 f^2)}$ is brought outside the integral sign because the integration is with respect to t and hence independent of f. If we now set

$$x = \frac{t}{\sqrt{2}\sigma} + j\sqrt{2}\pi\sigma f$$

and

$$dx = \frac{dt}{\sqrt{2}\sigma}$$

then

$$G(f) = \sqrt{2}\sigma e^{-2\pi^2\sigma^2 f^2} \int_{-\infty+j\sqrt{2}\pi\sigma f}^{\infty+j\sqrt{2}\pi\sigma f} e^{-x^2} dx$$

At this point, a knowledge of functions of a complex variable is necessary to show that it is permissible to drop the imaginary portions of the limits. Such a demonstration is beyond the scope of this book, so we must simply accept the fact that the imaginary portions can be dropped. Replacing the last integral by $\sqrt{\pi}$, we obtain

$$\mathscr{F}[e^{-t^2/(2\sigma^2)}] = \sqrt{2\pi}\sigma e^{-2\pi^2\sigma^2 f^2} \qquad (8.24)$$

Interestingly enough, when $\sigma = 1/\sqrt{2\pi}$, the last result becomes

$$\mathscr{F}[e^{-\pi t^2}] = e^{-\pi f^2} \qquad (8.25)$$

showing that the function and its transform are identical.

The Unit Impulse

As usual, the unit-impulse function $\delta(t)$ presents some difficulties. If the function is transformed directly

$$\mathscr{F}[\delta(t)] = \int_{-\infty}^{\infty} \delta(x)e^{-j2\pi fx}\, dx = 1 \qquad (8.26)$$

as in the case of the Laplace transform. The difficulty arises when we attempt to inverse transform $\delta(t)$ using Eq. (8.2).

$$\delta(t) \stackrel{?}{=} \int_{-\infty}^{\infty} e^{j2\pi ty}\, dy$$

This can only be demonstrated indirectly, since the integral simply does not exist in the ordinary sense. We can *define* the equation as correct, but this is not unlike defining π as 22/7. Sooner or later it will cause trouble.

For example, if 1 is the Fourier transform of $\delta(t)$, then according to Eq. (8.17), $\delta(f)$ is the transform of 1. But $f(t) = 1$ does not have finite area under it, and hence is not transformable. But in engineering, this need not stop us. What is wrong with $\delta(f)$ being the transform of unity—that is, d-c? This means that only one frequency, 0, is present in the function, and this coincides with the concept of *frequency* as it is used in engineering. Why not let $\delta(f-f_0)$ be the transform of $e^{j2\pi f_0 t}$ too? The impulse tells us that only one frequency is present.

There is sufficient physical reason for using the impulse for the Fourier transform of a constant, and vice versa, so this will be done; however, some difficulties may arise. To head these off it is convenient to define the impulse function $\delta(t)$ as the limiting form of any function of time whose transform approaches unity. There are many such functions, and a few are listed here.

1. The tall rectangular pulse of height $1/\epsilon$ and width ϵ. Its transform is known to be $(\sin \pi\epsilon f)/\pi\epsilon f$, which certainly approaches unity for any f if ϵ is made sufficiently small.

2. The tall triangular pulse of height $1/\epsilon$ and width 2ϵ, which has a transform of $(\sin^2 \pi\epsilon f)/(\pi\epsilon f)^2$. This approaches unity for any fixed f so long as ϵ is made sufficiently small.

3. The function

$$\frac{e^{-t^2/2\sigma^2}}{\sqrt{2\pi}\sigma}$$

has a transform of $e^{-2\pi^2\sigma^2 f^2}$ according to Eq. (8.24). But this transform can be made to approach unity for any value of f, however large, if σ is made small enough. Then

$$\delta(t) = \lim_{\sigma \to 0} \frac{e^{-t^2/2\sigma^2}}{\sqrt{2\pi}\sigma} \qquad (8.27)$$

is another choice for the definition of the delta function.

4. Since the delta function is real and even, any transform that is real and even and that approaches unity in a limit can be used for the transform of $\delta(t)$. How about $[\mathbf{1}(f+f_1) - \mathbf{1}(f-f_1)]$? This is unity in the region $-f_1 < f < f_1$, so the transform approaches unity for all f as f_1 becomes infinite. For any finite f_1, the inverse transform is

$$\int_{-f_1}^{f_1} e^{j2\pi ty} \, dy = \frac{\sin 2\pi f_1 t}{\pi t}$$

Thus we might define

$$\delta(t) = \lim_{f_1 \to \infty} \frac{\sin 2\pi f_1 t}{\pi t}$$

Although this is a useful definition mathematically, it is somewhat awkward to visualize as a function of time. If the numerator and denominator are multiplied by $2f_1$, the relation reads

$$\delta(t) = \lim_{f_1 \to \infty} 2f_1 \left[\frac{\sin 2\pi f_1 t}{2\pi f_1 t} \right] \qquad (8.28)$$

which is known to have a value of $2f_1$ at $t = 0$. Furthermore, the area under the function can be shown to be unity (since the area must equal the value of the transform at $f = 0$; see Prob. 8.10). Thus the function does become infinitely high at $t = 0$, and it does have the proper area under it. However, the envelope of the function does not go to zero as f_1

becomes infinite. In fact, if f_1 is considered a parameter, Eq. (8.28) defines a family of curves. No matter what f_1 is, the function will always touch the envelope given by $1/|\pi t|$. This is clear, because the sinusoid will attain maximum and minimum values of ± 1. For any fixed t then, as f_1 is made larger, the angle $2\pi f_1 t$ will continually go through odd multiples of $\pi/2$ and the magnitude of the function will be $\pm 1/\pi t$. The function is shown in Fig. 8.8 for one value of f_1. As f_1 is made larger, the "frequency" increases but the envelope remains the same. In spite of its shortcomings as an approximation of what we have come to think an impulse should look like, it is a convenient mathematical definition.

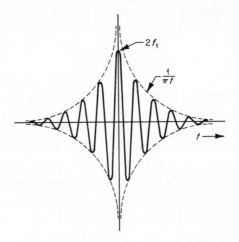

Fig. 8.8   *The function sin $(2\pi f_1 t)/(\pi t)$ plotted for a large value of f_1.*

5. Still another possibility is the transform pictured in Fig. 8.9. Again, as f_1 becomes infinite, the triangle approaches unity for all f, though it never gets there for any f but zero. We need transform the positive portion only; then we take twice the real part, since the transform is real and an even function of f. In the positive region, the function is given by

$$\left(1 - \frac{f}{f_1}\right) [\mathbf{1}(f) - \mathbf{1}(f - f_1)]$$

and the inverse transform is the same as the transform of

$$\left(1 - \frac{t}{f_1}\right) [\mathbf{1}(t) - \mathbf{1}(t - f_1)]$$

with f replaced by $-t$. The Laplace transform of the triangle is (positive portion only)

$$\frac{1}{s} - \frac{1}{f_1 s^2} + \frac{e^{-sf_1}}{f_1 s^2}$$

With $s = j2\pi f$, the Fourier transform is

$$\frac{1}{j2\pi f} - \frac{1}{f_1}\left[\frac{-1}{(2\pi f)^2}\right][1 - e^{-j2\pi f_1 f}]$$

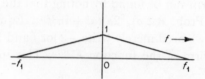

Fig. 8.9 *The triangular approximation of the transform of $\delta(t)$.*

Only the real part of this is needed, and thus $1/(j2\pi f)$ can be dropped. Since

$$1 - e^{-j2\pi f_1 f} = 1 - \cos(2\pi f_1 f) + j\sin(2\pi f_1 f)$$

the real part of the transform is simply

$$\frac{1 - \cos(2\pi f_1 f)}{(2\pi f)^2 f_1} = \frac{2\sin^2(\pi f_1 f)}{(2\pi f)^2 f_1}$$

Replacing f by $-t$ and doubling the result gives

$$\frac{4\sin^2 \pi f_1 t}{(2\pi t)^2 f_1}$$

the inverse transform of the function in Fig. 8.9. This can be verified by direct integration, since

$$f(t) = 2\,\text{Re}\left\{\int_0^{f_1}\left(1 - \frac{f}{f_1}\right)e^{j2\pi ft}\,df\right\}$$

We might now define

$$\delta(t) = \lim_{f_1 \to \infty}\frac{4\sin^2 \pi f_1 t}{(2\pi t)^2 f_1}$$

$$= \lim_{f_1 \to \infty} f_1\left(\frac{\sin \pi f_1 t}{\pi f_1 t}\right)^2 \tag{8.29}$$

Unlike the definition in Eq. (8.28), this function has an envelope that does go to zero as $f_1 \to \infty$ for all $t \neq 0$, and it is consequently somewhat more acceptable.

6. There are many more new definitions that could be constructed for the delta function. We shall present just one more. The transform

$$e^{-|f|f_1|}$$

is an even function of f and approaches unity as f_1 becomes infinite. Its inverse transform can be found by noting that the Fourier transform of $e^{-a|t|}$ is, from Prob. 8.2(a), $2\alpha/(\alpha^2+4\pi^2f^2)$. Equations (8.17) and (8.18) tell us that we need merely write $-t$ for f and $1/f_1$ for α to obtain the inverse transform of the function $e^{-|f|f_1|}$. This inverse transform is then

$$\frac{2/f_1}{(1/f_1{}^2) + (4\pi^2 t^2)}$$

Since f_1 is to be made large, we might let $a = 1/(2\pi f_1)$, and as f_1 becomes large, a will become small. Then the last expression becomes

$$\frac{2(2\pi a)}{(4\pi^2 a^2 + 4\pi^2 t^2)} = \frac{a/\pi}{(a^2 + t^2)}$$

Then

$$\delta(t) = \lim_{a \to 0} \frac{a/\pi}{a^2 + t^2} \tag{8.30}$$

This definition agrees well with the initial concept of the impulse, since at $t = 0$ it has the value $1/(\pi a)$, which becomes large as $a \to 0$. Also, for $t \neq 0$ the function approaches $a/(\pi t^2)$, or zero as $a \to 0$.

The Step Function

Because the Fourier transform of unity has been defined as $\delta(f)$, it should be possible to define the Fourier transform of the step function. Before we begin, it is well to note that from Eq. (8.5), the even part of the step function is

$$\tfrac{1}{2}\left[\mathbf{1}(t) + \mathbf{1}(-t)\right] = \tfrac{1}{2}$$

and the transform of this is, by definition, $\delta(f)/2$. But from Eq. (8.7), the real part of the transform of $\mathbf{1}(t)$ must be the same as the transform of the even part, so the real part of the Fourier transform of $\mathbf{1}(t)$ should be $\delta(f)/2$.

The transform of $\mathbf{1}(t)$ does not exist in the strict sense. The transform of $e^{-\alpha t}\mathbf{1}(t)$ does exist; it is $1/(j2\pi f+\alpha)$. This function approaches the step function as α approaches zero, so the transform of the step function must be $1/(j2\pi f)$. But this has no *real* part, yet it has already been established that the real part is $\delta(f)/2$.

If what has been done is correct

$$\mathscr{F}\,[\mathbf{1}(t)] = \lim_{\alpha \to 0} \frac{1}{j2\pi f + \alpha}$$

If we write the complex function in rectangular form by multiplying numerator and denominator by $(\alpha - j2\pi f)$, we have

$$\mathscr{F}[\mathbf{1}(t)] = \lim_{\alpha \to 0} \left\{\frac{\alpha}{\alpha^2 + (2\pi f)^2} - \frac{j2\pi f}{\alpha^2 + (2\pi f)^2}\right\}$$

The limit of the imaginary part is, as indicated before, $1/(j2\pi f)$, but the real part is, after we have divided the numerator and denominator by $4\pi^2$

$$\text{Re}\,\{\mathscr{F}[\mathbf{1}(t)]\} = \lim_{\alpha \to 0} \frac{\alpha/(4\pi^2)}{\alpha^2/(4\pi^2) + f^2}$$

If we set $a = \alpha/2\pi$, $a \to 0$ as $\alpha \to 0$, so

$$\text{Re}\,\{\mathscr{F}[\mathbf{1}(t)]\} = \lim_{a \to 0} \frac{a/(2\pi)}{a^2 + f^2}$$

But this is exactly one-half the expression for $\delta(f)$ given by Eq. (8.30), with t replaced by f. The real part of the transform is indeed $\delta(f)/2$ then, and

$$\mathscr{F}[\mathbf{1}(t)] = \frac{\delta(f)}{2} + \frac{1}{j2\pi f} \tag{8.31}$$

The Signum Function

The function "signum of t," abbreviated sgn (t), is equal to $+1$ when t is positive, -1 when t is negative, and 0 when $t = 0$. Thus

$$\text{sgn}\,(t) = \mathbf{1}(t) - \mathbf{1}(-t) \tag{8.32}$$

The Latin signum (sign) is used to avoid confusion with the homonym sin (t).

This function is Fourier transformable in the sense that a constant and a step function are transformable. From Eqs. (8.19), (8.31), and (8.32)

$$\mathscr{F}\left[\text{sgn}(t)\right] = \frac{\delta(f)}{2} + \frac{1}{j2\pi f} - \left[\frac{\delta(-f)}{2} - \frac{1}{j2\pi f}\right]$$

$$= \frac{1}{j\pi f} \tag{8.33}$$

Poles on the j axis in the p plane are inverse transformable then, because with $p = j2\pi f$

$$\mathscr{F}\left[\frac{\text{sgn}(t)}{2}\right] = \frac{1}{p} \tag{8.34}$$

$$\mathscr{F}\left[e^{j2\pi f_0 t}\frac{\text{sgn}(t)}{2}\right] = \frac{1}{p - j2\pi f_0} \tag{8.35}$$

EXAMPLE 8.9. Find the inverse Fourier transform of

$$\frac{4p^4 - 2p^3 + 6p^2 - 66p - 18}{p(p+1)(p-2)(p^2+9)}$$

Solution: Writing the partial fraction expansion of the expression above gives

$$\frac{1}{p} + \frac{2}{p+1} - \frac{1}{p-2} + \frac{1-j}{p-3j} + \text{conjugate}$$

1. The left-half p-plane poles have the same inverse transform as the Laplace transform; hence

$$\mathscr{F}^{-1}\left[\frac{2}{p+1}\right] = 2\,e^{-t}\mathbf{1}(t)$$

2. The right-half p-plane poles have the same inverse transform as the Laplace transform, but with $\mathbf{1}(t)$ replaced by $-\mathbf{1}(-t)$. Thus

$$\mathscr{F}^{-1}\left[\frac{-1}{p-2}\right] = e^{2t}\mathbf{1}(-t)$$

3. The j-axis p-plane poles have the same inverse transform as the Laplace transform, but with $\mathbf{1}(t)$ replaced by $\text{sgn}(t)/2$. Hence

$$\mathscr{F}^{-1}\left[\frac{1}{p} + \frac{1-j}{p-j3} + \text{conjugate}\right] = [1 + 2\sqrt{2}\cos(3t - 45°)]\frac{\text{sgn}(t)}{2}$$

Then

$$f(t) = 2e^{-t}\mathbf{1}(t) + e^{2t}\mathbf{1}(-t) + [1+2\sqrt{2} \cos (3t-45°)] \frac{\text{sgn } (t)}{2}$$

is the inverse Fourier transform of the function.

Periodic Functions

Since the transform of $e^{j2\pi f_0 t}$ is understood to be $\delta(f-f_0)$, any periodic or almost periodic function that is expressible in an exponential series has a Fourier transform. Thus with

$$f(t) = \sum_{k=-\infty}^{\infty} B_k e^{j2\pi f_k t} \tag{8.36}$$

$$\mathscr{F}[f(t)] = F(f) = \sum_{k=-\infty}^{\infty} B_k \delta(f-f_k) \tag{8.37}$$

PROBLEMS

8.28. Given that the Fourier transform of unity is $\delta(f)$, find the Fourier transforms of $\cos (2\pi f_0 t)$ and $\sin (2\pi f_0 t)$.

8.29. Using Eq. (8.35), find the inverse Fourier transforms of

(a) $\dfrac{p}{p^2+\beta^2}$ (b) $\dfrac{\beta}{p^2+\beta^2}$ (c) $\dfrac{2}{p(p+1)}$

Answer to (a): $\dfrac{1}{2} \cos \beta t$ sgn (t)

8.30. Find the Fourier transform of

(a) $\cos \beta t\ [\mathbf{1}(t)]$ (b) $\sin \beta t\ [\mathbf{1}(t)]$

Answer to (b): $\dfrac{\delta(f-\beta/2\pi)-\delta(f+\beta/2\pi)}{4j} + \dfrac{\beta}{p^2+\beta^2}$

8.31. Find the inverse Fourier transform of j sgn (f).

8.32. The energy density function, the square of the magnitude of the Fourier transform, has an area under it equal to the energy of the time function. However, with the exception of the Gaussian function, the energies associated with the functions of Sec. 8.5 are infinitely large. In fact, it was agreed that the delta function would never be squared; thus, one of the prices we must pay for our manipulations of the presumably "untransformable" functions is that we have permitted the energy density function to become meaningless. But it was noted in Prob. 8.24 that the transform of the correlation function $\phi(\tau)$ was the energy density function.

In Prob. 8.26, a different correlation function was defined and called $\psi(\tau)$. This function was defined especially for those $g(t)$ that were not Fourier transformable in the strict sense. Perhaps the transform of $\psi(\tau)$ can be thought of as some kind of density function. Test this by noting that the correlation function of $\cos(\beta t + \theta)$ in Prob. 8.26 was $\cos(\beta\tau)/2$. Find the Fourier transform of this autocorrelation function. Sketch the transform versus f and observe the area under the curve. What kind of a density function would you call this? Does the result make any physical sense?

8.33. The Fourier series of the rectangular square wave was found to be

$$f(t) = \frac{2A}{\pi} \sum_{\substack{k=-\infty \\ k \neq 0}}^{\infty} \frac{\sin(\pi k/2)}{k} e^{j2\pi kt/T}$$

where $C_0 = 0$. (See Prob. 7.14 and Fig. 7.8). Find the Fourier transform of $f(t)$ and sketch it versus f.

8.34. The function $(1/\sqrt{t})\mathbf{1}(t)$ has a Laplace transform $\sqrt{\pi/s}$, as shown in Prob. 3.63. It can be shown that the indefinite integral of $1/\sqrt{t}$ is $2\sqrt{t}$, and hence the function does not have finite area under it, nor does it, strictly speaking, have a Fourier transform. If, however, we define

$$\frac{\mathbf{1}(t)}{\sqrt{t}} = \lim_{\beta \to 0} \frac{e^{-\beta t}}{\sqrt{t}} \mathbf{1}(t)$$

it does have a Fourier transform, and the Fourier transform is simply the Laplace transform with s replaced by $j2\pi f$. Use the complex translation theorem to obtain the Laplace and Fourier transforms of $e^{-\beta t}\mathbf{1}(t)/\sqrt{t}$. Express the result in polar form as

$$\sqrt{\frac{\pi}{\sqrt{\beta^2 + (2\pi f)^2}}} \left/ -\frac{1}{2}\tan^{-1}\frac{2\pi f}{\beta} \right. = \frac{1}{\sqrt{2}(f^2 + b^2)^{1/4}} \left/ -\frac{1}{2}\tan^{-1}\frac{f}{b} \right.$$

where β is replaced by $2\pi b$ in the second expression. Show that as $b \to 0$, the second expression can be written as

$$\frac{1-j}{2\sqrt{f}} \quad \text{for} \quad f > 0$$

and

$$\frac{1+j}{2\sqrt{-f}} \quad \text{for} \quad f < 0$$

Then

$$\mathscr{F}\left[\frac{\mathbf{1}(t)}{\sqrt{t}}\right] = \frac{1}{2|f|^{1/2}} - j\frac{\operatorname{sgn} f}{2|f|^{1/2}}$$

Since the real part of the transform is known to be the transform of the even part of a function, show that the even part of $\mathbf{1}(t)/\sqrt{t}$ can be written as $|t|^{-1/2}/2$, and hence that the Fourier transform of $|t|^{-1/2}$ is $|f|^{-1/2}$, giving us *another identical pair*.

8.35. It was shown in the section on "Change of Scale" in Chapter 3 that the Laplace transform of $J_0(\alpha t)\mathbf{1}(t)$ is $1/\sqrt{s^2+\alpha^2}$. It is not at all obvious that the Fourier transform of this Bessel function can be obtained by the substitution of $j2\pi f$ for s, since as s approaches $\pm j\alpha$, the magnitude of the transform becomes large. These points in the s plane are not called poles in function theory, because in function theory the square root of any number is double-valued. They are called *branch points* (the reasons for this are beyond the scope of this text). Branch points are singularities, and since these occur on the j axis, we cannot obtain the Fourier transforms simply by substituting $s = j2\pi f$. It happens, however, that such a substitution is correct in this instance, and that the Fourier transform of $J_0(\alpha t)\mathbf{1}(t)$ is indeed $1/\sqrt{\alpha^2-(2\pi f)^2}$. *

The even portion of $J_0(\alpha t)\mathbf{1}(t)$ is $J_0(\alpha t)/2$, since $J_0(\alpha t)$ is known to be an even function of t. Find the Fourier transform of $J_0(\alpha t)$ [with no $\mathbf{1}(t)$] and show that it is defined for $|f| < \alpha/(2\pi)$ only. Sketch this transform versus f. *Note:* The result is derivable from pair 914.5 in Campbell and Foster (6), and it is derived by complex integration in Papoulis (7), pp. 184 and 185.

8.36. Let $g(t)$ be zero for $t < 0$. Show that if $g_e(t)$ is the even part of $g(t)$ and $g_o(t)$ is the odd part

$$g_e(t) = g_o(t) \operatorname{sgn}(t)$$

and

$$g_o(t) = g_e(t) \operatorname{sgn}(t)$$

8.37. If $g(t)$ is Fourier transformable with transform $G(f) = R(f) + jI(f)$, where $R(f)$ is the real part of $G(f)$, and $I(f)$ is its imaginary part, show that if $g(t)$ is zero for negative t, $g(t) = 2g_e(t)\mathbf{1}(t)$, where $g_e(t)$ is the even part of $g(t)$.

Since $g(t)$ is defined for positive t only, its Fourier transform must have left-half p-plane poles only, where $p = j2\pi f$. Then $G(f)$ can be obtained from its real part by making a partial fraction expansion of $2R(f)$, substituting $p = j2\pi f$ and retaining in the expansion only those terms that have left-half p-plane poles. Demonstrate this by finding $G(f)$ and $g(t)$ when $R(f) = a/(a^2+f^2)$.

8.38. If $g(t)$ is zero for negative t and has a Fourier transform $G(f) = R(f) + jI(f)$, then, as in Prob. 8.37, $g(t) = 2g_o(t)\mathbf{1}(t)$, where $g_o(t)$ is the odd part of $g(t)$. But from Eq. (8.8), the Fourier transform of $g_o(t)$ is $jI(f)$. Then $G(f)$ may be obtained from $I(f)$ by multiplying $I(f)$ by $2j$, replacing $j2\pi f$ by p, making a partial fraction expansion of the result, and

---

*See pair 557 in Campbell and Foster (6).

retaining the left-half p-plane poles only. Demonstrate this by finding $G(f)$ and $g(t)$ if $I(f)$ is $12f/(1+5\pi^2f^2+4\pi^4f^4)$.

$$\textit{Answer: } g(t) = \frac{8}{\pi}\left[e^{-2t}-e^{-t}\right]\mathbf{1}(t)$$

8.39. Evidently, from Probs. 8.36 through 8.38, not only the transform but the real part of the transform can be obtained from the imaginary part alone if it is known that $g(t)$ is zero for negative t. Similarly, the imaginary part and the transform can be obtained from the real part alone. There must be a general relation, then, between $R(f)$ and $I(f)$. Use Eq. (8.21)—convolution—and Eq. (8.33) with the results of Prob. 8.36 to show that

$$R(f) = \mathscr{F}[g_e(t)] = \frac{1}{\pi}\int_{-\infty}^{\infty}\frac{I(y)}{f-y}\,dy$$

and

$$I(f) = -j\mathscr{F}[g_o(t)] = -\frac{1}{\pi}\int_{-\infty}^{\infty}\frac{R(y)}{f-y}\,dy$$

$R(f)$ and $I(f)$ functions that satisfy these relations are known as *Hilbert pairs*, and the integrals are known as *Hilbert transforms*. The first equation is correct within a constant, for $R(f)$ can have any constant added to it and the result will still be a Hilbert pair. The first equation is more properly written

$$R(f) = R(\infty) + \frac{1}{\pi}\int_{-\infty}^{\infty}\frac{I(y)}{f-y}\,dy$$

8.40. Find $I(f)$, the Hilbert mate, if it is given that $R(f) = \delta(f)$. Use the equation of Prob. 8.39 to do this. After finding $I(f)$, inverse transform $R(f) + jI(f)$ and note that the result is zero for negative t.

8.41. The integral $\int_{-a}^{a} dy/(f-y)$ is improper for $-a < f < a$, because the integrand explodes in this interval.

    (a) For f in the interval $-a < f < a$, evaluate the integral by integrating from $-a$ to $f-b$, and from $f+b$ to a, and take the limit as $b \to 0$.

$$\textit{Answer: } \ln\left[\frac{a+f}{a-f}\right]$$

    (b) For $|f| > a$, evaluate the integral.

$$\textit{Answer: } \ln\left[\frac{f+a}{f-a}\right]$$

8.42. Since the integral in Prob. 8.41 can be written for all f as

$$\int_{-a}^{a} \frac{dy}{f-y} = \ln \left| \frac{f+a}{f-a} \right|$$

find $I(f)$, using the integral formula contained in Prob. 8.39, if it is given that $R(f) = A$ for $|f| < f_c$ and $R(f) = 0$ for $|f| > f_c$. Sketch $R(f)$ and $I(f)$ versus f.

chapter

9

Applications of the Fourier Transform

9.1 Modulation

Voice and music signals are generally band-limited. This means that the Fourier transform of any audio signal is usually negligibly small above 20 kc. Even if there are significant frequency components above 20 kc, the ear cannot detect them, so they might as well be eliminated. Actually, if everything above 10 kc is eliminated it takes an exceptional ear to notice distortion; however, most ears can notice distortion if everything above 2.5 kc is eliminated. A good example of this is the telephone, which generally uses a 2.5-kc frequency band. Distortion is quite noticeable with high-pitched voices, though relatively slight for altos and baritones.

Electric signals used to reproduce pictures, such as the picture portion of a television signal, are called *video signals*. The video frequencies usually lie in the range of 7.5 kc to 4 mc. This range is based on the commercial television system used in the United States, and these frequencies are acceptable to the extent that the pictures they reproduce are acceptable. In this television system, 525 lines are drawn on the screen 30 times a second, or a total of $525 \times 30 = 15{,}750$ lines per sec. To blank out one line then, a constant voltage must be applied to the control grid of the picture tube (kinescope) for at least $1/15{,}750$ sec. If this is viewed as the negative portion of a square wave, its fundamental frequency is $15{,}750/2 = 7875$ cps. This then is the lowest frequency required for the picture portion of the signal. (Actually, to synchronize the pictures vertically, a 60-cps synchronizing signal must be sent along with the picture information. Thus the actual signal has a lowest-frequency component of 60 cps.) If such a square wave were applied, the picture would have alternating black and white lines on it; that is, every other line would be blanked out. If similar fidelity were

380

required in the other direction—that is, if the definition of the picture had to be the same in the other direction, then we would have to project vertical dark lines on the screen with the same separation as that produced by the low-frequency signal in blanking out every other line. If the picture is assumed to be square (it is not, or at least it should not be), then 525/2 dark lines should appear vertically across the screen. Since it takes 1/(15,750) sec to draw one line, the time between one dark line and the next adjacent dark line would have to be 1/(15,750 × 525/2) sec. The reciprocal of this number, 4,134,375 cps, or approximately 4 mc, is the fundamental frequency of the signal required for this. For these reasons, the video band is usually defined as that band falling in the range 7.5 kc to 4 mc.

Neither of these signals, the audio of the lower portion of the video, are high enough in frequency to be radiated effectively. For one thing, the size of the radiator must be of the approximate magnitude of a quarter-wavelength of an electromagnetic wave. Since the product of the frequency and the wave-length is the velocity of light, the wavelength is given by

$$\lambda = \frac{3 \times 10^8}{f} \text{ meters}$$

Even when f is 1 mc, the wavelength is 300 meters, so a radiator would have to be about 75 meters long—nearly the length of a football field. If audio or video signals are to be transmitted by electro-magnetic radiation, and the size of the radiating unit is to be reasonably small, signals in the lower-frequency bands must be moved up in frequency.

Let $s(t)$ be a signal whose spectrum lies in the vicinity of f_c, a frequency high enough that radiation is economical and practical. f_c will be known as the carrier frequency. The most general signal that satisfies this requirement is the function

$$s(t) = A(t) \cos \left[2\pi f_c t + \theta(t) \right] \tag{9.1}$$

where $A(t)$ is some arbitrary function of time whose spectrum does not exceed the frequency f_c (it is usually small compared to f_c) and $\theta(t)$ is a signal whose maximum derivative does not exceed in magnitude the value $4\pi f_c/3$ *and* whose spectrum does not exceed $f_c/2$.

If an audio or video signal $s_m(t)$ is to be *carried* by the function of Eq. (9.1), either $A(t)$ must be some function of $s_m(t)$ or $\theta(t)$ must be some function of $s_m(t)$. If $A(t)$ is a function of $s_m(t)$ and $\theta(t)$ is a constant, the result is called *amplitude modulation* (AM). If $\theta(t)$ is some function of

$s_m(t)$ and $A(t)$ is a constant, the result is called *angle modulation*, the two most common examples of which are *phase modulation* (PM) and *frequency modulation* (FM).

In the following subsections, the *Fourier* spectrum will be used rather than the line spectrum or energy spectrum. This will be simply the transform of the signal, which, if plotted graphically in magnitude, will be simply the square root of the energy spectrum. In the case of sinusoids, the Fourier spectrum will be a pair of impulses.

Suppressed-Carrier Amplitude Modulation

Let $s_m(t)$ be the audio or video signal to be transmitted, and let $\cos(2\pi f_c t)$ be the carrier signal. With $A(t)$ of Eq. (9.1) equal to $s_m(t)$, the signal $s(t)$ is

$$s(t) = s_m(t) \cos 2\pi f_c t \tag{9.2}$$

where the choice of $\theta(t) = 0$ does not in any way make the equation less general, since we can always start measuring time when the sinusoid is at its peak maximum value.

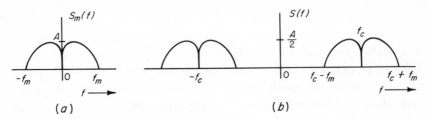

Fig. 9.1   (a) *The spectrum of some modulating signal $s_m(t)$. (b) The spectrum of the function $s(t) = s_m(t) \cos(2\pi f_c t)$.*

Let the Fourier transform of $s_m(t)$ be $S_m(f)$. We are certain that this transform exists, since the transforms of *all* practical signals exist. What then is the Fourier transform of $s(t)$?

Writing the cosine in exponential form, we have

$$s(t) = e^{j2\pi f_c t} \frac{S_m(t)}{2} + e^{-j2\pi f_c t} \frac{S_m(t)}{2}$$

But from Eq. (8.11), the transform of the first term is $S_m(f-f_c)/2$ and that of the second is $S_m(f+f_c)/2$. Thus the transform of $s(t)$, $S(f)$, is simply

$$S(f) = \frac{1}{2}\left[S_m(f-f_c) + S_m(f+f_c)\right] \tag{9.3}$$

But this means simply a *translation* of the original spectrum, f_c to the right and f_c to the left. This is easy to see graphically. Figure 9.1(*a*) shows a typical Fourier spectrum of some audio or video signal, and Fig. 9.1(*b*) shows this spectrum translated to the left and to the right; that is, the spectrum of $s(t)$ given in Eq. (9.2).

The result indicated by Eq. (9.3) is actually more general than this. It is not necessary at all that $s_m(t)$ be an audio or video signal. Whatever the spectrum of a signal, the spectrum of the signal obtained by multiplying this signal by $\cos 2\pi f_c t$ will be one-half the original shifted to the right f_c and one-half of original shifted to the left f_c. Figure 9.2 demonstrates the spectrum obtained when the $s(t)$ of Eq. (9.2) is multiplied again, this time by $\cos \pi f_c t$. This time the spectrum of Fig. 9.1(*b*) is shifted $f_c/2$ to the right and left, and this produces four spectra, each looking just like the $S_m(f)$, provided that f_c is not so small that the parts overlap.

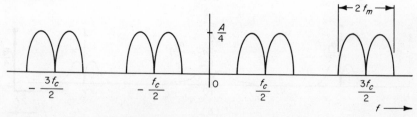

Fig. 9.2 *The spectrum that results when the signal whose spectrum appears in Fig. 9.1(b) is multiplied by* $\cos (\pi f_c t)$.

It is clear from Fig. 9.1(*b*) that if f_m is the maximum frequency component of the spectrum of $s_m(t)$, then f_c must be at least this value if no overlap is to occur. From Fig. 9.2 it is clear that if $f_c \gg f_m$, we can convert down in frequency with little fear of overlap.

The spectra of Figs. 9.1 and 9.2 have no impulses at the carrier positions if no impulse appears in the spectrum of $S_m(f)$. Since most communication signals have no d-c components, the spectra that result have no carrier frequency components, and hence this type of amplitude modulation is called *suppressed-carrier amplitude modulation*, which we shall abbreviate as AM–SC.

The method by which AM–SC is produced is based primarily on the ideas expressed in Chapter 7, where we discussed the application of several sinusoids to a nonlinear device. For example, suppose we have a square-law resistance for which the current is related to the voltage by

$$i(t) = a_0 + a_1 v(t) + a_2 v^2(t)$$

Then if $v(t) = s_m(t) + \cos 2\pi f_c t$, the current would be

$$i(t) = a_0 + a_1 s_m(t) + a_1 \cos 2\pi f_c t + a_2 s_m^2(t) + 2a_2 s_m(t) \cos 2\pi f_c t$$
$$+ a_2 \cos^2 2\pi f_c t$$

$$= a_0 + \frac{a_2}{2} + a_1 s_m(t) + a_2 s_m^2(t) + [a_1 + 2a_2 s_m(t)] \cos 2\pi f_c t$$
$$+ \frac{a_2}{2} \cos 4\pi f_c t$$

Figure 9.3(a) shows the spectrum of a typical $s_m(t)$. The spectrum

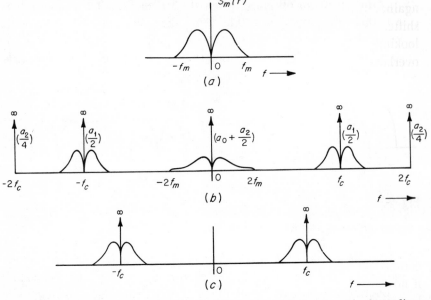

Fig. 9.3   (a) *The spectrum of* $s_m(t)$. *(b) The spectrum of the current in the nonlinear resistance. (c) The spectrum of the current after filtering out all but those components near* $f=f_c$.

of $s_m^2(t)$ is this spectrum convolved with itself, and this will have a maximum frequency component of $2f_m$. The spectrum of $i(t)$ will be that of Fig. 9.3(b) then. If $f_c > 3f_m$, there will be no overlap, and a filter with transfer function equal to unity in the frequency ranges $f_c - f_m < |f| < f_c + f_m$ (both positive and negative frequencies) and equal to zero outside of these bands will eliminate all but the spectrum appearing in Fig. 9.3(c). Here the carrier is present, as can be seen by the impulse. The carrier is not usually filtered out but is eliminated by the following technique.

Another nonlinear resistance just like the first is used, but the input voltage this time is $\cos 2\pi f_c t - s_m(t)$. After the signal is filtered as before, output signal (current) of $[a_1 - 2a_2 s_m(t)]\cos 2\pi f_c t$ is produced. If this signal is subtracted from the corresponding signal produced by the first resistance, the carrier will be balanced out, and only $4a_2 s_m(t)\cos 2\pi f_c t$ will remain.

The device used to produce AM–SC is shown schematically in Fig. 9.4. It is called a *balanced modulator*. If the transformers are considered

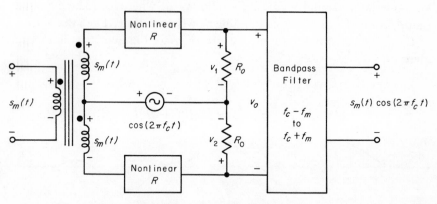

Fig. 9.4   *A balanced modulator.*

ideal with unity turns ratios, it can be seen that the emf across the top nonlinear resistance and the linear resistance R_0 in series with it is $\cos 2\pi f_c t + s_m(t)$. The current will then correspond to the $i(t)$ first obtained, and the voltage v_1 will be proportional to this current, since R_0 is a linear resistance. In the lower mesh, the emf across the lower nonlinear resistance and the lower R_0 is $\cos 2\pi f_c t - s_m(t)$, so v_2 will be proportional to the second current obtained. $v_0 = v_1 - v_2$ is the difference between the two, and the filter eliminates all but the signal desired.

When a signal is modulated in the manner described above, the receiver must unscramble or demodulate it. The Fourier transform of the output of the receiver must be identical to $S_m(f)$, so the receiver must shift the spectrum back to its original position. It can do this by multiplying by $\cos(2\pi f_c t)$ again. Since the entering spectrum is proportional to $S_m(f-f_c) + S_m(f+f_c)$, it will, after multiplication by $\cos 2\pi f_c t$, be shifted to the right and left f_c, giving one-half of $[S_m(f-2f_c) + 2S_m(f) + S_m(f+2f_c)]$. A low-pass filter will eliminate that part of the spectrum above f_m, yielding a spectrum proportional to $S_m(f)$. But this is the transform of the original signal, so the original signal can be recovered by a receiver that contains a balanced modulator and a low-pass filter.

If the receiver is to multiply the modulated signal by the carrier, it must have an oscillator in it to produce this signal. In practice, oscillators of this type tend to drift, and the result is a very poor reproduction of the original signal. Some idea of this can be seen by the following analysis.

Let the signal arriving at the receiver be $s_m(t) \cos 2\pi f_c t$, and let the local oscillator's signal be $\cos [2\pi(f_c + \Delta f)t + \phi]$, where it will be assumed that Δf is small and perhaps changing slowly with time. Then the output of the balanced modulator is, by use of a well-known trigonometric identity,

$$s_m(t) \cos 2\pi f_c t \cos [2\pi(f_c + \Delta f)t + \phi] =$$

$$\frac{s_m(t)}{2} \{\cos (2\pi\Delta ft + \phi) + \cos [2\pi(2f_c + \Delta f)t + \phi]\}$$

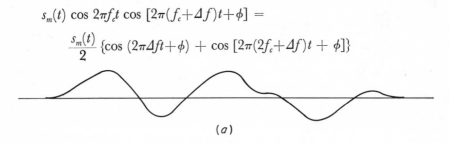

(*a*)

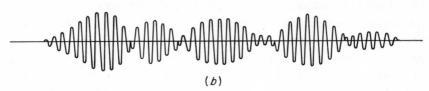

(*b*)

Fig. 9.5 (*a*) *A typical modulating signal* $s_m(t)$. (*b*) *The signal that results when* (*a*) *is multiplied by* $\cos (2\pi f_c t)$. *Thus* (*b*) *is the general form of a suppressed carrier amplitude-modulated signal.*

The double frequency terms are filtered out, leaving

$$\frac{1}{2} s_m(t) \cos (2\pi\Delta ft + \phi)$$

as the output signal. The spectrum of this will consist of $S_m(f)$ shifted to the right and left Δf, so there will be overlap. It is difficult to say what this does to voice signals, but the last equation clearly indicates that the amplitude level will change with frequency Δf. If the signal $s_m(t)$ is a steady sinusoid, the variation of Δf alters the frequency of the signal. Octaves will no longer sound like octaves, and the best that can be said of the system is that unless a very stable oscillator is employed, the results will not be very good. Stable oscillators of the crystal-controlled variety can be built for this purpose; however, the cost of such receivers is quite high.

The simplest way out of this difficulty is to send the carrier along with the signal. If a small portion of the total energy of the signal is used to transmit the carrier, this carrier can be used to synchronize or lock in the local oscillator at the receiver; then, even if the transmitter's oscillator drifts, the receiver will follow it.

Figure 9.5 shows a typical modulating signal $s_m(t)$; Fig. 9.5(b) shows the signal $s_m(t) \cos 2\pi f_c t$.

Single-Sideband Amplitude Modulation

Since $s_m(t)$ is a real function of time, its transform $S_m(f)$ is such that $S_m(-f) = S_m^*(f)$. Both halves of the transform carry duplicate information, so only one need be sent. Thus, after $s_m(t)$ is multiplied by cos $2\pi f_c t$ to provide the spectrum pictured in Fig. 9.6(a), either the upper or lower half of the spectrum can be filtered out. The spectrum that results when the upper portion is removed appears in Fig. 9.6(b), and the one that results when the lower portion is removed is shown in Fig. 9.6(c).

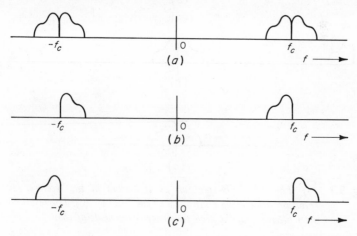

Fig. 9.6 (a) An AM-SC spectrum. (b) An AM-SSB spectrum obtained by filtering out the upper sideband of (a). (c) An AM-SSB spectrum obtained by filtering out the lower sideband of (a).

The upper portion of the spectrum of $s_m(t) \cos 2\pi f_c t$ is commonly called the *upper sideband* and the lower portion the *lower sideband*. When one or the other half is removed, the signal is said to have undergone single-sideband amplitude modulation, which we shall abbreviate as AM-SSB.

The advantages of this system over AM-SC are apparent in that only half as much bandwidth is required. Furthermore, if the portion of the frequency band that is being used has extraneous signals in it from other causes (we shall call this *noise*), then for a given amount of transmitter power the signal-to-noise ratio is doubled; that is, half as much noise power exists, since the band is cut in half.

Like AM-SC, AM-SSB is detected by multiplying the signal at the receiver by $\cos 2\pi f_c t$ and filtering out the frequencies above f_m. Figure 9.7(a) shows the AM-SSB signal as it arrives at the receiver. After being multiplied by $\cos 2\pi f_c t$, it is translated to the right and left by f_c, yielding the spectrum of Fig. 9.7(b). Observe that the positive sideband of Fig. 9.7(a) becomes the one just to the left of $f = 0$ in Fig. 9.7(b), and the negative portion in Fig. 9.7(a) becomes the portion just to the right of $f = 0$ in Fig. 9.7(b). In Fig. 9.7(c), the portions at $\pm 2f_c$ are filtered out, leaving $S_m(f)$.

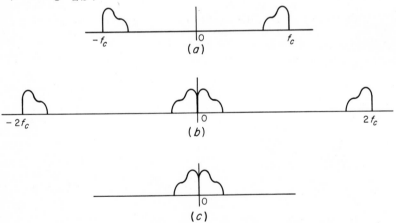

Fig. 9.7   (a) *The AM-SSB spectrum as it arrives at the receiver.* (b) *The spectrum after being multiplied by $\cos (2\pi f_c t)$. (c) The result obtained after filtering out the high frequency components of (b).*

As with AM-SC, the quality of the local oscillator is very important. Figures 9.8(a) and 9.8(b) demonstrate what happens to the spectrum at the output of the receiver if the oscillator is off by an amount $\varDelta f$, depending on whether the oscillator frequency is too small (producing overlap) or too large (producing separation).

The video portion of commercial television signals is sent AM-SSB, but to assure good reception a small carrier signal is sent along with the sideband to synchronize the local oscillators within receivers. This is sometimes referred to as *vestigial single-sideband transmission.*

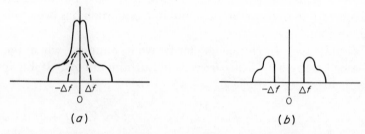

Fig. 9.8   *The low frequency spectra that result when the oscillator frequency of the receiver is (a) too low, (b) too high.*

Generally, AM-SSB is used by amateur radio operators only, or in other systems where faithful reproduction is not necessary but where the advantages of a narrow band and high signal-to-noise ratio are decisive.

It is not possible to demonstrate just what AM-SSB looks like in the time domain, given the shape of $s_m(t)$. It can be shown (see Probs. 9.7 and 9.9) that if the upper portion of the AM-SC signal is removed, the time signal that results is

$$s_{\text{SSB}}(t) = \frac{1}{2} \left[s_m(t) \cos 2\pi f_c t + s'_m(t) \sin 2\pi f_c t \right] \tag{9.4}$$

where

$$s'_m(t) = \frac{1}{\pi} \int\limits_{-\infty}^{\infty} \frac{s_m(y)}{t-y} \, dy \tag{9.5}$$

If $S_m(f)$ is the transform of $s_m(t)$, the transform of $s'_m(t)$ is

$$S'_m(f) = -j \, \text{sgn} \, (f) S_m(f) \tag{9.6}$$

so $s'_m(t)$ occupies the same frequency band as $s_m(t)$. If $s_m(t)$ is even, $S_m(f)$ is real and even and $S'_m(f)$ is imaginary and odd [since sgn (f) is odd]. Then $s'_m(t)$ is an odd function of time when $s_m(t)$ is even; conversely, $s'_m(t)$ is an even function of time if $s_m(t)$ is odd.

A discussion of the integral of Eq. (9.5) is well beyond the scope of this book, and this integral will not be evaluated for any signal here. (See Probs. 8.40 and 8.42 for two examples where identical integrals are evaluated.) The signal

$$\hat{s}_m(t) = s_m(t) + js'_m(t)$$

is referred to as the *analytic signal*, and s_m and s'_m are a Hilbert pair. Analytic signals will not be examined in this book, but a discussion of the applications of the analytic signal to modulation has been published by Bedrosian.*

Equation (9.4) can help clarify what happens when the local oscillator's frequency drifts from f_c by an amount Δf. If Eq. (9.4) is multiplied by $\cos [2\pi(f_c+\Delta f)t+\phi]$

$$s_{SSB}(t) \cos [2\pi(f_c+\Delta f)t+\phi] = \frac{1}{2} s_m(t) \cos 2\pi f_c t \cos [2\pi(f_c+\Delta f)t+\phi]$$

$$+ \frac{1}{2} s'_m(t) \sin 2\pi f_c t \cos [2\pi(f_c+\Delta f)t+\phi]$$

$$= \frac{1}{4} s_m(t) \cos (2\pi\Delta ft+\phi)$$

$$- \frac{1}{4} s'_m(t) \sin (2\pi\Delta ft+\phi) + \cdots$$

plus terms whose frequencies are near $2f_c$. If these are filtered out, only the last two terms above remain, and the output will be only $s_m(t)/4$ if both Δf and ϕ equal zero. This is the same as the result obtained with AM-SC but with a difference. With AM-SC, if $\Delta f = 0$ and $\phi = \pi/2$, the receiver produces silence; with AM-SSB, if $\Delta f = 0$ and $\phi = \pi/2$, the receiver produces $s'_m(t)$, whatever *that* is. One amateur radio operator described all SSB-receiver voice signals as sounding like Donald Duck. Whatever the description, it is clear that unless perfectly stable oscillators are used, AM-SSB (without the vestigial carrier) cannot be considered in the class of high-quality reproducing equipment.

Ordinary Amplitude Modulation

The term AM alone refers to what has come to be known as *ordinary amplitude modulation*. This is the type of amplitude modulation used in commercial broadcasting, and it has the advantage of requiring a very

---

*E. BEDROSIAN, "The Analytic Signal Representation of Modulated Waveforms," *Proc. I.R.E.*, Vol. 50 (1962), pp. 2071–2076.

simple circuit for demodulation; the receivers are relatively inexpensive and easy to construct.

AM differs from AM-SC only in that in AM, the carrier is not removed. A single nonlinear resistance circuit with the appropriate

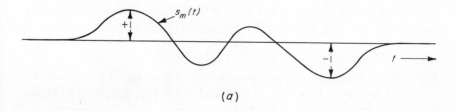

(a)

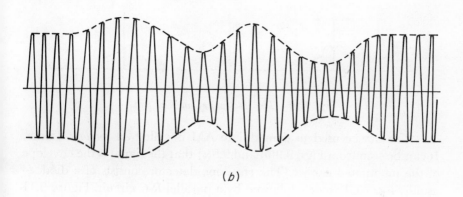

(b)

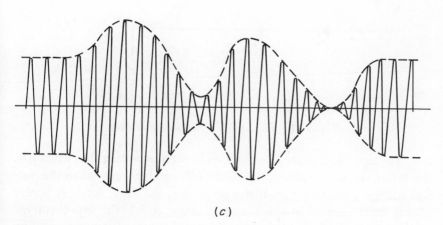

(c)

Fig. 9.9 (a) *An audio signal to be modulated by a carrier.* (b) *50 percent modulation.* (c) *100 percent modulation.*

filter will accomplish the modulation, and the only requirement is that the maximum amplitude of the modulating signal $s_m(t)$ never exceeds the peak amplitude of the carrier.

For purposes of this analysis, suppose that the maximum value of $s_m(t)$ is normalized at unity. Then, with m_a a constant (m_a is called the AM modulation index, with $m_a = 1$ indicating 100-percent modulation) between zero and one, the AM signal is proportional to

$$s(t) = [1+m_a s_m(t)] \cos (2\pi f_c t) \tag{9.7}$$

For a typical signal $s_m(t)$, pictured in Fig. 9.9(a), $s(t)$ is shown for two values of m_a: $m_a = \frac{1}{2}$ in Fig. 9.9(b) and $m_a = 1$ in Fig. 9.9(c). Figure 9.10 shows the spectrum of the AM wave.

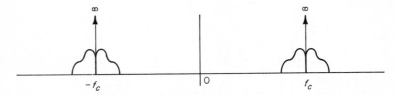

Fig. 9.10   *The spectrum of an AM wave.*

The device used to demodulate AM is called an *envelope detector.* It can be seen from Figs. 9.9(b) and 9.9(c) that the signal is the envelope of the modulated carrier. The envelope detector consists of a diode—usually a crystal diode—followed by a parallel *R-C* circuit. Figure 9.11 is a schematic diagram of this.

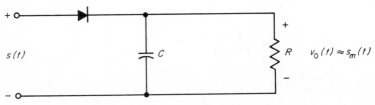

Fig. 9.11   *The circuit of the envelope detector.*

The operation of the detector can be seen by noting that when $s(t)$, the input signal, is positive, the diode will conduct only when the output voltage is less than $s(t)$. If this is the case, the diode acts very nearly like a short circuit, so the output voltage equals the input voltage whenever the diode conducts. Consider, for example, the signal of Fig. 9.12. Assume that the capacitor is initially uncharged. Then, as $s(t)$

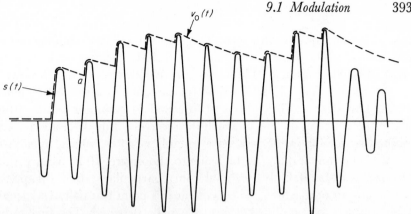

Fig. 9.12 *The solid curve is s(t) and the dashed curve is the output signal, which is approximately the envelope.*

becomes positive, the output voltage will equal the input voltage and will charge up the capacitor C. When $s(t)$ starts to fall after having reached its crest, the capacitor will still be at this peak voltage, so the diode will cease conducting, the voltage on its right now being greater than that on its left. The capacitor will then start to discharge through the resistance R with time constant RC, and nothing more will happen until $s(t)$ again exceeds the capacitor voltage. In Fig. 9.12, this will occur for the first time at point (a). From this point until $s(t)$ again reaches a crest, the input and output signals will be identical. This process is repeated, so the output signal is a choppy version of $s_m(t)$, the irregularities occurring at the carrier frequency. This output is shown in Fig. 9.13. Any low-pass filter following this will eliminate the "burrs" on the

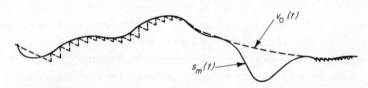

Fig. 9.13 *The output signal compared with $s_m(t)$. It is clear that the time constant RC cannot be too long.*

waveform. In fact, the speaker cannot respond to the carrier frequency, so the speaker itself is a low-pass filter and will eliminate the burrs automatically. Even if this were not true, no special filter would really be needed, because the ear could not hear the carrier even if it were actually reproduced.

It is seen from this discussion that a local oscillator is not needed in an AM receiver. Nevertheless, almost all AM receivers do have local oscillators. The reason for this has nothing to do with detection, however.

A radio receiver is designed not to detect one station or frequency band, but several. Thus, filters are needed to eliminate signals from stations other than the one to which the receiver is tuned. This is accomplished by having in the receiver a tunable r-f filter, which, by adjustment of the tuning dial, can be made to choose any 10-kc band within the broadcast band. Only the signal from a particular station will appear at the output of this filter. The signal at this point is usually very small and it has to be amplified before it can be detected. The first radio receivers used several stages of r-f amplification, with each stage tunable. When the operator changed stations, he had to tune every stage to the new frequency. Usually this was done with one control knob that operated a long metallic tape on a pulley. Turning the knob would adjust the capacitances of the r-f stages. This type of receiver was called a *tuned r-f* (TRF) receiver. After the r-f signal was sufficiently amplified, it was detected and put through one or more stages of audio amplification before being applied to the speaker.

The provision for retuning several stages automatically or with one manual knob added immeasurably to the price of the receiver. This could be avoided if no matter what the carrier frequency of the incoming signal, the center frequency of the signal to be amplified were always the same. This is achieved by converting all incoming carriers to a constant *intermediate frequency* (i-f). A local oscillator is installed in each receiver, the frequency of this oscillator being adjusted so that it always remains a fixed amount above the input frequency. In broadcast receivers, the intermediate frequency is set at 455 kc, and the operator, when tuning the r-f amplifier, also changes the frequency of the local oscillator so that it remains 455 kc above that to which the r-f amplifier is tuned. Inexpensive radios sometimes omit the r-f amplifier. To see what effect this has, refer to Prob. 7.33. A more efficient method of producing AM is described in the following section.

Pulse Modulation, Sampling

Consider the periodic function $\delta_p(t)$ consisting of impulses occurring every T_s sec and having an area of T_s units. This function is shown in Fig. 9.14. The Fourier series of $\delta_p(t)$ can be obtained by finding the Laplace transform of one period and letting $s = j2\pi k/T_s$. But the

Laplace transform of one period is simply T_s, and this contains no s at all. Then $C_k = T_s$, and the exponential series is

$$\delta_p(t) = \frac{1}{T_s} \sum_{k=-\infty}^{\infty} T_s e^{j2\pi k t/T_s}$$

$$= \sum_{k=-\infty}^{\infty} e^{j2\pi k t/T_s} \tag{9.8}$$

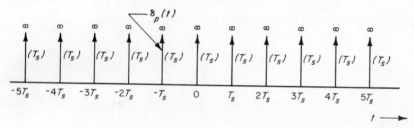

Fig. 9.14 *A periodic train of impulses of equal areas.*

If a function $s_m(t)$ is multiplied by $\delta_p(t)$, the product will be a series of impulses separated by T_s sec but whose areas are now T_s times the height or amplitude of $s_m(t)$ evaluated at the time of occurrence of each impulse. Then the result is only a sampling of $s_m(t)$ at the sampling instants, since only these values are now contained in the resulting function. Mathematically, the result of the multiplication can be expressed as

$$s_0(t) = s_m(t)\, \delta_p(t) \tag{9.9}$$

But

$$\delta_p(t) = \sum_{r=-\infty}^{\infty} T_s \delta(t - rT_s) \tag{9.10}$$

so

$$s_0(t) = \sum_{k=-\infty}^{\infty} T_s s_m(rT_s) \delta(t - rT_s) \tag{9.11}$$

or, using Eq. (9.8)

$$s_0(t) = \sum_{k=-\infty}^{\infty} s_m(t)\, e^{j2\pi k t/T_s} \tag{9.12}$$

Using Eq. (8.11), and with $S_m(f)$ the transform of $s_m(t)$, the Fourier transform $S_0(f)$ of $s_0(t)$ is, from Eq. (9.12)

$$S_0(f) = \sum_{k=-\infty}^{\infty} S_m(f - k/T_s) \tag{9.13}$$

Then the spectrum of the sampled signal is the same as $S_m(f)$ translated to the right and left $1/T_s$, $2/T_s$, $3/T_s$, and so forth, in addition to $S_m(f)$ itself when $k = 0$. Figure 9.15(a) shows a typical spectrum for $S_m(f)$, and Fig. 9.15(b) shows the spectrum of $s_0(t) = s_m(t)\delta_p(t)$. Note that if $1/T_s \geq 2f_m$, where f_m is the maximum frequency component of $S_m(f)$, the spectra will not overlap. This result is called the *sampling theorem*[*], which states that *if the maximum frequency component in $s_m(t)$ is f_m, $s_m(t)$ can be sampled at any rate greater than or equal to $2f_m$ and the original signal can be recovered from its samples by filtering.*

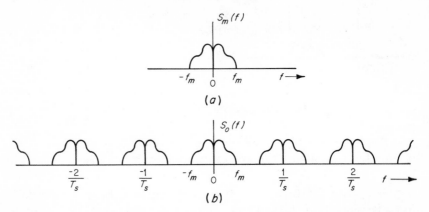

Fig. 9.15 (a) *The spectrum of a signal* $s_m(t)$. (b) *The spectrum of the sampled signal* $s_m(t)\delta_p(t)$.

Note that although a low-pass filter will indeed restore the original spectrum, a bandpass filter centered at $f = 1/T_s$, $2/T_s$, ... and $2f_m$ wide, will produce the signal AM-SC. Then amplitude modulation can be produced by pulse modulation and filtering as well as by the use of nonlinear devices.

Since impulses are impossible to produce, the question arises, "How well do finite pulses work?" If finite pulses are used, each having an area proportional to the amplitude of the signal sampled, the effect is the same as that of passing the impulse-modulated signal $s_m(t)\delta_p(t)$ through a device whose impulse response $h(t)$ is a pulse of the same type as the finite pulse used.

---

[*]E. T. Whittaker, "On the Functions Which Are Represented by the Expansions of the Interpolation Theory," *Proc. Royal Society of Edinburgh*, Vol. 35 (1914–1915), pp. 181–194. The particular interpretation of Whittaker's work used here was made by C. E. Shannon, "Communication in the Presence of Noise," *Proc. I.R.E.*, Vol. 37 (1949) pp. 10–21.

Suppose, for example, that we have a linear system whose impulse response is a narrow triangle whose base is Δt. After $s_m(t)$ is impulse-modulated—that is, multiplied by $\delta_p(t)$—the result is a series of impulses of varying areas. Each impulse will then produce a triangle at the output of the linear system, and the amplitude of each triangle will be proportional to the area of the impulse that produced it. This is the same result we would have obtained had the original sampling pulse been a triangle instead of an impulse.

But this description allows us to evaluate precisely what happens when a finite pulse is used for sampling, since the spectrum of the output is simply that pictured in Fig. 9.15(*b*) multiplied by the transfer function of the linear system. But if $H(f)$ is the Fourier transform of $h(t)$, this is also the transfer function of the system. Then we can conclude that if the Fourier transform of the pulse used in sampling is a constant over the frequency band concerned, the spectrum of the output will be the same as that of Fig. 9.15(*b*) in that frequency band. In general, it can be shown that, if the pulse width is Δt, the Fourier transform of the pulse is equal to the area under the pulse for all frequencies less than $1/(4\pi\Delta t)$, provided that the pulse is symmetric about its center. Even if the condition of symmetry is not met, there is still a pulse length for which the spectrum is very nearly a constant up to some maximum frequency. For symmetric pulses it is easier to prove:

Let $p(t)$ be a pulse of length Δt and $p(t)$ be an even function of t. Then

$$P(f) = \int_{-\Delta t/2}^{\Delta t/2} p(t)e^{-j2\pi ft}\, dt$$

$$= \int_{-\Delta t/2}^{\Delta t/2} p(t)\cos(2\pi ft)\, dt - j\int_{-\Delta t/2}^{\Delta t/2} p(t)\sin(2\pi ft)\, dt$$

The fact that $p(t)$ is an even function of t means that its transform is real, so the second integral vanishes. (It can be seen that it will vanish, because the integrand is odd and the limits of the integration are symmetric about the origin.) Then

$$P(f) = \int_{-\Delta t/2}^{\Delta t/2} p(t)\cos 2\pi ft\, dt$$

But for $f < 1/(4\pi\Delta t)$, $2\pi ft < t/(2\Delta t)$, so even at the upper limit, cos $2\pi ft = \cos \frac{1}{4} = \cos 14.3° \doteq 0.969$. The integrand is very nearly equal to $p(t)$ (within 3 percent) for all t within the range of integration, so, very nearly

$$P(f) = \int_{-\Delta t/2}^{\Delta t/2} p(t) \, dt = \text{area of } p(t)$$

for $f < 1/(4\pi\Delta t)$.

Now, if the objective of sampling is to recover $s_m(t)$ by ultimately using a low-pass filter, it is only necessary that $\Delta t < 1/(4\pi f_m)$, where f_m is the maximum frequency contained in $S_m(f)$. If the sampling is to be used to produce AM, the pulse length has to be about $1/(4\pi)$ times the period of the carrier frequency. Usually when sampling is used to produce AM, the first repetition of the spectrum is the one that is used, so the carrier frequency and the sampling frequency are the same. The sampling pulse has to be about $1/12.6 \doteq 8$ percent of the carrier period. With 360° to a cycle, the pulse should not be much larger than 28.6° wide.

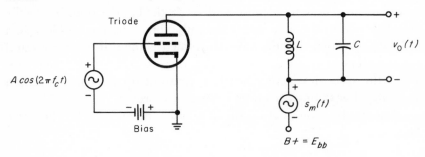

Fig. 9.16 *The plate-modulator.*

The plate modulator operates on this principle. Figure 9.16 is a diagram of this modulator. The modulating signal is placed in series with the d-c supply of the circuit so the plate voltage on the triode is very nearly $E_{bb} + s_m(t)$. The L-C resonant circuit provides a low-impedance path for the modulating signal and a high impedance to the carrier. The resonant circuit is also the filter that removes all but those frequencies near the carrier frequency.

The triode is biased well below cutoff, so when no carrier signal is applied to its grid the triode does not conduct at all. The carrier is applied to the control grid with an amplitude that insures that the tube will conduct only when the crest of the carrier is reached. If it conducts for less than 28.6 electrical deg, then the current can for all intents and purposes be considered an impulse as far as the band of frequencies near f_c is concerned. Furthermore, the amount of current produced will be proportional to the plate voltage at the moment of conduction, so the pulse will have an area under it proportional to $E_{bb} + s_m(t)$. The current pulses produced then pass through the bandpass filter represented by the L-C circuit, and the output voltage will be proportional to

$$[E_{bb} + s_m(t)] \cos 2\pi f_c t$$

If the maximum amplitude of $s_m(t)$ never exceeds E_{bb},* this is an ordinary AM signal. The simplicity of the resulting circuit is apparent; all the operations of impulse modulation (that is, sampling) and filtering are done in one stage. The plate modulator has the added advantage that nearly 100-percent modulation can be achieved with relatively little distortion.

Another practical application of pulse modulation is *time multiplexing*. If it is possible to send a message by sending only the samples, is there not some use that can be made of all the time in between samples? Yes; it can be used to send samples from other messages. Consider, for example, two signals $s_{m1}(t)$ and $s_{m2}(t)$. These might be two voice signals on a telephone line. Since 2.5 kc is the highest frequency needed or used in voice transmission, put both signals through a 2.5-kc low-pass filter and then sample each at a 5-kc rate. Now stagger the sampling pulses so that those belonging to one message are alternated with those of the other message. Two such signals appear in Fig. 9.17(a), and the alternating sample pulses appear in Fig. 9.17(b).

This pulse train is transmitted (note that its fundamental frequency is 10 kc), and the pulses at the other end of the line are separated out by some type of synchronized switching device or commutator; then each is passed through a 2.5-kc low-pass filter, and both signals are thus recovered simultaneously. Observe that the spectrum of the pulses that carry the sampled information must be transmitted by this channel without distortion, so the channel bandwidth must be determined not by the signals being modulated but by the pulses. To use this bandwidth efficiently, it is necessary to send more than two messages simultaneously.

---

*If $s_m(t)$ does exceed E_{bb} in a negative direction, the triode plate voltage becomes negative and the tube will not conduct at all. The output of the modulator will then be zero when $E_{bb} + s_m(t) < 0$. The effect of this is to cause the spectrum of the output to deviate markedly from that of ordinary AM, producing energy at other frequencies. Commercial stations cannot permit this to happen, for they will then interfere with other stations.

Practical systems have sent as many as eight messages, but the optimum appears to be in excess of twelve (see Prob. 9.15).

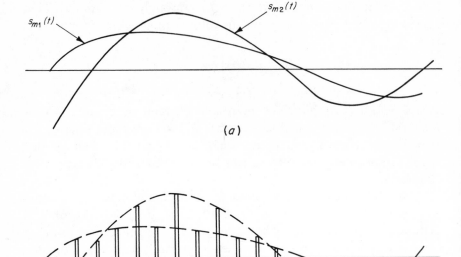

(a)

(b)

Fig. 9.17 (a) *Two signals* s_{m1} *and* s_{m2}. (b) *The sample pulses obtained by alternately sampling* s_{m1} *and* s_{m2}.

Another advantage of sampling is the possibility of using digital computers in connection with communication or control systems. Digital computers can only sample functions, just as data are collected in the laboratory to find the characteristics of different devices, such as motors, generators, vacuum tubes, and transistors. The low-pass filter used in the laboratory is called a *French curve*, and if samples are taken frequently enough (at least twice the frequency of the maximum frequency component), a smooth curve drawn through the data points will reproduce exactly the curve or characteristic of each device. (Refer to works on the Z-*transform* and *sampled data systems* for more on this topic.*)

---

*See for example D. K. Cheng, *Analysis of Linear Systems*. Reading, Mass.: Addison-Wesley Publishing Co. Inc., 1959, Chap. 10.

PROBLEMS

9.1. If the Fourier transform of $s_m(t)$ is $S_m(f)$, what is the Fourier transform of $s_m(t) \sin(2\pi f_c t)$?

9.2. Find and sketch the Fourier transform of the function $g(t) \cos 2\pi f_c t$ when $f_c = 10/b$ and $g(t)$ is
    (a) a rectangular pulse of height A and width b
    (b) a triangular pulse of height A and width $2b$.

9.3. Let $f(t)$ be a single cycle of a sinusoid, with

$$f(t) = \cos 2\pi t \left[\mathbf{1}\left(t+\frac{1}{2}\right) - \mathbf{1}\left(t-\frac{1}{2}\right) \right]$$

Sketch carefully, in the interval $-1 < t < 1$
    (a) $g_1(t) = f(t) \cos 40\pi t$
    (b) $g_2(t) = [1+f(t)] \cos 40\pi t$
    (c) $g_3(t) = [1+f(t)/2] \cos 40\pi t$
    (d) $g_4(t) = [1+2f(t)] \cos 40\pi t$
    Identify the different types of amplitude modulation.

9.4. Sketch carefully the Fourier spectrum of $\cos 2\pi f_m t \cos 2\pi f_c t$. When this signal is mixed with $\cos [2\pi(f_c + \alpha f_m)t]$, where $\alpha < 1$, and the frequency components above $2f_m$ are filtered out, what is the output signal? Draw the Fourier spectrum of this output signal.

Answer: $s_0(t) = \dfrac{1}{4}\{\cos [2\pi(1-\alpha)f_m t] + \cos [2\pi(1+\alpha)f_m t]\}$

9.5. Let $s_m(t) = \cos 440\pi t + \cos 880\pi t$, the A-major octave. Multiply this signal by $\cos(2\pi \times 10^6 t)$ to produce AM–SC, then multiply by $\cos [2\pi(10^6 - 110)t]$ to detect the AM–SC wave. Assuming that all but the audio frequencies are filtered out in the last step, what is the output signal? This will indicate what happens when music is received by an AM–SC receiver with a drifting local oscillator.

9.6. Suppose that in Prob. 9.5 only the lower sideband is retained when $s_m(t) = \cos 440\pi t + \cos 880\pi t$ is multiplied by $\cos(2\pi \times 10^6 t)$. Thus only those frequencies whose magnitudes are less than 1 mc are retained. What will the output be now when this signal is multiplied by $\cos [2\pi(10^6 - 110)t]$ and the frequencies above the audio range are filtered out?

Answer: $s_0(t) = \dfrac{1}{4}(\cos 220\pi t + \cos 660\pi t)$

9.7. Let the Fourier transforms of $s_m(t)$ and $s_m'(t)$ be $S_m(f)$ and $-j \operatorname{sgn}(f)S_m(f)$ respectively. Show that the Fourier transform of $[s_m(t) \cos 2\pi f_c t + s_m'(t) \sin 2\pi f_c t]$ is zero for $|f| > f_c$ and equal to $S_m(f-f_c) + S_m(f+f_c)$ for $|f| < f_c$.

9.8. (a) Let
$$s_m(t) = \frac{A}{\pi} \frac{\sin 2\pi f_c t}{t}$$
Find $S_m(f)$.

   (b) Multiply $S_m(f)$ by $-j$ sgn (f) and sketch the transform of $s_m'(t)$.
        Evaluate $s_m'(t)$ using the integral

$$s_m'(t) = \int_{-\infty}^{\infty} -j \text{ sgn } (f) S_m(f) e^{j2\pi ft} \, df$$

$$Answer: \quad \frac{2A}{\pi} \frac{\sin^2 \pi f_c t}{t}$$

9.9. If the Fourier transform of $1/(\pi t)$ is $-j$ sgn (f) [derivable from Eq. (8.33)],
      show by convolution that $s_m'(t)$, whose transform is $-j$ sgn $(f) S_m(f)$, is
      given by Eq. (9.5).

9.10. If
$$s_{\text{SSB}}(t) = s_m(t) \cos 2\pi f_c t - s_m'(t) \sin 2\pi f_c t$$

and $s_m'(t)$ is related to $s_m(t)$ as in Eqs. (9.5) and (9.6), show that the Fourier
transform of the function $s_{\text{SSB}}(t)$ vanishes for $|f| < f_c$ and is equal to
$S_m(f-f_c) + S_m(f+f_c)$ for $|f| > f_c$. $s_{\text{SSB}}(t)$ then, is the signal that results
if the lower sideband of the AM-SC signal is filtered out instead of the
upper sideband.

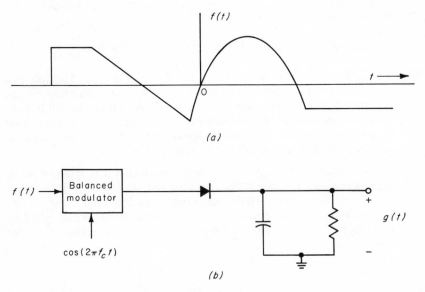

(a)

(b)

Fig. 9.18   *Problem 9.11.*

9.11. Given is $f(t)$ as pictured in Fig. 9.18(a). If $f(t)$ is the input signal to the
      circuit of Fig. 9.18(b), what is the waveform of the output $g(t)$?

9.12. The time constant RC of the envelope detector cannot be too long, nor should it be too short. The best compromise is a time constant whose length is such that for r-f peaks that are falling, the exponential will just intercept the next peak. This is shown in Fig. 9.19, where the height

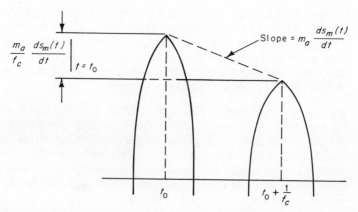

Fig. 9.19   *Two successive r-f peaks in an AM wave pictured at a time when the envelope is falling.*

of the first r-f peak is $1 + m_a s_m(t_0)$ [$s_m(t)$ is assumed to have a peak amplitude of unity, and m_a, the AM modulation index, is < 1] and the height of the second peak is very nearly equal to

$$1 + m_a s_m(t_0) + \frac{m_a}{f_c} \frac{ds_m(t)}{dt}\bigg|_{t=t_0}$$

This assumes that the period of the carrier $1/f_c$ is small enough that the slope of the line joining the peaks is equal to the derivative of the envelope at the time in question.

    Clearly, the amplitude will fall only when the slope of the envelope is negative. The output of the detector will have the form of an exponential decay; that is,

$$[1 + m_a s_m(t_0)]e^{-(t-t_0)/RC} \, \mathbf{1}(t-t_0)$$

and at $t = t_0 + 1/f_c$ it will have fallen to

$$[1 + m_a s_m(t_0)]e^{-1/(RC f_c)}$$

    Using the approximation $e^{-x} \doteq 1 - x$ for small x, show that the time constant RC should be no greater than the minimum value of the ratio $[1 + m_a s(t_0)]/[-m_a \dot{s}_m(t_0)]$, where $\dot{s}_m(t_0)$ is the value of the derivative $ds_m(t)/dt$ at the time t_0.

9.13. Let $s_m(t) = \cos 2\pi f_m t$. By differentiation with respect to t, find the minimum value of the function

$$\frac{1 + m_a \cos 2\pi f_m t}{2\pi f_m m_a \sin 2\pi f_m t} = \frac{1 + m_a s_m(t)}{-m_a \dot{s}_m(t)}$$

(see Prob. 9.12) and show that the time constant of the envelope detector should be given by

$$RC = \sqrt{1 - m_a^2}/(2\pi f m_a)$$

Observe that for $m_a = 0.707$ (70.7 percent modulation), RC is simply $1/(2\pi f_m)$, and that for 100 percent modulation, $RC = 0$. What would the output look like if $RC = 1/(2\pi f_m)$ and yet the modulation index were $m_a = 1$? To answer this, draw the signal $[1 + \cos{(2\pi f_m t)}] \cos{(2\pi f_c t)}$ for one cycle and observe that after $2\pi f_m t = \pi/2$, the exponential "misses" the r-f peaks for more than $\frac{1}{4}$ cycle.

9.14. The circuit appearing in Fig. 9.20 is called a *strain-gauge bridge*, since the resistance R_s is such that its ohmic value is proportional to its relative elongation when placed under mechanical stress (tension). Most wire will behave in this way, since the resistance of a wire is proportional to its length and inversely proportional to its cross section. If stretching does not change the cross section appreciably, changes in resistance will be proportional to changes in length.

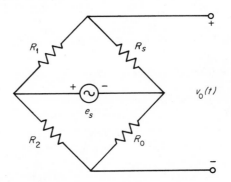

Fig. 9.20 *A strain-gauge bridge.*

If the resistance R_s is attached to something that moves very slightly, its resistance will change in proportion to this motion. Suppose the bridge is balanced when the resistance R_s is at rest—that is, when $R_1 = R_2$ and $R_s = R_0$. Under these conditions, $v_0(t) = 0$. If the length of the wire R_s at rest is l_0, then $R_s = R_0(1 + \Delta l/l_0)$ when the wire is elongated by a length Δl.

The source for the bridge is an a-c voltage $e_s = E_s \cos 2\pi f_c t$. If the resistance R_s is attached to some device that is moving in such a way that the elongation of the wire is $\Delta l(t)$, what is the voltage $v_0(t)$ as a function of time expressed in terms of $\Delta l(t)$? Assume that $\Delta l \ll l_0$. What kind of AM is this? If $v_0(t)$ is amplified, how would you detect a signal proportional to $\Delta l(t)$? If the vibration of the device to which R_s is attached were a sinusoid, would an envelope detector serve as an adequate detector? State your reasons why it would or would not be adequate.

Answer: $v_0(t) \doteq \dfrac{R_0 R_1 E_s}{l_0 (R_0 + R_1)^2} \; \Delta l(t) \cos 2\pi f_c t$

9.15. A certain pulse is used to sample audio signals for telephone applications. The pulse is such that a bandwidth of $1/b$ cps is required for it to pass with good fidelity, where b is the pulse length. The signal to be sampled has a bandwidth of 2.5 kc, so the samples must be taken at a 5-kc rate if the signal is to be recovered.

Now if the pulse length is $1/(4\pi)$ times the period of the maximum frequency that we desire to transmit, what must the pulse length b be? What must the bandwidth of the system be if these pulses are to be transmitted with good fidelity?

Since the bandwidth is very much greater than 2.5 kc, the space between pulses can be used to sample other messages. How many messages can be sampled without having two pulses overlap? Now suppose that this number of messages were amplitude modulated instead of being sampled, but with as many carrier frequencies as there are messages, each carrier frequency being 5 kc higher than the other so that the spectra of no two messages would overlap. For example, message number one would not be modulated, number two would be modulated with a 5-kc carrier, number three with a 10-kc carrier, and so forth. What total bandwidth is required?

This latter technique is called *frequency multiplexing*, and like time multiplexing it is another way of sending several messages simultaneously over one channel, with the cost of added bandwidth. How do the bandwidths compare for the two types of multiplexing?

Suppose that instead of using AM or AM-SC as suggested above, AM-SSB were used. Now the carriers would have to be only 2.5 kc apart. What would be the total bandwidth in this case for the same number of messages as with the time-multiplexed system?

Judging from this result, can you conclude that there is a direct relationship between information to be sent and the amount of bandwidth required to send it?

9.16. If the only difference between AM and AM-SC is the presence of the carrier, why not *add* the carrier to the incoming signal and use an ordinary envelope detector?

Let $s_m(t)$ be the modulation, and $\cos (2\pi f_c t)$ the carrier. Then the signal arriving at the receiver is

$$s_m(t) \cos (2\pi f_c t)$$

We must recognize that the carrier generated at the receiver will be neither in phase with, nor at the same frequency as, the carrier. Suppose that the signal generated by the local oscillator is

$$s_{LO}(t) = \cos [2\pi f_c t + x(t)]$$

where $x(t) = 2\pi \Delta f t + \phi$. Show that the signal obtained after adding

s_{LO} to the received signal can be expressed as

$$[s_m(t) + \cos x(t)] \cos 2\pi f_c t - [\sin x(t)] \sin 2\pi f_c t$$

Multiply and divide this expression by the square root of the sum of the squares of the coefficients of cos and sin $(2\pi f_c t)$ and show that the output of the envelope detector is

$$v_0(t) = \sqrt{1 + s_m^2(t) + 2s_m(t) \cos x(t)}$$

Sketch the output that results when $s_m(t)$ is a square wave (going from $+1$ to -1) with frequency 1 kc, when $x(t) = 2\pi \times 10^3 t$. Assume that $s_m(t)$ is positive when $\cos x(t)$ is positive.

Angle Modulation, FM and PM

Frequency and phase modulation are important applications of communication engineering. The two types of modulation are identical in form, the only distinction being the manner in which the signal is processed. These applications do not, however, represent examples in which the Fourier transform is extremely valuable. It is not possible, in general, to obtain the spectrum of a frequency-modulated wave, but it is possible to obtain bounds on this spectrum. It might be said that the frequency-domain understanding of FM leaves something to be desired.

If in Eq. (9.1) $A(t)$ is made a constant (say unity) and the carrier frequency is f_c, the general form of an angle-modulated wave is

$$s(t) = \cos [2\pi f_c t + \theta(t)] \tag{9.14}$$

If the modulating signal is $s_m(t)$, which we shall assume is normalized so that its maximum amplitude is unity, the modulation is called phase modulation if

$$\theta(t) = m_f s_m(t) \tag{9.15}$$

where m_f is called the *modulation index* for either phase or frequency modulation. Observe that $|\theta(t)|_{max} = m_f$, so m_f can be considered to be the maximum instantaneous *angle deviation* in radians.

The instantaneous frequency $f_i = f_i(t)$, a function of time, is given by $1/(2\pi)$ times the derivative of the argument of the cosine in Eq. (9.14). Thus

$$
\begin{aligned}
f_i(t) &= \frac{1}{2\pi} \frac{d}{dt} [2\pi f_c t + \theta(t)] \\
&= f_c + \frac{1}{2\pi} \frac{d\theta(t)}{dt}
\end{aligned}
\tag{9.16}
$$

The maximum instantaneous frequency deviation Δf is defined as the magnitude of the maximum deviation of $f_i - f_c$, and, from Eq. (9.16)

$$\Delta f = \frac{1}{2\pi} \left| \frac{d\theta(t)}{dt} \right|_{\text{max}} \qquad (9.17)$$

If the modulating signal is $s_m(t)$, again assumed to have a maximum amplitude of unity, and if $\theta(t)$ is defined by

$$\frac{1}{2\pi} \frac{d\theta(t)}{dt} = \Delta f s_m(t) \qquad (9.18)$$

Eq. (9.16) reads

$$f_i(t) = f_c + \Delta f s_m(t) \qquad (9.19)$$

and this relation defines frequency modulation. Thus PM and FM differ only in the form of $\theta(t)$. In PM the instantaneous angle is proportional to the modulating signal, and in FM the instantaneous derivative of the angle is proportional to the modulating signal. We need treat only one or the other type of modulation, since an FM system can be used to produce PM if the modulating signal is first differentiated with respect to time, and a PM system can be used to produce FM if the modulating signal is first integrated with respect to time. These distinctions will be brought out in the problems following this section, but only FM will be considered in the discussion.

THE INTUITIVE APPROACH

Equation (9.19) states that the instantaneous frequency in an FM signal is equal to the carrier frequency plus an amount proportional to the *amplitude* of the modulating signal. Notice that nothing at all is said about the frequency of the modulating signal. If the modulating signal is music, for example, the deviation in frequency will increase with the *loudness* of the music and will decrease as the music is played softly. During rests there will be no frequency deviation, and the signal will be merely the carrier sinusoid. This leads to what we might call the *modulation paradox*: In *amplitude* modulation, the bandwidth depends on the *frequency* of the modulating signal, but in *frequency* modulation, the bandwidth depends on the *amplitude* of the modulating signal.

Using intuition, we might expect the FM signal to occupy a band between $f_c - \Delta f$ and $f_c + \Delta f$. As we shall see, this is very nearly true if the maximum instantaneous frequency deviation is large compared to the maximum frequency of the modulating signal. Figure 9.21(a) shows a modulating signal $s_m(t)$, and Fig. 9.21(b) shows the effect of frequency modulating a carrier with this signal.

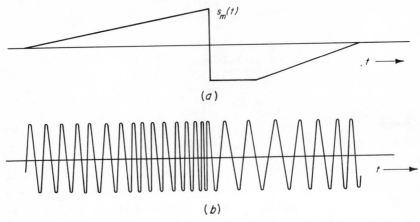

(a)

(b)

Fig. 9.21   (a) *A signal* $s_m(t)$. (b) *The result of frequency modulating a carrier with the* $s_m(t)$ *of* (a).

The total average power in the signal of Eq. (9.14) should be ½ watt if the sinusoid has an amplitude of unity. Thus it should be possible to calculate approximately the power spectrum of an FM wave by adding up the total *time* that the frequency is in a certain band. For example, suppose that the modulating signal is a sinusoid $\cos 2\pi f_m t$. Then the instantaneous frequency, from Eq. (9.19), is

$$f_i = f_c + \Delta f \cos 2\pi f_m t$$

Figure 9.22(a) shows $f_i - f_c$ plotted versus time; the result is periodic, and Fig. 9.22(b) shows half of one period, since in this time the entire frequency range from $f_c - \Delta f$ to $f_c + \Delta f$ is swept over once.

In Fig. 9.22(b), a particular frequency interval f to $f + df$ is outlined; notice that the frequency will remain in this interval for a time dt, located on the t axis. It can be intuitively assumed that the longer dt is, the greater will be the power that exists in this frequency range. For example, at $t = 0$ the frequency remains at $f_c + \Delta f$ for a relatively long time, but it passes through the carrier frequency quite rapidly and then seems to remain in the vicinity of $f_c - \Delta f$ for another extended period. We would expect, then, to find a spectrum that is large at $f_c \pm \Delta f$ and small at f_c. If the signal were a square wave instead of a sinusoid, intuition would tell us that only two frequencies would be present, one at $f_c + \varDelta f$ and one at $f_c - \varDelta f$. This would be something like the spectrum of a suppressed-carrier AM wave in which the modulating signal is a sinusoid of frequency $\varDelta f$. There is a difference, however. In the case of the suppressed-carrier AM, the sinusoids are always present in time; in the square-wave FM case, it is first one frequency and then the other.

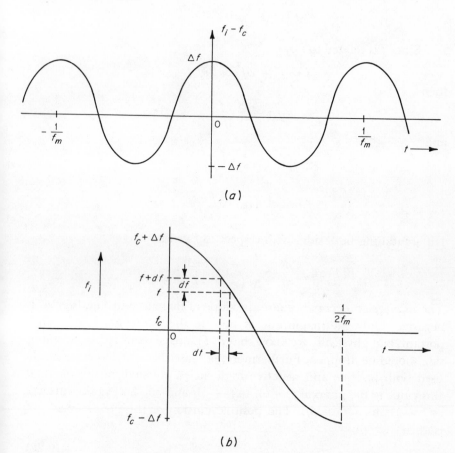

(a)

(b)

Fig. 9.22 (a) *The instantaneous frequency plotted as a function of time when the modulating signal is a sinusoid.* (b) *One half of one period of the wave of Fig. 9.22(a) showing that in this time the entire frequency range is swept over once.*

Continuing with the sinusoidal example, the ratio of the power in the band f to $f + df$ to the total power should be equal to the ratio of dt to $1/(2f_m)$ (one-half the period). In equation form, if $P(f)$ is the power density, the power in the band will be $P(f)\,df$, so

$$\frac{P(f)\,df}{1/2} = \frac{dt}{1/(2f_m)} \tag{9.20}$$

$$P(f)\,df = f_m\,dt$$

or

$$P(f) = f_m \frac{dt}{df} \tag{9.21}$$

Since f is related to t by

$$f = f_c + \varDelta f \cos 2\pi f_m t$$

then

$$\cos 2\pi f_m t = \frac{f - f_c}{\varDelta f}$$

and

$$2\pi f_m t = \cos^{-1}\frac{f - f_c}{\varDelta f}$$

$$f_m t = \frac{1}{2\pi}\cos^{-1}\frac{(f - f_c)}{\varDelta f}$$

Differentiating both sides with respect to f yields

$$P(f) = f_m \frac{dt}{df} = \frac{-1/(2\pi\varDelta f)}{\sqrt{1 - (f - f_c)^2/(\varDelta f)^2}}$$

The minus sign occurs because the slope of the curve in Fig. 9.22(*b*) is negative. Only the magnitude of time in the frequency band is important, and physically we know that $P(f)$ must be positive, so the minus sign should be dropped. Furthermore, because this text has consistently used both positive and negative frequencies, we shall assign one-half this value to the interval $f_c - \varDelta f$ to $f_c + \varDelta f$ and one-half to the interval $-f_c - \varDelta f$ to $-f_c + \varDelta f$. The positive portion of the power spectrum is then

$$P(f) = \frac{1}{(4\pi\varDelta f)\sqrt{1 - (f - f_c)^2/(\varDelta f)^2}} \tag{9.22}$$

The positive portion of this spectrum appears in Fig. 9.23. Remember that this is only an *intuitive spectrum*, and our intuition is limited.

It is possible to generalize Eq. (9.21). Because the instantaneous frequency deviation is proportional to the modulating signal, then a given frequency f_0 may occur several times in one period. In this event the total time that the frequency is in a given band $f_0 < f < f_0 + df$

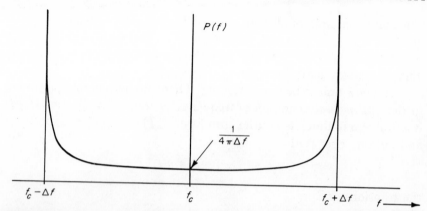

Fig. 9.23 *An* intuitive *spectrum of the frequency-modulated sinusoid, with sinusoidal modulation and maximum frequency deviation Δf. Only the positive frequency portion is shown.*

will be the sum of all the $\mid dt_k \mid$, $k = 1, 2, \cdots$ that correspond to this frequency interval. Then

$$P(f) = \frac{1}{4} f_m \sum_k \left| \frac{dt_k}{df} \right|$$

where the summation is made over one cycle of the modulating signal. In our example this was not necessary because the modulating signal swept the frequency band back and forth in a symmetric fashion and only one branch of the signal had to be chosen. There is really no object in this approach, however, unless the results obtained make sense.

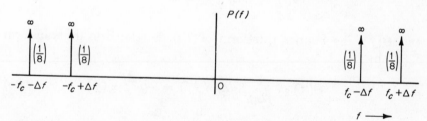

Fig. 9.24 *An intuitive spectrum of a sinusoid modulated with a square wave. Again, Δf is the maximum instantaneous frequency deviation.*

Figure 9.24 shows what intuition tells us the spectrum should be if the modulating signal is a square wave: an impulse at $f_c - \Delta f$ and another at $f_c + \Delta f$. Since both positive and negative frequencies have been considered, there are two more impulses at $-f_c - \Delta f$ and $-f_c + \Delta f$.

The combined area of all four must be ½, so each must have an area of ⅛.

The Mathematical Approach

It is now time to be more exacting. There has been nothing intuitive in the *mathematical* definition of frequency or frequency spectra. If $g(t)$ is a function of time, its Fourier transform $G(f)$ determines its spectrum and nothing else. With

$$s(t) = \cos\left[2\pi f_c t + \theta(t)\right]$$

the transform is

$$S(f) = \int_{-\infty}^{\infty} \cos\left[2\pi f_c t + \theta(t)\right] e^{-j2\pi ft} \, dt \tag{9.23}$$

One glance at Eq. (9.23) may be enough to convince us that we did not want to study FM anyway. The situation is not as bad as it appears, however. Although it is true that we cannot make general statements about the shape of the spectra, as we could with AM, it will prove to be very fruitful if we compare the actual spectra for the square wave and the sinusoid to the spectra obtained intuitively, and these actual spectra can be found.

As a first approach, let us assume that the maximum angle deviation m_f is ¼ rad or less. We are discussing FM, with $s_m(t)$ the modulating signal, so from Eq. (9.18)

$$\theta(t) = 2\pi \Delta f \int_{-\infty}^{t} s_m(x) \, dx \tag{9.24}$$

and $\Theta(f)$, the Fourier transform of $\theta(t)$, is related to the transform $S_m(f)$ by

$$\Theta(f) = \frac{1}{j2\pi f} 2\pi \Delta f \, S_m(f) = -j \frac{\Delta f}{f} S_m(f) \tag{9.25}$$

where we shall assume that $s_m(t)$ has zero average value. Therefore, $S_m(0) = 0$ and the transform $\Theta(f)$ does exist.

If the maximum value of $\theta(t)$ is m_f and consequently the maximum angle variation is m_f, the amplitude of $s_m(t)$ must be such that its integral with respect to t has a maximum value of $m_f/(2\pi\Delta f)$. This means that nothing can be said about the relative amplitude of $s_m(t)$ unless its variation with time is known.

From the trigonometric identity for the cosine of the sum of two angles we can obtain

$$\cos\,[2\pi f_c t + \theta(t)] = \cos 2\pi f_c t \cos \theta(t) - \sin 2\pi f_c t \sin \theta(t) \qquad (9.26)$$

With the maximum angle deviation limited to $\frac{1}{4}$ rad, $\cos \theta(t) \doteq 1$ and $\sin \theta(t) \doteq \theta(t)$, both within 3 percent. Then Eq. (9.26) can be written approximately as

$$\cos\,[2\pi f_c t + \theta(t)] \doteq \cos 2\pi f_c t - \theta(t) \sin 2\pi f_c t \qquad (9.27)$$

But this is just like ordinary AM, except that the carrier portion is 90 deg out of phase with the modulated signal. The transform of the cosine term is simply a pair of impulses of area $\frac{1}{2}$ located at $\pm f_c$, and the transform of the second term is $1/(2j)$ times the transforms of $-\theta(t)$ shifted to the right f_c and $\theta(t)$ shifted to the left f_c. Then, for m_f small, using Eq. (9.25),

$$S(f) \doteq \frac{1}{2}\,\delta(f - f_c) + \frac{1}{2}\,\delta(f + f_c)$$

$$+ \frac{\varDelta f}{2}\left[\frac{S_m(f - f_c)}{f - f_c} - \frac{S_m(f + f_c)}{f + f_c}\right] \qquad (9.28)$$

A typical $S_m(f)$ appears in Fig. 9.25(a), and $S_m(f)/f$ appears in Fig. 9.25(b). The FM spectrum (positive-frequency portion only) is shown in Fig. 9.25(c).

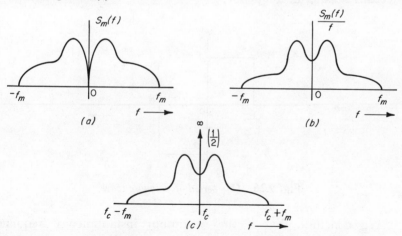

Fig. 9.25 (a) The spectrum of $s_m(t)$, $S_m(f)$. (b) The spectrum of $S_m(f)/f$. (c) The positive-frequency portion of the spectrum of the narrow-band FM wave with $m \leqslant \frac{1}{4}$.

The bandwidth is seen to depend on the maximum frequency component of $s_m(t)$ and not at all on Δf. All this depends, of course, on the assumption that m_f is less than $\frac{1}{4}$. Observe that if $s_m(t)$ were periodic, with a maximum amplitude of A, and that if the fundamental frequency were f_m, the maximum value of the integral of $s_m(t)$ with respect to t would be $A/(2f_m)$, since $s_m(t)$ is assumed to have zero average value. This can be seen by sketching a square wave of amplitude A and period $1/f_m$ and seeing that no periodic wave with equal positive and negative areas in any cycle can possibly have an amplitude not exceeding $\pm A$ in either direction and still have a maximum integral that exceeds $A/(2f_m)$.

Thus, no matter what $s_m(t)$ is, if it is periodic with fundamental frequency f_m and if the maximum value of the signal is unity, the maximum value of the integral must be less than or equal to $1/(2f_m)$. From Eq. (9.24) then, the maximum value of $\theta(t)$ must be $2\pi\Delta f/(2f_m) = \pi\Delta f/f_m$. If this is to be less than $\frac{1}{4}$ rad, then Eq. (9.28) will be true only if $\Delta f/f_m \leq 1/(4\pi)$. In other words, the spectrum of Fig. 9.25(c) is correct only if the maximum instantaneous frequency deviation is *small* compared to the maximum frequency to be transmitted. Actually the bound specified here is small, because most signals do not have the complexity in the frequency domain that the square wave has. In practice, a frequency deviation of one-quarter of the maximum frequency to be transmitted will in general lead to a bandwidth of about twice this maximum frequency.

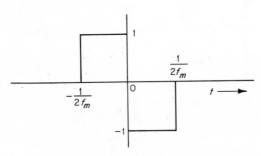

Fig. 9.26 *One period of a square wave.*

We conclude that if the maximum instantaneous frequency deviation is less than one-quarter f_m, where f_m is the maximum frequency component in the modulating signal, the FM spectrum will extend from $f_c - f_m$ to $f_c + f_m$ and be independent of the deviation Δf.

Equation (9.28) indicates that the magnitude of the spectrum will then be proportional to Δf. This is known as *narrow-band FM*.

When the maximum instantaneous frequency deviation is large compared to f_m, the analysis yields an entirely different result. Suppose, for example, we want to find the FM spectrum of the square pulse pictured in Fig. 9.26. The fundamental frequency is chosen as f_m cps. Recall that the Fourier transform of one pulse is the envelope of the Fourier series, so the Fourier transform of one period only is required.

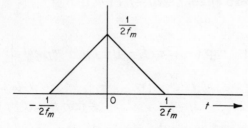

Fig. 9.27 *The integral of the pulse of Fig. 9.26.*

When the pulse is integrated with respect to t, the triangle appearing in Fig. 9.27 results. Since its amplitude is $1/(2f_m)$, we have, from Eq. (9.19) and (9.24)

$$f_i = f_c + \Delta f s_m(t)$$

where $s_m(t)$ is the pulse of Fig. 9.26 and

$$\theta(t) = \frac{2\pi \Delta f}{2f_m} \times \begin{cases} 1 + 2f_m t & -1/(2f_m) < t < 0 \\ 1 - 2f_m t & 0 < t < 1/(2f_m) \\ 0 & |t| > 1/(2f_m) \end{cases}$$

For simplicity we shall set

$$m_f = \pi \Delta f / f_m$$

the maximum angle deviation in radians, and call it the modulation index for this wave. If we assume that the carrier is turned on at $t = -1/(2f_m)$ and off at $t = 1/(2f_m)$, since the signal only exists in this interval [the rest of the wave is only the carrier, for when $s_m(t) = 0$ the signal is $\cos(2\pi f_c t)$, whose spectrum we know to be an impulse at $f = f_c$] then, the Fourier transform of the FM pulse is

$$S(f) = \int_{-1/(2f_m)}^{0} \cos\left[2\pi f_c t + m_f(1 + 2f_m t)\right] e^{-j2\pi f t}\, dt$$

$$+ \int_{0}^{1/(2f_m)} \cos\left[2\pi f_c t + m_f(1 - 2f_m t)\right] e^{-j2\pi f t}\, dt$$

If the first integral is called $S_1(m_f, f)$ and the second $S_2(m_f, f)$, it can be shown that

$$S_1(m_f, f) = S^*(-m_f, f)$$

by replacing m_f by $-m_f$ and t by $-t$ in the second integral. Then only the second integral need be evaluated. Writing the cosine term in exponential form and using $\pi \Delta f = m_f f_m$ gives

$$S_2 = \frac{1}{2} \left\{ \int_0^{1/(2f_m)} \exp\{j[2\pi(f_c - \Delta f - f)t + m_f]\} \, dt \right.$$

$$\left. + \int_0^{1/(2f_m)} \exp\{-j[2\pi(f_c - \Delta f + f)t + m_f]\} \, dt \right\}$$

$$= \frac{1}{2} \left\{ \frac{e^{jm_f} \left[e^{j\pi(f_c - \Delta f - f)/f_m} - 1 \right]}{j2\pi(f_c - \Delta f - f)} + \frac{e^{-jm_f} \left[e^{-j\pi(f_c - \Delta f + f)/f_m} - 1 \right]}{-j2\pi(f_c - \Delta f + f)} \right\}$$

Observe that the second term in the last equation is small for f near f_c, since the denominator is near $2f_c$. Then the first term is the positive-frequency part of S_2, so if we replace m_f by $-m_f$, Δf by $-\Delta f$, and take the conjugate, the first term will yield the positive-frequency portion of S_1. Then, for $f > 0$

$$S(f) = S_1(m_f, f) + S_2(m_f, f) \doteq \frac{e^{jm_f}}{j4\pi} \left[\frac{e^{j\pi(f_c - \Delta f - f)/f_m} - 1}{f_c - \Delta f - f} \right.$$

$$\left. - \frac{e^{-j\pi(f_c + \Delta f - f)/f_m} - 1}{f_c + \Delta f - f} \right]$$

$$S(f) = \frac{e^{jm_f}}{2\pi} \left[\frac{e^{j\pi(f_c - \Delta f - f)/(2f_m)} \sin[\pi(f_c - \Delta f - f)/(2f_m)]}{f_c - \Delta f - f} \right.$$

$$\left. + \frac{e^{-j\pi(f_c + \Delta f - f)/(2f_m)} \sin[\pi(f_c + \Delta f - f)/(2f_m)]}{f_c + \Delta f - f} \right]$$

The functions

$$F_1 = \frac{\sin[\pi(f_c - \Delta f - f)/(2f_m)]}{2\pi(f_c - \Delta f - f)}$$

and

$$F_2 = \frac{\sin[\pi(f_c + \Delta f - f)/(2f_m)]}{2\pi(f_c + \Delta f - f)}$$

have values of $1/(4f_m)$ at $f = f_c - \Delta f$ and $f = f_c + \Delta f$ respectively, and are shown in Fig. 9.28. They are drawn for the case of very little overlap (large Δf). Each function goes to zero everytime f changes by an amount $2f_m$, and the amplitude becomes small only when the frequency is more than $2f_m$ cps away from $f_c \pm \Delta f$. Thus, there will never actually be a condition of *no* overlap, but practically speaking the overlap is negligible when $\Delta f = 10f_m$. For this value of Δf, each of the functions F_1 and F_2 has a magnitude at the carrier frequency that is less than or equal to $1/(20\pi f_m)$, or $1/(5\pi)$ times its maximum value.

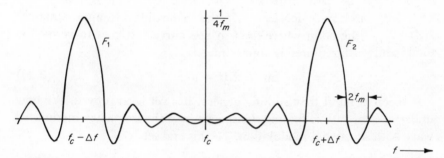

Fig. 9.28 *The positive portion of the spectrum of the square pulse FM signal for the case $\Delta f \gg 2f_m$.*

If we assume that there is no overlap, then since the magnitudes of the exponentials that multiply F_1 and F_2 in the transform $S(f)$ are unity, the energy-density function for positive frequencies will merely be the sum of the magnitudes squared of F_1 and F_2

$$\Phi(f) = |S(f)|^2 \doteq \frac{\sin^2\left[\pi\,(f_c - \Delta f - f)/(2f_m)\right]}{4\pi^2(f_c - \Delta f - f)^2}$$
$$+ \frac{\sin^2\left[\pi\,(f_c + \Delta f - f)/(2f_m)\right]}{4\pi^2(f_c + \Delta f - f)^2}$$

If either term in the last equation is compared with Eq. (8.29)

$$\delta(t) = \lim_{f_1 \to \infty} f_1 \left[\frac{\sin \pi f_1 t}{\pi f_1 t}\right]^2 \tag{8.29}$$

some similarities can be noted. In fact, if in Eq. (8.29) t is replaced by $(f_c - \Delta f - f)$ and f_1 by $1/(2f_m)$, the equation will read

$$\delta(f_c - \Delta f - f) = \lim_{f_m \to 0} \frac{2f_m}{\pi^2} \frac{\sin^2\left[\pi(f_c - \Delta f - f)/(2f_m)\right]}{(f_c - \Delta f - f)^2}$$

or

$$\lim_{f_m \to 0} \frac{1}{8f_m}\delta(f_c - \Delta f - f) = \lim_{f_m \to 0} \frac{\sin^2\left[\pi(f_c - \Delta f - f)/(2f_m)\right]}{4\pi^2(f_c - \Delta f - f)^2}$$

so as $f_m \to 0$, the energy spectrum approaches four impulses at $\pm f_c \pm \Delta f$, each of area $1/(8f_m)$. If f_m approaches zero, the period $1/f_m$ becomes infinite. If the energy is divided by $1/f_m$, the length of the signal, the spectrum will become a *power-density spectrum* consisting of four impulses, each of area $\frac{1}{8}$. This is exactly the conclusion we reached intuitively.

Observe that we can now draw some conclusions from this. Since for Δf small the bandwidth was shown to be $2f_m$, that is, $f_c - f_m < f < f_c + f_m$, and since for large Δf the bandwidth is approximately $2(\Delta f + 2f_m)$—the point where the $(\sin x)/x$ curve first goes to zero—the total bandwidth required is approximately

$$\text{bw} = 2\Delta f + 4f_m \tag{9.29}$$

Keep in mind that nothing general has yet been proved. We now undertake the task of finding the spectrum of the frequency-modulated wave with sinusoidal modulation. To this end let

$$s_m(t) = \cos 2\pi f_m t \tag{9.30}$$

so

$$f_i = f_c + \Delta f \cos 2\pi f_m t \tag{9.31}$$

Then, from Eq. (9.24)

$$\theta(t) = \frac{2\pi\Delta f}{2\pi f_m} \sin 2\pi f_m t$$

$$= \frac{\Delta f}{f_m} \sin 2\pi f_m t \tag{9.32}$$

It is seen that for this signal

$$m_f = \frac{\Delta f}{f_m} \tag{9.33}$$

Since

$$s(t) = \cos [2\pi f_c t + m_f \sin 2\pi f_m t] \tag{9.34}$$

is periodic, we shall look for its Fourier series instead of its Fourier transform. But $s(t)$ can be written as

$$s(t) = 2 \, Re[e^{j2\pi f_c t} \, e^{jm_f \sin 2\pi f_m t}] \tag{9.35}$$

Then if the Fourier series for $\exp (jm_f \sin 2\pi f_m t)$ can be found, then that of $s(t)$ can be found also. If then

$$f(t) = e^{jm_f \sin 2\pi f_m t} \tag{9.36}$$

$$= \frac{1}{T} \sum_{k=-\infty}^{\infty} C_k \, e^{j2\pi kt/T} \tag{9.37}$$

then with $T = 1/f_m$

$$C_k = \int_0^{1/f_m} e^{jm_f \sin 2\pi f_m t}\, e^{-j2\pi f t}\, dt$$

If we let $x = 2\pi f_m t$, $dx = 2\pi f_m\, dt$, then the limits on the integral become 0 and 2π, so

$$C_k = \frac{1}{2\pi f_m} \int_0^{2\pi} e^{j(m_f \sin x - kx)}\, dx \qquad (9.38)$$

A form of *Sommerfeld's integral* for $\mathcal{J}_n(m_f)$ is

$$\mathcal{J}_n(m_f) = \frac{1}{2\pi} \int_0^{2\pi} e^{j(m_f \sin x - nx)}\, dx \qquad (9.39)$$

where $\mathcal{J}_n(m)$ is the Bessel function of the first kind, order n. The integral is correct, provided that n is an integer.

Comparison of Eqs. (9.39) and (9.38) indicates that

$$C_k = \frac{1}{f_m}\, \mathcal{J}_k(m_f) \qquad (9.40)$$

and so

$$f(t) = \sum_{k=-\infty}^{\infty} \mathcal{J}_k(m_f) e^{j2\pi f_m k t} \qquad (9.41)$$

Then

$$e^{j2\pi f_c t} f(t) = \sum_{k=-\infty}^{\infty} \mathcal{J}_k(m_f) e^{j2\pi(f_c + k f_m)t} \qquad (9.42)$$

Now

$$e^{j2\pi f_c t} f(t) = e^{j(2\pi f_c t + m_f \sin 2\pi f_m t)}$$

and it is seen that the real part of this expression is just $s(t)$. But the real part of any complex number is one-half the sum of itself and its conjugate, and so

$$s(t) = \frac{1}{2} \sum_{k=-\infty}^{\infty} \mathcal{J}_k(m_f) e^{j2\pi(f_c + k f_m)t} + \frac{1}{2} \sum_{k=-\infty}^{\infty} \mathcal{J}_k(m_f) e^{-j2\pi(f_c + k f_m)t} \qquad (9.43)$$

Then the positive frequencies in $s(t)$ are $f_c, f_c \pm f_m, f_c \pm 2f_m, \ldots,$ $f_c \pm k f_m$, with amplitudes $\mathcal{J}_k(m_f)/2$. It is known that

$$\mathcal{J}_{-k}(m_f) = (-1)^k \mathcal{J}_k(m_f) \qquad (9.44)$$

so that when k is odd the amplitude of the frequency $|k f_m|$ below f_c is the negative of that $|k f_m|$ above f_c.

The magnitude of the kth harmonic which is $|kf_m|$ cps away from the carrier is

$$\frac{1}{2}\, \mathcal{J}_k(m_f) \tag{9.45}$$

It is interesting to inquire about the behavior of this function as m_f is made large. Since the frequency corresponding to k is

$$f = f_c + kf_m$$

then

$$k = \frac{f - f_c}{f_m}$$

Since f_m is to be made small compared to $\varDelta f$, then for fixed $\varDelta f$ and fixed frequency f how does $\mathcal{J}_k(m_f)$ vary as both k and m_f become large? An asymptotic formula* for this has been worked out and is

$$\mathcal{J}_k(m_f) \sim \sqrt{\frac{2}{\pi m_f}} \frac{\cos \phi}{[1 - (f - f_c)^2/(\varDelta f)^2]^{1/4}} \tag{9.46}$$

where $\phi = \phi(m_f,\, k)$ and varies in a random fashion as m_f and k are changed. Then if $\cos \phi = 1$, Eq. (9.46) becomes a *bound* on $\mathcal{J}_k(m_f)$.

The power spectrum of the signal must be a line spectrum, because the signal is periodic. However, as $f_m \to 0$ the separation between lines is small, and thus we can approach a continuous spectrum whose area represents power by squaring Eq. (9.46) and dividing by $4f_m$. The factor of 4 comes from the fact that the coefficients of the Fourier series are one-half of $\mathcal{J}_k(m_f)$, and division by f_m, the separation between lines, converts the line to an area. When $\cos \phi$ is squared then it will in general have an average value of $\frac{1}{2}$ and so the expression

$$P(f) \sim \frac{1}{4f_m} \cdot \frac{2}{\pi m_f} \cdot \frac{\cos^2 \phi}{\sqrt{1 - (f - f_c)^2/(\varDelta f)^2}}$$

has an upper bound of

$$P(f)_{\max} = \frac{1}{2\pi \varDelta f \sqrt{1 - (f - f_c)^2/(\varDelta f)^2}} \tag{9.47}$$

but an average value of

$$P(f)_{\mathrm{av}} = \frac{1}{4\pi \varDelta f \sqrt{1 - (f - f_c)^2/(\varDelta f)^2}} \tag{9.48}$$

---

*See for example Papoulis (7), p. 143.

But Eq. (9.48) is exactly the same as Eq. (9.22). Again we conclude that our intuition is correct, provided that $\Delta f/f_m$ is large.

In order to see what happens to the bandwidth between the limits of m_f small and m_f large, it is convenient to plot a few curves. Define

$$h = \frac{f-f_c}{\Delta f} \tag{9.49}$$

and with

$$m_f = \frac{\Delta f}{f_m} \tag{9.50}$$

then

$$hm_f = \frac{f-f_c}{f_m} \tag{9.51}$$

Then when hm_f is an integer it will be k, the kth sideband above the carrier frequency. Since the complex amplitude of each frequency component is $\mathcal{J}_k(m_f)/2$, then the function

$$P(h,m_f) = \frac{\mathcal{J}_{hm_f}^2(m_f)}{4} \tag{9.52}$$

represents the envelope of the line power spectrum for any fixed m_f at a frequency whose deviation from the carrier is the fraction h of the maximum frequency deviation Δf.

Figure 9.29 shows a plot of the function $P(h, m_f)$ versus h for values of $m_f = 1, 2, 4, 8,$ and 20. Notice that on each curve a small circle appears at the point at which the band corresponds to $\Delta f + 2f_m$ on either side of the carrier, and that most of the area under the curves appears to the left of this point. Whatever the value of m_f, it appears that for the sinusoidal modulation it is also true that the total bandwidth required to pass an FM signal is very nearly

$$\text{bw} = 2\Delta f + 4f_m \tag{9.53}$$

which is exactly the same as Eq. (9.29). We are now in a position to state that this relation is a reasonable limit for the bandwidth of an FM signal.

It must be made clear again, however, that the curves in Fig. 9.29 are not power-density curves, but merely envelopes of the line spectra. For example, when $m_f = 20$, then the spectrum will consist of a line at $h = 0$, and lines at $h = 0.05, 0.10, 0.15, \ldots 0.95, 1.00, 1.05, 1.10, 1.15, \ldots$. Beyond 1.10 the lines almost vanish. Recall too, that this is just the upper half of the positive-frequency portion of the spectrum.

There is a symmetric lower sideband as well as another pair of sidebands centered at $f = -f_c$.

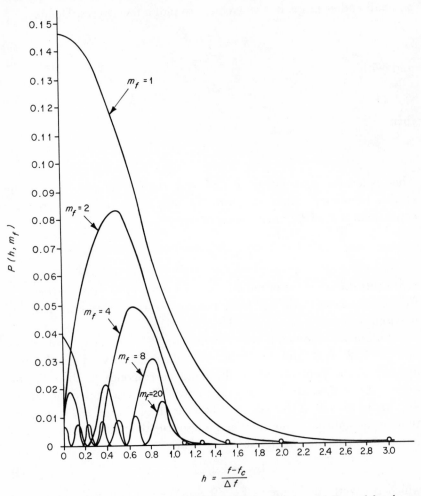

$$h = \frac{f - f_c}{\Delta f}$$

Fig. 9.29 $P(h, m_f)$, *the envelope of the line spectrum of a sinusoidally modulated wave as a function of percent frequency deviation h and modulation index m_f. For any m_f, the kth line occurs when $h = k/m_f$.*

Table 9.1 lists some values for the Bessel functions of the first kind.* Two examples using this table will now be given.

---

* For a more complete list, with a greater number of significant figures, see Jahnke and Emde(9).

EXAMPLE 9.1. Given

$$s(t) = 10 \cos (200\pi t + 20 \sin 2\pi t)$$

Table 9.1

Values of $J_k (m_f)$ for Certain Values of k and m_f

k	$J_k(1)$	$J_k(2)$	$J_k(4)$	$J_k(8)$	$J_k(12)$	$J_k(16)$	$J_k(20)$	$J_k(24)$	k
0	0.765	0.224	−0.397	0.172	0.048	−0.175	0.167	−0.056	0
1	0.440	0.577	−0.066	0.235	−0.223	0.090	0.067	−0.154	1
2	0.115	0.353	0.364	−0.113	−0.085	0.186	−0.160	0.043	2
3	0.020	0.129	0.430	−0.291	0.195	−0.044	−0.099	0.161	3
4	0.002	0.034	0.281	−0.105	0.183	−0.203	0.131	−0.003	4
5		0.007	0.132	0.186	−0.073	−0.057	0.151	−0.162	5
6		0.001	0.049	0.338	−0.244	0.167	−0.055	−0.065	6
7			0.015	0.321	−0.170	0.183	−0.184	0.130	7
8			0.004	0.224	0.045	−0.007	−0.074	0.140	8
9			0.001	0.126	0.230	−0.190	0.125	−0.036	9
10				0.061	0.301	−0.206	0.187	−0.168	10
11				0.026	0.270	−0.068	0.061	−0.103	11
12				0.010	0.195	0.112	−0.119	0.073	12
13				0.003	0.120	0.237	−0.204	0.176	13
14				0.001	0.065	0.272	−0.146	0.118	14
15					0.032	0.240	−0.001	−0.039	15
16					0.014	0.178	0.145	−0.166	16
17					0.006	0.115	0.233	−0.183	17
18					0.002	0.067	0.251	−0.093	18
19					0.001	0.035	0.219	0.043	19
20						0.017	0.165	0.162	20
21						0.008	0.111	0.226	21
22						0.003	0.068	0.234	22
23						0.001	0.038	0.203	23
24							0.020	0.155	24
25							0.010	0.107	25
26							0.005	0.068	26
27							0.002	0.040	27
28							0.001	0.022	28
29								0.011	29
30								0.006	30
31								0.003	31
32								0.001	32

Plot the line power spectrum of the function for positive frequencies. If $s(t)$ represents an FM wave, what is $s_m(t)$? If $s(t)$ represents a PM wave, what is $s_m(t)$?

Solution: The maximum angle deviation is clearly 20 radians, and so $m_f = 20$. Then the magnitude of the sidebands would be $J_k^2(20)/4$ if the amplitude were unity. Since the amplitude is 10, however, then each sideband will be multiplied by $10^2 = 100$. Table 9.2 lists the calculations, and the line spectrum appears in Fig. 9.30.

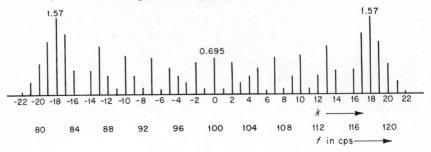

Fig. 9.30   *The line spectrum of* $s(t)$.

Table 9.2

k	$J_k(20)$	$J_k^2(20)$	$25J_k^2(20)$
0	0.167	2.78 × 10⁻²	0.695
1	0.067	0.445 ,,	0.111
2	−0.160	2.57 ,,	0.643
3	−0.099	0.973 ,,	0.243
4	0.131	1.70 ,,	0.425
5	0.151	2.28 ,,	0.570
6	−0.055	0.302 ,,	0.076
7	−0.184	3.38 ,,	0.845
8	−0.074	0.542 ,,	0.136
9	0.125	1.56 ,,	0.390
10	0.187	3.46 ,,	0.865
11	0.061	0.375 ,,	0.094
12	−0.119	1.41 ,,	0.353
13	−0.204	4.15 ,,	1.038
14	−0.146	2.14 ,,	0.535
15	−0.001	0.000 ,,	0.000
16	0.145	2.10 ,,	0.525
17	0.233	5.41 ,,	1.353
18	0.251	6.28 ,,	1.570
19	0.219	4.76 ,,	1.190
20	0.165	2.70 ,,	0.675
21	0.111	1.21 ,,	0.303
22	0.068	0.455 ,,	0.114

Since $\Delta f = 20$ cps, and $f_m = 1$ cps, the spectrum was carried out only to $20 + 2 = 22$ cps on either side of the carrier. The total power in a 10-volt sinusoidal wave is $10^2/2 = 50$ watts on a one-ohm level. Then the positive portion should add up to 25 watts. The sum of the line lengths of the positive portion can be obtained by adding all but the first number in the last column of Table 9.2. This is the sum of the upper sideband only. The lower portion will have the same sum. The carrier power is 0.695 watt, and so the total is twice the sum of the numbers excluding 0.695, plus 0.695. The sum is 12.054, and so the total of all 25 lines is $2 \times 12.054 + 0.695 = 24.803$. Then there must be about 0.2 watt in the lines omitted, or 0.8 per cent.

If $s(t)$ is an FM wave, then $s_m(t)$ is simply the derivative of 20 sin $2\pi t$; that is,

$$s_m(t)_{\mathrm{FM}} = 40\pi \cos 2\pi t$$

If $s(t)$ is a PM wave, then $s_m(t)$ is simply

$$s_m(t)_{\mathrm{PM}} = 20 \sin 2\pi t$$

Strictly speaking, both of these $s_m(t)$ terms should have unity coefficients since the text has been normalizing the modulating signals to unity.

EXAMPLE 9.2. A student, not realizing that the FM band extends beyond Δf, attempts to demodulate the following signal by using a band-pass filter that passes everything between 99 and 101 cps, and eliminates everything below 98.5 and above 101.5 cps:

$$s(t) = \cos (200\pi t + \sin 2\pi t)$$

He runs into some trouble, and looks at the output of his filter on an oscilloscope. He observes some AM on the wave, which puzzles him greatly. Not knowing the source of the AM, and realizing it does not belong there, he puts the output of his filter into a *limiter*, which has the effect of chopping off the top and bottom of the wave and hence removing the AM. He then puts the wave into a discriminator to demodulate it. He should get a signal proportional to $\cos 2\pi t$, the derivative of $\sin 2\pi t$. What does he get, and what did the AM look like? *Solution:* The maximum angle deviation is 1 rad, so $m_f = 1$. From Table 9.1, $J_k(1)$ has only three sidebands or values of importance: $J_k(1) = 0.765$, 0.440, and 0.115. Evidently he chopped off the second line away from the carrier.

It is convenient to write the signal as a Fourier cosine series for this problem. From Eq. (9.43)

$$s(t) \doteq \frac{1}{2} [0.765 \, e^{j200\pi t} + 0.440 \, e^{j202\pi t} - 0.440 \, e^{j198\pi t}$$
$$+ 0.115 \, e^{j204\pi t} + 0.115 \, e^{j196\pi t} \text{ plus conjugates}]$$

Observe that the odd harmonics change sign at frequencies less than the carrier frequency. Then $s(t)$ can be written as

$$s(t) \doteq 0.765 \cos 200\pi t + 0.44 \cos 202\pi t - 0.44 \cos 198\pi t$$
$$+ 0.115 \cos 204\pi t + 0.115 \cos 196\pi t$$

Since he cut off the last two terms, the output of his filter must be

$$s_0(t) = 0.765 \, (\cos 200\pi t + 0.575 \cos 202\pi t - 0.575 \cos 198\pi t)$$
$$= 0.765 \, (\cos 200\pi t - 1.15 \sin 2\pi t \sin 200\pi t)$$

where the last two terms were combined by using the cosine of the sum and difference of two angles, the two angles being $200\pi t$ and $2\pi t$ in both cases.

If the last result is multiplied and divided by

$$\sqrt{1^2 + (1.15 \sin 2\pi t)^2}$$

then, with

$$\cos \phi = \frac{1}{\sqrt{1 + 1.32 \sin^2 2\pi t}} \qquad \sin \phi = \frac{1.15 \sin 2\pi t}{\sqrt{1 + 1.32 \sin^2 2\pi t}}$$

the expression for s_0 may be written

$$s_0(t) = 0.765 \sqrt{1 + 1.32 \sin^2 2\pi t} \, (\cos \phi \cos 200\pi t - \sin \phi \sin 200\pi t)$$
$$= 0.765 \sqrt{1 + 1.32 \sin^2 2\pi t} \, [\cos (200\pi t + \phi)]$$

Then the AM must be the coefficient of the cosine, or

$$s_{AM}(t) = 0.765 \sqrt{1 + 1.32 \sin^2 2\pi t}$$

This wave appears in Fig. 9.31.

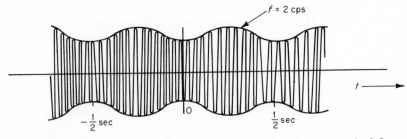

Fig. 9.31 *The AM signal seen on the oscilloscope of Example 9.2.*

The discriminator is an **FM** detector, and thus the output of the discriminator will be $d\phi/dt$ after the signal has had the AM removed. From the definitions of $\cos\phi$ and $\sin\phi$ it is clear that $\tan\phi = 1.15\sin 2\pi t$ and so $\phi = \tan^{-1}(1.15\sin 2\pi t)$. If this is differentiated with respect to t, then

$$\frac{d\phi}{dt} = \frac{2\pi \times 1.15 \cos 2\pi t}{1 + 1.32 \sin^2 2\pi t}$$

The output of the discriminator will be proportional to this last expression, as plotted in Fig. 9.32. The dashed curve is $\cos 2\pi t$.

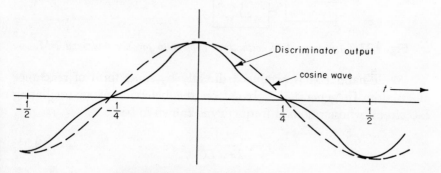

Fig. 9.32   *The discriminator output.*

PRODUCTION OF FM

The first successful system of frequency modulation was developed by E. H. Armstrong,* who produced narrow-band FM by devising a system based on the approximation used in Eq. (9.27), which is repeated here for convenience:

$$\cos[2\pi f_c t + \theta(t)] \doteq \cos 2\pi f_c t - \theta(t) \sin 2\pi f_c t \qquad (9.27)$$

Since $\theta(t)$ is the integral of the modulating signal, $s_m(t)$ was first put into an integrating network and then applied to a balanced modulator to produce the AM-SC term $\theta(t) \sin 2\pi f_c t$. Then the carrier was shifted 90° in phase and added to the output of the balanced modulator to produce Eq. (9.27), which represents narrow-band FM. To convert to wide-band FM, the resulting signal was fed into one or more harmonic generators, which have the effect of multiplying the instantaneous

*E. H. Armstrong, "A Method of Reducing Disturbances in Radio Signaling by a System of Frequency Modulation," *Proc. I.R.E.*, Vol. 24 (May, 1936), p. 689.

frequency by an integer (see Prob. 7.32). Three cascaded triplers, for example, would multiply the carrier frequency and the frequency deviation by 27. If m_f was originally $\frac{1}{4}$, then after three stages of tripling it would become $2\frac{7}{4}$, which is well within the range of what is called wide-band FM. The Armstrong system appears in block diagram form in Fig. 9.33.

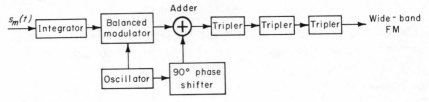

Fig. 9.33 *Armstrong FM with three triplers to produce wideband FM.*

Wide-band FM is produced directly by some form of reactance modulator. In general it is based on the behavior of an oscillating L-C circuit whose resonant frequency is known to be

$$f = \frac{1}{2\pi\sqrt{LC}} \tag{9.54}$$

If either L or C can be made to vary with time according to the dictates of a modulating signal, then intuition tells us that FM will be produced. In particular, suppose that C is given by

$$C = C_0 + ks_m(t) \tag{9.55}$$

where the maximum value of $ks_m(t)$ is presumed to be small compared to C_0. Then, substitution of Eq. (9.55) in Eq. (9.54) yields

$$f = \frac{1}{2\pi\sqrt{LC_0[1+ks_m(t)/C_0]}} \tag{9.56}$$

Now if we define

$$f = \frac{1}{2\pi\sqrt{LC_0}} \tag{9.57}$$

as the carrier frequency, then Eq. (9.56) can be written as

$$f = f_c\,[1+ks_m(t)/C_0]^{-\frac{1}{2}} \tag{9.58}$$

Since ks_m is assumed to be small compared to C_0, the radical may be expanded by the binomial theorem, with only the first-degree term in $ks_m(t)$ retained:

$$f = f_c\left[1-\frac{ks_m(t)}{2C_0}\right] \tag{9.59}$$

This expression indicates that the frequency deviation from the carrier is proportional to the modulating signal $s_m(t)$.

The actual manner in which the capacitance is altered with time is an interesting study in itself. One technique for achieving this change involves the use of a reactance-tube modulator.

In the reactance-tube modulator a tube is not really necessary. Any device having a small-signal equivalent circuit that is approximately a current source whose output current varies as some nonlinear function of the applied signal will do. We shall choose a vacuum tube of the "variable g_m" type. It is not necessary to be trained in electronics to understand what follows. Suffice it to say that the small-signal equivalent circuit of the reactance tube is a current source whose output current depends on the grid voltage of the tube. The equivalent circuit appears in Fig. 9.34(a) and the current source i_s is given by

$$i_s = g_{mo}e_g(t) + g_m e_g^2(t) \qquad (9.60)$$

plus negligible terms of higher order.

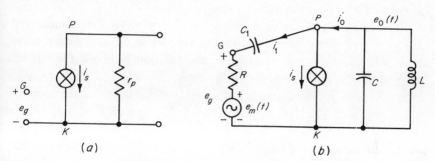

Fig. 9.34 (a) *The equivalent circuit of the reactance tube.* (b) *The equivalent circuit of the reactance-tube modulator with its oscillator.*

Figure 9.34(b) shows the equivalent circuit of such a tube when it is connected to perform as a reactance-tube modulator. The resistance r_p in Fig. 9.34(a) is missing, since it appears in parallel with the L-C tank circuit. In the figure this circuit is presumed to be lossless, inasmuch as it is really an equivalent circuit for an oscillator. Losses that are attributable to r_p and the resistance of the actual coil used are taken care of by an oscillator tube, which is not shown in the figure. Problem 5.61 describes such an oscillator.

Notice in Fig. 9.34(b) that the plate of the reactance-tube (point P) is connected to the grid (point G) by a capacitance C_1. To proceed with the analysis the following assumptions are made:

1. The product RC_1 is very much smaller than the reciprocal of the carrier frequency; that is,

$$RC_1 \leq \frac{1}{20\pi f_c} \tag{9.61}$$

2. The impedance of the tank circuit to signals having frequencies that differ markedly from the carrier frequency is substantially zero. In particular, although $i_0(t)$ may contain frequencies both in the audio range and twice the carrier frequency, the output voltage $e_0(t)$ will have only frequencies at or near f_c.

The source $e_m(t)$ is the modulating signal, and is assumed to have a spectrum in the audio or video range. Then the voltage e_g will have a spectrum that will contain both audio- and carrier-frequency components. Suppose we let

$$e_g(t) = e_{gc} + e_{gm} \tag{9.62}$$

where e_{gc} is the portion of e_g that contains only frequencies near the carrier and e_{gm} has an audio or video spectrum.

The objective of the following analysis is to show that the current $i_0(t)$ has frequency components in the vicinity of f_c, and hence these alone will affect $e_0(t)$. Furthermore, the relation between the carrier component of i_0 and e_0 is to be of the type

$$i_0 = C(t)\frac{de_0(t)}{dt}$$

where $C(t)$ varies as the modulating signal $e_m(t)$. This then will provide the varying capacitance required to produce FM.

From the circuit we note that

$$\frac{e_g - e_m}{R} = C_1\frac{d(e_0 - e_g)}{dt}$$

or, by rearranging terms

$$RC_1\frac{de_g}{dt} + e_g = RC_1\frac{de_0}{dt} + e_m \tag{9.63}$$

If we take the Fourier transform of this equation the coefficient of the transform of e_g, $E_g(f)$, will be $j2\pi fRC + 1$, and by assumption 1 the first term is negligibly small. Then the Eq. (9.63) can be written as

$$e_g \doteq RC_1\frac{de_0(t)}{dt} + e_m \tag{9.64}$$

Equating this to the right-hand side of Eq. (9.62) yields the two results

$$e_{gm} = e_m \tag{9.65a}$$

$$e_{gc} = RC_1 \frac{de_0(t)}{dt} \tag{9.65b}$$

We shall be interested in knowing the carrier component of the current i_0, because only this component can affect the output voltage e_0 according to assumption 2. The carrier component of i_0 consists of the carrier component of i_1 and the carrier component of i_s. The carrier component of i_1 is

$$i_{1c} = C_1 \frac{d}{dt}(e_0 - e_{gc}) \doteq C_1 \frac{de_0}{dt} \tag{9.66}$$

again using the assumption 1 and Eq. (9.65b).

With this tube i_s is given by Eq. (9.60), so

$$i_s = g_{mo}(e_{gc} + e_m) + g'_m(e_{gc} + e_m)^2 \tag{9.67}$$

where Eq. (9.62) and Eq. (9.65a) have been used. Expanding Eq. (9.67) gives

$$i_s = g_{mo}e_{gc} + g_{mo}e_m + g'_m(e_{gc}^2 + 2e_m e_{gc} + e_m^2) \tag{9.68}$$

Only the carrier components of the last equation are desired, and thus the $g_{mo}e_m$ term and the $g'_m e_m^2$ terms may be dropped, inasmuch as they contain only low-frequency components. The e_{gc}^2 term may be dropped because it will have frequency components near zero and $2f_c$. If this is not apparent, think about the spectrum of

$$s_m^2 \cos^2 2\pi f_c t = s_m^2 \left(\frac{1 + \cos 4\pi f_c t}{2}\right)$$

Then i_{sc}, the carrier component of i_s, is

$$i_{sc} = g_{mo}e_{gc} + 2g'_m e_m e_{gc} = (g_{mo} + 2g'_m e_m)e_{gc} \tag{9.69}$$

If the e_{gc} is replaced by Eq. (9.65b), then

$$i_{sc} = (g_{mo} + 2g'_m e_m)RC_1 \frac{de_0}{dt} \tag{9.70}$$

Adding this to Eq. (9.66) will yield the total carrier component of the current i_0:

$$i_{0c} = C_1 \left[(1 + g_{mo}R) + 2g'_m Re_m\right] \frac{de_0}{dt} \tag{9.71}$$

But this is the volt-ampere relation of a capacitance $C(t)$, whose value is

$$C(t) = C_1 \left[(1 + g_{mo} R) + 2g'_m Re_m \right] \text{ farads} \qquad (9.72)$$

Then the entire circuit to the left of the L-C tank circuit is nothing but a time-varying capacitance. The total capacitance of the entire circuit is simply

$$C_t = C + C_1 (1 + g_{mo} R) + 2 C_1 g'_m Re_m \qquad (9.73)$$

When $e_m = 0$, the situation for zero modulation, then define

$$C_0 = C + C_1 (1 + g_{mo} R) \qquad (9.74)$$

and

$$k = 2 C_1 g'_m R \qquad (9.75)$$

Then Eq. (9.73) can be written as

$$C_t = C_0 + ke_m \qquad (9.76)$$

which is identical to Eq. (9.55) with $e_m = s_m(t)$.

From Eq. (9.59) the frequency deviation can be seen to be

$$f_i - f_c = \frac{f_c k e_m}{2C_0}$$

$$= \frac{f_c R C_1 g'_m}{C_0} e_m \qquad (9.77)$$

It is possible to produce large frequency deviations with these circuits, given a good square-law device, hence it is not always necessary to employ harmonic generators when reactance-tube modulators are used.

DETECTION OF FM

Since the general expression for a frequency-modulated carrier is

$$s(t) = \cos \left[2\pi f_c t + \theta(t) \right]$$

differentiating both sides yields

$$\frac{ds(t)}{dt} = - \left(2\pi f_c + \frac{d\theta(t)}{dt} \right) \sin \left[2\pi f_c t + \theta(t) \right] \qquad (9.78)$$

But the last expression is in the form of an ordinary AM wave whose carrier happens to be frequency modulated. Since

$$\frac{d\theta(t)}{dt} = 2\pi \Delta f s_m(t)$$

from Eq. (9.24),

$$\frac{ds(t)}{dt} = -2\pi \left[f_c + \Delta f s_m(t)\right] \sin \left[2\pi f_c t + \theta(t)\right] \tag{9.79}$$

and since $f_c > \Delta f$, it is seen to be ordinary AM. Detection can then be accomplished by an envelope detector.

Observe that differentiating with respect to t is equivalent to multiplication by f in the frequency domain. Actually any device whose transfer function is linear in the region of the carrier will perform the differentiation. Various refinements of this general technique have evolved, but these belong to a study of electronics. (See Prob. 9.24 and 9.25.)

PROBLEMS

9.17. By using the ideas and technique presented in the intuitive approach to FM, sketch the shape of the power-density spectra of a frequency-modulated carrier when the modulating signals are those appearing in Fig. 9.35(a), (b), and (c). These will be accurate if the frequency deviation is large compared to the frequency of the waves. Assume that $s_m(t)_{\max}$ yields a frequency deviation of Δf cps.

9.18. Using Table 9.1, draw the positive-frequency portion of the line power spectrum of

$$s(t) = 100 \cos (2\pi 10^7 t + m_f \sin 2\pi 10^4 t)$$

when

(a) $m_f = 1$
(b) $m_f = 2$
(c) $\Delta f = 40$ kc
(d) $\Delta f = 80$ kc
(e) Find Δf for (a) and (b) and m_f for (c) and (d). Is $s(t)$ a PM wave or an FM wave?

9.19. The signal $s_m(t)$ in Fig. 9.36 is phase modulated and the output is
$$s(t) = A \cos \left[6.73 \times 10^7 t + b s_m(t)\right]$$

(a) What is the smallest bandwidth the phase-modulated signal can have assuming that b, but nothing else, can be altered at will $[b \neq 0$ of course!] and $s_m(t)$ is a 1-kc sinusoid.

(b) If $s_m(t) = \sin 377t$ and $b = 1000$, what is the maximum instantaneous frequency deviation? What is the carrier frequency? What is the bandwidth occupied by the signal?

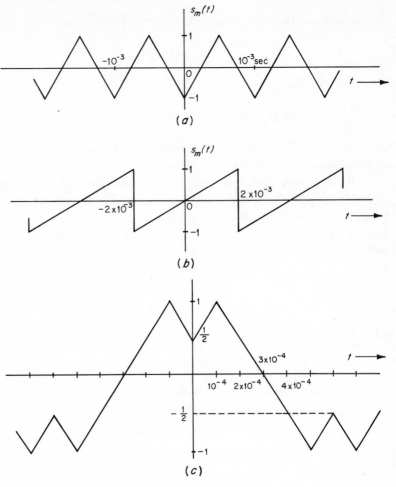

Fig. 9.35   *Problem 9.17.*

9.20. You are asked to design a reactance-tube modulator so that a one-volt (peak) signal will produce a frequency deviation of 50 kc at 10 mc. You are given a tube for which $g_{mo} = 10^{-3}$ mho and $g'_m = 0.3 \times 10^{-3}$ mho/volt. In addition you are required to use no capacitances smaller than 10 pf ($10^{-11}f$) and a coil whose inductance does not exceed 100 mh (0.1 h).

Fig. 9.36   *Problem 9.19.*

(a) The internal impedance of the signal generator is 600 ohms, so you decide to set $R = 600$ and $C_1 = 10$ pf. What limit does this place on f_c if assumption 1, inequality (9.61), is to be satisfied?

(b) In order to use the binomial theorem to arrive at Eq. (9.59), then the variable portion of C should be ten per cent of C_0, or smaller. What then is the smallest C_0 can be?

Answer: 36 pf

(c) With this choice of C_0 and the largest possible value of L, what is the minimum value the carrier frequency may have?

(d) Choose a carrier frequency between the limits obtained in the answers to (a) and (c) so that two cascaded doublers will produce both the desired carrier frequency of 10 mc and the desired deviation of 50 kc. What must L and C_0 be for this?

Answer: $L = 11.2$ μh

(e) Instead of solution (d), choose C_0 as the minimum value obtained in (b) and choose a carrier frequency to give a 50-kc deviation. What value of L is now required? Specify a frequency with which the resulting signal may be mixed to raise the carrier to 10 mc. What filters (if any) are required after mixing?

9.21. A reactance-tube modulator produces a signal
$$s(t) = 50 \cos \left[\pi \times 10^8 t + 4 \cos (2\pi \times 10^5 t) \right]$$

(a) Using Table 9.1, plot the line spectrum of $s(t)$ versus f (positive frequencies only).

(b) If $s(t)$ represents a phase-modulated signal, $s_m(t)_{PM}$, what is this signal? Normalize its amplitude.

(c) If $s(t)$ represents a frequency-modulated signal, $s_m(t)_{FM}$, what is this signal? Normalize its amplitude.

(d) What are the maximum frequency and angle deviations, and what is m_f?

(e) What percentage of the power is contained in the two bands centered on $\pm f_c$ and $2\Delta f$ wide?

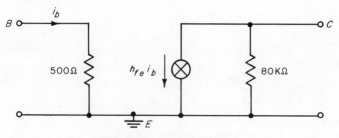

Fig. 9.37 *Problem 9.22.*

9.22. The equivalent circuit for a certain grounded emitter transistor appears in Fig. 9.37, where B, E, and C are the base, emitter, and collector terminals respectively. What must h_{fe} be in order to use this device in a reactance-transistor modulator? What circuit would produce the desired result, assuming, of course, that h_{fe} has the appropriate functional relation?

9.23. The Federal Communications Commission has decreed that the maximum frequency deviation for FM stations will be 75 kc.

   (a) If the maximum and minimum modulation frequencies it is desired to transmit are 15 kc and 20 cps, then what range will m_f have?

   (b) What bandwidth will this require?

   (c) If AM-SSB with vestigial carrier were used instead of FM for the same signals as in (a), what bandwidth would be required? What is the ratio of the FM bandwidth to the AM-SSB bandwidth?

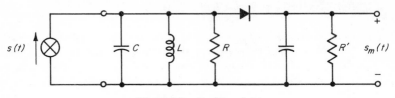

Fig. 9.38 *Problem 9.24.*

9.24. An *L-C* tank circuit and an envelope detector are to be used to detect an FM signal. The circuit appears in Fig. 9.38. The magnitude of the frequency response of the tank circuit is known to be

$$\left|\frac{V_0}{I}\right| = |H(j2\pi f)| = \frac{R}{\sqrt{1+Q_0^2\,(f/f_0-f_0/f)^2}}$$

(see Example 5.17 in Sec. 5.4 and Prob. 4.31) where

$$Q_0 = R\sqrt{\frac{C}{L}}$$

and

$$f_0 = \frac{1}{2\pi\sqrt{LC}}$$

It is assumed here that the envelope detector draws negligible current. Assume also, for simplicity, that $f \approx f_0$, and thus

$$\frac{f}{f_0} - \frac{f_0}{f} = \frac{f^2-f_0^2}{f_0 f} = \frac{(f+f_0)\,(f-f_0)}{f_0 f} \doteq 2\frac{f-f_0}{f_0},$$

where f_0 is used for f in every term except the difference term.

   (a) Show that the maximum *slope* of the transfer function occurs when $f - f_0 = \pm f_0/(2\sqrt{2}Q_0)$, and that this maximum slope is $4RQ_0/(\sqrt{27}f_0)$.

   (b) If the carrier of an FM wave, $s(t)$, is set so that

$$f_c = f_0\left(1 - \frac{1}{2\sqrt{2}\,Q_0}\right)$$

and with representative values of $Q_0 = 50$, $f_0 = 10$ mc, and $R = 100$ k, then plot the amplitude of the ratio of the magnitude of the output voltage to the input current for $f - f_c = 70.71$ kc; 35.36 kc; 0; -35.36 kc; -70.71 kc. Use 0.7071 for $1/\sqrt{2}$. How linear is this detector? What could you do to extend its range of linearity to ± 75 kc?

9.25. Most discriminators (a special name for a certain class of FM detectors) operate on a very simple principle. The algebra required to demonstrate their operation is, however, extremely tedious. The principle can be demonstrated by placing two circuits just like that of the previous problem back to back, as shown in Fig. 9.39. The top circuit is tuned to a frequency f_1, and the bottom circuit to f_2. These frequencies are so chosen that $f_1 > f_2$ and the carrier frequency is at $(f_1+f_2)/2$.

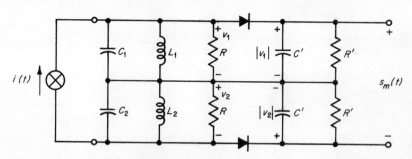

Fig. 9.39 *Problem 9.25.*

The values of Q_0 and R of the two circuits are identical, so the magnitudes of V_1/I and V_2/I are

$$\left|\frac{V_1}{I}\right| = \frac{R}{\sqrt{1+4Q_0^2\,(f-f_1)^2/f_1^2}}$$

and

$$\left|\frac{V_2}{I}\right| = \frac{R}{\sqrt{1+4Q_0^2\,(f-f_2)^2/f_2^2}}$$

where the same approximation has been made that was made previously. If f_1 and f_2 are practically equal, then $Q_0^2/f_1^2 \doteq Q_0^2/f_c^2 \doteq Q_0^2/f_2^2$, where $f_c = (f_1+f_2)/2$ is the carrier frequency.

Notice that the envelope detectors are so placed that the output voltage, labeled $s_m(t)$ in Fig. 9.39, is $|V_1| - |V_2|$ since the diodes conduct only when current exists in them in the direction of the arrow. Then the magnitude of the output will be

$$\frac{|V_1| - |V_2|}{|I|} = \frac{R}{\sqrt{1+4Q_0^2\,(f-f_1)^2/f_c^2}} - \frac{R}{\sqrt{1+4Q_0^2\,(f-f_2)^2/f_c^2}}$$

Clearly the output will be zero when $f = f_c$, since $(f_c-f_1)^2 = (f_c-f_2)^2$.

If f_c is chosen when each term is $R/2$, it will be seen that a very linear characteristic is obtained. For this situation

$$\frac{4Q_0^2 (f_c - f_1)^2}{f_c^2} = \frac{4Q_0^2 (f_c - f_2)^2}{f_c^2} = 3$$

In Fig. 9.40, notice how the frequency responses of the two networks are offset just enough to make their difference as linear as possible.

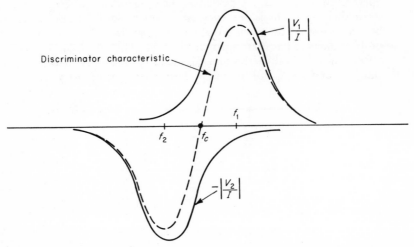

Fig. 9.40   *The two amplitude characteristics of Prob. 9.25 plotted so that the stagger tuning is made evident. The dashed line indicates the difference of the two curves, that is the discriminator characteristic.*

(a)   Write out the required relations between f_1 and f_c and f_2 and f_c.

(b)   Set $f = f_c(1 + \delta)$, where δ will be the percent deviation from the carrier frequency, and hence it will be small. Show that the output expression above can be written as

$$\frac{|V_1| - |V_2|}{|I|} = \frac{R}{\sqrt{1 + (2Q_0\delta - \sqrt{3})^2}} - \frac{R}{\sqrt{1 + (2Q_0\delta + \sqrt{3})^2}}$$

(c)   Choose values of $2Q_0\delta$ from -3 to $+3$ and plot carefully the characteristic of this discriminator. If $Q_0 = 50$ and $R = 100$ K, as in the previous problem, how do the linearity and maximum deviation compare with the results of Prob. 9.24 for a 10-mc carrier?

Note: The circuit above leads to a rather simple explanation of discriminators, but does not lead to the simplest circuit. The *balanced discriminator* has identical characteristics and the stagger tuning is achieved by using inductively coupled parallel tuned circuits.

9.26. When the reflector voltage of a klystron or the anode voltage of a voltage-tunable magnetron (VTM) are varied, the frequency of these oscillators changes almost linearly with voltage. Then these devices are ideal for high-frequency FM generators (1 to 25 gc).

The *tuning rate* of such devices is defined as the change in frequency in megacycles per volt change of reflector or anode voltage. A convenient method of measuring this tuning rate is to apply a sinusoidal modulating voltage to the tube and to observe the spectrum of the output signal on a spectrum analyzer. As the modulating voltage is gradually increased from zero, two sidebands and the carrier appear (narrow-band FM), then two more pips—one on either side—appear. As the amplitude of the modulating signal is still further increased the carrier pip decreases, until at one point it disappears.

(a) What is the m_f at the point where the carrier disappears? You may approximate this by interpolating Table 9.1. It would be more accurate to look up the number in Jahnke and Emde (9).

(b) What is the tuning rate in megacycles per volt of the device (klystron or VTM) if the modulating frequency is 10 kc and the rms a-c modulating voltage is 10 mv at the point at which carrier pip disappears.

9.2 Filters

The sections concerned with modulation depended heavily on the fact that unwanted sidebands or portions of a spectrum could be filtered out. The Fourier transform is used not to design filters but rather to establish criteria for them. It will tell us what is possible and what is not possible, and explain some characteristics of practical filters.

A *physically realizable filter* is one whose impulse response is necessarily zero for t less than zero.* This is fairly obvious, for it is certainly not possible for a physical device to anticipate the fact that an impulse is about to strike it and hence produce an output before the arrival of the input.

In the frequency domain it is not as easy to specify criteria for physical realizability. For example, if $h(t)$ is the impulse response of a realizable filter, then $h(t) = 0$ for $t < 0$. Its transform $H(f)$, on the other hand, can be expressed in two ways:

$$H(f) = R(f) + jI(f) \tag{9.80}$$

and

$$H(f) = |H(f)| \, e^{j\theta(f)} \tag{9.81}$$

---

*It should not be inferred that *any* function, $h(t)$, that is zero for $t < 0$ can be the impulse response of an R-L-C network. Some can be realized with transmission lines, others can be only approximated arbitrarily closely. A system, realizable or not, is referred to as being *causal* if its impulse response vanishes for $t < 0$.

In filter theory it is Eq. (9.81) that interests the engineer. For example, a bandpass filter should have a constant magnitude over the passband and a magnitude of zero outside the band. Hence it is the magnitude of the transfer function that concerns us. The phase function, $\theta(f)$, has an extremely simple standard. This can be deduced as follows:

Suppose a band-limited signal with frequency components in the interval $|f| < f_c$ is put through a filter whose magnitude is constant over this frequency range, but can be anything at all at other frequencies. Let the transform of this band-limited signal be $S(f)$, and the magnitude of the transfer function be A. Then the transform of the output signal will be simply

$$S_0(f) = AS(f)e^{j\theta(f)}$$

But if the device is to reproduce the signal without distortion of waveshape, the ideal in filtering, then $S_0(f)$ should be proportional to $S(f)$ This means that $\theta(f) = 0$. However, $\theta(f) = -j2\pi ft_0$ would not be objectionable, since

$$S_0(f) = AS(f)e^{-j2\pi ft_0}$$

has an inverse transform which is simply the input signal changed in amplitude by the factor A and *delayed* t_0 sec. Then, assuming a time delay of t_0 sec is not objectionable, the criterion for distortionless filtering is a phase function that is *linear* with frequency (*not* constant phase shift!).

The ideal bandpass filter then has the following properties:

1. The magnitude of the transfer function is a constant in the passband, and zero otherwise.

2. The phase function, $\theta(f)$, must be a linear function of frequency in the passband with negative slope of $-2\pi t_0$, where t_0 is the delay time.

As with all ideals, the ideal filter is unattainable. It turns out, however, that the ideal can be approached arbitrarily closely if one is willing to increase the delay time t_0.

The criterion that the amplitude of the transfer function must meet to insure that the impulse response will be zero for negative t is called the *Paley-Wiener condition*. This criterion states that $|H(f)|$ *may* be the magnitude of the Fourier transform of a function which is zero for t less than some time t_1 if, and only if, the integral

$$\int_{-\infty}^{\infty} \frac{\ln|H(f)|}{1+f^2}\, df \tag{9.82}$$

converges—that is, if it is less than infinity.

If the integral converges, there exists a phase function, not necessarily linear, that can be associated with $|H(f)|$ so that its inverse transform is zero for negative t.

Expression (9.82) is not quite so hopeless as it looks. For example, we may conclude that $H(f)$ cannot be zero over any finite range of frequencies; if it were, $\ln |H(f)| = -\infty$ in this interval and the integral over this finite range alone would explode. Therefore, no ideal filter is possible. Yet the integral (9.82) does not exclude the possibility that $H(f)$ could be very small in magnitude.

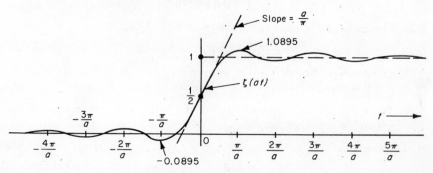

Fig. 9.41 $\zeta(at)$ *versus* t.

In spite of the fact that we know in advance that an ideal low-pass filter is unrealizable, we proceed to find its impulse response with the hope that it may tell us how we can achieve a nearly ideal filter. Before doing this, however, it will be convenient to define a function $\zeta(t)$, which will appear several times in the next section:

$$\zeta(t) = \frac{1}{\pi} \int_{-\infty}^{t} \frac{\sin y}{y}\, dy \tag{9.83}$$

The integral cannot be evaluated in closed form, but a similar integral, called the *sine integral*, Si(t), has been tabulated and appears, for example, in Jahnke and Emde (9). Si(t) is defined as

$$\text{Si}(t) = \int_{0}^{t} \frac{\sin y}{y}\, dy \tag{9.84}$$

and is related to the function $\zeta(t)$ by

$$\zeta(t) = \frac{1}{2} + \frac{1}{\pi}\, \text{Si}(t) \tag{9.85}$$

If t is replaced by at and y by ay in Eq. (9.83), we have

$$\zeta(at) = \frac{1}{\pi} \int_{-\infty}^{t} \frac{\sin (ay)}{y} \, dy \tag{9.86}$$

Figure 9.41 shows $\zeta(at)$ as a function of t. Observe that its slope at $t = 0$ is a/π.

PROBLEMS

9.27. Use Eqs. (9.83) and (9.84) to obtain Eq. (9.85).

9.28. Obtain Eq. (9.86) from Eq. (9.83).

9.29. Differentiate Eq. (9.86) with respect to t and show that the slope at $t = 0$ is a/π.

9.30. Prove that the maxima and minima of $\zeta(at)$ occur at $t = \pm k\pi/a$, where k is an integer other than zero.

9.31. Show that

$$\frac{1}{\pi} \int_{c}^{t} \frac{\sin (ay)}{y} \, dy = \zeta(at) - \zeta(ac)$$

9.32. Use Expression (9.82), the Paley-Wiener condition, to prove that a time-limited signal cannot have a Fourier transform that is band-limited.

9.33. Since the Fourier transform and its inverse are symmetrical, then the criterion for a band-limited transform must be

$$\int_{-\infty}^{\infty} \frac{\ln |f(t)|}{1+t^2} \, dt < \infty$$

Show that this implies that a band-limited signal must exist for all t.

The Ideal Low-Pass Filter

The transfer function of the ideal low-pass filter is

$$H(f) = A \left[\mathbf{1}(f+f_c) - \mathbf{1}(f-f_c) \right] e^{-j2\pi f t_0} \tag{9.87}$$

where f_c will be the *cut off* frequency and t_0 the (positive) delay time. The inverse transform of this is the impulse response:

$$h(t) = \frac{A}{\pi} \frac{\sin \left[2\pi f_c \, (t-t_0) \right]}{t-t_0} \tag{9.88}$$

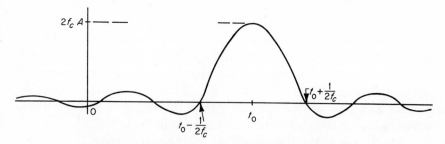

Fig. 9.42 *The impulse response of the ideal low-pass filter.*

This function appears in Fig. 9.42 and, as expected, it starts "wiggling" before $t = 0$ and hence is not realizable. The unit step-function response of this filter is

$$\frac{A}{\pi} \int_{-\infty}^{t} \frac{\sin\left[2\pi f_c \left(t-t_0\right)\right]}{t-t_0} \, dt = A\zeta[2\pi f_c \left(t-t_0\right)] \tag{9.89}$$

or the function of Fig. 9.41 with the amplitude altered to A and the constant $a = 2\pi f_c$; this function resembles a step function. If f_c is made large, the frequency of the wiggles is large (this frequency is f_c) and the response approaches that shown in Fig. 9.43. Notice, however, that no matter how large f_c is made, there will always be an *overshoot* and an *undershoot* at the discontinuity, each about 8.95 percent of the magnitude of the discontinuity.

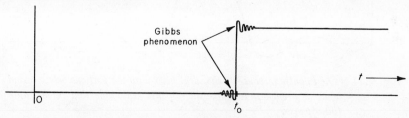

Fig. 9.43 *The response of an ideal low-pass filter to a step-function input when f_c is very large. Observe the 8.95-percent overshoot, referred to as Gibbs' phenomenon.*

Even though the filter above is not realizable, it will be shown that realizable filters demonstrate this overshoot if the magnitude of the transfer function falls rapidly in the vicinity of f_c. This peculiarity is known as the *Gibbs' phenomenon.*

Observe also that the *rise time* of the step response is very nearly equal to the reciprocal of the slope of $\zeta\left[2\pi f_c(t-t_0)\right]$ at $t = t_0$. Then the rise time of the output is $\pi/a = 1/(2f_c)$. If the input were a rectangular pulse instead of a step function, then the output could be viewed as a positive step followed by a negative step. If the output is to look anything like a pulse, then the step function rise time should not exceed one-half the pulse length. This has led to a rule of thumb: *the bandwidth of a filter must be at least the reciprocal of the pulse length if the pulse is not to be seriously altered in amplitude.* This rule was used in Prob. 9.15.

It is clear from Fig. 9.42 that if the delay time t_0 is large,

$$\frac{\sin [2\pi f_c (t - t_0)]}{t - t_0}$$

will be small for negative t. Therefore, we should be able to approximate the ideal filter by making the impulse response of a filter

$$\frac{A}{\pi} \frac{\sin [2\pi f_c (t - t_0)]}{t - t_0} \mathbf{1}(t)$$

Unfortunately this function is not symmetric about the time $t = t_0$, so when this is transformed the result will not have linear phase. Symmetry can be achieved, however, by chopping off the response of the ideal filter for $t > 2t_0$ as well. The result appears in Fig. 9.44.

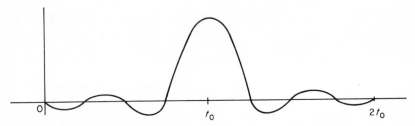

Fig. 9.44   *The impulse response of the ideal filter with the portions below t_0 and above $2t_0$ removed to make the response realizable and to maintain linear phase.*

Finding the transform of this function can be approached in two different ways. The impulse response above can be viewed as the original impulse response multiplied by $[\mathbf{1}(t) - \mathbf{1}(t-2t_0)]$. The transform of the latter function is

$$e^{-j2\pi f t_0} \frac{\sin 2\pi f t_0}{\pi f}$$

and this can be convolved with the transform of the ideal filter to find the transfer function of the almost-ideal filter. If $H_{ai}(f)$ is the transfer function of this realizable approximation to the ideal filter, then

$$H_{ai}(f) = \int\limits_{-f_c}^{f_c} \frac{Ae^{-j2\pi y t_0}\, e^{-j2\pi(f-y)t_0} \sin 2\pi(f-y)t_0}{\pi(f-y)}\, dy$$

$$= \int\limits_{-f_c}^{f_c} \frac{A}{\pi} \frac{\sin 2\pi\,(f-y)t_0}{f-y}\, e^{-j2\pi f t_0}\, dy$$

Since the exponential and the constants under the integral sign are independent of y, they may be brought outside of the integral sign. If the new variable $x = f - y$ is used, with $dx = -dy$ and the limits changed to $f + f_c$ and $f - f_c$,

$$H_{ai}(f) = \frac{A}{\pi} e^{-j2\pi f t_0} \int\limits_{f+f_c}^{f-f_c} - \frac{\sin 2\pi t_0 x}{x}\, dx$$

$$= \frac{A}{\pi} e^{-j2\pi f t_0} \int\limits_{f-f_c}^{f+f_c} \frac{\sin\,(2\pi t_0 x)}{x}\, dx \tag{9.90}$$

But this is simply the integral appearing in the defiintion of $\zeta\,(t)$, and so

$$H_{ai}(f) = A\{\zeta[2\pi t_0(f+f_c)] - \zeta\,[2\pi t_0(f-f_c)]\}\, e^{-j2\pi f t_0} \tag{9.91}$$

This result can also be obtained by direct integration, as indicated in Prob. 9.34. The magnitude and phase of the transfer function are plotted as a function of frequency in Fig. 9.45. Notice that since the ζ function becomes negative for alternate intervals below $-f_c$ and above f_c, the phase function has discontinuities in it of magnitude π every time a change in sign occurs. This in no way detracts from the linearity requirement of the phase. Observe that the ripple frequency at the band edges is t_0, and so the ripples are spread out in Fig. 9.45(a) for small t_0 and squeezed together in Fig. 9.45(b) for large t_0.

We can now draw two conclusions from this result: (1) the delay time of a filter will be a function of the slope of the frequency response at the cutoff frequency. The larger this slope, the larger will be the delay. Furthermore, the price we must pay for a good low-pass filter would appear to be delay in the response. (2) Finally, the response of such a filter will be accompanied by about a 9 percent overshoot and undershoot at points where the input is discontinuous.

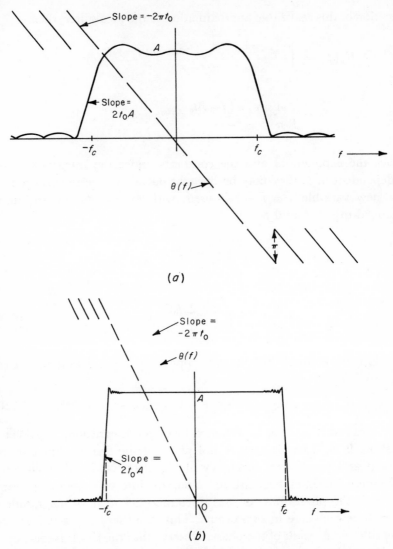

Fig. 9.45 (a) *The magnitude and phase functions for the almost ideal low-pass filter with small delay time* t_o. *(b) The magnitude and phase of the almost ideal filter for large* t_o.

It is not necessary that the magnitude of the low-pass filter exhibit the ripple effect shown in Fig. 9.45 at the band edges. We could have avoided this, for example, by multiplying the impulse response of the ideal filter by a triangle of height unity and centered at $t = t_0$, with base $2t_0$. This would lead to an impulse response not unlike that of Fig. 9.44, but the ripples would be decreased in magnitude as we moved away from the center of the response. It is not obvious, but this does lead to a no-overshoot condition in the magnitude of the transfer function, but, of course, the step-function response would still have the characteristic ripples in it. This approximation is called the Fejér filter.*

PROBLEMS

9.34. Evaluate $H_{ai}(f)$ by direct integration. To do this note that

$$H_{ai}(f) = \frac{A}{\pi} \int_0^{2t_0} \frac{\sin 2\pi f_c(t-t_0)}{t-t_0} e^{-j2\pi ft} dt$$

Substitute $y = t - t_0$ for the new dummy variable of integration and obtain

$$H_{ai}(f) = \frac{A}{\pi} e^{-j2\pi ft_0} \int_{-t_0}^{t_0} \frac{\sin 2\pi f_c y}{y} e^{-j2\pi fy} dy$$

Since the limits on the integral are symmetric about $y = 0$, only the even part of the integrand will contribute to the result. Why? Using this fact show that

$$H_{ai}(f) = \frac{2A}{\pi} e^{-j2\pi ft_0} \int_0^{t_0} \frac{\sin 2\pi f_c y \cos 2\pi fy}{y} dy$$

Now use the trigonometric identity

$$\sin A \cos B = \frac{1}{2} [\sin (A+B) + \sin (A-B)]$$

and obtain Eq. (9.91).

9.35. Notice that if t_0 is chosen less than or equal to $1/(2f_c)$ then there will be no ripple in the step response—that is, no overshoot. Show this by drawing the impulse response for $t_0 = 1/(2f_c)$ for the approximately ideal filter and graphically integrate this to obtain a sketch of the step response. In particular you should be able to show that the step response equals $1.179\,A$ for $t > 2t_0$. For this value of t_0 what is the slope of the magnitude of $H_{ai}(f)$ at $f = f_c$?

9.36. Suppose a low-pass filter with cutoff frequency f_c is such that for $f > f_c$

$$|H(f)| \doteq \frac{B}{f^n}$$

---

*See for example Papoulis (7), pp. 106 ff.

(a) Show that the ratio of the slope of the function $H(f)$ to the magnitude of $H(f)$ at the cutoff frequency is $-n/f_c$.

(b) Show that the magnitude of $H(f)$ falls at the rate of $6n$ db per octave; that is, the magnitude falls by a factor of 2^n every time the frequency doubles.

(c) For the almost ideal filter of Prob. 9.35, show that the ratio of the slope to the magnitude at cutoff is $-2/f_c$ and hence that it falls off at the rate of 12 db per octave. Since this filter is the one which just fails to produce overshoot, we *might* conclude that overshoot in the step response will occur if the transfer function falls off at a rate greater than 12 db per octave at $f = f_c$.

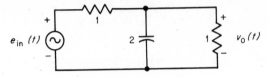

Fig. 9.46   *Problem 9.37.*

9.37. Show that the unit step response of the circuit of Fig. 9.46 is $0.5(1 - e^{-t})\mathbf{1}(t)$. Show also that this response has no overshoot and that, for large f, its transfer function falls off at a rate of 6 db per octave.

9.38. Show that the unit step response of the circuit of Fig. 9.47 is

$$0.5 \left[1 - \sqrt{2}\, e^{-t/\sqrt{2}} \cos\left(\frac{t}{\sqrt{2}} - \frac{\pi}{4}\right)\right]\mathbf{1}(t)$$

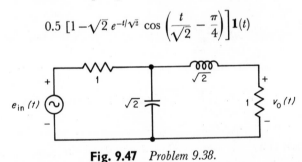

Fig. 9.47   *Problem 9.38.*

Show that this response has a 4.3 percent overshoot at $t = \sqrt{2}\pi$ and that, for large f, its transfer function falls off at a rate of 12 db per octave.

The High-Pass Filter

A filter with transfer function $Ae^{-j2\pi f t_0}$ for *all* frequencies is physically realizable (in fact it is a lossless transmission line whose length corresponds to a delay time of t_0 sec). Therefore, if we subtract the transfer function for the low-pass filter from the function given, the resulting transfer function will be physically realizable. Thus

$$H_h(f) = Ae^{-j2\pi ft_0}\{1 - \zeta\,[2\pi t_0\,(f+f_c)] - \zeta\,[2\pi t_0\,(f-f_c)]\}$$

will have an impulse response equal to an impulse of value A at $t = t_0$, *minus* the impulse response of the low-pass filter with the same cutoff frequency. This appears in Fig. 9.48(a). Its integral will be the step

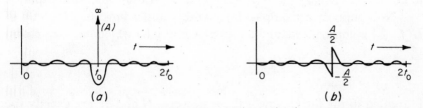

(a)   (b)

Fig. 9.48.   *The impulse and step responses of an almost ideal high-pass filter.*

response, which will be the upside-down version of the low-pass step response but with a positive discontinuity of A at $t = t_0$, as shown in Fig. 9.48(b). The magnitude and phase functions for this filter are shown in Fig. 9.49.

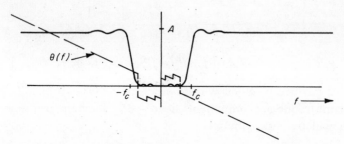

Fig. 9.49   *The magnitude and phase functions for the almost ideal high-pass filter.*

The Bandpass Filter

The bandpass filter may be thought of as the result of subtracting from a constant both a high-pass and a low-pass filter, the cutoff frequency of the low-pass filter being less than that of the high-pass filter. Although this particular view is not very helpful, it does make it clear that such a filter can be constructed. It is easier to think of such a filter as having been evolved from the low-pass filter by a simple translation to the left and right of f_0 cps, where f_0 is the center frequency of the filter.

The advantage of this latter view is that the impulse response must be the same as that of the low-pass filter multiplied by $\cos 2\pi f_0 t$. In fact, this result can be made to apply approximately to any signal applied to a bandpass filter. For example, let $H(f)$ be the transfer function of the low-pass filter, and let $S_{in}(f)$ be the transform of the input signal to this filter. Then $S_o(f) = H(f)S_{in}(f)$ is the transform of the output.

Now suppose a bandpass filter with transfer function $H(f+f_0) + H(f-f_0)$ is constructed, and an input signal $s_{in}(t)$ which has a transform

$$\frac{S_{in}(f+f_0) + S_{in}(f-f_0)}{2}$$

is applied to the filter. Now if the transforms H and S_{in} are exactly the same as those used with the low-pass filter, then the input signal in the case of the bandpass filter is the signal used in the low-pass filter but multiplied by $\cos 2\pi f_0 t$. The output signal from the bandpass filter will have a transform

$$\frac{1}{2} [S_{in}(f+f_0) + S_{in}(f-f_0)] [H(f+f_0) + H(f-f_0)] =$$

$$\frac{1}{2} [S_{in}(f+f_0)H(f+f_0) + S_{in}(f-f_0)H(f-f_0)$$

$$+ S_{in}(f+f_0)H(f-f_0) + S_{in}(f-f_0)H(f+f_0)]$$

The last two products will be small, in general, if the $S_{in}(f)$ has no significant frequency components near $\pm 2f_0$. Thus the transform of the output will be approximately

$$\frac{1}{2} [S_{in}(f+f_0)H(f+f_0) + S_{in}(f-f_0)H(f-f_0)]$$

which is simply the transform of the output of the low-pass filter multiplied by $\cos 2\pi f_0 t$. Then if the *envelope* of the signal applied to the bandpass filter is the same signal as that applied to the low-pass filter, the output of the low-pass filter will be the envelope of the output of the bandpass filter. This is an extremely valuable rule, since the response of a low-pass filter is generally easier to obtain than that of a bandpass filter. For example, the step response of the bandpass filter with large delay is simply the step response of the low-pass filter, shown in Fig. 9.50(a), multiplied by $\cos 2\pi f_0 t$. The result appears in Fig. 9.50(b).

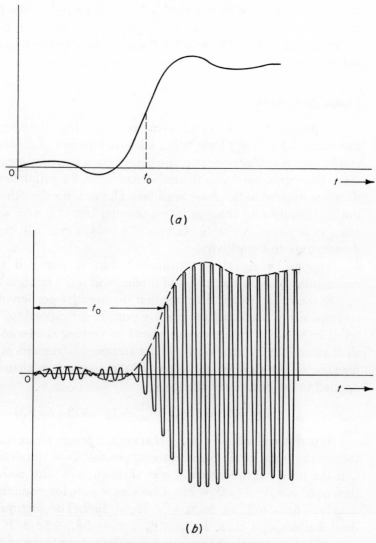

Fig. 9.50   (a) *The step response of the almost ideal low-pass filter of bandwidth* f_c. (b) *The step response of the almost ideal band-pass filter with bandwidth* $2f_c$. *Observe that the input to the bandpass filter is cos* $(2\pi f_0 t)\ \mathbf{1}(t)$ *and not simply* $\mathbf{1}(t)$.

The bandwidth required, however, is twice as large for the same envelope response, because of the duplication that occurs when the translation takes place. The positive frequency band is $2f_c$ wide for the bandpass filter with an envelope response that is the same as the response of a low-pass filter with bandwidth f_c. Then r-f pulses, the product of low-frequency pulses and $\cos 2\pi f_0 t$, require a bandwidth that is *twice* the reciprocal of the pulse length if the envelope is to reach its maximum value.

Phase Distortion

Not many general statements can be made about the effects of phase distortion—that is $\theta(f)$ not being a linear function of f. About all that can be said is that nonlinear phase causes distortion of waveshape. This seems to be unimportant with audio frequencies, for within limits the ear does not appear to be phase sensitive. The eye, on the other hand, is not too sensitive to changes in magnitude, but it is very sensitive to changes in phase. A simple example of a video signal will be chosen to demonstrate this sensitivity.

Suppose a signal is transmitted that is intended to display rectangular bars on the screen of a television set. The signal will be a square wave, and we shall assume that the negative portion of the wave corresponds to black and the positive portion corresponds to white. All levels in between these two correspond to varying shades of gray. We shall assume further that only the first and third harmonics of the signal manage to get through the filters of the receiver so that the signal applied to the grid of the kinescope is

$$s(t) = A \left[\cos\left(\omega_0 t + \theta_1\right) + \tfrac{1}{3}\cos\left(3\omega_0 t + \theta_3\right)\right]$$

If both harmonics of this signal are in the proper phase relationship, then both should go through zero with positive slope simultaneously. If t_0 is the time the fundamental goes through zero with positive slope, then $\omega_0 t_0 + \theta_1 = -\pi/2 + 2n\pi$. Choosing $n = 0$, for example, requires $\omega_0 t_0 = -\theta_1 - \pi/2$; so $3\omega_0 t_0 = -3\theta_1 - 3\pi/2$. The argument of the third harmonic is then $3\omega_0 t_0 + \theta_3 = \theta_3 - 3\theta_1 - 3\pi/2$. If this is to be $-\pi/2$ also, then the harmonics are in the proper phase and $\theta_3 = 3\theta_1 + \pi$. Thus, as asserted earlier, the phase must vary linearly with frequency.

Figure 9.51(a) shows the transmitted signal and Fig. 9.51(b) shows the signal received when the phase relation between the fundamental and third harmonics is correct. Fig. 9.51(c) shows what happens when the third harmonic is delayed an additional 180°. Directly under each waveform is a shaded drawing indicating the way one of the lines on the screen would appear depending on the signal applied to the picture tube. It will be observed that the loss of the higher harmonics is not serious; however, the phase error is serious since the black level is cut down in width by about one-half. Good video contrast and distinction between shades of gray requires linear phase.

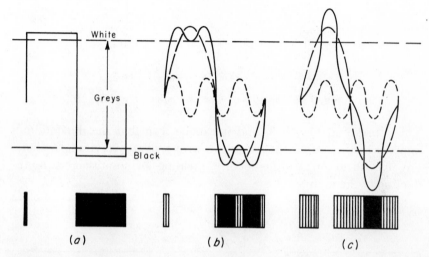

Fig. 9.51 *The effect of missing harmonics and phase error on a video presentation of black and white spots. (a) The picture as transmitted. (b) The signal as received with all harmonics above the third missing, but with proper phase relationship. (c) The result of a phase error in the third harmonic.*

Another example of the distortion caused by nonlinear phase is given by the circuit of Fig. 9.52. This circuit has a transfer function of

$$H(s) = \frac{E_0(s)}{E_{in}(s)} = \frac{(1/\sqrt{LC}) - s}{(1/\sqrt{LC}) + s}$$

and, when $s = j\omega = j2\pi f$ this becomes

$$H(j2\pi f) = \frac{(1/\sqrt{LC}) - j2\pi f}{(1/\sqrt{LC}) + j2\pi f} = 1 \underline{/-2\tan^{-1}(f/f_0)}$$

where $f_0 = 1/(2\pi\sqrt{LC})$. Then this circuit in no manner affects amplitude, but does change the phase, and change it in the fashion of most inexpensive filters. The result of this alteration in phase can be studied by observing the response of such a network to a step function. With $E_{in}(s) = 1/s$

$$E_0(s) = \frac{(1/\sqrt{LC}) - s}{s[(1/\sqrt{LC}) + s]} = \frac{1}{s} - \frac{2}{s + 1/\sqrt{LC}}$$

making

$$e_0(t) = [1 - 2e^{-t/\sqrt{LC}}]\mathbf{1}(t) = [1 - 2e^{-2\pi f_0 t}]\mathbf{1}(t)$$

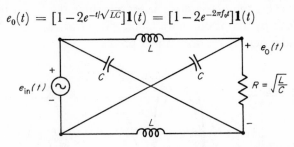

Fig. 9.52   *An all-pass filter that affects only phase.*

This appears in Fig. 9.53, and it can be seen that the discontinuity appears in the output, but with the wrong sign. Everything is there, but it is all grouped rather poorly, yielding an unsatisfactory reproduction of the input.

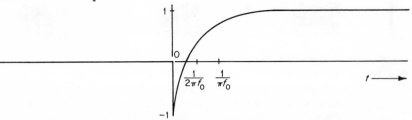

Fig. 9.53   *The unit step response of the filter of Fig. 9.52.*

Figure 9.54 shows a plot of $\theta(f)$ versus f for the circuit of Fig. 9.52. Notice that near $f = 0$ the curve is quite linear, so that signals whose frequency band lies near $f = 0$ should be passed with relatively small distortion. Now if the slope had been linear for all frequencies, then $\theta(f) = -2\pi f t_0$, with t_0 the delay time. For this reason the function

$$t_g = t_g(f) = -\frac{1}{2\pi}\frac{d\theta(f)}{df} = -\frac{d\theta(f)}{d\omega} \qquad (9.92)$$

is defined as the *group* delay time. It means that for signals whose band lies near the frequency f the filter would appear to be linear to a group of frequencies near this value, and the signal whose transform corresponds to this frequency group would be delayed by t_g sec. For the phase function of Fig. 9.54 it is seen that

$$t_g = -\frac{1}{2\pi}\frac{d\theta(f)}{df} = \frac{1}{\pi f_0} \cdot \frac{1}{1+(f/f_0)^2}$$

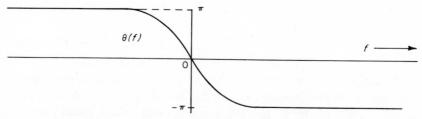

Fig. 9.54 *The phase function $\theta(f)$ of the filter of Fig. 9.52.*

and so low-frequency signals are delayed by $1/(\pi f_0)$ sec. This can be seen in Fig. 9.53 since the d-c steady-state is reached in just about two time constants or $1/(\pi f_0)$ sec. Notice that for large f the phase is also nearly linear but with nearly zero slope or delay time. The high-frequency components of the step function occur at the discontinuity, and this is seen to come through with no delay at all. The fact that the high-frequency phase is $\pm 180°$ accounts for the fact that the step is inverted.

No general rules are available for predicting what nonlinearity of phase will do to a waveform. Therefore, if we wish to avoid distortion we must insist upon linear phase.

Practical Filters

The first filter designs were used in audio work, so there was little concern for linear phase functions. Whatever the design criterion, if a bandpass filter or a high-pass filter is to be designed using lumped elements—R, L, and C—it is necessary only to design the equivalent low-pass filter with a cutoff frequency of one rad per sec ($f = 1/2\pi$ cps) and a one-ohm impedance level. This is such a time-saving principle that a little space will be spent on its demonstration.

Suppose we have been given a low-pass filter constructed of R, L, and C elements, and we know its circuit diagram. What would happen if all inductances and capacitances were removed and replaced by inductances and capacitances half as large? If we think about this a while, we realize that the filter will have exactly the same characteristics as it did before, but with *twice* the bandwidth. The reason is that frequency enters into impedance calculations only when associated with an L or a C. Thus $j2\pi fL$ and $j2\pi fC$ are, respectively, the impedance of an inductance and the admittance of a capacitance as a function of frequency. If the C terms are halved, then at twice the former frequency the admittances of the new C elements will be the same as that of the old ones. The same thing can be said of the impedance of the L elements. We can draw the following conclusion:

If all L and C terms of a network are reduced in size by a factor a, then the transfer function of the network will have the same amplitude and phase variation but with the frequency axis multiplied by the constant a. If, for example, a filter has a 10-kc cutoff, and the L and C terms are divided by 4, then the new filter will have a transfer function with exactly the same shape but with the cutoff occurring at 40 kc.

If we are quite satisfied with the cutoff frequency of the filter, but dissatisfied with the impedance level, then the impedance level can be raised by a factor b if all impedances are multiplied by this factor. This means that the R and L terms are multiplied by b, but the C terms are divided by b, since the impedance of a capacitance is $1/(j\omega C)$.

If, then, we design a low-pass filter with cutoff frequency $1/(2\pi)$ cps and a one-ohm impedance level, then to convert it to a low-pass filter with cutoff frequency f_c and impedance level R_0 we simply

Multiply all resistances by R_0

Multiply all inductances by $R_0/(2\pi f_c)$

Divide all capacitances by $2\pi f_c R_0$

If we wish to design a bandpass filter with impedance level R_0 and bandwidth f_c, then it is necessary to design the corresponding low-pass filter with the same impedance level and cutoff frequency f_c, and then place (1) in series with every inductance a capacitance that is series resonant with it at the desired center frequency f_0, and (2) in parallel with every capacitance of the low-pass filter an inductance that is parallel resonant with it at the center frequency f_0.

Since the foregoing operations mean that the impedance of an inductance is replaced by a series resonant circuit, then $j\omega L = j2\omega f L$ is replaced by $j2\pi f L - j1/\omega C$ where C is related to L by

$$C = \frac{1}{4\pi^2 f_0^2 L}$$

if it is to be resonant with it at f_0. This amounts to replacing $j\omega L = j2\pi f L$ by $j2\pi L \left(f - f_0^2/f\right)$. It can be shown in a similar manner that placing an L in parallel with each capacitance is also equivalent to replacing the admittances $j2\pi f C$ by $j2\pi C \left(f - f_0^2/f\right)$, where the inductance used in each case must be related to the capacitance C by

$$L = \frac{1}{4\pi^2 f_0^2 C}$$

in order that each pair will be resonant at the frequency f_0. Both of these operations can be expressed mathematically by saying that the frequency f is replaced by

$$f - \frac{f_0^2}{f} = \frac{(f-f_0)\,(f+f_0)}{f}$$

This is not quite equivalent to a translation to the left and right as we have been viewing bandpass filters. For frequencies near f_0, however, the function $(f-f_0)(f+f_0)/f$ behaves like $2(f-f_0)$, and so if the cutoff frequency of the original low-pass filter is f_c, then the upper cut off frequency of the band-pass filter will be about $f_0 + f_c/2$ and the lower cutoff frequency near $f_0 - f_c/2$. The transfer function has thus shrunk in size, but the resulting bandwidth is the same. Actually, as is brought out in Prob. 9.39, the new cutoff frequencies are related to each other by

$$f_H - f_L = f_c$$

and

$$f_H f_L = f_0^2$$

so that the bandwidth is exactly f_c but the center frequency is at the geometric mean of the upper and lower cutoff frequencies f_H and f_L, respectively.

Finally, if it is required to design a high-pass filter with cutoff frequency f_c and impedance level R_0, then we need only design a low-pass filter with the same level and cutoff frequency and then replace all C terms by L terms that are resonant with the C terms at the cutoff frequency f_c, and replace all L terms by C terms that are resonant with the L terms at the cutoff frequency. This can be seen fairly easily since at resonance the impedances of the new elements equal exactly those they replace, and so the transfer function will have the same magnitude at f_c for both. The phase angle will change sign, however. Why? On either side of the frequency f_c the variation of the impedances of the new elements with frequency will be just the opposite of those they replaced and so the opposite transfer function will be obtained. It is as though the frequency f were replaced by f_c^2/f.

Since high-pass and bandpass filters can be obtained from a low-pass filter, and since the frequency and impedance levels are unimportant to the design, then we shall confine our attention to designing only low-pass filters on a one-ohm, one-rad-per-sec basis. They will be compared with the ideal low-pass filter, which has an equivalent delay time for low frequencies and which has the same bandwidth. The step response of this ideal filter will be $\zeta(t)$. Examples that extend the design to other types of filters will be given in the next section.

BUTTERWORTH FILTERS

The low-pass Butterworth filter of order n has a transfer function with a magnitude of

$$|H_{Bn}(j\omega)| = \frac{1}{\sqrt{1+\omega^{2n}}} \tag{9.93}$$

It is seen that the magnitude of the transfer function is $1/\sqrt{2}$ at $\omega = 1$ rad per sec, and this is called its cutoff frequency.

It is well known that the magnitude squared of a complex number is equal to the product of the number and its conjugate, and so

$$|H_{Bn}(j\omega)|^2 = H_{Bn}(j\omega)H_{Bn}^*(j\omega) = \frac{1}{1+\omega^{2n}} \tag{9.94}$$

But the conjugate of $H_{Bn}(j\omega)$ is $H_{Bn}(-j\omega)$ since the Laplace transfer function $H_{Bn}(s)$ has all real coefficients; that is, it is real when s is real. Then Eq. (9.94) can be written as

$$H_{Bn}(j\omega)H_{Bn}(-j\omega) = \frac{1}{1+\omega^{2n}} \tag{9.95}$$

If we now go backwards, and put $s = j\omega$, or $\omega = -js$, Eq. (9.95) will read

$$H_{Bn}(s)H_{Bn}(-s) = \frac{1}{1+(-js)^{2n}} = \frac{1}{1+(-1)^n s^{2n}} \tag{9.96}$$

Now, we are fortified with the knowledge that if $H_{Bn}(s)$ is the transfer function of a realizable filter, then its poles must be in the left-half s plane. Then $H_{Bn}(-s)$ must have poles in the right-half s plane. It is then necessary only to factor the denominator of Eq. (9.96) and keep the left-half s-plane poles and throw the others away. The roots of the denominator that are in the left-half plane are the $(2n)$th roots of -1 or $+1$, depending on whether n is even or odd. Thus the roots lie on the unit circle in the s plane, and it can be shown that those lying in the left-half plane are

$$s_k = -\sin\left[\frac{\pi(1+2k)}{2n}\right] + j\cos\left[\frac{\pi(1+2k)}{2n}\right] \tag{9.97}$$

for $k = 0, 1, 2, \ldots n-1$. You are asked to show this in Prob. 9.40.

If these roots are put in the appropriate factors, then

$$H_{Bn}(s) = \frac{1}{(s-s_0)\,(s-s_1)\,\cdots\,(s-s_{n-1})} \tag{9.98}$$

EXAMPLE 9.3. Find the transfer function and step response of a third-order Butterworth filter.

Solution: Since $n = 3$, then the roots of $H_{B3}(s)$ are

$$s_0 = -\sin\frac{\pi}{6} + j\cos\frac{\pi}{6}$$

$$= -\frac{1}{2} + j\frac{\sqrt{3}}{2}$$

$$s_1 = -\sin\frac{3\pi}{6} + j\cos\frac{3\pi}{6}$$

$$= -1 + j0$$

$$s_2 = -\sin\frac{5\pi}{6} + j\cos\frac{5\pi}{6}$$

$$= -\frac{1}{2} - j\frac{\sqrt{3}}{2}$$

Then the denominator polynomial is

$$\left(s + \frac{1}{2} - j\frac{\sqrt{3}}{2}\right)\left(s + \frac{1}{2} + j\frac{\sqrt{3}}{2}\right)(s+1) = (s^2 + s + 1)\,(s+1)$$

$$= s^3 + 2s^2 + 2s + 1$$

and

$$H_{B3}(s) = \frac{1}{s^3 + 2s^2 + 2s + 1}$$

The unit step response will be the inverse Laplace transform of $H_{B3}(s)/s$; that is,

$$\frac{1}{s(s+1)\,(s+1/2 - j\sqrt{3}/2)\,(s+1/2 + j\sqrt{3}/2)} = \frac{1}{s} - \frac{1}{s+1}$$

$$+ \frac{1/\sqrt{3}\;\underline{/90°}}{s+1/2 - j\sqrt{3}/2}$$

plus the conjugate of the last term. This makes the step response:

$$\left[1 - e^{-t} + \frac{2}{\sqrt{3}}e^{-t/2}\cos\left(\frac{\sqrt{3}}{2}t + 90°\right)\right]\mathbf{1}(t)$$

$$= \left[1 - e^{-t} - \frac{2}{\sqrt{3}}e^{-t/2}\sin\frac{\sqrt{3}}{2}t\right]\mathbf{1}(t)$$

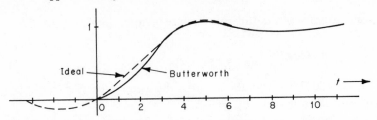

Fig. 9.55 *The unit step response of the third-order Butterworth (solid curve) and the step response of the ideal filter with the same delay (dashed curve.)*

This response appears in Fig. 9.55 along with the response of the ideal filter. The low-frequency group delay of the Butterworth filter can be calculated by noting that, for $s = j\omega$, the transfer function is

$$H_{B3}(j\omega) = \frac{1}{(1+j\omega)\,[1/2+j(\omega-\sqrt{3}/2)]\,[1/2+j(\omega+\sqrt{3}/2)]}$$

for which the angle is

$$\theta(f) = -\tan^{-1}\omega - \tan^{-1}2\left(\omega-\frac{\sqrt{3}}{2}\right) - \tan^{-1}2\left(\omega+\frac{\sqrt{3}}{2}\right)$$

The negative derivative of this with respect to ω will yield the group delay, t_g, given by equation (9.92). This is

$$t_g = -\frac{d\theta(f)}{d\omega} = \frac{1}{1+\omega^2} + \frac{2}{1+4(\omega-\sqrt{3}/2)^2} + \frac{2}{1+4(\omega+\sqrt{3}/2)^2}$$

At $\omega = 0$ this is 2 sec, and so the response of the ideal filter is drawn with this delay.

The overshoot in the third-order Butterworth is about 8 percent, but there is no undershoot. Since the transfer function falls off like $1/f^3$ for large frequencies, this is a factor of 2^3 per octave or 18 db per octave.

EXAMPLE 9.4.

1. Show that the transfer function $V_0(s)/I_s(s)$ for the circuit shown in Fig. 9.56 is a Butterworth third-order filter. Plot the magnitude and phase of its transfer function.

2. Use the filter given to design a low-pass filter with an impedance level of 10 K and a cutoff frequency of 15 kc.

3. Use the circuit of 2 to design a bandpass filter with a bandwidth of 15 kc but centered at 100 kc with a 10-K impedance level.

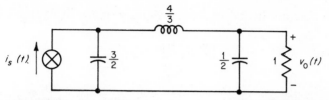

Fig. 9.56 *The circuit of a third order Butterworth filter.*

4. Use the circuit of 2 to design a high-pass filter with a cutoff frequency of 15 kc and an impedance level of 10 K.

Solution: 1. We shall use a circuit technique applicable only to ladder networks to obtain the transfer function. Start by assuming that the *load* voltage is a unit impulse, so $V_0(s) = 1$. Then use Ohm's and Kirchhoff's laws to work back to the input current. Figure 9.57 shows how this is done. Since the transform of v_0 is 1, then the current in the one-ohm resistance has a transform of 1 also. The transform of the current in the $\frac{1}{2} f$ capacitance must be $s/2$, and so the current in the inductance must be $1 + s/2$. The voltage across the $\frac{4}{3}h$ inductance has to be $4s(1+s/2)/3$ and so the voltage across the input capacitance has a transform of $1 + 4s(1+s/2)/3$. Multiplication of the latter value by $3s/2$ gives the transform of the current in the front capacitance, and adding this to $1 + s/2$ gives the transform of the input current. Then

$$\frac{I_s(s)}{V_0(s)} = \frac{1+s/2+3s\,[1+4s(1+s/2)/3]/2}{1}$$

or

$$\frac{V_0(s)}{I_s(s)} = \frac{1}{s^3+2s^2+2s+1}$$

which is the $H_{B3}(s)$ of Example 9.3.

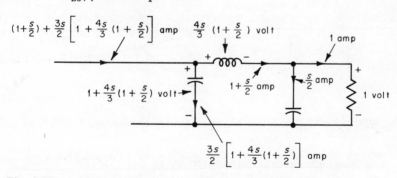

Fig. 9.57 *Finding the transform of the input current by setting that of the output voltage equal to unity and working backwards.*

The magnitude and phase functions, as given in Example 9.3, are

$$|H_{B3}(j\omega)| = \frac{1}{\sqrt{1+\omega^6}}$$

and

$$\theta(f) = -\left[\tan^{-1}\omega + \tan^{-1}2\left(\omega - \frac{\sqrt{3}}{2}\right) + \tan^{-1}2\left(\omega + \frac{\sqrt{3}}{2}\right)\right]$$

Since

$$H_{B3}(s) = \frac{1}{(s+1)(s^2+s+1)}$$

then

$$H_{B3}(j\omega) = \frac{1}{(1+j\omega)(1-\omega^2+j\omega)}$$

and $\theta(f)$ could be written as

$$\theta(f) = -\left[\tan^{-1}\omega + \tan^{-1}\frac{\omega}{(1-\omega^2)}\right]$$

The magnitude and phase functions appear in Fig. 9.58.

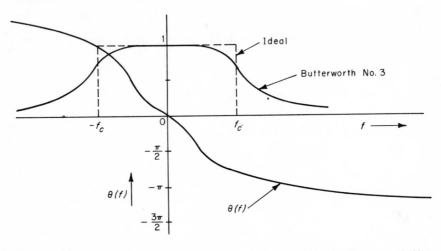

Fig. 9.58 *The magnitude and phase functions of the third-order Butterworth filter.*

2. Since the level is to be raised by $10K = 10^4$, multiply R and L by 10^4, divide C by 10^4. The frequency level is to go to 15×10^3 from $1/2\pi$; hence

$$R = 1 \text{ to } R = 10^4$$

$$L = \frac{4}{3} \text{ to } L = \frac{4 \times 10^4/3}{2\pi \times 15 \times 10^3} = \frac{4}{9\pi} \text{ h}$$

$$C = \frac{1}{2} \text{ to } C = \frac{1/2}{10^4 \times 2\pi \times 15 \times 10^3} = \frac{10^{-8}}{6\pi} = \frac{10^{-2}}{6\pi} \mu\text{f}$$

and $C = \frac{3}{2}$ goes to three times the latter, or $C = 10^{-2}/2\pi$ μf. The circuit appears in Fig. 9.59.

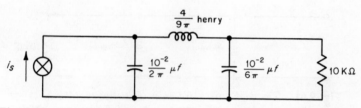

Fig. 9.59 *The third-order Butterworth filter with an impedance level of 10 K and a cutoff frequency of 15 kc.*

3. Go to a bandpass filter centered at $f_0 = 10^5$; in series with $4/(9\pi)$ h put a C such that

$$C = \frac{1}{4\pi^2 f_0^2 L} = \frac{900}{16\pi} \text{ pf}$$

In parallel with the $10^{-2}/(6\pi)$ μf capacitance put an

$$L = \frac{1}{4\pi^2 f_0^2 C} = \frac{3}{200\pi} \text{ h}$$

Finally put an inductance of one-third the last value in parallel with the $10^{-2}/(2\pi)$ μf capacitance and obtain the circuit of Fig. 9.60.

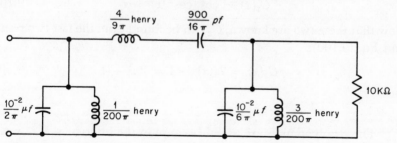

Fig. 9.60 *The bandpass third-order Butterworth filter with an impedance level of 10 K and a bandwidth of 15 kc, centered at 100 kc.*

4. For the high-pass filter with cutoff at 15 kc replace the L and C terms by elements resonant with them at 15 kc:

$$L = \frac{4}{9\pi} \text{ h is replaced by } C = \frac{1}{4\pi^2 f_c^2 L} = \frac{10^{-2}}{16\pi} \text{ } \mu f$$

$C = 10^{-2}/(2\pi) \text{ } \mu f$ is replaced by $L = 2/\pi$ h, and the $10^{-2}/(6\pi) \text{ } \mu f$ capacitance becomes $L = 2/(3\pi)$ h. The circuit appears in **Fig.** 9.61.

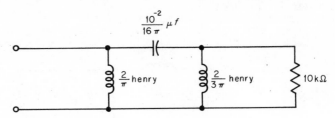

Fig. 9.61   *The high-pass third-order Butterworth filter with an impedance level of 10 K and a cutoff frequency of 15 kc.*

CHEBYSHEV FILTERS

The Chebyshev polynomials are defined by

$$C_n(x) = \cos (n \cos^{-1} x) \tag{9.99}$$

It can be shown that these polynomials satisfy the recurrence formula

$$C_n(x) = 2x \, C_{n-1}(x) - C_{n-2}(x) \tag{9.100}$$

and so if the first two can be obtained then the others also can.

Letting $n = 0$ in Eq. (9.99) yields

$$C_0(x) = \cos (0) = 1 \tag{9.101}$$

Letting $n = 1$ gives

$$C_1(x) = \cos (\cos^{-1} x) = x \tag{9.102}$$

Now that these two are known, C_2 can be found from the last two results and Eq. (9.100):

$$C_2(x) = 2x(x) - 1 = 2x^2 - 1 \tag{9.103}$$

and

$$C_3(x) = 2x(2x^2 - 1) - x = 4x^3 - 3x \tag{9.104}$$

These polynomials are useful because in the interval $-1 \leqslant x \leqslant 1$ the polynomials oscillate back and forth from $+1$ to -1, and are always equal to $+1$ at $x = 1$ and either ± 1 at $x = -1$. The polynomials are odd if n is odd, and even if n is even. Figure 9.62 shows C_0, C_1, C_2, and C_3 plotted versus x.

The nth-order Chebyshev filter has the general form

$$|H_{Cn}(j\omega)| = \frac{1}{\sqrt{1+\epsilon^2 C_n^2(\omega)}} \qquad (9.105)$$

where ϵ is commonly chosen to be less than or equal to one. A choice of $\epsilon = 1$ leads to a 3-db variation in the transfer function in the passband, and this is usually considered large.

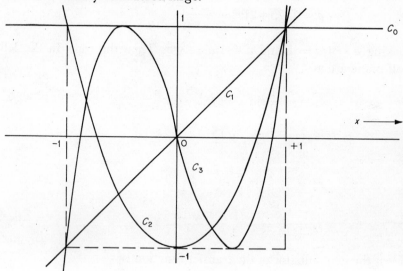

Fig. 9.62 *The first four Chebyshev polynomials: C_0, C_1, C_2, C_3.*

If, as was done with the Butterworth filters, the magnitude squared is formed, with ω set equal to $-js$, then the roots of the resulting denominator that lie in the left-half s plane can be shown to be at

$$s = -\frac{(a-1/a)}{2}\sin\left[\frac{\pi(1+2k)}{2n}\right] + j\frac{(a+1/a)}{2}\cos\left[\frac{\pi(1+2k)}{2n}\right] \qquad (9.106)$$

where $k = 0, 1, \ldots, n-1$, and

$$a = [\sqrt{1+1/\epsilon^2} + 1/\epsilon]^{1/n} \qquad (9.107)$$

These poles lie on an *ellipse* whose semimajor axis lies on the j axis and whose length is $(a+1/a)/2$ and whose semiminor axis lies on the real axis and is $(a-1/a)/2$ in length.

EXAMPLE 9.5. Choose $\epsilon = \frac{1}{2}$ and determine the magnitude, phase, and step response of a third-order Chebyshev low-pass filter.

Solution: Since $C_3(\omega) = 4\omega^3 - 3\omega$, then $C_3^2(\omega)/4$ is $4\omega^6 - 6\omega^4 + 9\omega^2/4$ and so the transfer function is

$$|H_{C3}(j\omega)| = \frac{1}{\sqrt{1+9\omega^2/4-6\omega^4+4\omega^6}}$$

with $\epsilon = \frac{1}{2}$. Then from Eq. (9.107)

$$a = [\sqrt{5}+2]^{1/3} = \frac{\sqrt{5}+1}{2}$$

making $a - 1/a = 1$ and $a + 1/a = \sqrt{5}$. Then the roots in the left-half plane are at

$$s_0 = -\frac{1}{2}\sin\frac{\pi}{6} + j\frac{\sqrt{5}}{2}\cos\frac{\pi}{6}$$

$$= -\frac{1}{4} + j\frac{\sqrt{15}}{4}$$

$$s_1 = -\frac{1}{2}\sin\frac{\pi}{2} = -\frac{1}{2}$$

$$s_2 = s_0^* = -\frac{1}{2} - j\frac{\sqrt{15}}{4}$$

Then the denominator of the transfer function is

$$\left(s+\frac{1}{2}\right)\left(s+\frac{1}{4} - j\frac{\sqrt{15}}{4}\right)\left(s+\frac{1}{4} + j\frac{\sqrt{15}}{4}\right) =$$

$$\left(s+\frac{1}{2}\right)\left(s^2+\frac{s}{2}+1\right) = s^3 + s^2 + \frac{5s}{4} + \frac{1}{2}$$

Then $H(s)$ has to be

$$H(s) = \frac{1}{2s^3+2s^2+5s/2+1}$$

where the denominator polynomial had to be multiplied by two to make the constant term unity.

Since $\theta(f)$ is the negative of the angle of the denominator polynomial, then

$$\theta(f) = -\left[\tan^{-1}2\omega + \tan^{-1}\frac{\omega}{2(1-\omega^2)}\right]$$

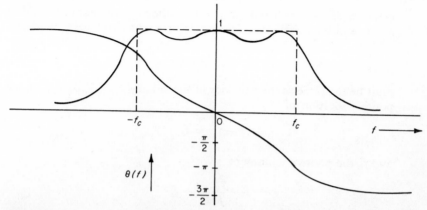

Fig. 9.63   *The magnitude and phase functions of the Chebyshev third-order low-pass filter with $\epsilon=\frac{1}{2}$.*

If $\theta(f)$ is differentiated with respect to ω and ω set equal to zero, then the delay time for low frequencies can be shown to be 2.5 sec. Figure 9.63 shows the magnitude and phase functions and Fig. 9.64 shows the step response with the step response of the ideal filter having a 2.5-sec delay.

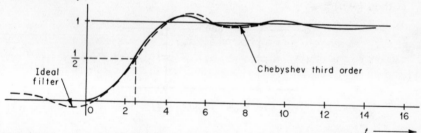

Fig. 9.64   *The step response of the Chebyshev third-order low-pass filter (solid curve) shown with the response of the ideal filter (dashed curve).*

The step response can be shown to be

$$\left(1-e^{-t/2}-\frac{2}{\sqrt{15}}\,e^{-t/4}\,\sin\frac{\sqrt{15}t}{4}\right)\mathbf{1}(t)$$

PROBLEMS

9.39. For the low-pass to bandpass conversion let us suppose that the low-pass filter has a cutoff frequency at f_c. Since the alteration of the circuit described in Sec. 9.2 is equivalent to replacing f by $f-f_0^2/f$, the behavior of the new circuit at f_0 will be the same as that of the old at $f = 0$, and the behavior of the new circuit at the frequencies f given by

$$f - \frac{f_0^2}{f} = \pm f_c$$

must be the same as the behavior of the old at $f = \pm f_c$. Let f_H be the positive solution of

$$f - \frac{f_0^2}{f} = f_c$$

and f_L the positive solution of

$$f - \frac{f_0^2}{f} = -f_c$$

  (a) Find f_H and f_L in terms of f_0 and f_c.
  (b) Show that $f_H - f_L = f_c$.
  (c) Show that $f_H f_L = f_0^2$.

9.40. Show that, if, as in Eq. (9.97)

$$s = -\sin\left[\frac{\pi(1+2k)}{2n}\right] + j\cos\left[\frac{\pi(1+2k)}{2n}\right]$$

then $(-js)^{2n} = -1$.

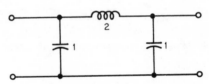

Fig. 9.65 *Problem 9.41.*

9.41. The constant-k low-pass filter is shown in Fig. 9.65. This has a nominal impedance level of one ohm and a cutoff frequency of $1/(2\pi)$ cps.
  (a) Design a high-pass constant-k filter with impedance level of 5 K and cutoff frequency of 30 kc.
  (b) Design a bandpass filter with bandwidth 10 kc, center frequency 80 kc, and a 10-K impedance level.

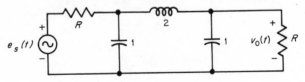

Fig. 9.66 *Problems 9.42, 9.43, and 9.50.*

9.42. If the constant-k filter of Fig. 9.65 is terminated in one ohm and driven by a source with a one-ohm internal impedance, as shown in Fig. 9.66 with $R = 1$, then find the transfer function of the filter. Show in particular that with this resistance level the filter is a third-order Butterworth.

9.43. Repeat Prob. 9.42, but this time use $R = 2$ in Fig. 9.66 and show that this is now a third order Chebyshev filter with $\epsilon = 1/2$.

9.44. In Eq. (9.107) let $a = e^{a/n}$ so that

$$e^a = \sqrt{1 + \frac{1}{\epsilon^2}} + \frac{1}{\epsilon}$$

(a) Show that since

$$\frac{e^{a/n} - e^{-a/n}}{2} = \sinh \frac{\alpha}{n}$$

and

$$\frac{e^{a/n} + e^{-a/n}}{2} = \cosh \frac{\alpha}{n}$$

then Eq. (9.106) can be written

$$-js = \omega = \cosh \frac{\alpha}{n} \cos \left[\frac{\pi(1+2k)}{2n} \right] + j \sinh \frac{\alpha}{n} \sin \left[\frac{\pi(1+2k)}{2n} \right]$$

(b) Using the formula for the cosine of the difference of two angles and the fact that $\cos(\pm jx) = \cosh x$ and $\sin(\pm jx) = \pm j \sinh x$, show that the equation in (a) above can be written as

$$\omega = \cos \left[\frac{\pi(1+2k)}{2n} - j\frac{\alpha}{n} \right]$$

(c) Now since $C_n(\omega) = \cos(n \cos^{-1}\omega)$, show that

$$C_n(\omega) = \cos \left[\frac{\pi(1+2k)}{2} - j\alpha \right]$$

$$= \cosh \alpha \cos \left[\frac{\pi(1+2k)}{2} \right] + j \sinh \alpha \sin \left[\frac{\pi(1+2k)}{2} \right]$$

(d) But since $\cos[\pi(1+2k)/2] = 0$ for all k and $\sin[\pi(1+2k)/2] = (-1)^k$, show that

$$C_n^2(\omega) = -\sinh^2 \alpha = -\frac{1}{\epsilon^2}$$

This proves the correctness of Eq. (9.106) for the roots of $1 + \epsilon^2 C_n^2(\omega) = 0$.

9.45. Show that the network of Fig. 9.67 can be considered a first-order Butterworth or Chebyshev filter (with $\epsilon = 1$). Find its step response and determine whether or not it has overshoot.

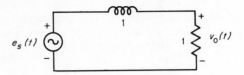

Fig. 9.67 *Problem 9.45.*

9.46. Show that the circuit of Fig. 9.68 is a second-order Butterworth filter. Find and plot carefully its step response. Does it have overshoot?

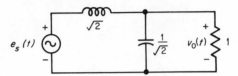

Fig. 9.68 *Problem 9.46.*

9.47. Choosing $\epsilon = \frac{3}{4}$, find the transfer function of a second-order Chebyshev filter. Plot the magnitude of the transfer function versus frequency. Choose values of $\omega = 0, 0.5, 1/\sqrt{2}, 1,$ and 1.5.

$$\textit{Answer: } H(s) = \frac{1}{3s^2/2 + \sqrt{6}\,s/2 + 5/4}$$

9.48. Show that the circuit appearing in Fig. 9.69 is a Chebyshev second-order filter with $\epsilon = \frac{3}{4}$. (See the answer to Prob. 9.47). Find its step response. Does it have overshoot?

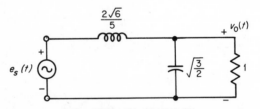

Fig. 9.69 *Problem 9.48.*

9.49. Show that for an nth-order Chebyshev filter with $\epsilon \leq 1$ the 3-db point does not occur at $\omega = 1$ but rather at

$$\omega = \cosh\left[\frac{\cosh^{-1}(1/\epsilon)}{n}\right]$$

9.50. (a) Using the circuit of Fig. 9.66, design an audio low-pass third-order Butterworth filter (see Prob. 9.42) to work into a 50-K resistor from a 50-K source so that the cutoff frequency occurs at 20 kc.

(b) Repeat (a) but design a third-order Chebyshev filter (see Prob.

9.43) to be used in the same application as the Butterworth filter of (*a*).

(*c*) Convert the filter obtained in (*a*) to a bandpass filter centered at 100 kc with bandwidth 20 kc, and the same impedance level (50 K).

(*d*) Convert the filter obtained in (*b*) to a bandpass filter centered at 80 kc with a 20-kc bandwidth, and the same impedance level (50 K).

9.3 Noise

The word *noise* usually refers to unpleasant sound. In general, it has little to do with the kind of sound, or its waveshape, but rather the mental state of the auditor. The sound of children playing might seem like music at three in the afternoon, but it is noise at eleven in the evening. No such indefinite standard can be used in engineering; noise must be something more specific.

The word *random* is the key to an engineering definition of noise. A purely random signal is one whose magnitude cannot be predicted with certainty. However, if a waveform is known, it is not considered noise. Thus, even though the output of a radio may be swamped by a 60-cps hum, the interfering signal is not considered noise, because it has a familiar half-wave rectified sinusoidal waveform and its variation with respect to time in the future is completely predictable. The reasons for this are clear if we realize that the hum in a radio is symptomatic of a defective part, usually a filter capacitor in the power supply, and hence can be eliminated. To be classified as noise the signal must have an element of unpredictibility—it must be random. Therefore, its emotional effect does not enter into this definition.

The simplest view we can take of noise is that the noise signal may be considered to be a large collection of short pulses, each of which is similar in shape but occurring in time in a random fashion. The pulses may overlap or not, the essential elements being that there are a large number of these pulses and that there is no regularity in their appearance.

If the shower in the bathroom is dripping, then one drop of water falls every few seconds. The audio signal caused thereby is a periodic set of pulses. A signal of this kind will not be considered noise by an electrical engineer simply because it is periodic, and hence predictable. (In fact, it is its periodicity that is so annoying to the listener!) If the water is turned on, many drops will strike the shower walls and floor at various points. The result is a hissing sound, like rain on the roof, which is not altogether unpleasant to the ear, and in fact can operate as an excellent sedative. Consider, for example, the group of drops leaving the shower head at any instant. Because the directions they take are all different, each drop strikes the wall or floor at a time different from the others. These individual collisions produce audio pulses that are nearly identical in waveform but are distributed in time in a random fashion.

Noise, such as that produced by the shower, is annoying only when it interferes with the transmission of signals. If the level of the signal is small compared to the level of the noise, the signal may well become completely unintelligible or undetectable. The ultimate limitation of any piece of electronic equipment is always noise. The reception of radio signals from transmitters distantly located is limited by the relative amplitudes of the signal and the noise at the receiver's antenna.

In this section a mathematical description of noise will be presented, and some of the types of noise encountered by engineers will be discussed. A thorough understanding of these ideas rests upon the *theory of probability*, a mathematical study much too extensive to include in this book. Moreover, a knowledge of probability is not a prerequisite for this study. As a result, we will be required to take some statements on faith.

Random Pulse Trains

Let $p(t)$ represent a pulse—a time-limited signal with a finite maximum value. Then $p(t)$ has a Fourier transform, which will be denoted by $P(f)$. Now consider a train of N of these pulses all identical in waveform and amplitude, but occurring at times t_1, t_2, t_3, ..., t_N. The t_k may be widely separated or they may be close together so that pulses overlap.

It will be supposed that N, the number of pulses, is very large, and that the total time between the first and last pulse, $t_N - t_1 = T$, is very large compared to the length of one pulse.

The pulse train has a Fourier transform $P_t(f)$ which, from the real translation theorem, can be written as

$$P_t(f) = P(f) \left[e^{-j2\pi f t_1} + e^{-j2\pi f t_2} + \ldots + e^{-j2\pi f t_N} \right] \qquad (9.108)$$

Figure 9.70(*a*) depicts a pulse of the type referred to in this discussion, and Fig. 9.70(*b*) shows the result of a random group of such pulses.

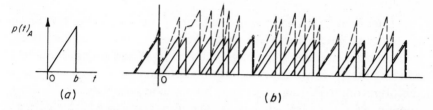

Fig. 9.70   (a) *A pulse.* (b) *A random group of such pulses. The dashed line in* (b) *indicates the sum of the pulses.*

The energy density spectrum $\Phi(f)$ of any signal is the magnitude squared of its transform, and so the spectrum of the random pulse train is

$$\Phi(f) = |P(f)|^2 |e^{-j2\pi f t_1} + e^{-j2\pi f t_2} + \dots + e^{-j2\pi f t_N}|^2 \qquad (9.109)$$

It is clear that the spectrum cannot be calculated unless the times t_k are known. It is possible, however, to find an *average* spectrum for such a signal.

Let us assume that we have a group of several pulse trains, each made by using exactly N pulses of the same type and distributed over the same time interval T. Thus there are infinitely many different pulse trains we could construct in this manner, the only difference between any two being the choice of the times t_k. Such a set of signals is called an *ensemble*. We might then ask: If all conceivable pulse trains are taken and their spectra computed, what would the average of all these spectra look like?

Equation (9.109) indicates that each spectrum would have $|P(f)|^2$ as a multiplier. Then on the assumption that the t_k are chosen at random, we shall attempt to find the average of the magnitude squared of

$$e^{-j2\pi f t_1} + e^{-j2\pi f t_2} + \dots + e^{-j2\pi f t_N}$$

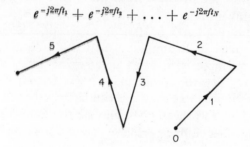

Fig. 9.71   *The addition of five complex numbers all of whose amplitudes are unity but whose angles are chosen at random.*

Each term in this expression is a complex number whose magnitude is unity and whose angle is $-2\pi f t_k$. Figure 9.71 shows the sum of five such complex numbers, the angles chosen in some random fashion. It will be noted that we could be anywhere from 0 to N steps away from the origin after adding N such numbers together. What we want to know is, *on the average*, what is the magnitude squared of the distance from the origin after N steps?

This problem is known as a two-dimensional *random-walk* problem. In the theory of probability the problem would be stated in another way:

Starting at the origin, proceed to take one step in any arbitrary direction. After that take another step in some other arbitrary direction. For example, you might have a small spinning pointer on a 360° scale and, after each step, spin the needle and take the next step in the direction indicated by the needle when it stops spinning. Now suppose that 5000 people, each with a spinner, start from 5000 different origins and each takes 100 steps. Upon concluding the experiment the number of steps displaced from the origin of each is noted and squared. The squares are then averaged. What do you think the average would be? In fact, what do you think the average distance from the origins would be? (The average square is always larger than the square of the average.)

It is possible that a few people could get as far away as 100 steps, but this seems unlikely since the spinner would have to come to rest in the same direction every time. It is even more likely that many of the people will be back near the point of departure, having walked around in circles. The rest will be scattered at varying distances from 0 to 100 steps from their respective origins. Although this may seem difficult to believe, the average distance from the origin will be near 9 steps and the average square of the distance from the origin will be near 100, the same as the number of steps.

Because this result may be difficult to accept, a simpler problem in probability is given in Example 9.6 with the solution included. The object of the example is to assist in assessing intuition in problems involving *chance*. Try this problem on your friends (both male and female) and see if your experience is similar to the author's.

EXAMPLE 9.6. Two people are playing the following game: While sitting on a park bench one person will write down the last two digits of the license plates of each car as it passes in the street. Some number N (to be determined) of these double-digit numbers will be recorded. (We shall assume that no letters appear—only pairs of digits 0 through 9.) The one writing the numbers down (observed carefully by the other for purposes of accuracy) bets five dollars that *at least* two double-digit numbers will match. The observer bets five dollars that *no two* will match. Thus, for example, the writer wins the bet if two 36's or two 91's or three 16's appear (and so on), and the observer wins if all the two-digit numbers are different.

Since the bet carries 50/50 odds (even money), the number N cannot be too large to keep the game fair. How large should N be for a fair game? Do not attempt to solve the problem (if you know how), just guess!

Solution: If $N = 12$, the observer has a slight edge over the writer (the odds in his favor are about 81/80); if $N = 13$, the writer has a definite edge over the observer (the odds are about 5/4 in *his* favor). For the game to be fair, N should be set at 12 and the two persons should alternate in the roles of observer and writer.

As a rule women *who do not gamble* usually come fairly close to 12 or 15. The others respond much the same way men do, who usually say N should be 50, which accounts for the ruin of so many would-be gamblers. Some men have said 101. These men should never bet on anything!

The simplest way to solve the problem is to calculate the probability that the observer will win. Assuming the last two numbers on the license plates are random then the probability that the second pair will *not* match the first is 99/100, since no matter what the first number was the second can be any of 99 others and no match will occur. The probability that the third will not match the first or second is now 98/100 since there are only 98 numbers now which are not duplicates of the two already observed and recorded. If one continues in this fashion then the probability of no match in 12 cars is

$$1 \times .99 \times .98 \times \ldots \times .89 \doteq 0.503$$

Then the probability of at least one match is 0.497 and the odds are $0.503/0.497 \doteq 81/80$ that no match will occur.

It may seem difficult to believe that the average squared magnitude of the exponential series in Eq. (9.109) is N, the number of pulses, provided that N is large. Although the following is not rigorous, it may help us to appreciate the result:

Suppose each of the 5000 people have taken n random steps. Let R_n represent the distance of any one man from his point of origin after the nth step. Then he will have polar coordinates R_n and θ, where θ is his angular position relative to some coordinate axis, as shown in Fig. 9.72.

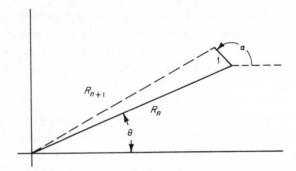

Fig. 9.72   *The distances R_n and R_{n+1} from the origin after the nth and $(n+1)$st steps in the random walk.*

In the next spin of the needle suppose the angle of his next step is α. Then his new position R_{n+1} from the origin will be given by

$$
\begin{aligned}
R_{n+1}^2 &= (R_n \cos \theta + \cos \alpha)^2 + (R_n \sin \theta + \sin \alpha)^2 \\
&= R_n^2 \cos^2 \theta + 2R_n \cos \theta \cos \alpha + \cos^2\alpha + R_n^2 \sin^2 \theta \\
&\qquad + 2R_n \sin \theta \sin \alpha + \sin^2 \alpha \\
&= R_n^2 + 1 + 2R_n \cos (\theta - \alpha)
\end{aligned}
$$

But the angle α is independent of the angle θ, and so, on the average, $\cos (\theta - \alpha)$ will be zero. Then, on the average,

$$
R_{n+1}^2 = R_n^2 + 1
$$

After the first step R_1 must equal one, so

$$
R_n^2 = n
$$

will be the average squared distance from the origin of a large number of random walks consisting of n steps.

We have assumed that the angles $-2\pi f t_k$ are random simply because the t_k are random. For any nonzero f this can be shown to be true. For $f = 0$, however, all the angles are zero, and the squared magnitude of the series becomes N^2. As the numbers N and T become large, the energy grows and the spectrum approaches infinity everywhere. This can be avoided by defining the *power density spectrum*, $\Psi(f)$, of the pulse train as the energy density divided by T. Then, if on the average n pulses occur per sec, $N = nT$ and $\Psi(f)$ approaches

$$
\frac{nT |P(f)|^2}{T} = n |P(f)|^2 \qquad \text{for } f \neq 0
$$

and approaches $n^2T|P(0)|^2$ as f approaches zero. As T becomes infinite this can be shown to approach an impulse at $f = 0$ since $P(0)$ is simply the area under the pulse, and if this is not zero then there will be an average value to the signal, a constant, which will have a constant average (d–c) power associated with it. In fact, if the pulse were a current or a voltage pulse on a one-ohm level, the area of the pulse times the number of pulses per sec gives the zero-frequency average: $NP(0)/T = nP(0)$. The average power associated with this is simply $n^2P^2(0)$ watts per ohm, and the power density spectrum for this average is simply an impulse of area $n^2P^2(0)$ at $f = 0$. Then Eq. (9.109) can be altered to yield the *power density spectrum*, $\Psi(f)$, as

$$\Psi(f) = n^2P^2(0)\,\delta(f) + n\,|P(f)|^2 \qquad (9.110)$$

watts per cps (one-ohm level).

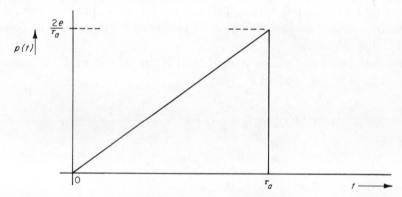

Fig. 9.73   *The current pulse induced in a circuit connected to a high-vacuum diode, caused by the transit of one electron from cathode to plate.*

EXAMPLE 9.7. The current pulse induced in the circuit connected to a high-vacuum diode by an electron traveling from the cathode to the plate in the diode can be shown to be given by

$$p(t) = \frac{2e}{\tau_a^2}\,t[\mathbf{1}(t) - \mathbf{1}(t-\tau_a)] \text{ amp}$$

where τ_a is the transit time of the electron in sec—that is, the length of time it takes the electron to go from the cathode to the plate. The diode is assumed to have parallel-plane electrodes separated by d meters, and e is the magnitude of the charge of the electron, 1.6×10^{-19} coulomb. It is also assumed that the electron leaves the cathode with zero velocity and the anode is V volts above the cathode. As a result it can be shown that

$$\tau_a = d \sqrt{\frac{2m}{eV}}$$

where m is the mass of the electron in kilograms, 9.11×10^{-28}. Specifically, $e/m = 1.759 \times 10^{11}$ coul/kg and so

$$\tau_a = 3.36 \times 10^{-6} \frac{d}{\sqrt{V}} \text{ sec}$$

Figure 9.73 shows a sketch of $p(t)$.

Express the power density spectrum of the diode current in terms of its average or d–c value, I_{d-c}, and plot the spectrum. Assume that the flight of any one electron is independent of any other, so that the current is truly a random pulse train. This will be the case in practice when the diode is *temperature limited*. The noise produced by these current pulses is called *shot* noise.

Solution: Since $P(f)$ is desired, then it is simplest to find the Laplace transform of $p(t)$, and set $s = j2\pi f$:

$$\mathscr{L}\left[p(t)\right] = \frac{2e}{\tau_a^2} \cdot \frac{1}{s^2}(1 - e^{-s\tau_a}) - \frac{2e}{\tau_a} \cdot \frac{1}{s} e^{-s\tau_a}$$

$$= \frac{2e}{s^2 \tau_a^2}\left[1 - e^{-s\tau_a} - s\tau_a e^{-s\tau_a}\right]$$

Notice that s always appears with a τ_a, and so $s\tau_a = j2\pi f\tau_a$ will yield the Fourier transform. For convenience let

$$\theta = \pi f \tau_a$$

so that $s\tau_a = j2\theta$. Then

$$P(f) = \frac{2e}{-4\theta^2}\left[1 - e^{-j2\theta} - j2\theta e^{-j2\theta}\right]$$

$$= \frac{-e}{2\theta^2}\left[1 - \cos 2\theta + j \sin 2\theta - j2\theta (\cos 2\theta - j \sin 2\theta)\right]$$

$$= \frac{-e}{2\theta^2}\left[1 - \cos 2\theta - 2\theta \sin 2\theta + j(\sin 2\theta - 2\theta \cos 2\theta)\right]$$

Since the magnitude squared of this is desired, then the sum of the squares of the real and imaginary parts is

$$|P(f)|^2 = \frac{e^2}{4\theta^4}[2 + 4\theta^2 - 2(\cos + 2\theta \sin 2\theta)]$$

$$= \frac{e^2}{\theta^4}[\theta^2 + \sin^2 \theta - \theta \sin 2\theta]$$

$$= \frac{e^2}{\theta^4}(\theta^2 + \sin^2 \theta - \sin \theta \cos \theta)$$

We can find $P(0)$ from the last expression by using L'Hôpital's rule, but it is easier to find the area of $p(t)$. From Fig. 9.73 this area is seen to be e, and so $p^2(0) = e^2$.

Since $I_{d-c} = ne$, the magnitude of the impulse at $f = 0$ is I_{d-c}^2 and so

$$\Psi(f) = I_{d-c}^2\delta(f) + \frac{I_{d-c}}{e}\frac{e^2}{\theta^4}(\theta^2 + \sin^2 \theta - 2\theta \sin \theta \cos \theta)$$

$$= I_{d-c}^2\delta(f) + I_{d-c}e\frac{(\pi f \tau_a)^2 + \sin^2 \pi f \tau_a - 2\pi f \tau_a \sin \pi f \tau_a \cos \pi f \tau_a}{(\pi f \tau_a)^4}$$

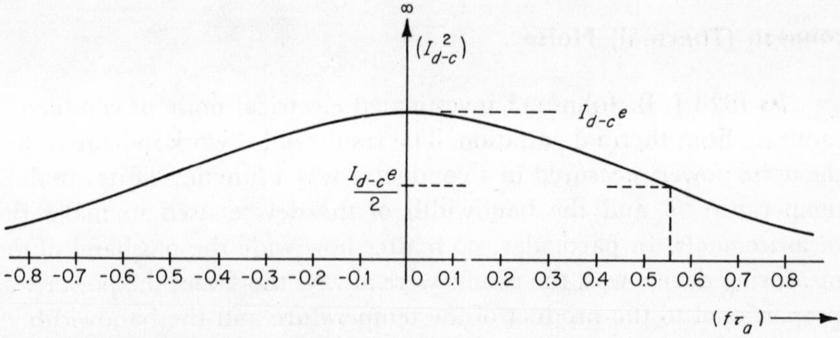

Fig. 9.74 *The spectrum of the diode current in* temperature-limited *operation.*

The spectrum is plotted in Fig. 9.74. Note that for low frequencies it is nearly a constant of value $I_{d-c}e$. Observe that the half-power point comes at about $0.554/\tau_a$ and that the spectrum is flat below $f = 0.1/\tau_a$. For a diode spacing of about 2 mm and a voltage of 100 volts the half-power point occurs at about 8.3 mc and the spectrum is nearly constant below 2 mc. For audio work the spectrum may certainly be considered flat.

PROBLEMS

9.51. Find the power density spectrum of a random pulse train of current each pulse of which has the waveform shown in Fig. 9.75. Assume that, on the average, $n = 10^{10}$ pulses occur per second.

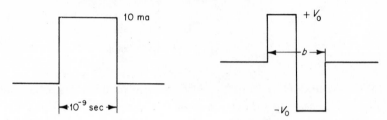

Fig. 9.75 *Problem 9.51.*   **Fig. 9.76** *Problem 9.52.*

9.52. Find the power density spectrum of a random voltage pulse train each pulse of which has the waveform shown in Fig. 9.76. Assume that an average of n pulses occur per sec.

$$\text{Answer: } \Psi(f) = \frac{4nV_0^2}{\pi^2 f^2} \sin^4 \frac{\pi f b}{2}$$

Johnson (Thermal) Noise

In 1928 J. B. Johnson[*] investigated electrical noise in conductors resulting from thermal agitation. The results of his work indicated that the noise power measured in a conductor was a function of its absolute temperature T and the bandwidth of the device used to make the measurements. In particular, no matter how wide the passband of the measuring device was, the results were always the same: the power was proportional to the product of the temperature and the bandwidth.

Then the power density spectrum of Johnson noise must be a constant with frequency and independent of the size of the conductor. In particular,

$$\Psi(f) = 2kT \text{ watts/cps} \tag{9.111}$$

for as high a frequency as it has been possible to measure. Boltzmann's constant k is 1.374×10^{-23} joule/°K. Noise signals, such as this, that

---

[*]J. B. Johnson, "Thermal Agitation of Electricity in Conductors," *Phys. Rev.*, Vol. 32 (July, 1928), p. 97.

have a constant-amplitude spectrum are referred to as *white noise* since all frequencies are present in equal amounts. The analogy is with white light, which is the presence of all colors.

Since power in a resistance is given by v^2/R, the noise voltage in a resistance of R ohms has a spectral density or a transform squared of $2kTR$. Similarly, the spectral density function of the current is $2kT/R$. Thus, denoting these spectra by $\Psi_v(f)$ and $\Psi_i(f)$ for voltage and current, respectively,

$$\Psi_v(f) = 2kTR \text{ volt}^2/\text{cps} \tag{9.112}$$

and

$$\Psi_i(f) = 2kT/R \text{ amp}^2/\text{cps} \tag{9.113}$$

If this noise is the input of an ideal low-pass filter, then the output power is

$$P_n = \int_{-f_c}^{f_c} \Psi(f) \, df$$

$$= 4kTf_c \text{ watts/cps} \tag{9.114}$$

Because this expression tends to infinity as f_c, the cutoff frequency, becomes infinite, it is clear that the density spectrum cannot remain constant all the way out to $f = \infty$, for then the power would be infinite. The half-power frequency has not been discovered and seems to be well beyond the frequency range at which it is proper to refer to the notions of the lumped elements R, L, and C.

In amplifiers the magnitude of the noise voltage or current is more important than the actual power involved, and so the mean-square voltage or current are usually of primary interest. As a result the spectra given by Eqs. (9.112) and (9.113) will be used exclusively.

Probably the most curious result of this study is the fact that the total noise power density does not depend on the size of the conductor at all. The noise power density produced in a miniature resistor of any size is the same as that of the large resistors used on locomotives to dissipate the heat caused by dynamic braking. Furthermore, the act of soldering two resistors together will have the effect of cutting the total noise power in half, since the act of soldering makes the two resistors become one.

When combinations of resistances occur, we can readily calculate the noise mean-square voltage or current density functions of the combination by using Eqs. (9.112) and (9.113) by first finding the equivalent resistance of the combination and using this value for R in those equations.

We can also define equivalent circuits for resistances involving what look like noise-voltage or noise-current sources in series or in parallel with a *noiseless* resistance. This is shown in Fig. 9.77, where it will be noted that the sources are not labeled in volts or amperes but rather with their spectral density functions Ψ_v or Ψ_i whose units are volts-squared per cps (to be abbreviated v²/cps) or amperes-squared per cps (abbreviated a²/cps) respectively. Observe also that no polarity marks or arrows are used, since the value of the source is the magnitude of the spectral density function. This leads to a technique which might be called the *circuit theory of noise.*

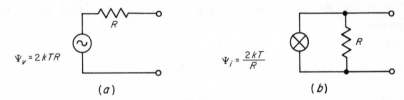

$\Psi_v = 2kTR$ (a) $\Psi_i = \dfrac{2kT}{R}$ (b)

Fig. 9.77   (a) *The equivalent circuit of a noisy resistance represented by a noise voltage source in series with a noiseless resistance.* (b) *The equivalent circuit of a noisy resistance represented by a noise current source in parallel with a noiseless resistance. Observe that the units of the sources are v²/cps and a²/cps respectively, since the sources are labeled with the magnitude of the spectrum density functions.*

Circuit Theory of Noise

If two resistors are connected in series, then the total noise power density of the combination is

$$\Psi(f) = 2kT \text{ watts/cps}$$

Then the mean-square noise voltage density must be

$$\frac{\Psi_v}{(R_1+R_2)} = 2kT$$

or

$$\Psi_v = 2kT\,(R_1+R_2)$$

since Ψ_v has units of v²/cps and power is v^2/R. Now before connecting the two resistors the mean-square voltage density of R_1 alone was $2kTR_1$ and that of R_2 was $2kTR_2$. It appears then that the act of connecting them in series is equivalent to adding the mean-square voltage *densities* and not in adding the two voltages as one would normally do with sources in series.

If two resistors are connected in parallel then the current source representation of the resistance will lead to the appropriate equivalent circuit for the combination if the mean-square current densities are added rather than the currents themselves. This can be seen since for a resistance R_1 alone the mean-square current density is $2kT/R_1$ and for a resistance R_2 alone the density would be $2kT/R_2$. The sum of these densities is $2kT(1/R_1+1/R_2)$ which is the same result we would have obtained if we had first calculated the equivalent resistance of the parallel combination and divided this into $2kT$. It is assumed, of course, that all resistors are at the same temperature, for otherwise the addition process would have to take the different temperatures into account.

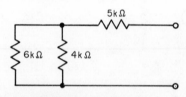

Fig. 9.78 *Example 9.8.*

EXAMPLE 9.8. In the circuit of Fig. 9.78 find the equivalent mean-square noise voltage and current of the combination of resistances shown by two methods: (1) by finding the equivalent resistance of the combination and using Eqs. (9.112) and (9.113), and (2) by drawing an equivalent circuit for each resistor and combining the mean-square sources in the conventional manner. Assume that all resistors are at 68°F. *Solution:* Using method (1) we find that the equivalent resistance of the combination is $5 + (6 \times 4)/(6 + 4) = 7.4$ K. Since $2kT = 8.06 \times 10^{-21}$ when $T = 293°K$ ($=20°C=68F°$) then

$$\Psi_v = 8.06 \times 10^{-21} \times 7400 = 5.96 \times 10^{-17} v^2/cps$$

and the mean-square current density function is

$$\Psi_i = \frac{8.06 \times 10^{-21}}{7400} = 1.09 \times 10^{-24} a^2/cps$$

Using method (2) we get a circuit (Fig. 9.79) that shows equivalent sources for each resistance. In (*a*) the parallel sources are current sources and the series source with the 5-K resistor is a voltage source.

Figure 9.79(b) shows the two current sources combined into one by addition of density functions:

$$\frac{2kT}{6000} + \frac{2kT}{4000} = \frac{5 \times 10^{-3}\, kT}{6}$$

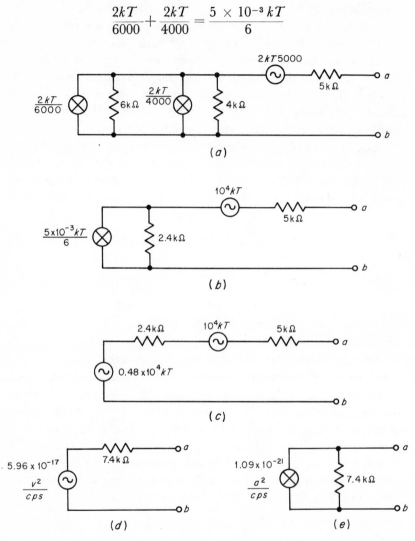

Fig. 9.79   *The reduction of a noise-resistance equivalent circuit to a circuit involving only one resistance and one source.*

The equivalent resistance of the 6-K and 4-K resistors is 2.4 K. In Fig. 9.79(c) the current source and the 2.4-K resistance are replaced by their Thévènin equivalent, the mean-square voltage density function being simply the current density function multiplied by R^2—that is, 5×10^{-3}

$kT/6$ multiplied by $(2400)^2$. This yields $0.48 \times 10^4 kT$ v²/cps, and when added to $2kT5000 = 10^4 kT$, the density function of the 5-K resistance, results in $1.48 \times 10^4 kT = 5.96 \times 10^{-17}$ v²/cps. Dividing this voltage density function by $(7400)^2$ yields the equivalent current source representation appearing in Fig. 79.9(*e*).

EXAMPLE 9.9. Find the equivalent noise voltage density function for the voltage across the 500-ohm resistor in Fig. 9.80.

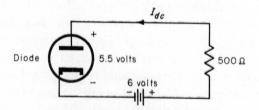

Fig. 9.80 *Example 9.9.*

Solution: Since the circuit of Fig. 9.80 indicates that the d–c voltage across the 500-ohm resistor is 0.5 volt, then the current must be 1 ma. Assuming that the diode is temperature limited, the density function of the shot-noise current produced by 1 ma d-c is $I_{d-c} e = 10^{-3} \times 1.6 \times 10^{-19} = 1.6 \times 10^{-22}$ a²/cps. If the resistance were noiseless this would produce a mean-square noise voltage density of $1.6 \times 10^{-22}(500)^2 = 4 \times 10^{-17}$ v²/cps. The resistance by itself would produce a noise density function of $2kT(500) = 0.403 \times 10^{-17}$ v²/cps again assuming that $T = 293°$K. Now since the two sources of noise are unrelated or independent of each other, the density functions add. It will be assumed here that the diode noise is flat also. This is a legitimate assumption unless the system to be affected by the noise has a bandwidth that goes well into the megacycle region.

It is not at all obvious that the density functions caused by shot noise and Johnson noise will add. This can be proved using probability theory or it can be demonstrated in the laboratory. Whenever the noise sources are produced independently it is correct to add density functions, so

$$\Psi_v = 4.4 \times 10^{-17} \text{ v²/cps}$$

LOSSLESS ELEMENTS

Lossless elements have the effect of altering the shape of the spectral density functions. For example, if a signal whose transform is $V(f)$ is applied to a filter whose transfer function is $H(f)$, the output transform is simply $V(f)H(f)$. The energy spectrum of the input is $|V(f)|^2$ and that of the output is $|V(f)|^2|H(f)|^2$. It is entirely reasonable to assume that with a power density function of the input equal to $\Psi_v(f)$, then the power density function of the output is simply $\Psi_v(f)|H(f)|^2$. This is true because the power density spectrum was obtained by simply dividing the energy density function by T, the duration of the signal. If this is done to both the input and output signals, their ratio must still be $|H(f)|^2$.

With shot or thermal noise the spectral densities are essentially constants at most usable frequencies, although the diode noise can fall off noticeably if transit times are large. For the purposes of this section, however, the diode spectrum will be considered a constant.

Then the spectrum of the noise after having passed through a device whose transfer function is $H(f)$ will simply be proportional to $|H(f)|^2$, the proportionality factor being the spectral density of the input.

EXAMPLE 9.10. For the circuit of Fig. 9.81 find the spectral density function of the resistance voltage and find the total mean-square noise voltage across the resistor. Also find the root-mean-square (rms) voltage across the resistor due only to the noise.

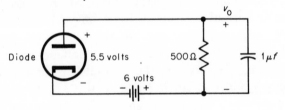

Fig. 9.81   *Example 9.10.*

Solution: Observe that the circuit is exactly the same as the circuit of Fig. 9.80 except for the 1-μf capacitor connected across the 500-ohm resistor. Then, in the absence of the capacitor the noise spectrum would have been 4.4×10^{-17} v²/cps, which could be represented by a voltage source with this noise density in series with a 500-ohm noiseless resistance. This is shown in Fig. 9.82. The output voltage, v_o, of the network is evidently the voltage across the capacitance which is the same as the voltage across the resistance in the original network. The transfer function of the R-C network is

$$H(f) = \frac{1/Cs}{R+1/Cs}\bigg/_{s=j2\pi f}$$

$$= \frac{1}{1+j2\pi RCf} = \frac{1}{1+j(f/f_c)}$$

where $f_c = 1/(2\pi RC) = 10^3/\pi = 318$ cps since $R = 500$ and $C = 10^{-6}$. Then

$$|H(f)|^2 = \frac{1}{1 + (f/f_c)^2}$$

and so the spectral density of the output voltage* must be

$$\Psi_v = \frac{4.4 \times 10^{-17}}{1 + (f/318)^2} \text{ v}^2/\text{cps}$$

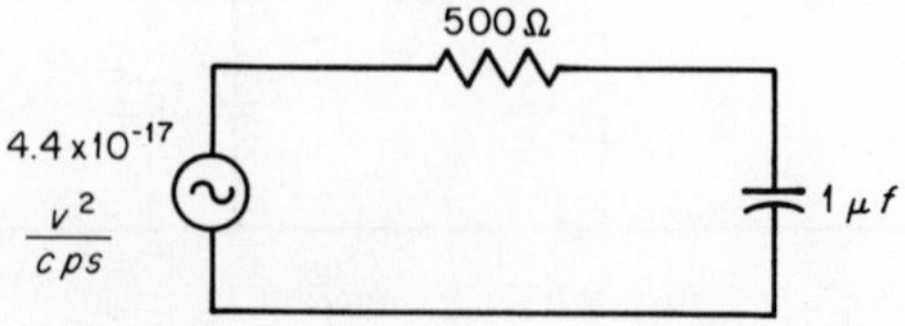

Fig. 9.82 *A noise equivalent circuit for the circuit of Fig. 9.81.*

To find the total mean-square noise voltage it is now necessary to integrate the density function over all frequencies:

$$\overline{v^2} = \int_{-\infty}^{\infty} \Psi_v \, df = \int_{-\infty}^{\infty} \frac{4.4 \times 10^{-17}}{1 + (f/f_c)^2} \, df = 2f_c \int_{0}^{\infty} \frac{4.4 \times 10^{-17}}{1 + (f/f_c)^2} \, d\left(\frac{f}{f_c}\right)$$

$$= 2 \times 318 \times 4.4 \times 10^{-17} \tan^{-1} \frac{f}{f_c} \Big|_{0}^{\infty} = 2.8 \times 10^{-14} \times \frac{\pi}{2}$$

$$= 4.4 \times 10^{-14} \text{ v}^2$$

The symbol $\overline{v^2}$ means the *average* of the voltage squared. The rms noise voltage is the square root of the last result or

$$v_{\text{rms}} = 0.21 \ \mu\text{v}$$

Observe that the presence of the capacitor has the effect of filtering out the noise at the high-frequency end of the spectrum.

The previous example demonstrates the general procedure for solving for rms noise voltages produced in a circuit in which lossless elements create a bandpass or low-pass filter. For high-pass filters, of course, the result would be infinite, since it has been assumed that the spectrum of the noise source is constant all the way out to infinity. For the

---

*There is, of course, an impulse at $f = 0$ of area $(\frac{1}{2})^2 = \frac{1}{4}$ as a result of the d-c component of the voltage.

latter situation it is necessary to specify the upper frequency being considered or else be content with the spectral density function alone. Another example will prove instructive.

EXAMPLE 9.11. In the circuit of Fig. 9.83, find the spectral density function and rms value of the output noise voltage, v_0, across the 5-K resistance.

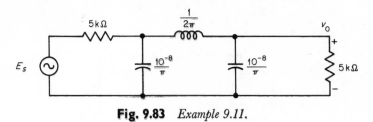

Fig. 9.83   *Example 9.11.*

Solution: Note in Fig. 9.83 the third-order Butterworth filter with cutoff frequency at 10^4 cps. This can be deduced by working from the circuit pictured in Fig. 9.84 towards that of Fig. 9.83 by making the appropriate impedance-level and bandwidth changes.

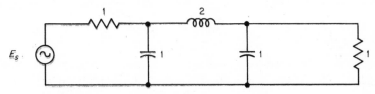

Fig. 9.84   *A third-order Butterworth low-pass filter.*

Now it must be noted that there are two sources of noise, the two 5-K resistors. Both resistors will be affected by the action of the filter, but the noise of the output resistor will not be affected in the same manner as that of the input resistor. This can be seen by solving the problem by superposition. The actual source will be removed since it is not involved in the computation and two equivalent noise-current sources will be inserted in parallel with noiseless resistances. (Although voltage sources would do as well, the circuit is more amenable to the nodal method). Figure 9.85 shows the noise equivalent circuit, the noise-current sources each being represented by spectral density functions of $2kT/5000 = 1.61 \times 10^{-24}$ a²/cps. Call the current source on the left I_1 and that on the right I_2. It is now necessary to obtain *two* transfer functions, one relating V_2 (the transform of the output voltage in Fig. 9.85) to I_1 and one relating V_2 to I_2.

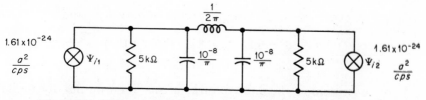

Fig. 9.85 *The equivalent noise circuit for the circuit of Fig. 9.83.*

Forgetting for the moment about noise, and writing the nodal equations of the network:

$$\left(\frac{10^{-8}}{\pi}s + \frac{1}{5000} + \frac{2\pi}{s}\right)V_1 - \frac{2\pi}{s}V_2 = I_1$$

$$-\frac{2\pi}{s}V_1 + \left(\frac{10^{-8}}{\pi}s + \frac{1}{5000} + \frac{2\pi}{s}\right)V_2 = I_2$$

or

$$(s^2 + 2\pi \times 10^4 s + 2\pi^2 \times 10^8)V_1 - 2\pi^2 \times 10^8 V_2 = \pi \times 10^8 s I_1$$

$$-2\pi^2 \times 10^8 V_1 + (s^2 + 2\pi \times 10^4 s + 2\pi^2 \times 10^8)V_2 = \pi \times 10^8 s I_2$$

Solving for V_2 gives

$$V_2 = \frac{2\pi^3 \times 10^{16} I_1 + \pi \times 10^8 (s^2 + 2\pi \times 10^4 s + 2\pi^2 \times 10^8) I_2}{s^3 + 4\pi \times 10^4 s^2 + 8\pi^2 \times 10^8 s + 8\pi^3 \times 10^{12}}$$

Thus the two transfer functions sought are

$$\frac{V_2}{I_1} = \frac{2\pi^3 \times 10^{16}}{s^3 + 4\pi \times 10^4 s^2 + 8\pi^2 \times 10^8 s + 8\pi^3 \times 10^{12}}$$

and

$$\frac{V_2}{I_2} = \frac{\pi \times 10^8 (s^2 + 2\pi \times 10^4 s + 2\pi^2 \times 10^8)}{s^3 + 4\pi \times 10^4 s^2 + 8\pi^2 \times 10^8 s + 8\pi^3 \times 10^{12}}$$

If s is set equal to $j2\pi f$ the transfer functions become

$$\frac{V_2}{I_1} = \frac{2500}{1 - 2(f/10^4)^2 + j[2(f/10^4) - (f/10^4)^3]}$$

and

$$\frac{V_2}{I_2} = \frac{2500\,[1 - 2(f/10^4)^2 + j2(f/10^4)]}{1 - 2(f/10^4)^2 + j[2(f/10^4) - (f/10^4)^3]}$$

Since the magnitude squared of these transfer functions is desired, then

$$\left|\frac{V_2}{I_1}\right|^2 = \frac{6.25 \times 10^6}{1 + (f/10^4)^6}$$

as might be expected since it is a third-order Butterworth, and

$$\left|\frac{V_2}{I_2}\right|^2 = \frac{6.25 \times 10^6 \, [1 + 4(f/10^4)^4]}{1 + (f/10^4)^6}$$

By superposition, then, the spectral density at the output due to the noise source Ψ_{i1} alone is

$$\Psi_{v_2 i_1} = \frac{1.61 \times 10^{-24} \times 6.25 \times 10^6}{1 + (f/10^4)^6} = \frac{1.01 \times 10^{-17}}{1 + (f/10^4)^6} \quad \text{v}^2/\text{cps}$$

and that due to Ψ_{i2} alone is

$$\Psi_{v_2 i_2} = \frac{1.01 \times 10^{-17} \, [1 + 4(f/10^4)^4]}{1 + (f/10^4)^6} \quad \text{v}^2/\text{cps}$$

The *sum* of these two spectra is the total spectral density

$$\Psi_{v_2} = \frac{2.02 \times 10^{-17} \, [1 + 2(f/10^4)^4]}{1 + (f/10^4)^6} \quad \text{v}^2/\text{cps}$$

The mean-square noise voltage is obtained by integrating this result over all f:

$$\overline{v^2} = \int_{-\infty}^{\infty} \frac{2.02 \times 10^{-17} \, [1 + 2(f/10^4)^4] \, df}{1 + (f/10^4)^6}$$

Since the integrand is even, the integral may be taken over 0 to ∞ and multiplied by 2. Letting $x = f/10^4$ this expression becomes

$$\overline{v^2} = 4.04 \times 10^{-13} \int_0^{\infty} \frac{1 + 2x^4}{1 + x^6} \, dx$$

It can be shown by using the Beta function $B(m, n - m)$ that

$$\int_0^{\infty} \frac{x^{m-1}}{1 + x^n} \, dx = \frac{\pi}{n \sin (m\pi/n)}$$

if $0 < m < n$, and so

$$\int_0^{\infty} \frac{dx}{1 + x^6} = \frac{\pi}{3} \quad \text{and} \quad \int_0^{\infty} \frac{x^4 dx}{1 + x^6} = \frac{\pi}{3\sqrt{3}}$$

which makes

$$\overline{v^2} = 4.04 \times 10^{-13} \left[\frac{\pi}{3} + \frac{2\pi}{3\sqrt{3}}\right] = 9.12 \times 10^{-13} \text{ v}^2$$

and

$$v_{\text{rms}} = 0.956 \ \mu\text{v}$$

The examples above may be summarized in the following manner: To find the voltage spectral density function at any point in a circuit it is necessary to isolate all *independent* sources of noise power. As many as possible of these sources should be combined into fewer sources, if this can be done. Thus resistances in series or parallel should be combined into single resistances, and if a diode or other vacuum tube or transistor appears it may be possible to add its noise current or voltage spectrum to those of parallel or series resistances. When it is impossible to combine any more sources of noise resulting from the intercession of an L or a C in the network, it is then necessary to find all the transfer functions relating these sources (whether current or voltage) to the voltage or current whose noise spectrum is sought. The *sum* of all the individual spectra due to all combinations of sources and the appropriate transfer functions will then yield the desired spectrum. For a simplification of this technique applicable only to circuits not containing nonlinear devices see Probs. 9.61 and 9.62.

PROBLEMS

9.53. Find the voltage spectral density function at the terminals a and b for each of the circuits appearing in Fig. 9.86. Assume $T = 293°$K.

   Answers: (a) $8.06 \times 10^{-16} \text{ v}^2/\text{cps}$. (d) $3.49 \times 10^{-16} \text{ v}^2/\text{cps}$
   (f) $0.403 \times 10^{-16} \text{ v}^2/\text{cps}$.

9.54. Find the current spectral density function in the wires labeled with arrows in each of the circuits pictured in Fig. 9.87. Assume $T = 293°$ K.

   Answers: (b) $8.06 \times 10^{-25} \text{ a}^2/\text{cps}$ (d) $\dfrac{1.612 \times 10^{-24}}{1 + (2\pi f/10^4)^2} \text{ a}^2/\text{cps}$
   (e) $1.612 \times 10^{-21} \text{ a}^2/\text{cps}$

9.55. The circuit in Fig. 9.88 consists of a resistor R in parallel with a coil having an inductance of L henrys. Draw the equivalent noise voltage source for the resistance and, by using the transfer function relating this voltage to the current, deduce that the average energy stored in the coil is $kT/2$ joules.

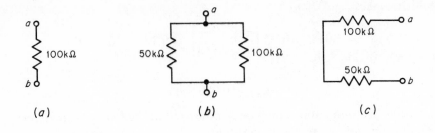

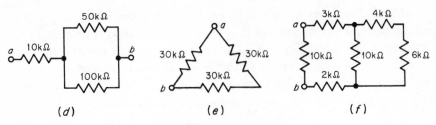

Fig. 9.86   *Problem 9.53.*

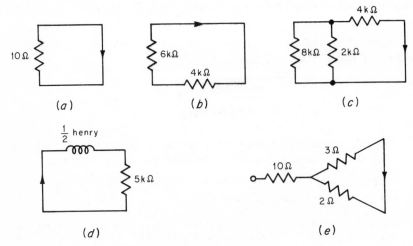

Fig. 9.87   *Problem 9.54.*

Fig. 9.88   *Problem 9.55.*   **Fig. 9.89**   *Problem 9.56.*

9.56. Draw the equivalent noise-current source in the circuit of Fig. 9.89 and show, as in Prob. 9.55, that the average stored energy in the capacitance is also $kT/2$.

9.57. Find the rms noise output voltage in the circuit of Fig. 9.90. Use $T = 293°K$.

Answer: 0.275 μv

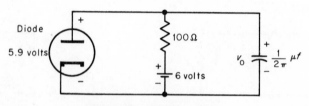

Fig. 9.90   *Problem 9.57.*

9.58. Find the spectral density function of the noise output voltage in the circuit of Fig. 9.91. Use $T = 293°K$.

Answer: $8.06 \times 10^{-18} \dfrac{1/3 + (f/1500)^2}{1 + (f/1500)^2}$

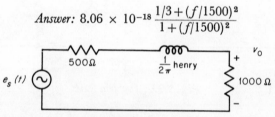

Fig. 9.91   *Problem 9.58.*

9.59. Prove that, for a low-pass first-order Butterworth filter the effective noise bandwidth is $\pi/2$ times the half-power frequency of the filter. Thus, if f_c is the positive half-power frequency, the noise power at the output due only to a resistance at the input would be $2kTR(2f_{\text{eff}}) = 4kTRf_{\text{eff}}$, where $f_{\text{eff}} = \pi f_c/2$.

9.60. Prove that, for an nth-order Butterworth low-pass filter the effective noise bandwidth is

$$f_{\text{eff}} = f_{\text{co}} \frac{\pi}{2n \sin (\pi/2n)}$$

where f_{co} is the positive half-power frequency of the filter and, for an input noise signal with a constant amplitude spectrum N, the mean-square value of the output noise is this amplitude N multiplied by $2f_{\text{eff}}$. Show that as $n \to \infty, f_{\text{eff}} \to f_{\text{co}}$.

9.61. For a linear bilateral network (one without vacuum tubes or transistors, for example, and only lumped R, L, and C terms) the spectral density of the noise voltage can be shown to be $2kTR(f)$, where $R(f)$ is the real part of the input impedance $Z(j\omega)$ at the terminals at which the spectral density is sought. Show that this is the case for each of the networks appearing in Fig. 9.92 by (1) finding the density function by ordinary use of transfer functions as is done in the text, and (2) finding the real part of the impedance between the appropriate terminals—that is, those for which the spectral density is sought. Assume that all the sources pictured in the figures are noiseless.

Answers: (b) $\dfrac{2kTL^2\omega^2/R}{1+(\omega L/R)^2}$ (c) $\dfrac{2kT[R_1(R_2C\omega)^2 + R_2 + R_2(R_1C\omega)^2]}{1 + [(R_1 + R_2)\,C\omega]^2}$

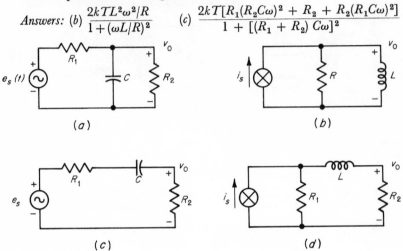

(a)   (b)

(c)   (d)

Fig. 9.92 *Problem 9.61.*

9.62. Calculate the real part of the impedance of the network in Fig. 9.83 when looking into the terminals labeled v_o. Show that $2kT$ times this real part is simply the spectral density function of the output voltage by comparing your result with the solution given to Example 9.11.

9.63. The equivalent noise circuit for an amplifier* can be shown to be the two-resistance network pictured in Fig. 9.93. The resistance R_g is usually made purposely large and the resistance R_{eq} represents the noise introduced by the vacuum tube and its associated resistances. The amplifier A has a voltage gain of A and is assumed to have infinite input impedance and to be noiseless.

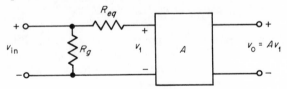

Fig. 9.93 *Problem 9.63.*

---

*For a description and derivation of this equivalent circuit see M. Schwartz (8), pp. 221-224.

Assume that the input signal is a noise source whose voltage spectral density function is a constant, $\mathcal{N}$, in the interval $|f| < f_m$, where f_m is some very large number. The amplifier will be assumed to be ideal and hence has a transfer function of A for all frequencies.

A signal is now applied to the input terminals of the amplifier through a generator whose internal impedance is R_s ohms, and hence the noise equivalent circuit can be represented as in Fig. 9.94. Note that the source labeled $\Psi_{vs} = \mathcal{N}$ has the constant spectrum previously

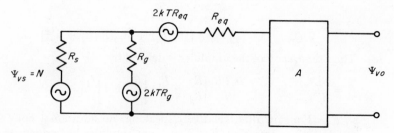

Fig. 9.94 *The equivalent noise circuit of the amplifier in Fig. 9.93.*

mentioned but that this may be greater than $2kTR_s$ if the signal comes from a signal generator with vacuum tubes and/or transistors in it. $\mathcal{N}$ cannot be less than $2kTR_s$. The resistances in Fig. 9.94 are assumed to be noiseless and at temperatures of $T = 293°K$. The labels on the sources are the respective voltage-noise density functions.

(a) Show that the spectral density Ψ_{vo} of the output noise voltage is

$$\Psi_{vo} = A^2 \mathcal{N} \left\{ \left[\frac{R_g}{R_s + R_g} \right]^2 + \frac{2kT}{\mathcal{N}} \left[R_g \left(\frac{R_s}{R_s + R_g} \right)^2 + R_{eq} \right] \right\}$$

(b) By applying a noiseless signal $v_{in}(t)$ to the amplifier as in Fig. 9.95, where R_s and R_g are assumed to be noiseless also, show that the noiseless output voltage will be

$$v_0(t) = \frac{AR_g}{R_s + R_g} v_{in}(t)$$

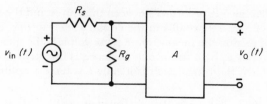

Fig. 9.95 *Problem 9.63(b).*

(c) If the signal-to-noise ratio when $v_{in}(t)$ and the noise are both present is defined as the ratio of the squared average of the signal voltage to the mean-square noise voltage, then the signal-to-noise ratio S/N at the input is

$$\frac{S}{N_{\text{in}}} = \frac{\overline{v_{\text{in}}^2}}{2Nf_m}$$

where the bandwidth of the noise is assumed finite since the noise cannot have infinite average power. The bar over $\overline{v_{\text{in}}^2}$ indicates the average.

Show that the signal-to-noise ratio at the output is

$$\frac{S}{N_{\text{out}}} = \frac{\overline{v_{\text{in}}^2}}{2Nf_m} \times \frac{1}{1 + (2kT/N)\,[(R_s^2/R_g) + R_{\text{eq}}(R_s/R_g + 1)^2]}$$

(d) The *noise figure* F of the amplifier is defined by

$$F = \frac{S/N_{\text{in}}}{S/N_{\text{out}}} = 1 + \frac{2kTR_s}{N}\left\{\frac{R_s}{R_g} + \frac{R_{\text{eq}}}{R_s}\left[\frac{R_s}{R_g} + 1\right]^2\right\}$$

so $F = 1$ means that, relatively speaking, no additional noise is added by the amplifier. For $F > 1$ the amplifier has added proportionally more noise power to the total signal than it has added signal power.

First, assuming that $N = a2kTR_s$, where $a \geq 1$, show that the minimum noise figure attainable by varying R_g and keeping a, R_s, and R_{eq} fixed is

$$F' = 1 + \frac{R_{\text{eq}}}{aR_s}$$

Second, assuming again that $N = a2kTR_s$, where $a \geq 1$, show that the minimum noise figure attainable by varying R_s and keeping a, R_g, and R_{eq} fixed occurs when

$$R_s = \sqrt{\frac{R_g R_{\text{eq}}}{1 + R_{\text{eq}}/R_g}}$$

and is

$$F'' = 1 + \frac{2}{a}\sqrt{\frac{R_{\text{eq}}}{R_g}}\,[\sqrt{R_{\text{eq}}/R_g} + \sqrt{1 + R_{\text{eq}}/R_g}]$$

9.64. *Continuation.* Placing a transformer between the source and the amplifier in the circuit of Fig. 9.93 results in the circuit shown in Fig. 9.96. The effect is that of raising the mean-square noise voltage, the mean-square signal voltage, and R_s by a factor of n^2, where n is the turns ratio of the transformer. Then the transformer is ideally a voltage amplifier with a noise figure of 1.

The amplifier of Fig. 9.96 is identical in form to that of Prob. 9.63, but with R_s replaced by n^2R_s, and N by n^2N. Then no matter what a is for the source in Prob. 9.63 ($N = a2kTR_s$), it will be the same for the new amplifier. Then the turns ratio can be chosen to produce the minimum noise figure F'' of Prob. 9.63(d). The only added effect is that the new amplifier will have a voltage gain n times that of problem 9.63.

(a) A certain amplifier has $R_{eq} = 1250$ ohms and $R_g = 100$ K. If $R_s = 600$ ohms, what must n be to achieve the minimum noise figure F'' of Prob. 9.63(d)?

Answer: $n = 4.31$

(b) What will this minimum noise figure be if $a = 10$? if $a = 1$?

(c) What would the noise figure be for the circuit without the transformer, everything else remaining the same, when $a = 10$? when $a = 1$?

Answers: 1.2116 and 3.116

(d) Noise figures for amplifiers are often given in db, where noise figure in db $= 10 \log_{10} F$. Express the answers to (b) and (c) in db.

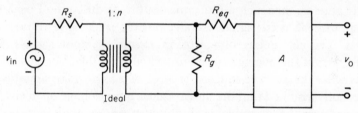

Fig. 9.96 *Problem 9.64.*

Optimum Filters

In Sec. 9.2, filters were discussed in the light of the elimination of unwanted signals. It was assumed that the signals had spectra that could be separated into nonoverlapping parts, and so attention was directed toward the elimination of those parts or frequency bands that were not desired. If the spectra of the desired signal and the undesired signals overlapped, then we either threw up our hands in frustration or carefully avoided mentioning that the possibility might exist.

However, as the previous section shows, noise spectra will overlap with the spectrum of any signal, and so efforts were expended in the late nineteen thirties and early nineteen forties toward the design of filters that can remove noise within the signal's band. It will be seen that such analyses quickly become very complicated, but the general idea can be understood and appreciated by a study of the simple *matched filter*. The general problem of noise filtering is usually referred to as *optimum filtering*, which signifies that the filter to be designed optimizes the signal-to-noise ratio in some sense.

Suppose that we are concerned with a communication system that uses pulses as the fundamental signal. Examples of such systems are radar, digital-computer circuitry, and telegraphy. Suppose further that the system uses pulses that are all of the same shape, and that the information desired can be deduced if only the *time of arrival* of the pulse is the important factor. Thus if words were coded in some form of pulse train, it would be possible to decode the message simply by receiving this pulse train with each pulse appearing in its proper position relative to the others. Then the question we ask is this: When such a pulse train is corrupted by noise, what type of filter can be devised to insure that the signal amplitude will be as large as possible relative to the noise amplitude, so that noise pulses will not drown out the pulses or be large enough to be mistaken by the receiver for pulses?

It appears that such a filter must optimize the ratio of peak signal voltage to peak noise signal voltage. But the peak noise voltage is unknown. The rms noise voltage of an *ensemble* of noise signals can be deduced from the average spectrum of the ensemble, but this does not tell us what the average squared voltage of a *single* noise signal will be. It is usually assumed that the mean-square noise voltage of an ensemble, averaged over the ensemble, and the mean-square noise voltage of any member of the ensemble averaged over time will be the same. For any such ensemble the group of noise signals is said to constitute a *stationary time series*. In other words, the hurdle presented by comparing averages over a group and averages of any one member over time is cleared by saying that they are the same. Experimental evidence and the theory of probability show this assumption to be sound. In fact, it is sometimes assumed that noise signals are such that no matter what statistical property the ensemble possesses when averaged over the ensemble, each member of the ensemble possesses the same property when averaged over time. Such an ensemble is called *ergodic*.

Noise signals having spectra that are flat over wide frequency bands almost always behave as though they were ergodic. Thus the engineer may draw the following conclusion: Since random noise has been shown[*] to have an amplitude distribution that follows the Gaussian process, then, with σ equal to the mean-square noise voltage, the probability that the magnitude of the voltage will be in a certain interval $v_0 < v < v_0 + dv$ at some arbitrary time is

$$\frac{1}{\sqrt{2\pi}\sigma} e^{-v_0^2/2\sigma^2} dv$$

----

[*]W. B. Davenport, Jr., and W. L. Root, *An Introduction to the Theory of Random Signals and Noise*, New York: McGraw-Hill Book Company, Inc., 1958.

Without our going into detail, this means that the chances that the magnitude (plus or minus) of the voltage does not exceed a voltage v_0 at an arbitrary time is proportional to the area under the curve $y = \exp\left(-v^2/2\sigma^2\right)/(\sqrt{2\pi}\sigma)$ between $-v_0$ and $+v_0$. The function y, plotted in Fig. 9.97, is known as the *normal* distribution function. σ is called the *standard deviation* and for $v_0 = \sigma$ the area under the curve from $-\sigma$ to σ is about two-thirds of the total area. Then about two times out of three the noise voltage will be less than $v_{\text{rms}} = \sigma$.

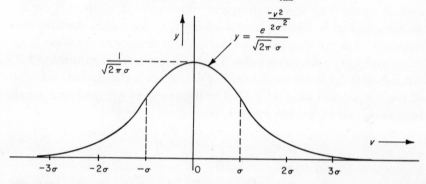

Fig. 9.97 *The Gaussian or normal density function, with standard deviation σ and zero mean (average).*

The integral of the function in Fig. 9.97 is not elementary, but the total area (from $-\infty$ to $+\infty$) is normalized to unity by the factor $\sqrt{2\pi}\,\sigma$ (see Sec. 8.5). The integral is related to the *error integral* and the latter is tabulated in Jahnke and Emde (9). We can conclude from the tables that the probability that the noise will be smaller than its rms value is 0.684; hence, the probability that it will exceed this value is $1 - 0.684 = 0.316$. Thus the odds that it will not exceed this value are $0.684/0.316$ or $2.16/1$. The probability that the voltage magnitude will not exceed twice v_{rms} (again in either the positive or negative direction) is 0.9545, making the odds $0.9545/0.0455$ or $20.7/1$. The probability that the voltage will not exceed three times v_{rms} is 0.99729, making the odds $369/1$.

Now if the signal level is the same as v_{rms}, chances are that at least one-third of the message will be garbled and hence impossible to de-cipher. With signal voltages twice v_{rms} (this would be a power ratio of $4/1$) our chances are much better but, even so, 5 percent of the message will be lost or incorrect. However, with the signal voltage three or more times v_{rms}, we are fairly well assured that the message may be properly decoded with little error.

For these reasons, when the time of arrival of a pulse is the only information desired, it seems reasonable to attempt to maximize the ratio of peak output signal to rms noise voltage by using a special filter. We define the signal-to-noise ratio at the output of the filter as the ratio of the squared amplitude of the peak of the output signal to the mean-square noise voltage at the output.

Suppose we desire to find a linear filter with transfer function $H(f)$ and impulse response $h(t)$ such that the ratio of the peak signal voltage output squared to the mean-square noise voltage at the output is a maximum. Figure 9.98 depicts such a filter, which will be assumed to be noiseless. N is the magnitude of the spectral density of the noise at the input and $p_{in}(t)$ is the input pulse. The noise spectrum is assumed to have a bandwidth far in excess of any filter we care to use and so the spectrum of the output will be $N|H(f)|^2$. The total noise power will then be the integral of this expression over all f or

$$\overline{v_{rms}^2} = N \int_{-\infty}^{\infty} |H(f)|^2 \, df \tag{9.115}$$

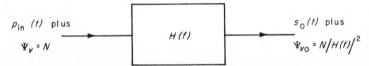

Fig. 9.98 *Schematic for an optimum filter.*

But from Eq. (8.22), Chapter 8, the last integral can be written as

$$\overline{v_{rms}^2} = N \int_{-\infty}^{\infty} h^2(\tau) \, d\tau \tag{9.116}$$

By the convolution theorem the output signal must be

$$s_0(t) = \int_{-\infty}^{\infty} h(\tau) \, p_{in}(t - \tau) \, d\tau \tag{9.117}$$

Suppose we assume that the maximum value of the output signal occurs at some time t_0. Then the peak-signal-to-noise power ratio at the output must be

$$\frac{S}{N} = \frac{\left[\int_{-\infty}^{\infty} h(\tau) p_{in}(t_0 - \tau) \, d\tau \right]^2}{N \int_{-\infty}^{\infty} h^2(\tau) \, d\tau} \tag{9.118}$$

and this is the expression it is desired to maximize.

Notice that this is not an ordinary maximum or minimum problem, because we are not looking for the value of a single variable but rather a *whole function* $h(t)$ that maximizes the ratio in Eq. (9.118). The *calculus of variations*, another recommended study, is designed to solve this type of problem very easily. However, with a little additional effort and thought the solution can be found without this discipline.

The first thing to note is that a maximum should exist. Suppose, for example, that the transform of the input pulse is predominantly in the frequency range $|f| < f_m$. Then, since the noise occupies a range much larger than this, an ordinary low-pass filter could be used to eliminate all the noise outside of the signal's band. If the bandwidth of the filter were made smaller than f_m still more noise would be eliminated, but some signal power would be eliminated as well. It seems reasonable to expect that some filter exists (which is approximately a low-pass filter) that could optimize the S/N ratio at the output.

Since an optimum $h(t)$ is presumed to exist, let $h_0(t)$ be the impulse response of this optimum filter. Then any other impulse response will not be as good. In fact, for any function $h'(t)$ and for any constant ϵ,

$$h(t) = h_0(t) + \epsilon h'(t) \tag{9.119}$$

will definitely be inferior to $h_0(t)$ alone. In particular, the ratio

$$\frac{S}{N} = \frac{\left[\int\limits_{-\infty}^{\infty} [h_0(\tau) + \epsilon h'(\tau)]\, p_{\text{in}}\,(t_0 - \tau)\, d\tau \right]^2}{N \int\limits_{-\infty}^{\infty} [h_0(\tau) + \epsilon h'(\tau)]^2\, d\tau} \tag{9.120}$$

must have a maximum at $\epsilon = 0$ *no matter what* $h'(t)$ *is.*

The last paragraph is the crux of the development that follows.

Writing Eq. (9.120) out by performing the squaring operations and using the fact that the integral of a sum is equal to the sum of the integrals, we obtain

$$\frac{S}{N} = \frac{\left[\int\limits_{-\infty}^{\infty} h_0(\tau) p_{\text{in}}(t_0 - \tau)\, d\tau \right]^2 + 2\epsilon \left[\int\limits_{-\infty}^{\infty} h_0(\tau) p_{\text{in}}(t_0 - \tau)\, d\tau \right] \left[\int\limits_{-\infty}^{\infty} h'(\tau) p_{\text{in}}(t_0 - \tau)\, d\tau \right] + \epsilon^2 \left[\int\limits_{-\infty}^{\infty} h'(\tau) p_{\text{in}}(t_0 - \tau)\, d\tau \right]^2}{N \left[\int\limits_{-\infty}^{\infty} h_0^2(\tau)\, d\tau + 2\epsilon \int\limits_{-\infty}^{\infty} h_0(\tau) h'(\tau)\, d\tau + \epsilon^2 \int\limits_{-\infty}^{\infty} h'^2(\tau)\, d\tau \right]} \tag{9.121}$$

Now if we imagine $h_0(t)$, $p_{in}(t)$, and $h'(t)$ as fixed functions of time, then the integrals are all constants and S/N is a function of ϵ alone. Letting

$$a = \int_{-\infty}^{\infty} h_0(\tau) p_{in}(t_0 - \tau) d\tau \qquad b = \int_{-\infty}^{\infty} h'(\tau) p_{in}(t_0 - \tau) d\tau$$

$$c = \int_{-\infty}^{\infty} h_0^2(\tau) d\tau \qquad d = \int_{-\infty}^{\infty} h_0(\tau) h'(\tau) d\tau \qquad e = \int_{-\infty}^{\infty} h'^2(\tau) d\tau$$

then Eq. (9.121) becomes

$$\frac{S}{N} = \frac{a^2 + 2ab\epsilon + b^2\epsilon^2}{N(c + 2d\epsilon + e\epsilon^2)}$$

The derivative of this with respect to ϵ must vanish at $\epsilon = 0$ since the ratio has a maximum at that point. But

$$\frac{d(S/N)}{d\epsilon} = \frac{(c + 2d\epsilon + e\epsilon^2)(2ab + 2b\epsilon) - (a^2 + 2ab\epsilon + b^2\epsilon^2)(2d + 2e\epsilon)}{N(c + 2d\epsilon + e\epsilon^2)^2}$$

which, at $\epsilon = 0$, is

$$\frac{d(S/N)}{d\epsilon}\bigg|_{\epsilon=0} = \frac{2a(bc - ad)}{Nc^2} \tag{9.122}$$

This derivative vanishes at $\epsilon = 0$ only if

$$bc = ad \tag{9.123}$$

or, using the definitions of these quantities,

$$\left[\int_{-\infty}^{\infty} h'(\tau) p_{in}(t_0 - \tau) d\tau \right] \left[\int_{-\infty}^{\infty} h_0^2(\tau) d\tau \right]$$

$$= \left[\int_{-\infty}^{\infty} h_0(\tau) p_{in}(t_0 - \tau) d\tau \right] \left[\int_{-\infty}^{\infty} h_0(\tau) h'(\tau) d\tau \right] \tag{9.124}$$

But this should be *independent* of $h'(t)$; that is, it should not matter *what* $h'(t)$ is. The only way this can happen is to have the two terms containing $h'(\tau)$ be proportional to each other so that they cancel out of Eq. (9.124). Then

$$\int_{-\infty}^{\infty} h'(\tau) p_{in}(t_0 - \tau) d\tau = A \int_{-\infty}^{\infty} h_0(\tau) h'(\tau) d\tau$$

$$\int_{-\infty}^{\infty} h'(\tau) [p_{in}(t_0 - \tau) - A h_0(\tau)] d\tau = 0$$

The only way this can vanish, no matter what $h'(t)$ is, is to have

$$Ah_0(\tau) = p_{in}(t_0 - \tau) \tag{9.125}$$

Then Eq. (9.125) must be the impulse response of the optimum filter. We conclude that the impulse response of the filter that maximizes the ratio of peak signal to rms noise for a particular pulse $p(t)$ is the *mirror image* of $p(t)$ shifted to the right far enough that $h_0(t)$ is realizable. Then t_0, must be at least as large as the pulse length. Usually it is set equal to the pulse length.

If Eq. (9.125) is substituted into Eq. (9.120), the peak-signal-to-noise ratio (power) becomes

$$
\left.
\begin{aligned}
\frac{S}{N} &= \frac{\displaystyle\int_{-\infty}^{\infty} p_{in}^2 (t_0 - \tau) \, d\tau}{N} \\[2ex]
&= \frac{\text{Energy in } p_{in}(t)}{N}
\end{aligned}
\right\} \tag{9.126}
$$

where both the energy and N are taken on a one-ohm level. Actually the level is unimportant, as long as it is the same for both signal and noise.

EXAMPLE 9.12. Find the impulse response of the matched filter that optimizes the ratio of peak signal to rms noise for the pulse pictured in Fig. 9.99. Calculate the S/N ratio (power) at the output of such a filter, assuming that the spectral density of the input noise is a constant N.

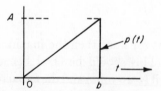
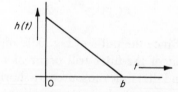

Fig. 9.99 *Example 9.12.*

Fig. 9.100 *The impulse response of the matched filter for the signal in Fig. 9.99.*

Solution: The mirror image shifted b units to the right appears in Fig. 9.100. This is the impulse response of the matched filter. The S/N ratio at the output, from Eq. (9.126), is simply $A^2b/3N$ since the square of the triangle is a parabola, and the area of a parabolic triangle is one-third the base times the height.

EXAMPLE 9.13. The signal in Fig. 9.100 looks somewhat like the exponential decay, and a circuit with an impulse response that is an exponential decay is very easy to construct. One is shown, for example, in Fig. 9.101.

Since the transfer function of the filter shown in Fig. 9.101 is

$$H(f) = \frac{1/RC}{s+1/RC}$$

then

$$h(t) = \frac{1}{RC} e^{-t/RC} \mathbf{1}(t)$$

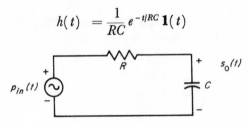

Fig. 9.101   *Example 9.13.*

This function will look like the triangle of Fig. 9.100 if the time constant RC is about b sec. Find the time constant that will maximize the signal-to-noise ratio and compare it with the ratio obtained with the optimum filter.

Solution: The mean-square noise voltage will be N times the integral of $h^2(t)$ and so

$$N \int_{-\infty}^{\infty} \frac{e^{-2t/RC}\mathbf{1}(t)}{(RC)^2} dt = \frac{N}{2RC}\left(- e^{-2t/RC}\right)\bigg/_0^{\infty} = \frac{N}{2RC} \text{ v}^2$$

Since the pulse of Fig. 9.99 only lasts for b sec then the maximum output of the filter will occur at $t = b$. This should be clear because beyond that time the source is a short circuit (zero volts) and the capacitor then simply discharges through the resistor. Until $t = b$ the source is a ramp function with slope A/b and so the transform of the output for the first b sec is

$$S_0(s) = \frac{A}{bRC} \cdot \frac{1}{s^2(s+1/RC)}$$

$$= \frac{A/b}{s^2} - \frac{ARC/b}{s} + \frac{ARC/b}{s+1/RC}$$

making

$$s_0(t) = \frac{A}{b}[t - RC(1 - e^{-t/RC})] \qquad \text{for} \quad 0 \leqslant t \leqslant b$$

and so, at $t = b$ the peak output voltage is

$$s_0(b) = \frac{A}{b} \left[b - RC \left(1 - e^{-b/RC} \right) \right] = A \left[1 - \frac{RC}{b} \left(1 - e^{-b/RC} \right) \right]$$

If we now set

$$a = \frac{b}{RC}$$

then

$$s_0(b) = A \left[1 - \frac{1 - e^{-a}}{a} \right]$$

The ratio of peak signal squared to mean-square noise voltage is then

$$\frac{S}{N} = \frac{A^2 [1 - (1 - e^{-a})/a]^2}{N/2RC} = \frac{2A^2 RC}{N} \left(1 - \frac{1 - e^{-a}}{a} \right)^2$$

If this is divided by the S/N ratio of the optimum filter, which was found to be $A^2 b / 3N$ in Example 9.12, then

$$\frac{S/N_{(RC)}}{S/N_{(Opt)}} = \frac{6RC}{b} \left(1 - \frac{1 - e^{-a}}{a} \right)^2 = \frac{6}{a} \left(1 - \frac{1 - e^{-a}}{a} \right)^2$$

By differentiating this ratio with respect to a and setting the result equal to zero, we find the maximum s/N ratio for the $R\text{-}C$ filter.

$$\frac{d(S/N)}{da} = \frac{6}{a^4} (a - 1 + e^{-a}) [3 - a - e^{-a} (2a + 3)]$$

which vanishes at a value of a for which

$$e^a = \frac{2a + 3}{3 - a}$$

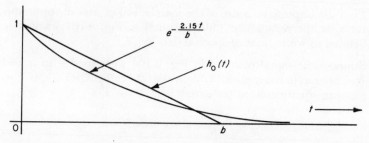

Fig. 9.102 *The impulse response of the optimum filter and that of the best low-pass filter for the pulse of Fig. 9.99.*

The solution of this equation, found by trial and error, is about $a = 2.15$ and so

$$RC = \frac{b}{2.15}$$

is the time constant that leads to the best low-pass filter. The relative signal-to-noise ratios are

$$\frac{S/N_{(RC)}}{S/N_{(Opt)}} = 0.968 = -0.14 \text{ db}$$

The impulse response of the R-C filter and that of the optimum filter appear in Fig. 9.102.

PROBLEMS

9.65. Sketch the impulse response of the matched filter that optimizes the ratio of peak signal to rms noise when the input pulse is $p_{in}(t) = Ae^{-t/a}\mathbf{1}(t)$. Is this filter realizable? If a filter whose impulse response is that shown in Fig. 9.103 were used instead of the optimum filter, what is the pulse length b that will maximize the signal to noise ratio? By how much is this S/N ratio less than the optimum in db?

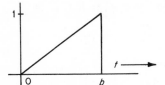

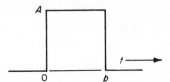

Fig. 9.103   *Problem 9.65.*   **Fig. 9.104**   *Problems 9.66 and 9.67.*

9.66. Find the impulse response of the matched filter and the optimum S/N ratio for the rectangular pulse pictured in Fig. 9.104 when it is embedded in white noise of spectral density N.

9.67. Suppose the signal pictured in Fig. 9.104 were used with a low-pass R–C filter as in Example 9.13. Show that the ratio of peak signal squared to mean-square noise at the output is

$$\frac{S}{N} = \frac{2A^2RC}{N}\left(1 - e^{-b/RC}\right)^2$$

Show also that the ratio of this S/N to that of the optimum obtained in Prob. 9.66 has a maximum value when $b/RC \doteq 2\pi/5$. What is this maximum ratio in db? How does the half-power frequency of the filter compare with the reciprocal of the pulse length?

Answer: -0.895 db.

9.68. The impedance of a lossless short-circuited transmission line can be shown to be

$$Z(s) = Z_0 \frac{1 - e^{-s\tau}}{1 + e^{-s\tau}}$$

where τ is the two-way delay time of the line. For a transmission line with air dielectric $\tau = 2d/c$, where d is the length of the line in meters and $c = 3 \times 10^8$ m/sec is the velocity of light.

(a) Show that the transfer function $V_0(s)/I_s(s)$ of the circuit in Fig. 9.105 is

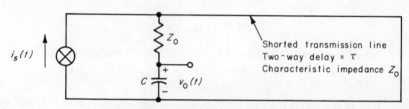

Fig. 9.105 *The Rochefort matched filter.*

$$\frac{V_0(s)}{I_s(s)} = \frac{\dfrac{1}{2C}(1 - e^{-s\tau})}{\left(s + \dfrac{1}{2Z_0C}\right)\left(1 + \dfrac{e^{-s\tau}}{1 + 2Z_0Cs}\right)}$$

Z_0 is simply a constant and is known as the characteristic or surge impedance of the line.

(b) Find the impulse response of the filter for $0 < t < 2\tau$ given that $Z_0C = 50\tau$. Do this by expanding the exponential factor in the denominator of the transfer function into the series

$$1 - \frac{e^{-s\tau}}{100\tau s + 1} + \frac{e^{-2s\tau}}{(100\tau s + 1)^2} - \cdots$$

and use the real translation theorem in reverse.

(c) Observe that for $Z_0C \geqslant 50\tau$

$$h(t) \doteq \frac{1}{C}[\mathbf{1}(t) - \mathbf{1}(t - \tau)]$$

within 2 percent. This is the Rochefort* matched filter for the rectangular pulse.

*J. S. ROCHEFORT, "Matched Filters for Detecting Pulsed Signals in Noise," *I.R.E. Convention Record*, Vol. 2, Pt. 4, *Electronic Computers and Information Theory*, 1954, pp. 30–34.

9.69. Find $H(f)$, the transfer function of the matched filter for the pulse

$$p_{in}(t) = e^{-at^2/b^2}$$

Answer: $\sqrt{\dfrac{\pi}{a}}\; b\, e^{-j2\pi f t_0}\, e^{-(\pi f b)^2/a}$

9.70. Find the impulse response and transfer function for the matched filter when

$$p_{in}(t) = A\,\frac{\sin\,[a(t-t_0)]}{a(t-t_0)}$$

Show that the output of the matched filter will have the same form as $p_{in}(t)$. Is the matched filter thus obtained physically realizable?

9.71. The spectral density function of a noise signal is given by

$$\Psi(f) = \frac{10^6}{10^{10}+f^2}\; \text{v}^2/\text{cps}$$

A 1-volt rectangular pulse of 1 msec duration is embedded in this noise.
(a) What is the signal-to-noise power ratio, S/N?

Answer: 0.0318:1

(b) If the mixture is put into a matched filter, calculate the (power) ratio of peak signal to noise at the output. Do not get involved in integrations but observe that the input noise spectrum is nearly constant over the bandwidth of the filter.

Answer: 10.0:1.

9.72. Prove that the output signal of a matched filter is the autocorrelation function of the input signal (see Prob. 8.24).

References

1. GARDNER, M. F., and J. L. BARNES, *Transients in Linear Systems.* New York: John Wiley & Sons, Inc., 1942.
    There is little doubt that a large share of the popularity of the Laplace transform in the area of operational calculus is directly attributable to these men and their volume. The bibliography at the end of this book is very extensive.
2. GUILLEMIN, E. A., *Introductory Circuit Theory.* New York: John Wiley & Sons, Inc., 1953.

A slightly different point of view in the approach to connection matrices and the s plane is taken in this book. The reader can hardly afford to be unfamiliar with it.

3. *The Mathematics of Circuit Analysis.* New York: John Wiley & Sons, Inc., 1949.
The most complete collection of those portions of mathematics that are essential to the electrical engineer.

4. Kron, G., *Tensor Analysis of Networks.* New York: John Wiley & Sons, Inc., 1939.
The point of view taken by Kron in this volume has been used in conjunction with the work of Guillemin in the presentation of the matrix analysis of networks. In physical systems the matrices used in this work possess the properties of *tensors* and Kron exploits this fact.

5. *IRE Transactions on Circuit Theory*, Vol. CT-5, March 1958, No. 1.
This issue contains four important papers on network topology. A translation of G. Kirchhoff's paper on the subject, p. 4, a paper entitled, "Kirchhoff's 'Third and Fourth' Laws," by L. Weinberg (in which, for example, he proves that the number of trees $= detB^TB$), p. 8, and "Some Topological Considerations in Network Theory" by F. Reza, on p. 30, which also includes a large bibliography. The fourth paper, on p. 42, is "General Topological Formulas for Linear Network Functions" by C. L. Coates.

6. Campbell, G. A., and R. M. Foster. *Fourier Integrals for Practical Applications.* Princeton, N.J.: D. Van Nostrand Company, Inc., 1948.
To the author's knowledge this is the largest collection of transform pairs available.

7. Papoulis, A. *The Fourier Integral and Its Applications.* New York: McGraw Hill Book Company, Inc., 1962.
This excellent volume presents nearly every important use of the Fourier transform. It is required reading for those who would continue work in this field.

8. Schwartz, Mischa, *Information Transmission, Modulation, and Noise.* New York: McGraw-Hill Book Company, Inc., 1959.
An appropriate sequel to this text in that it extends the work of Chapter 9.

9. Jahnke, E., and F. Emde. *Tables of Functions with Formulae and Curves.* New York: Dover Publications, Inc., 1945.
Extensive tabulation of Bessel functions and most of the functions encountered in engineering practice.

10. Ramo, S., and J. R. Whinnery. *Fields and Waves in Modern Radio.* New York: John Wiley & Sons, Inc., 1953.
An excellent introduction to the study of field theory. The proof that $M_{12} = M_{21}$ appears in Sec. 5.10, pp. 220–221.

Index